ELECTROMAGNETIC SCATTERING

ICES II

ELECTROMAGNETIC SCATTERING

Proceedings of the Second Interdisciplinary Conference on Electromagnetic Scattering held at the University of Massachusetts at Amherst, June 1965

Edited by

ROBERT L. ROWELL

and

RICHARD S. STEIN

University of Massachusetts

With an introduction by Peter Debye

Sponsored by
Air Force Cambridge Research Laboratories
Office of Aerospace Research
United States Air Force

GORDON AND BREACH SCIENCE PUBLISHERS

New York London Paris

Science Publishers, Inc.
150 Fifth Avenue, New York, N.Y. 10011

Editorial office for the United Kingdom:

Gordon and Breach, Science Publishers Ltd.
61 Carey Street, Chancery Lane
London W.C.2, England

Editorial office for France:

Gordon and Breach
7-9 rue Emile Dubois
Paris 14

Library of Congress Catalog Card Number: 63-15613

Distributed in France by:

Dunod Editeur
92, rue Bonaparte
Paris 6, France

Distributed in Canada by:

The Ryerson Press
299 Queen Street West
Toronto 2B, Ontario

Printed in the United States of America

PREFACE

This volume is primarily a collection of papers presented at the Second Interdisciplinary Conference on Electromagnetic Scattering and a report of the discussion of those papers. All papers were by invitation and all were presented at the Conference with the exception of the contribution in Session II by Birnboim, Magill, and Berry and the contribution in Session III by van de Hulst which are included because of their relevance to the Conference discussion. The papers have been edited since the time of their presentation and in many cases extended somewhat to be as timely as possible and to reflect changes suggested by independent readers who served to referee each contribution, especially with respect to clarity of exposition to interdisciplinary readers. We have included also in this volume a report on the discussion that went on at ICES-II. The discussion was assembled by tape-recorder and by discussion question-answer sheets. Each person contributing to the discussion was given a chance to edit his remarks. Nevertheless, the edited discussion follows very closely the oral presentation at the conference and, most of it is verbatim. When appropriate, the editors have allowed amplification of the discussion which we feel will be of considerable value to interdisciplinary readers, particularly when the reader is looking at a work out of his own particular speciality.

The Conference was sponsored by the Air Force

Cambridge Research Laboratories of the Office of Aerospace Research. The host institution was the University of Massachusetts at Amherst, through the Department of Chemistry and the Polymer Research Institute. The organization of the Conference including the division into Sessions and the organization of the general format of each session was under the direction of a Steering Committee consisting of: P. Debye (Cornell, Physics and Chemistry), J. Howard (AFCRL, Optical Physics), M. Kerker (Clarkson, Colloid Science), R. Mack (AFCRL, Microwave Physics), R. Penndorf (AVCO, Geophysics), W. Prins (Delft, Physical Chemistry), R. Rowell (U. Mass., Physical Chemistry), R. Stein (U. Mass., Polymer Physical Chemistry), V. Twersky (Sylvania, Mathematical Physics), R. Ullmann (Ford, Polymer Chemistry).

The selection of papers for each session and the particular plans for each session was carried out through the session chairmen, working in conjunction with the Conference Co-chairmen and the Steering Committee and accepting the suggestions from experts in different disciplines. The sessions and chairmen were: Session I: Particulate Scattering, Chairman, J. Mayo Greenberg (Department of Physics, Rensselaer Polytechnic Institute); Session II: Non-Particulate Scattering, Chairman, W. Prins (Laboratory for Physical Chemistry, Technical University of Delft, Delft, Netherlands); Session III: Multiple Scattering, Chairman, Zdenek Sekera (Chairman, Department of Meteorology, University of California at Los Angles); Session IV: Related Non-Electromagnetic Scattering, Chairman, Victor Twersky (Sylvania Electronics Systems, Mountain View, California).

The Conference was held on the Campus of the University of Massachusetts at Amherst on June 28-30, 1965. The speakers and participants, numbering one hundred fifty-one, wer drawn from Astronomy, Chemistry, Engineering, Mathematics, Meteorology, and Physics, and came from twenty-eight states and eight nations. Representatives from academic institutions, industrial research laboratories, and other research laboratories were present.

This book is divided into four sections corresponding to the sessions of the Conference. In planning the Conference, the Steering Committee designed the approach to the problem of electromagnetic scattering according to four fundamental interdisciplinary idea categories: 1. The idea of scattering from a discrete particle, 2. The idea of the correlation function approach to scattering which we found difficult to describe other than to designate it as non-particulate scattering, 3. The idea of scattering from systems of many particles where multiple scattering effects must be considered, 4. Ideas that might be obtained by analogy with related areas of scattering which were not necessarily electromagnetic in nature.

The general format of each session was suggested largely as a result of a survey of the participants of the First Interdisciplinary Conference on Electromagnetic Scattering which was held at Clarkson College of Technology in August of 1962 under the Chairmanship of Milton Kerker who later edited the proceedings of that conference (Electromagnetic Scattering, Vol. 5, in International Series of Monographs on Electromagnetic Waves, Pergamon, Oxford, 1963). Each session was introduced by a tutorial paper or papers which also included some new material. Thus, in Session I, the tutorial presentations were by Professors Greenberg and Kerker, in Session II by Professor J. A. Prins, and in Session III by Professor Zdenek Sekera. In Session IV all of the papers were essentially tutorial in nature with an introduction by Chairman V. Twersky.

A highlight of the Conference was the banquet on Tuesday night at which we all enjoyed a presentation by Dr. John Howard of the Air Force Cambridge Research Laboratories on "The Scientific Papers of Lord Raleigh". Dr. Howard reviewed the life and work of Lord Raleigh with emphasis given to his studies on scattering, optics, and wave motion. In Dr. Howard's words, "Raleigh was a remarkable combination of thoroughly trained theorist and careful and ingenious experimenter. Working for the most part alone with homemade apparatus, he designed experiments that varified his theoretical predictions and formulated simplified criteria for optical instruments, and is best known for the theory of Raleigh Scattering, which explained the blue of the sky. His 'theory of sound' is still the Bible of accoustics, and even after his death much of his wave theory was reapplied to quantum wave mechanics." Dr. Howard's talk was both a fitting testimonial to one of the founders of electromagnetic scattering theory, as well as an inspirational and interesting presentation. Much of the material of his talk was drawn from the special October 1964 issue of Applied Optics, and consequently is not republished here.

In preparing any conference, especially an interdisciplinary one, it is a tremendous job to get all of the people together at the same time. Thus, we were not able to obtain the presence of Prof. van de Hulst, but we have included a short contribution from him in Session III. We were also disappointed that scheduling conflicts did not allow the presence of Prof. Debye at the Conference, although we benefited greatly from his assistance in organizing the Conference, by his service on the Steering Committee, and we obtained his "presence" in this book in the form of an introduction to the Conference which Prof. Debye consented to write, provided he could first read all the manuscripts.

It is difficult to fully appreciate the problems of style, notation, and format until one attempts to assemble the collection of manuscripts from experts in many disciplines and from many lands. We have taken great pains to provide as much uniformity as possible in style and notation, although there is still considerable variation. We felt, however, that some variation must be allowed in order to preserve the natural language of each discipline. Electromagnetic scattering is a broad field and we recognize that there may be some areas that have been omitted, some emphases that have not been covered, and certainly some background that has not been included. It should be noted, however, that this is not an attempt to provide a complete and authoritative, coherent and unified treatise on electromagnetic scattering, but rather it is a collection of papers presented at a conference by a number of outstanding workers in a variety of disciplines and remarks and comments on those papers presented by their collegues in an inter-disciplinary discussion. The purpose of the conference was to bring together, to inspire, to instruct, and to hear what might be new. It is hoped that this volume will carry these objectives to a much wider audience and provide both an index as to what is currently going on in electromagnetic scattering as well as a report on what the editors, the steering committee and session chairmen hope to be some of the most significant and interesting work now underway in various laboratories throughout the world.

Finally, as Conference Co-chairmen and editors of this volume we should like to express a special thanks to all of those who have contributed to the work of the conference and to the preparation of this work. We are grateful to the Air Force Cambridge Research Laboratories for the financial support that made this Conference possible and to the University of Massachusetts as host institution. Such a task is not the work of two men alone, but rather a result which requires thanks to many people: to the Steering Committee, to the Session Chairmen, to the many others with whom we have corresponded in organizing the conference, to the secretarial staff especially Mrs. Young and Mrs. Zimnosky of the Polymer Institute, to the audio-visual team under the able direction of Mr. Daniel Keedy, to our Conference Office and Conference Co-ordinator, Mr. Harold Durgin, to Mrs. D. G. Smith, our able style reader, to the local arrangements committee especially our collegues Prof. E. Ernest Lindsey and Prof. Phillips Jones, and finally to our wives for their patience and understanding.

R. L. Rowell

R. S. Stein

Conference Co-Chairmen and Co-Editors
Amherst, Massachusetts, 1966

INTRODUCTION

When van der Hulst wrote his introduction to ICES I he emphasized how broad the field is covered by the conferences. It comprises indeed not only light-radio- waves and X-rays but any other kind of radiation as well, since as we know now every radiation has its wavelength and the phenomenon of interference is universal.

In ICES I about 1/3 of the space was devoted to the discussion of single particles. This is still true for ICES II but now we also encounter a good deal of discussion about how to determine the distribution of sized of scattering particles from the observed scattering. In one contribution it is reported that the scattering cross-section of spherically symmetrical gas-molecules is experimentally found bigger than theoretically anticipated. If this should be confirmed it would be disturbing, to say the least.

A second session of the Conferences devoted to non-particulate scattering is the longest. Here the interparticle-scattering is emphasized by the introduction of a Correlation-Function, which by measuring the correlation in space of the fluctuations determines the angular distribution of the scattered intensity. A special application is the analysis of hole-structures, like they are used in heterogeneous catalysts. The simplest and most straightforward result is a method for determining the surface of such catalysts. However more detailed analysis of the scattering seems to give promise to find out more about the geometry of the hidden surface.

In objects like solid polymer films we not only have frozen in density-fluctuations but also fluctuations of orientation of crystalline regions. These and their correlation lead to a range of phenomena in their effect on polarized light, revealing the structure of such films.

Finally the same method of attack is discussed in its application to critical opalescence where very near the critical point deviations from classically expected behavior are predicted from more sophisticated theories, whereas experimentally such deviations are hard to find except perhaps in the immediate vicinity of the critical point. Correlation in the classical range is here characterized by very long correlation-distances many times longer than the average distance over which molecular forces act. In one other contribution the analogous correlation in time and its effect on the spectral changes induced by scattering is discussed.

In a third session of the conferences, of nearly the same length as the first, multiple scattering is treated. This can be done theoretically in a way which is beyond reproach, but therefore also leads to a rather complicated mathematical formulation. In practice, for instance in the paint industry, a formulation of an approximate character (Kubelka-Munk) is often preferred Both approaches are discussed here. In both there is a central problem, unanswered as yet, namely how to understand and to calculate the bulk properties of the medium from the optical properties of the single particles. The only way to make advances in this direction seems to be following the experimental method. Efforts in this direction are reported also.

This report of the conferences closes with a fourth session called; "Related Non-electromagnetic Scattering." It is very short only three papers: Atomic Scattering is discussed, An optical Model of the nucleus is used for describing nuclear scattering, Velocity and attenuation of waves in a random medium are calculated. This certainly is a fitting finale illuminating the broad field of possible applications of the subject discussed in ICES II.

P. DEBYE

CONTRIBUTORS

Dr. Joseph T. Atkins
E.I. duPont deNemours
P. O. Box 1217
Parkersburg, W. Va.

Dr. Meyer H. Birnboim
Mellon Institute
4400 Fifth Ave.
Pittsburg, Pa.

Prof. Sidney Borowitz
Chairman, Dept. of Physics
New York University
Bronx 53, New York

Dr. R. K. Bullough
Department of Mathematics
College of Science and Technology
Manchester 1, England

Professor Benjamin Chu
University of Kansas
Chemistry Dept.
Lawrence, Kansas

Dr. H. L. Frisch
Bell Research Labs.
Murray Hill, N. J.

Dr. T. V. George
Gaseous Electronics Lab
University of Illinois
Urbana, Illinois

Prof. J. Mayo Greenberg
Department of Physics
Rensselaer Polytechnic Inst.
Troy, New York

Prof. Dr. C.C. Grosjean
University of Ghent
J. Plateaustr 22
Ghent, Belgium

Prof. Benjamin Herman
University of Arizona
Inst. of Atmos. Physics
Tucson, Arizona

Dr. Jaap Hijmans
Konig-Shell Labs
Amsterdam, Netherlands

Dr. Joseph Keller
Courant Inst. Math. Sci.
New York University'
Div. of Electromagnetic Res.
251 Mercer St.
New York, N. Y. 10012

Dr. Edward M. Kennaugh
Department of Electrical Engineering
Ohio State Univ.
Columbus, Ohio

Prof. Milton Kerker
Dean, School of Science
Clarkson College of Tech.
Potsdam, New York

Prof. Samuel Levine
University of Manchester
Department of Mathematics
Manchester, England

Dr. Donald McIntyre
Chief, Polymer Solutions
National Bureau of Standards
Washington, D. C.

Prof. T. W. Mullikin
Purdue University
Department of Mathematics
Lafayette, Indiana

Dr. R. M. Patrick
AVCO - Everett Res. Lab.
2385 Revere Beach Parkway
Everett, Mass. 02149

Dr. Robert Pecora
Department of Chemistry
Stanford University
Stanford, Calif. 94305

Prof. Dr. G. Porod
Physiklisches Institut
Der Universitat Gras
Austria

Prof. J. A. Prins
Technische Hogeschool Delft
Lorentzweg 1,
Delft, Nederland

Prof. Willim Prins
Delft Technical Univ.
Lorentzweg 1,
Delft, Netherlands

Prof. E. Saxon
Department of Physics
UCLA
405 Hilgard Ave.
Los Angeles, Calif.

Prof. Paul W. Schmidt
University of Missouri
Physics Dept.
Columbia, Mo.

Prof. Z. Sekera, Chairman
Dept. of Meteorology
USLA
405 Hilgard Ave.
Los Angeles, Calif.

Prof. K. S. Shifrin
Main Geophysical Observatory
Leningrad, K-18
U. S. S. R.

Prof. Richard S. Stein
Polymer Research Institute
Univ. of Mass.
Amherst, Mass.

Dr. Victor Twersky
Department of Mathematics
Univ. of Illinois at Chicago
Circle, Box 4348
Chicago, Illinois 60680

Prof. H. C. van de Hulst
Sterrewacht, Leyden
Holland

CONTENTS

SESSION II: NON-PARTICULATE SCATTERING

SESSION III: MULTIPLE SCATTERING

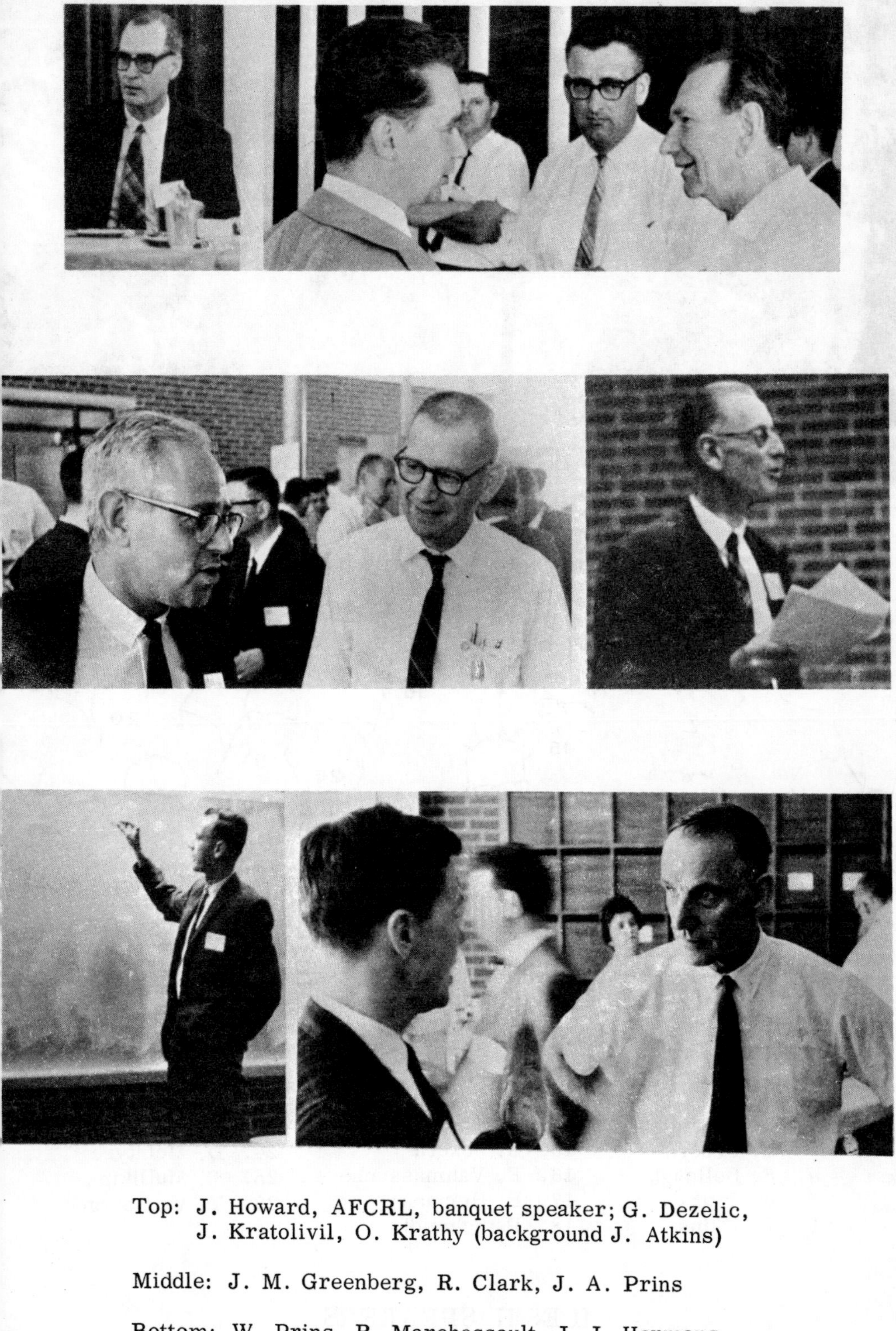

Top: J. Howard, AFCRL, banquet speaker; G. Dezelic, J. Kratolivil, O. Krathy (background J. Atkins)

Middle: J. M. Greenberg, R. Clark, J. A. Prins

Bottom: W. Prins, R. Marchessault, J. J. Hermans

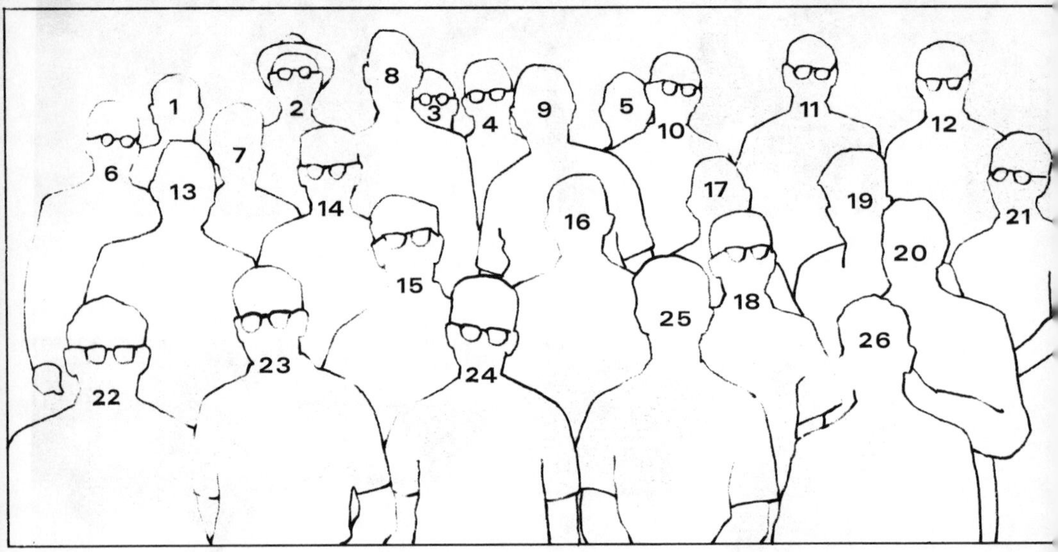

1. R. Stein
2. J. A. Prins
3. R. Mack
4. M. Kerker
5. E. Kennaugh
6. R. Pecora
7. R. Bullough
8. W. Prins
9. J. Atkins
10. J. Greenberg
11. J. Howard
12. D. Saxon
13. R. Rowell
14. P. Latimer
15. Z. Sekera
16. F. Vanmassenhove
17. B. Herman
18. P. Schmidt
19. J. Hijmans
20. G. Porod
21. V. Twersky
22. S. Levine
23. H. Frisch
24. D. McIntyre
25. T. Mullikin
26. T. V. George

ICES II SPEAKERS

SESSION I:

PARTICULATE SCATTERING

Scattering by Nonspherical Systems *

J. Mayo Greenberg†, Arthur C. Lind, Ru T. Wang
Rensselaer Polytechnic Institute, Troy, New York

and

Louis F. Libelo‡
U. S. Naval Ordnance Laboratory, White Oak, Maryland

ABSTRACT

Theoretical and experimental results on the scattering by nonspherical particles whose size is of the order of the wave length are presented.

A method of solution of the problem of scattering by axially symmetric penetrable particles using approximate matching of boundary conditions is applied to the scattering by prolate spheroids. Application is made specifically to the scattering of a scalar wave incident along the symmetry axis.

---

*Work Supported by grants from the National Aeronautic and Space Administration and the National Science Foundation.

†Currently on leave of absence as a member at the Institute for Advanced Study, Princeton, New Jersey.

‡Part of this paper is taken from a thesis submitted by L. F. Libelo in partial fulfillment of the degree of Doctor of Philosophy at Rensselaer Polytechnic Institute.

In comparison with exact scattering coefficients for the sphere, it is shown that the "approximate" method yields results as close as one wishes to the exact results. Calculations are presented for particle sizes ranging from those small enough to be calculated by the Rayleigh approximation to sizes generally beyond the first major resonance in the total cross-section curve.

Numerical caluclations are made for the tilted infinite dielectric cylinder. Some new and interesting properties of the scattering efficiency as a function of orientation are demonstrated. Particularly noted is the existence of a polarization reversal as a consequence of tilt for thin cylinders.

A new and improved method for obtaining microwave scattering by small particles is applied to the consideration of the detailed dependence on orientation of the cross-section of prolate spheroidal particles. The particle sizes range from slightly beyond the Rayleigh approximation to somewhat larger than the first major resonance in the extinction curve. The results are, where appropriate, compared with the Rayleigh approximation and a simple ray approximation. The ray approximation is shown to yield better results in certain than had been anticipated although there exists an intermediate but reasonably defined span of particle sizes for which the approximation is even qualitatively poor.

I. INTRODUCTION

The method of scattering is applied as an investigatory tool in studies ranging from the character of atomic nuclei through sizes and shapes of large molecules to the character of disturbances in the solar corona. The demands made upon the theory of the scattering process have often not been met even for application to situations which involve well-known physical processes and basic mathematical equations.

Disregarding the possibilities of complicated interactions between waves and obstacles there still are important gaps in the theoretical procedures. As a matter of fact the special case of the scattering of light by simple nonspherical particles is adequately treated only when the particles are either very small or very large compared with the wave length of light.

Van de Hulst (17) has surveyed the domain of m (m = index of refraction) and ka (ka = $2\pi a/\lambda$, a = a characteristic linear dimension, λ = wave length) for the regions of simple approximations and simple physical interpretations. The ranges of ka and m with which we are concerned here are just those which do not satisfy the simplicity criteria. We consider here those particles for which ka $\gtrsim$ 1, (m - 1) not $\ll$ 1, 2ka (m - 1) $\gtrsim$ 1; i.e., neither the Rayleigh (11) nor the Rayleigh-Gans-Born (12, 13, 2, 1) approximations are applicable.

The primary aim of this paper is to report on some progress that has been made at Rensselaer in extending our range of information, both actual and potential, concerning the scattering by nonspherical sharply bounded obstacles. We believe that the results which are present are new and that they indicate the possibilities for obtaining complete solutions to a useful range of problems in the near future. In other words, we believe that the problem of single scattering will soon be essentially solved.

The work described in the following three sections is abstracted from separate and more detailed accounts which are reported on elsewhere.

In section II we describe a method (5) for obtaining the numerical solution to the scattering by an axially symmetric penetrable particle whose size ranges from the very small to a value essentially limited by computing machine time. Although the problem treated here is limited to that of a scalar wave propagated along the axis of the particle, there does not appear to be any difficulty to generalize at least to the electromagnetic case. This has been done, but a formal solution and procedure are too lengthy to give here.

The numerical solution to the scattering of electromagnetic waves by an arbitrarily dielectric cylinder is discussed in section III.

In section IV we give some results obtained by an experimental method using microwaves for the study of scattering by arbitrarily oriented penetrable spheroids. The value of the microwave method lies in its applicability to the wides range of anisotropy of shape and optical properties.

II. SOLUTION TO THE SCATTERING PROBLEM BY APPROXIMATING BOUNDARY CONDITIONS

We consider here the problem of the scattering of a plane scalar wave which is incident along the axis of a smooth convex cylindrically symmetric body. The boundary conditions which we apply will correspond to the scattering of Schrödinger waves by a square well potential and to the scattering of acoustic waves by a body whose density is equal to that of the surrounding medium. Our results will thus be the scalar wave analog of the electromagnetic scattering problem.

The method of approximation is applied first to the case of the sphere as a means of checking the accuracy of the method by comparison with exact solutions. Application is then made to prolate spheroids up to elongations of two.

As we shall see, the solutions which are obtained are complete in the sense of being valid not only in the asymptotic region, but at all interior and exterior points. Furthermore, it is reasonable to expect the solutions to have reliability equal to that of Mie (8) series expansions so long as appropriate restrictions are imposed on the range of applicability.

a. Outline of the computational procedure

We desire solutions to the scalar wave equation

$$\nabla^2 \psi + k^2(\mathbf{r})\, \psi = 0 \tag{1}$$

where $k(\mathbf{r}) = 2\pi/\lambda(\mathbf{r})$ is the wave number at the point $\mathbf{r}$. The problems which we treat will be limited to homogeneous scatterers which are characterized by having a wave number inside, κ, which is a constant, m (index of refraction) times the wave number outside, k.

The boundary conditions on the solution are that the wave function and its normal derivative be continuous

$$\left.\begin{aligned} \psi_{inside} &= \psi_{outside} \\ n \cdot \nabla\psi_{in} &= n \cdot \nabla\psi_{out} \end{aligned}\right\} \text{ at the surface of the scatterer} \qquad \begin{matrix}(2a)\\(2b)\end{matrix}$$

where n is the normal to the surface.

We further impose the radiation condition

$$\psi_{r \to \infty} \to e^{ikz} + \frac{f(\theta)}{kr} e^{ikr} \tag{2c}$$

We may expand the solutions inside and outside in the standard forms which satisfy the differential equation and the radiation condition (2c)

$$\psi_{inc} = e^{ikz} = \sum_{l=0}^{\infty} (2l + 1)\, i^l\, j_l(kr)\, P_l(\cos\theta)$$

$$\psi_{sc} = \sum_{l=0}^{\infty} (2l + 1)\, i^l A_l\, h_l^{(1)}(kr)\, P_l(\cos\theta) \tag{3}$$

$$\psi_t = \sum_{l=0}^{\infty} (2l + 1)\, i^l B_l\, j_l(\kappa r)\, P_l(\cos\theta)$$

where ψ_{inc} is the incident wave, ψ_{sc} is the scattered wave, ψ_t is the transmitted wave, and where $j_l(z)$ is the spherical Bessel function and $h_l^{(1)}(z)$ is the spherical Hankel function of the first kind.

It is now only necessary to impose the conditions (2a) and (2b) and to solve for the coefficients A_l and B_l. Note that $\psi_{in} = \psi_t$ and $\psi_{out} = \psi_{inc} + \psi_{sc}$.

In the case of the sphere these B.C. (boundary condition) equations separate and one gets an infinite set of independent pairs of equations in the A's and B's which may be readily solved. If the bounding surface is nonspherical, the infinity of equations are coupled and a simple solution no longer exists.

The series expressions (3) are generally not rapidly converging. However, it is well known that the number of terms which are required for a good representation of the solution is of the order of $n = ka = 2\pi a/\lambda$ where a is a typical linear dimension of the scatterer. In the limit of very small scatterers it would only be necessary to find A_0 and B_0 in which case we see that the functions in Eq. (3) are independent of angle. For small scatterers it is then obvious that if the boundary conditions are satisfied at only one point they are automatically satisfied at all points on the surface. It is to be expected that the shorter the wave length, the more points on the boundary need to be considered. In other words, the number of points at which the boundary condition is satisfied should be at least of the same order (ka) as the number of important terms in the series expressions(3). Because of cylindrical symmetry each point corresponds of course to a circle about the symmetry axis.

Our procedure consists in choosing some finite number N of points at which to satisfy the boundary conditions (2a) or (2b) and then truncating the series so that we obtain an equal number of unknowns. We then solve the 2N inhomogeneous equations in the 2N unknowns A_l and B_l, $l = 0$ to $N - 1$. Each point (circle) on the boundary is represented by some angle θ. It should be noted that because of the reflective symmetry of the scatterers we have chosen, if the boundary conditions are satisfied for a given value of θ, they are then automatically satisfied for the angle $\pi - \theta$.

We shall choose s angles θ_i in the first quadrant to define an approximation of order $N = 2s$. We denote the approximate solutions by

$$\psi_{inc}^{(2s)} = \sum_{l=0}^{2s-1} (2l+1)\, i^l\, j_l(kr)\, P_l(\mu)$$

$$\psi_{sc}^{(2s)} = \sum_{l=0}^{2s-1} (2l+1)\, i^l\, A_l^{(2s)} h_l^{(1)}(kr)\, P_l(\mu) \tag{4}$$

$$\psi_t^{(2s)} = \sum_{l=0}^{2s-1} (2l+1)\, i^l\, B_l^{(2s)} j_l(\kappa r)\, P_l(\mu)$$

where $\mu = \cos\theta$.

The boundary conditions (2a) and (2b) are to be replaced by the sets of equations

$$\psi_t^{(2s)}(\mu_i) = \psi_{inc}^{(2s)}(\mu_i) + \psi_{sc}^{(2s)}(\mu_i) \tag{5a}$$

$$n(\mu_i) \cdot \overline{\nabla}\{\psi_t^{(2s)}(\mu_i) = \psi_{inc}^{(2s)}(\mu_i) + \psi_{sc}^{(2s)}(\mu_i)\} \tag{5b}$$

where $\mu_i = \cos\theta_i$.

We evaluate the scattering efficiency from the optical theorem

$$Q = \frac{4\pi}{(ka)^2}\,\mathrm{Im}\{f(0)\}$$

which for the exact solution is given by

$$Q = -\frac{4}{(ka)^2}\sum_{l=0}^{\infty}(2l+1)\,\mathrm{Re}A_l$$

and for the approximate solution is given by

$$Q = -\frac{4}{(ka)^2}\sum_{l=0}^{2s-1}(2l+1)\,\mathrm{Re}A_l^{(2s)} \tag{6}$$

b. Approximate scattering by a sphere

The sphere is used as a test case for the method because we may compare with exact results. The exact solution for the sphere is given by the coefficients

$$A_l = \frac{\kappa a\, j_l(ka) j_l'(\kappa a) - ka\, j_l'(ka)\, j_l(\kappa a)}{ka\, h_l'(ka) j_l(\kappa a) - \kappa a\, h_l(ka) j_l'(\kappa a)}$$

$$B_l = \frac{ka[h_l'(ka) j_l(ka) - h_l(ka) j_l'(ka)]}{ka\, h_l'(ka) j_l(\kappa a) - \kappa a\, h_l(ka) j_l'(\kappa a)} \tag{7}$$

It is instructive and possible to apply the approximation Eq. (5) piecemeal to the sphere. We consider three successive procedures: (1) Exact boundary condition for normal component of the gradient of ψ but approximate boundary condition for ψ; (2) Exact boundary condition on ψ but approximate one for the gradient of ψ; (3) Full approximation as given in Eq. (5). In all cases the coefficients are solved by the same truncation of the series expressions. We denote the solutions obtained by procedures (1), (2) and (3) by $A_{l,1}^{(2s)}$, $A_{l,2}^{(2s)}$, and $A_l^{(2s)}$ etc., respectively.

Procedure (1) involves the simultaneous solution of:

From (5a) and (4)

$$\exp(ika\mu_i) + \sum_{l=0}^{2s-1} (-1)^l (2l+1) A_{l,1}^{(2s)} h_l(ka) P_l(\mu_i)$$

$$= \sum_{l=0}^{2s-1} (-1)^l (2l+1) B_{l,1}^{(2s)} j_l(\kappa a) P_l(\mu_i) \tag{8a}$$

and from (2b) and (3)

$$ka[j'_l(ka) + h'_l(ka) A_l] = \kappa a B_l j'_l(\kappa a) \tag{8b}$$

In simultaneously solving for the A's and B's in Eqs. (8a) and (8b), we let the A_l and B_l of Eq. (8b) be equated to the $A_{l,1}^{(2s)}$ and $B_{l,1}^{(2s)}$ of Eq. (8a).

As a simplification in the numerical analysis the equation (8a) may be separated into two sets of equations, each of which is either even or odd in μ_i.

The result of combining (8a) and (8b) is

$$A_{l,1}^{(2s)}(ka) = \{1 + \rho_l^{(2s)}(ka)\} A_l(ka) \tag{9}$$

where

$$\rho_l^{(2s)} = \left\{ \frac{\Lambda_l^{(2s)}(ka) - 1}{1 - \left[\frac{ka\, j'_l(ka) j_l(ka)}{\kappa a\, j_l(ka) j'_l(\kappa a)}\right]} \right\} \tag{10}$$

and $\Lambda_l^{(2s)}(ka)$ is a rather complicated algebraic expression which we shall not present here. Instead we give the expansions of $\Lambda_l^{(2s)}(ka)$ in powers of ka which, for even and odd values of l are

$$\Lambda_{2l}^{(2s)}(ka) = \sum_{n=0}^{s-l-1} \frac{(-1)^n (ka)^{2n+2l} c_{2n+2l,2l}}{(2n+2l)!(4l+1) j_{2l}(ka)} + L^{(2s)}(\mu_i) \tag{11a}$$

and

$$\Lambda_{2l+1}^{(2s)}(ka) = \sum_{n=0}^{s-l-1} \frac{(-1)^n (ka)^{2n+2l+1} c_{2n+2l+1,2l+1}}{(2n+2l+1)!(4l+3) j_{2l+1}(ka)} + M^{(2s)}(\mu_i) \tag{11b}$$

where $L^{(2s)}(\mu_i)$ and $M^{(2s)}(\mu_i)$ are functions of the angles at which the B.C.'s are satisfied. Both $L^{(2s)}$ and $M^{(2s)}$ are expansions in (ka) in which the lowest order term is $(ka)^{2s}$ and $(ka)^{2s+1}$ respectively. The quantities $c_{2n,2}$ and $c_{2n+1,2m+1}$ are coefficients in the expansions

$$\mu^{2n} = \sum_{i=0}^{n} c_{2n,2i} P_{2i}(\mu), \quad \mu^{2n+1} = \sum_{i=0}^{n} C_{2n+1,2i+1} P_{2i+1}(\mu)$$

Procedure (2) involves the simultaneous solution of:

From (5b) and (4)

$$ika\,\mu_i \exp(ika\mu_i) + ka \sum_{l+1}^{2s-1} (2l+1) i^l A_{l,2}^{(2s)} h_l'(ka) P_l(\mu_i) \tag{12a}$$

$$= \kappa a \sum_{l=0}^{2s-1} (2l+1) i^l B_{l,2}^{(2s)} j_l'(\kappa a) P_l(\mu_i)$$

and from (2a) and (3)

$$[j_l(ka) + h_l(ka) A_l] = j_l(\kappa a) B_l \tag{12b}$$

Similarly to our previous treatment we consider the A_l and B_l in (12b) as approximate values $A_{l,2}^{(2s)}$ and $B_{l,2}^{(2s)}$ and combine (12a) and (12b) to obtain

$$A_{l,2}^{(2s)} = [1 + \xi_l^{(2s)}(ka)] A_l \tag{13}$$

where

$$\xi_l^{(2s)}(ka) = \frac{\Gamma_l^{(2s)}(ka) - 1}{1 - [\frac{\kappa a j_l(ka) j_l'(\kappa a)}{ka j_l'(ka) j_l'(\kappa a)}]} \tag{14}$$

The quantities $\Gamma_l^{(2s)}(ka)$ when expanded in powers of (ka) are very similar to the $\Lambda_l^{(2s)}$ and are given by (for l even and odd respectively)

$$\Gamma_{2l}^{(2s)}(ka) = \sum_{n=0}^{s-l-1} \left[\frac{(-1)^n (ka)^{2n+2l-1} c_{2n+2l,2l}}{(2n+2l-1)!(4l+1) j'_{2l}(ka)} \right] + N^{(2s)}(\mu_i) \tag{15a}$$

$$\Gamma_{2l+1}^{(2s)}(ka) = \sum_{n=0}^{s-l-1} \frac{(-1)^n (ka)^{2n+2l} c_{2n+2l+1,2l+1}}{(2n+2l)!(4l+3) j'_{2l+1}(ka)} + 0^{(2s)}(\mu_i) \tag{15b}$$

where only the functions of the higher powers of (ka) involve the choice of B.C. angles μ_i.

Finally then we use the full approximation to obtain from Eq. (8a) and (12a) the coefficients

$$A_l^{(2s)} = \frac{\kappa a\, j_l(ka)\, j'_l(\kappa a) \Lambda_l^{(2s)}(ka) - ka\, j'_l(ka) j_l(\kappa a) \Gamma_l^{(2s)}(ka)}{ka\, h'_l(ka) j_l(\kappa a) - \kappa a\, h_l(ka) j'_l(ka)} \tag{16a}$$

$$B_l^{(2s)} = \frac{ka[h'_l(ka) j_l(ka) \Lambda_l^{(2s)}(ka) - h_l(ka) j'_l(ka) \Gamma_l^{(2s)}(ka)]}{ka\, h'_l(ka) j_l(\kappa a) - \kappa a\, h_l(ka) j'_l(\kappa a)} \tag{16b}$$

where the modifying coefficients $\Lambda_l^{(2s)}$ and $\Gamma_l^{(2s)}$ are identical to those defined by Eqs. (11) and (15).

We may then write

$$A_l^{(2s)} = [1 + \rho_l^{(2s)}(ka) + \xi_l^{(2s)}(\kappa a)] A_l \tag{17}$$

Several general facts are rather evident. It can be seen by tracing back along the trail of definitions of ρ_l and ξ_l that both of these quantities are real (for real κ) and that consequently the phases of the exact and approximate A_l are identical. Further we see that the approximation is independent of the choice of angles up to some power of (ka) [at least $(ka)^{2s}$]. This means that for $l = 2s - 1$ we obtain only the leading term in the expansion (in ascending powers of ka) but that for smaller values of l we obtain successively more and more terms which are independent of the choice of boundary points. Finally as ka → 0 the $A_l^{(2)}$ go as $(ka)^{2l+1}$ and become identical with the Rayleigh approximation.

The approximate expressions are so complicated that it is certainly not easy to draw any more general inferences if indeed they exist. At this point we must resort to demonstrating the two features which imply the usefulness of our approximation: (1) The values of the coefficients converge reasonably rapidly to some value; and (2) this value is the correct one.

Extensive numerical analysis was carried out in evaluating the quantities A_l, B_l, $\rho_l^{(2s)}$ and $\xi_l^{(2s)}$. We present in Tables 1 and 2 some sets of values of $\rho_l^{(2s)} + \xi_l^{(2s)}$ (full approximation procedure) for spheres with refractive index m = 1.3.

TABLE 1

Numerical Values of the $\rho_l^{(2s)}$(ka) for the Refractive Index m = 1.3

s = 2

$\rho_l^{(4)}$ka	ka = 0.2	ka = 0.4	ka = 0.6	ka = 0.8	ka = 1.0	ka = 1.5	ka = 2. 0
0	2.2(-5)	3.5(-4)	1.8(-3)	5.9(-3)	1.4(-2)	7.6(-2)	2.5(-1)
1	-1.7(-4)	-1.3(-3)	-1.3(-3)	-2.1(-3)	-2.7(-3)	-1.3(-3)	1.0(-1)
2	2.4(-1)	2.3(-1)	2.4(-1)	2.1(-1)	2.0(-1)	1.8(-1)	9.2(-1)
3	1.9(-1)	2.6(-1)	2.5(-1)	2.6(-1)	2.5(-1)	2.2(-1)	1.9(-1)

s = 3

$\rho_l^{(6)}$ka	ka = 0.2	ka = 0.4	ka = 0.6	ka = 0.8	ka = 1.0	ka = 1.5	ka = 2.0
0	2.1(-9)	1.3(-7)	1.6(-6)	8.9(-6)	3.5(-5)	4.3(-4)	2.7(-3)
1	1.1(-7)	1.7(-6)	8.1(-6)	2.3(-5)	4.6(-5)	4.9(-5)	-7.7(-4)
2	-1.6(-4)	-6.3(-4)	-1.4(-3)	-2.4(-3)	-3.5(-3)	-6.3(-3)	-7.0(-3)
3	-1.3(-4)	-5.4(-4)	-1.2(-3)	-2.1(-3)	-3.2(-3)	-6.5(-3)	-9.7(-3)
4	2.9(-1)	2.9(-1)	2.8(-1)	2.8(-1)	2.8(-1)	2.6(-1)	2.3(-1)
5	-1.6	-7.3(-1)	-7.2(-1)	-7.2(-1)	-7.1(-1)	-6.9(-1)	-6.5(-1)

s = 4

$\rho_l^{(8)}$ka	ka = 0.2	ka = 0.4	ka = 0.6	ka = 0.8	ka = 1.0	ka = 1.5	ka = 2.0
0	-6.1(-13)	-1.6(-11)	-4.1(-10)	-4.2(-9)	-2.5(-8)	-6.9(-7)	-7.2(-6)
1	3.6(-12)	1.5(-10)	1.5(-9)	7.7(-9)	2.4(-8)	6.0(-8)	-1.7(-6)
2	-1.3(-8)	-2.0(-7)	-9.8(-7)	-3.0(-6)	-7.0(-6)	-2.9(-5)	-5.8(-5)
3	6.2(-7)	3.7(-7)	1.9(-6)	5.9(-6)	1.4(-5)	6.5(-5)	1.8(-4)
4	-4.3(-3)	-4.4(-5)	-9.6(-4)	-1.7(-3)	-2.6(-3)	-5.5(-3)	-9.0(-3)
5	-1.5(-2)	-6.4(-3)	5.5(-4)	1.7(-3)	2.7(-3)	5.8(-3)	9.8(-3)
6	3.1(-1)	3.1(-1)	3.1(-1)	3.1(-1)	3.0(-1)	2.9(-1)	2.8(-1)
7	9.2(-1)	9.1(-1)	9.1(-1)	9.1(-1)	9.0(-1)	8.8(-1)	8.5(-1)

Noting that the validity of the approximation is justified only if the quantities $\rho_l^{(2s)}$ and $\xi_l^{(2s)}$ are small, it is rather interesting to observe the numerically experimental fact that the full approximation procedure is not consistently worse and is in many cases better than procedure (1) in which the B.C.'s are presumably better satisfied.

TABLE 2

Numerical Values of the $\tau_l^{(2s)}(ka) = \rho_l^{(2s)}(ka) + \zeta_l^{(2s)}(ka)$ for m = 1.3

s = 2

$\tau_l^{(4)}$ka	ka = 0.2	ka = 0.4	ka = 0.6	ka = 0.8	ka = 1.0	ka = 1.5	ka = 2.0
0	9.0(-4)	-3.6(-3)	-4.2(-2)	-9.0(-3)	-8.4(-3)	4.3(-2)	2.2(-1)
1	5.6(-4)	2.2(-3)	7.6(-2)	1.5(-2)	1.8(-2)	4.2(-2)	-7.6(-2)
2	-1.1	-7.5(-1)	-1.1	-1.1	-1.1	-1.0	-9.8(-1)
3	1.1	-1.7(-1)	-1.9(-1)	-1.9(-1)	-2.1(-1)	-2.0(-1)	-2.1(-1)

s = 3

$\tau_l^{(6)}$ka	ka = 0.2	ka = 0.4	ka = 0.6	ka = 0.8	ka = 1.0	ka = 1.5	ka = 2.0
0	-1.4(-6)	-2.2(-5)	-1.1(-4)	-3.3(-4)	-7.6(-4)	-3.0(-3)	-4.1(-3)
1	-6.8(-7)	-1.1(-5)	-5.6(-5)	-1.8(-4)	-4.5(-4)	-2.4(-3)	-9.9(-3)
2	5.6(-4)	1.5(-3)	5.1(-3)	9.1(-3)	1.4(-2)	3.2(-2)	5.9 -2)
3	1.8(-4)	7.3(-3)	1.6(-3)	2.9(-3)	4.7(-3)	1.1(-2)	2.0(-2)
4	6.4(-1)	6.5(-1)	6.5(-1)	6.4(-1)	6.4(-1)	6.1(-1)	5.8(-1)
5	-18.7	2.8(-1)	3.0(-1)	3.0(-1)	3.0(-1)	3.2(-1)	3.4(-1)

s = 4

$\tau_l^{(8)}$ka	ka = 0.2	ka = 0.4	ka = 0.6	ka = 0.8	ka = 1.0	ka = 1.5	ka = 2.0
0	-2.2(-11)	-1.4(-9)	-1.6(-8)	-8.9(-8)	-3.4(-7)	-2.4(-6)	-1.7(-5)
1	-2.0(-11)	-1.2(-9)	-1.4(-8)	-8.1(-8)	-3.1(-7)	-3.2(-6)	2.4(-5)
2	3.8(-8)	4.1(-7)	3.1(-6)	10.0(-5)	2.5(-5)	1.3(-4)	4.4(-4)
3	-1.6(-6)	-8.0(-6)	-3.9(-6)	-1.3(-5)	-3.1(-5)	-1.6(-4)	-5.3(-4)
4	-9.2(-3)	8.1(-4)	9.8(-3)	1.8(-3)	3.0(-3)	6.4(-2)	1.2(-2)
5	-2.0(-1)	-1.5(-2)	-1.7(-3)	-1.4(-3)	-2.2(-3)	-5.2(-3)	-9.6(-3)
6	-1.0(-1)	-1.0(-1)	-1.1(-1)	-1.0(-1)	-1.1(-1)	-1.1(-1)	-1.1(-1)
7	-2.6(-1)	-2.6(-1)	-2.6(-1)	-1.2(-1)	-2.7(-1)	-2.8(-1)	-2.9(-1)

We have explicitly evaluated the $\rho_l^{(2s)}$ and $\xi_l^{(2s)}$ only for values of ka up to ka = 2 (implicitly they were calculated up to ka = 5.8). In any case it is clear to see that for s = 2, the first two scattering coefficients $A_l^{(2s)}$ are good to within a few percent up to ka = 2. For s = 3 we obtain the first four scattering coefficients to this order of accuracy; and finally for s = 4, the first six are so defined. Although one would expect the values of $\rho_l^{(2s)}$ to be consistently smaller for smaller values of ka than for larger values of ka, we have found this not to be true. For example, the value of $\rho_3^{(4)}$ is largest for ka = 0.2 and is almost constant from ka = 0.4 to ka = 2.0. It should be pointed out that for smaller values of ka it is possible that numerical errors may have accumulated in the inversion of the simultaneous equation matrix so that the value of $\rho_3^{(4)}$ might be in error. In general, the computational procedure of inverting the matrices is such that if ka is small, it is preferable to use an approximation whose order is not much larger than the minimum one required.

Tables 3 and 4 are to be compared term by term for differences in the complex scattering coefficients which show up as dependent on varying the selection of angles at which the B.C.'s are satisfied. Several conclusions are evident after a careful perusal of these two tables. One conclusion is that over the expected range of validity of the spproximation ($l < s$, $ka < s$) the differences in these scattering coefficients is trivial except where the coefficients themselves become so small as to be negligible. As has already been pointed out the phases of the scattering coefficients should be and are invariant to the choice of angles. The tables have been spot checked for this as an indication of the possibility of numerical error and no deviations have been detected.

Tables 5 and 6 indicate again how the important terms in the series are independent of the choice of B.C. angles. In particular we see that for $s = 6$ the values of the scattering coefficients for sizes up to $ka = 5$ are given within better than one percent up to $l = 7$ (8th term) where the coefficients may already be neglected.

For calculating the total cross-section for a given value of ka it appears from Table 7 that one can be guaranteed of an accuracy considerably better than one percent by using the approximation which involves a number of B.C. points equal to the nearest integer less than ka.

c. Approximate scattering by prolate spheroids.

The configuration appropriate to this problem is shown in Fig. 1. We consider a prolate spheroid of length 2b and width 2a ($b > a$) whos symmetry axis is along the direction of propagation of the scalar radiation.

The equation for the surface of the spheroid is

$$\frac{r}{a} = (1 - \eta^2 \cos^2 \theta)^{-\frac{1}{2}} \tag{18}$$

where $\eta^2 = 1 - (a/b)^2$. Although there might be some advantage in using spheroidal coordinates we have found it

TABLE 3

Scattering Coefficients $A_l^{(8)}$ for a Sphere of Refractive Index m = 1.3
Angular Positions at which Boundary Conditions are Satisfied are
$\theta_1 = 10°, \theta_2 = 32.5°, \theta_3 = 55°, \theta_4 = 77.5°$

ka	$A_0^{(8)}$	$A_1^{(8)}$	$A_2^{(8)}$	$A_3^{(8)}$
1.0	-0.049, 534, 84 i0.216, 981, 8	-2.095, 560(-4) i0.014, 475, 2	-1.646, 739(-7) i4.057, 968(-4)	-4.873, 225(-11) i6.470, 687(-6)
2.0	-0.423, 076, 0 i0.494, 041, 9	-0.146, 019, 9 i0.353, 127, 0	-1.927, 607(-3) i0.043, 859, 41	-7.381, 245(-6) i2.716, 772(-3)
3.0	-0.486, 047, 5 i0.499, 869, 7	-0.665, 144, 1 i0.471, 970, 6	-0.299, 405, 8 i0.457, 759, 2	-6, 855, 142(-3) i0.082, 501, 63
4.0	-0.939, 155, 5 i0.244, 630, 7	-0.716, 439, 4 i0.450, 687, 1	-0.838, 190, 8 i0.365, 549, 5	-0.508, 918, 1 i0.499, 542, 4
5.0	-0.991, 155, 4 i0.119, 272, 8	-0.996, 484, 7 i0.014, 720, 876	-0.877, 347, 5 i0.328, 293, 3	-0.945, 681, 7 i0.223, 482, 4

TABLE 3 (Continued)

ka	$A_4^{(8)}$	$A_5^{(8)}$	$A_6^{(8)}$	$A_7^{(8)}$
1.0	-1.003, 705(-13) i6.583, 169(-8)	5.244, 207(-14) i4.640, 630(-10)	2.691, 890(-18) i2.028, 563(-12)	1.154, 230(-18) i8.836, 961(-15)
2.0	-1.245, 258(-8) i1.115, 763(-4)	-1.026, 259(-11) i3.211, 343(-6)	-3.745, 451(-15) i5.585, 579(-8)	-2.406, 651(-18) i1.117, 888(-9)
3.0	-5.298, 698(-5) i7.274, 703(-3)	-2.252, 085(-7) i4.776, 254(-4)	-4.164, 604(-10) i1.837, 003(-5)	-7.261, 956(-13) i8.727, 847(-7)
4.0	-0.017, 535, 81 i0.130, 993, 5	-2.056, 689(-4) i0.014, 530, 29	-1.121 423(-6) i9.316, 697(-4)	-6.749, 310(-9) i8.438, 223(-5)
5.0	-0.730, 802, 8 i0.434, 599, 0	-0.040, 915, 22 i0.203, 205, 4	-3.996, 412(-4) i0.016, 984, 88	-6.097, 832(-6) i2.545, 918(-3)

TABLE 4

Scattering Coefficients $A_l^{(8)}$ for a Sphere of Refractive Index m = 1.3
Angular Positions at which Boundary Conditions are Satisfied are
$\theta_1 = 0°$, $\theta_2 = 22.5°$, $\theta_3 = 45°$, $\theta_4 = 67.5°$

ka	$A_0^{(8)}$	$A_1^{(8)}$	$A_2^{(8)}$	$A_3^{(8)}$
1.0	-0.049, 534, 32 i0.216, 979, 5	-2.095, 557(-4) i0.014, 474, 52	-1.646, 443(-7) i4.057, 418(-4)	-4.429, 208(-11) i6.470, 727(-6)
2.0	-0.422, 831, 5 i0.493, 756, 3	-0.146, 019, 17 i0, 353, 125, 1	-1.923, 037(-3) i0.043, 755, 42	-7, 381, 756(-6) i2.716, 960(-3)
3.0	-0.488, 770, 3 i0, 502, 669, 9	-0.665, 107, 3 i0, 471, 944, 5	-0.295, 333, 8 i0.451, 533, 5	-6.857, 578(-3) i0, 082, 530, 94
4.0	-1.045, 818 i0.272, 414, 2	-0.716, 441, 3 i0.450, 744, 9	-0.801, 279, 1 i0.349, 451, 7	-0.509, 469, 7 i0.500, 083, 8
5.0	-1.197, 145 i0.144, 061, 1	-1.000, 568 i0.014, 781, 20	-0.878, 284, 0 i0.328, 643, 7	-0.947, 674, 3 i0.223, 953, 35

TABLE 4 (Continued)

ka	$A_4^{(8)}$	$A_5^{(8)}$	$A_6^{(8)}$	$A_7^{(8)}$
1.0	-2.162, 455(-15) i6.536, 006(-8)	1.849, 599(-13) i2.604, 276(-11)	-4.208, 555(-19) i1.173, 327(-12)	-7.256, 898(-19) i2.497, 293(-16)
2.0	-1.207, 444(-8) i1.081, 871(-4)	-1.014, 600(-11) i3.185, 952(-6)	-2.072, 432(-15) i3.122, 903(-8)	9.036, 006(-18) i7.667, 151(-10)
3.0	-4.897, 194(-5) i6.723, 468(-3)	-2.207, 244(-7) i4.681, 155(-4)	-2.122, 014(-10) i9.360, 192(-6)	-4.769, 251(-13) i5.732, 091(-7)
4.0	-0.014, 826, 46 i0.110, 754, 5	-1.972, 147(-4) i0.013, 933, 01	-4.864, 164(-7) i4, 041, 107(-4)	-4.148, 749(-9) i5.186, 912(-5)
5.0	-0.525, 503, 7 i0.312, 510, 3	-0.037, 784, 93 i0.187, 658, 8	-1.290, 071(-4) i5. 482, 845(-3)	-3.406, 539(-6) i1.422, 271(-3)

TABLE 5

Scattering Coefficients for a Sphere of Refractive Index m = 1.3

Angular Positions at which Boundary Conditions are Satisfied are
$\theta_1 = 8°$, $\theta_2 = 22°$, $\theta_3 = 36°$, $\theta_4 = 50°$, $\theta_5 = 64°$
$\theta_6 = 78°$

	ka = 4	ka = 5
$A_0^{(12)}$	-0.936, 519, 3 i0.243, 944, 0	-0.985, 896, 9 i0.118, 640, 0
$A_1^{(12)}$	-0.716, 423, 2 i0.450, 733, 6	-0.999, 776, 7 i0.014, 769, 50
$A_2^{(12)}$	-0.840, 176, 5 i0.366, 415, 5	-0.877, 252, 7 i0.328, 357, 8
$A_3^{(12)}$	-0.509. 296, 1 i0.499, 913, 4	-0.947, 106, 47 i0.223, 819, 1
$A_4^{(12)}$	-0.017, 603, 28 i0.131, 497, 4	-0.738, 400, 7 i0.439, 114
$A_5^{(12)}$	-2.003, 107(-4) i0.014, 151, 74	-0.038, 962, 97 i0.193, 509, 6
$A_6^{(12)}$	-1.447, 620(-6) i1.202, 370(-3)	-5.520, 048(-4) i0.023, 460, 39
$A_7^{(12)}$	-6.398, 064(-9) i7.998, 417(-5)	-5.736, 642(-6) i2.395, 116(-3)
$A_8^{(12)}$	-1.762, 039(-11) i4.155, 607(-6)	-3.896, 484(-8) i1.957, 383, 6(-4)
$A_9^{(12)}$	-3.913, 989(-14) i1.776, 048(-7)	-1.811, 698(-10) i1.349, 351(-5)
$A_{10}^{(12)}$	-9.873, 709(-17) i5.030, 706(-9)	-4.395, 214(-13) i5.904, 508(-7)
$A_{11}^{(12)}$	-1.009, 969(-17) i1.748, 354(-10)	-1.114, 085(-15) i3.368, 192(-3)

TABLE 6

Scattering Coefficients for a Sphere of Refractive Index m = 1.3

Angular Positions at which Boundary
Conditions are Satisfied are
$\theta_1 = 0°$, $\theta_2 = 15°$, $\theta_3 = 30°$, $\theta_4 = 45°$, $\theta_5 = 60°$
$\theta_6 = 75°$

	ka = 4	ka = 5
$A_0^{(12)}$	-0.936, 698, 8 i0.243, 990.8	-0.986, 421, 9 i0.118, 703, 2
$A_1^{(12)}$	-0.716, 423, 4 i0.450, 733, 7	-0.999, 782, 7 i0.014, 769, 59
$A_2^{(12)}$	-0.840, 119, 5 i0.366, 390, 7	-0.877, 455, 1 i0.328, 333, 5
$A_3^{(12)}$	-0.509, 296, 3 i0.499, 913, 6	-0.947, 107, 9 i0.223, 819, 5
$A_4^{(12)}$	-0.017, 597, 82 i0.131, 456, 7	-0.737, 409, 0 i0.438, 527, 6
$A_5^{(12)}$	-2.003, 091(-4) i0.014, 151, 63	-0.038, 961, 65 i0.193, 502, 9
$A_6^{(12)}$	-1.444, 638(-6) i1.200, 190(-3)	-5.488, 371(-4) i0.032, 235, 76
$A_7^{(12)}$	-6.401, 423(-9) i7.998, 753(-5)	-5.737, 106(-6) i2.395, 310(-3)
$A_8^{(12)}$	-1.707, 119(-11) i4.056, 325(-6)	-3.735, 678(-8) i1.876, 609(-4)
$A_9^{(12)}$	-1.499, 002(-13) i1.764, 777(-7)	-1.790, 520(-10) i1.334, 291(-5)
$A_{10}^{(12)}$	-6.721, 264(-17) i3.735, 586(-9)	-3.131, 437(-13) i4.209, 051(-7)
$A_{11}^{(12)}$	-9.904, 413(-17) i1.393, 141(-10)	-8.466, 696(-16) i2.613, 487(-8)

TABLE 7

Exact and Approximate Scattering Efficiency Factors
for a Sphere with Refractive Index m = 1.3

	ka = 0.4	ka = 0.8	ka = 1.0	ka = 1.4	ka = 1.8	ka = 2.0
Q	5.527, 85(-3)	0.088, 425	0.200, 655	0.487, 09	0.703, 52	0.870, 83
$Q^{(8)}$	5.530, 11(-3)	0.088, 488	0.200, 658	0.487, 272	0.703, 522	0.870, 826
$Q^{(10)}$	5.528, 50(-3)	0.088, 488	0.200, 658	0.487, 273	0.703, 524	0.870, 829
$Q^{(12)}$		0.088, 488	0.200, 657	0.487, 273	0.703, 524	0.870, 831

	ka = 2.4	ka = 2.8	ka = 3.0	ka = 3.2	ka = 3.6	ka = 4.0
Q	1.273, 64	1.573, 81	1.790, 19		2.340, 13	2.753, 11
$Q^{(8)}$	1.273, 626	1.573, 636	1.789, 767	2.019, 190	2, 338, 452	2.750, 422
$Q^{(10)}$	1.273, 637	1.573, 762	1.790, 077	2.019, 776	2.339, 667	2.752, 484
$Q^{(12)}$	1.273, 643	1.573, 807	1.709, 189	2.020, 001	2, 340, 117	2.753, 100

	ka = 4.6	ka = 5.0	ka = 5.4	ka = 5.8
Q		3.533, 64		
$Q^{(8)}$	3.175, 907	3.523, 152	3.663, 221	3.990, 987
$Q^{(10)}$	3.178, 406	3.521, 577	3.642, 263	3.924, 411
$Q^{(12)}$	3.182, 225	3.533, 232	3.656, 848	3.937, 768

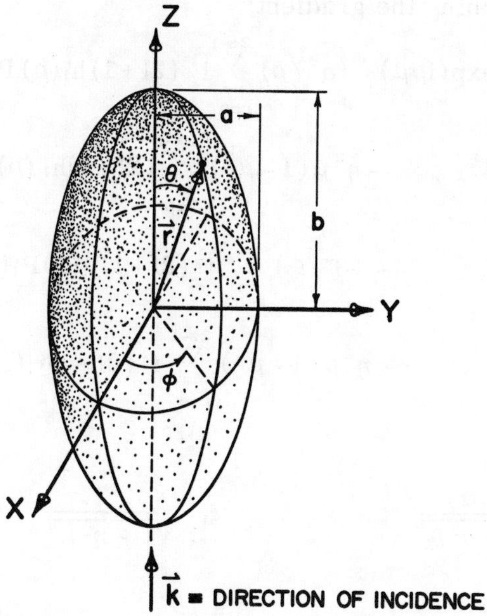

Fig. 1. Orientation of spheroid scatterer and direction of incidence of scalar plane wave

easier, at least in this first approach, to continue to use spherical coordinates. The expansions for the interior and exterior wave functions are then formally exactly the same as they were for the sphere and the equations defining the approximate wave functions are the same as Eq. (4).

The boundary conditions (Eqs. (2) or (5)) are to be applied now at the surface defined by Eq. (18). Applying the boundary conditions we get the resulting sets of equations for matching the function:

$$\exp(i\rho\mu) + \sum_{l=0}^{2s-1} i^l (2l+1) h_l(\rho) A_l^{(2s)} P_l(\mu)$$

$$= \sum_{l=0}^{2s-1} i^l (2l+1) j_l(\xi) B_l^{(2s)} P_l(\mu) \qquad (19a)$$

and for matching the gradient:

$$i\rho\mu(1-\eta^2)\exp(i\rho\mu) + (\alpha^2/\rho)\sum_{l=0}^{2s-1} i^l(2l+1)h'_l(\rho)P_l(\mu)A_l^{(2s)}$$

$$-\eta^2\mu(1-\mu^2)\sum_{l=0}^{2s-1}(2l+1)h_l(\rho)P'_l(\mu)A_l^{(2s)} \tag{19b}$$

$$= (\beta^2/\xi)\sum_{l=0}^{2s-1} i^l(2l+1)j'_l(\xi)P_l(\mu)B_l^{(2s)}$$

$$-\eta^2\mu(1-\mu^2)\sum_{l=0}^{2s-1} i^l(2l+1)j_l(\xi)P'_l(\mu)B_l^{(2s)}$$

where

$$\rho = \frac{\alpha}{\sqrt{1-\eta^2\mu^2}}, \qquad \xi = \frac{\beta}{\sqrt{1-\eta^2\mu^2}}$$

$$\alpha = ka \qquad \beta = \kappa a \qquad \mu = \cos\theta$$

Equations (19a) and (19b) may be separated into equations which are even and odd in μ and which involve respectively the even and odd values of l.

The expressions become so formidable that little can be deduced from them. We therefore go immediately to a representation of some numerical results.

Table 8 is presented to show how (by comparison with Table 7), the range of validity of the approximation depends on the degree of elongation. It is to be expected that the number of scattering coefficients required to give a certain degree of accuracy should be $l \sim (b/a)ka$ if it is $l \sim ka$ for the sphere. The reason for this is clear when one notes that the phase shift for a ray parallel to the axis of the spheroid is exactly b/a times as large as that for a ray traversing a sphere of radius a. One may reasonably conclude that the order of approximation required for an accuracy of one percent is obtained when s is one less than the nearest integer to (b/a)ka.

Figures 2 and 3 contain a graphic portrayal of differences between various orders of approximation for two

TABLE 8

Scattering Efficiency Factors for a Prolate Spheroid with b/a = 2 and m = 1.3

	ka = 0.4	ka = 0.8	ka = 1.0	ka = 1.4	ka = 1.8	ka = 2.0
$Q^{(8)}$	0.011, 920, 8	0.236, 553	0.484, 639	1.758, 542	3.193, 689	3.450, 687
$Q^{(10)}$	0.011, 920, 8	0.236, 554	0.483, 859	1.758, 101	3.196, 556	3.450, 397
$Q^{(12)}$			0.484, 743	1.759, 671	3.194, 680	3.450, 037
$Q^{(14)}$						3.450, 548

	ka = 2.4	ka = 2.8	ka = 3.0	ka = 3.2	ka = 3.6	ka = 4.0
$Q^{(8)}$	4.854, 463	5.171, 704	4.650, 036	5.525, 259	6.930, 284	7.298, 593
$Q^{(10)}$	4.796, 134	5.184, 812		6.152, 740	5.922, 495	6.288, 430
$Q^{(12)}$	4.798, 951	5.138, 471		6.268, 150	6, 061, 440	6.261, 153
$Q^{(14)}$	4.799, 104	6.139, 032		6.273, 697	6, 071, 912	6.265, 153
$Q^{(16)}$	4.798, 918	5.139, 445		6.272, 457	6.071, 789	6.265, 833

	ka = 4.5	ka = 5.0	ka = 5.4	ka = 5.8
$Q^{(8)}$	5.262, 951	4.222, 431	2.752, 570	1.447, 217
$Q^{(10)}$	5.544, 403	4.305, 276	2.919, 845	2.334, 681
$Q^{(12)}$	5.186, 779		2.873, 365	2.059, 084
$Q^{(14)}$	5.373, 065		3.260, 315	2.206, 513
$Q^{(16)}$	5.420, 588		3.290, 666	2.189, 633

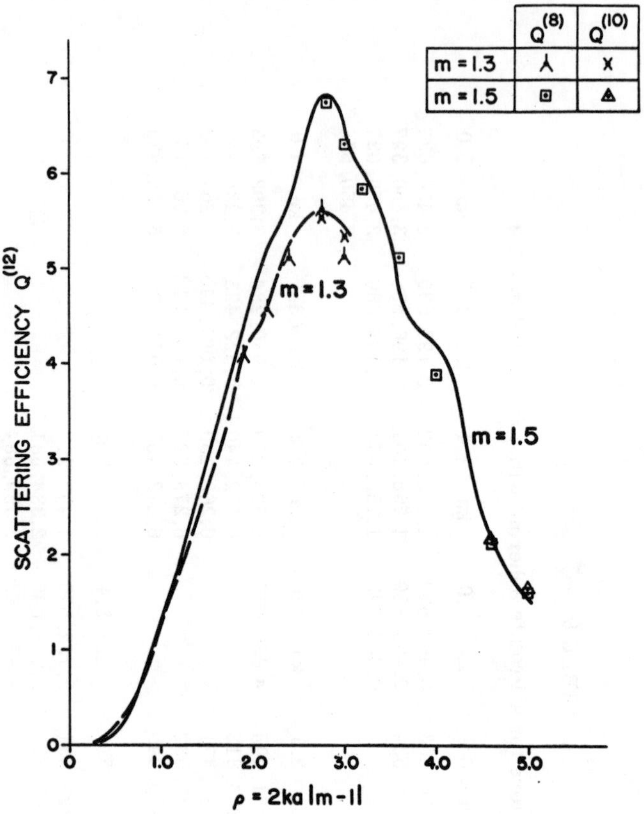

Fig. 2. Scattering efficiencies for b/a = 1.5, s = 6 and a sampling of s = 4 and 5

elongations (b/a = 1.5 and b/a = 2). Here we have plotted the total scattering efficiency versus the parameter $\rho = 2ka(m - 1)$ which is the phase shift of a ray traversing the spheroid along its symmetry axis. The extra points are shown only for ρ values greater than those for which they would fall on the curves. For example we see in Fig. 2 that the eight point (s = 4) approximation is acceptable on the m = 1.5 curve up to about $\rho = 3$ (perhaps slightly less) whereas on the m = 1.3 curve, it is acceptable only to about $\rho = 2.2$. Note that this is reasonable because the corresponding values of ka are both about ka = 3.

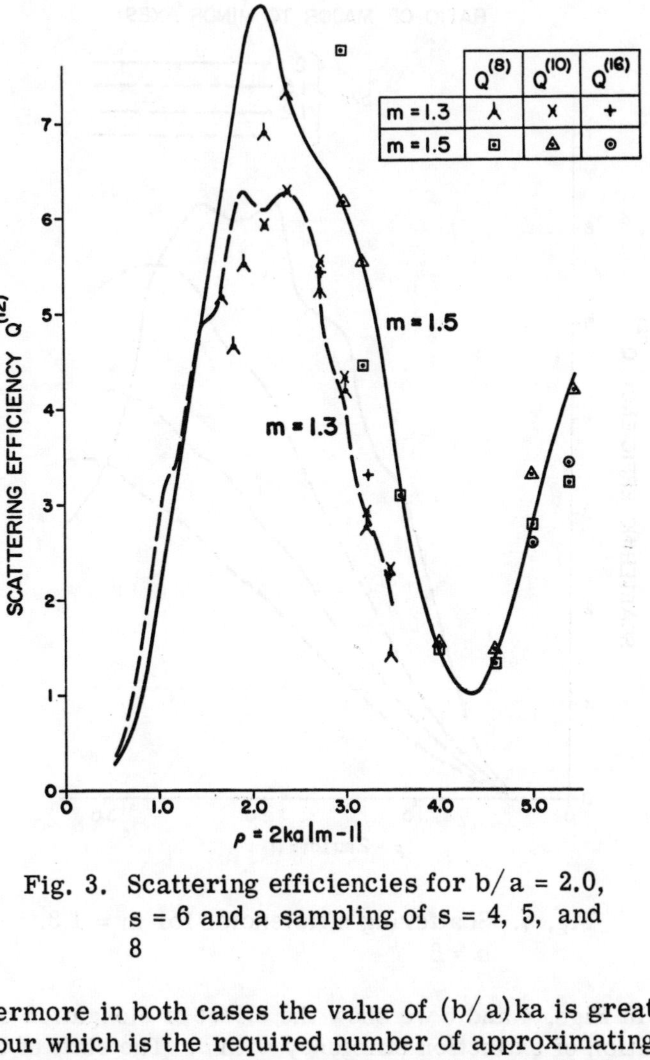

Fig. 3. Scattering efficiencies for b/a = 2.0, s = 6 and a sampling of s = 4, 5, and 8

Furthermore in both cases the value of (b/a)ka is greater than four which is the required number of approximating points. We could apply this argument to the results for b/a = 2 presented in Fig. 4. We should expect, for example that for s = 5 the approximation should be good for ka = 2.5 or ρ = 2.5 and ρ = 1.5 for m = 1.5 and 1.3 respectively. It can be seen that actually the approximation appears to be good up to and somewhat beyond ρ = 3 and ρ = 2 for the two indices of refraction.

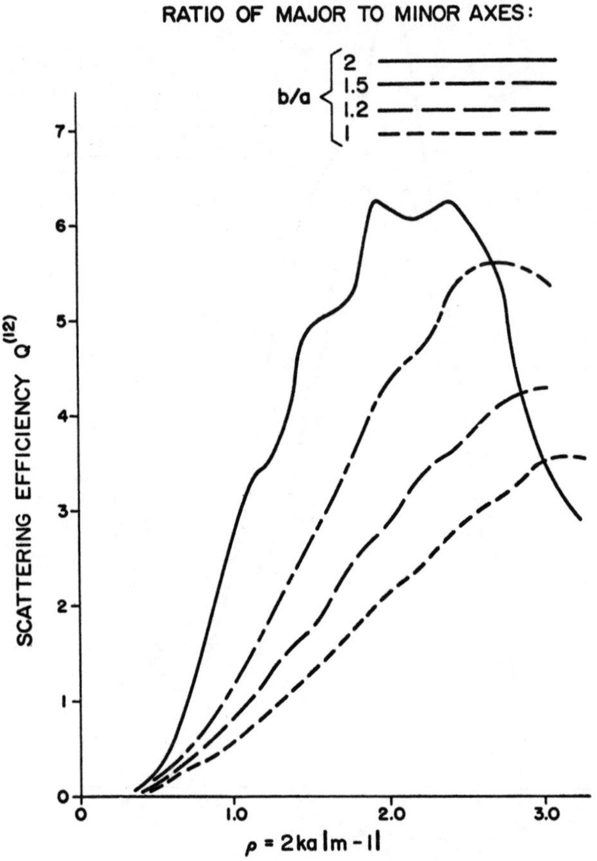

Fig. 4. Scattering efficiencies for m = 1.3, s = 6

In Figs. 4 and 5 we show the effect of elongation on the variation of extinction efficiency with ρ. The shift of the maximum in the total cross-section curves toward shorter values of ρ (by the factor a/b) with increasing b/a has an obvious explanation in terms of a ray approximation (3). However the interesting result which is lost in the simple ray approximation is the tendency toward increasing the height of the first broad maximum in the efficiency curve as b/a increases, and simultaneously introducing a deeper

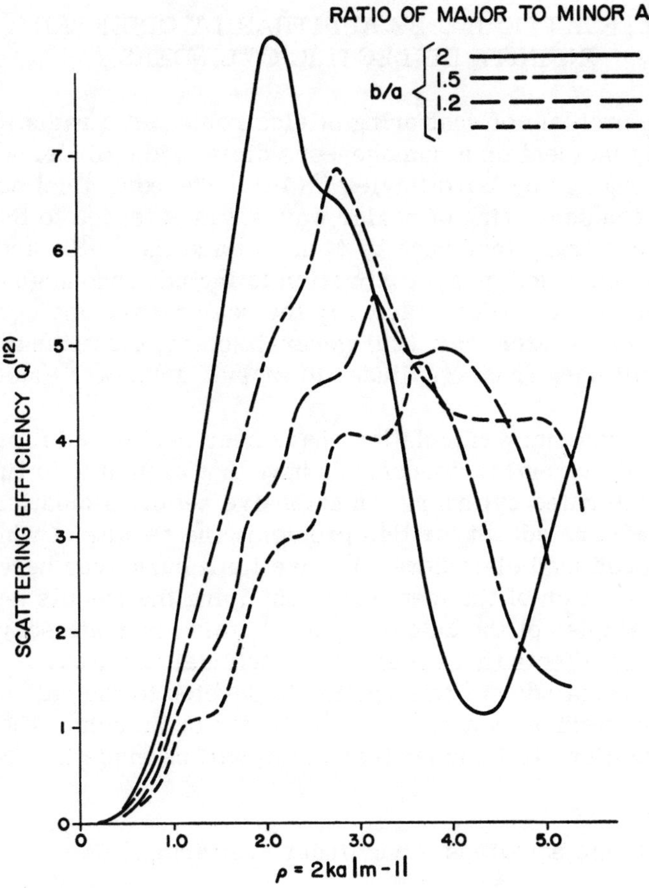

Fig. 5. Scattering efficiencies for m = 1.5, s = 6

dip in the first minimum. It should be remarked that this confirms at least these qualitative aspects of early experimental data on scattering by dielectric spheroids (4). So far no simple theoretical explanation has been given for these effects.

III. SCATTERING BY ARBITRARILY ORIENTED INFINITE DIELECTRIC CYLINDERS

The problem of scattering of electromagnetic radiation normally incident on a homogeneous dielectric cylinder was solved long ago by Lord Rayleigh (14). The equivalent solution for the scattering of scalar waves was extended to the case of arbitrary incidence by Montroll and Hart (10) and later (9) extended by approximation to include inhomogeneous dielectric cylinders (actually the scalar wave analogue). Several years later Wait (20) generalized the electromagnetic scattering from a cylinder to include arbitrary orientation.

Although many calculations have been performed for the case of normal incidence, we have not been able to find any for the tilted cylinder. An extensive set of calculations are being carried out for this problem, the results of which will be published elsewhere (6). We limit ourselves here to a demonstration of the method for obtaining the results and some examples of the calculations. We also indicate some interesting effects that occur as the cylinder is tilted.

The remainder of this section is devoted to the calculation of scattering by a dielectric cylinder in vacuum. The generalizations to include other cases will be made in a later paper.

a. Basic equations for cylinder scattering.

We follow the notation of van de Hulst (18). Let U and V be two solutions of the scalar wave equation

$$\overline{\nabla}^2 \psi + m^2 k^2 \psi = 0 \tag{20}$$

We define the associated solutions M and N of the vector wave equation

$$\mathbf{M}_\psi = \overline{\nabla} \times (\hat{z}\psi) \tag{21}$$

$$mk\, \mathbf{N}_\psi = \overline{\nabla} \times \mathbf{M}_\psi$$

where $\hat{z}$ is a unit vector along the cylinder axis.

The electric and magnetic fields are then given by

$$\begin{aligned} \mathbf{E} &= \mathbf{M}_V + i\,\mathbf{N}_U \\ \mathbf{H} &= m(-\mathbf{M}_U + i\,\mathbf{N}_V) \end{aligned} \tag{22}$$

Referring to Fig. 6 we write the solutions U and V corresponding to the "E" or "H" case; i.e., radiation linearly polarized with the electric and magnetic vector in the plane containing the cylinder axis and the propagation vector k.

"E" case

$$r > a \quad \begin{aligned} U &= \sum_{n=-\infty}^{\infty} F_n \left[J_n(lr) - b_n^E H_n(lr) \right] \\ V &= \sum_{n=-\infty}^{\infty} F_n \left[-a_n^E H_n(lr) \right] \end{aligned}$$

"H" case (23)

$$r > a \quad \begin{aligned} U &= \sum_{n=-\infty}^{\infty} F_n \left[-b_n^H H_n(lr) \right] \\ V &= \sum_{n=-\infty}^{\infty} F_n \left[J_n(lr) - a_n^H H_n(lr) \right] \end{aligned}$$

"E" case

$$r < a \quad \begin{aligned} U &= \sum_{n=-\infty}^{\infty} F_n d_n^E J_n(l_1 r) \\ V &= \sum_{n=-\infty}^{\infty} F_n c_n^E J_n(l_1 r) \end{aligned}$$

"H" case (24)

$$r < a \quad \begin{aligned} U &= \sum F_n d_n^H J_n(l_1 r) \\ V &= \sum F_n c_n^H J_n(l_1 r) \end{aligned}$$

where

$$F_n = (-i)^n \exp(i\omega t - ikz \sin\alpha + i n\theta)$$

$$l = k\cos\alpha,\; l_1 = k\sqrt{m^2 - \sin^2\alpha},\; \alpha = \frac{\pi}{2} - \chi$$

a = radius of cylinder

J_n = cylindrical Bessel function of the first kind

H_n = cylindrical Hankel function of the second kind.

Applying the appropriate boundary conditions on E and H at the surface of the cylinder we obtain the coefficients a_n, b_n, c_n, d_n,

$$\text{"E"}\left\{\begin{aligned}
a_n^E &= i n \sin\alpha\, SR_n \frac{B_n(\mu) - A_n(\mu)}{A_n(\epsilon)A_n(\mu) - n^2S^2\sin^2\alpha} \\
b_n^E &= R_n \frac{A_n(\mu)B_n(\epsilon) - n^2S^2\sin^2\alpha}{A_n(\epsilon)A_n(\mu) - n^2S^2\sin^2\alpha} \\
c_n^E &= -\sqrt{\mu}\,\frac{(la)^2 H_n(la)}{(l_1a)^2 J_n(l_1a)}\, a_n^E \\
d_n^E &= \sqrt{\epsilon}\,\frac{(la)^2}{(l_1a)^2 J_n(l_1a)}\left[J_n(la) - H_n(la)\, b_n^E\right]
\end{aligned}\right. \qquad (25)$$

$$\text{"H"}\left\{\begin{aligned}
a_n^H &= R_n \frac{A_n(\epsilon)B_n(\mu) - n^2S^2\sin^2\alpha}{A_n(\epsilon)A_n(\mu) - n^2S^2\sin^2\alpha} \\
b_n^H &= -a_n^E \\
c_n^H &= \sqrt{\mu}\,\frac{(la)^2}{(l_1a)^2 J_n(l_1a)}\left[J_n(la) - H_n(la)\, a_n^H\right] \\
d_n^H &= -\sqrt{\epsilon}\,\frac{(la)^2 H_n(la)}{(l_1a)^2 J_n(l_1a)}\, b_n^H
\end{aligned}\right.$$

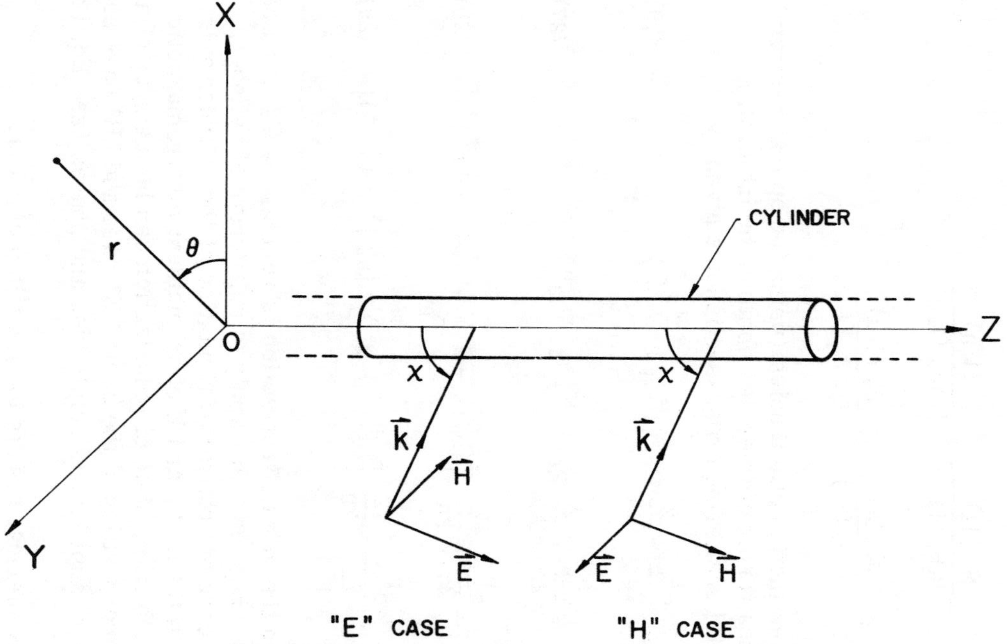

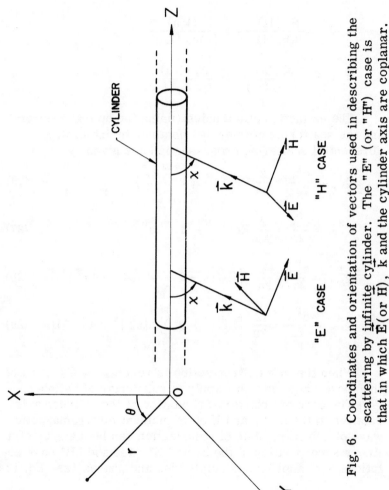

Fig. 6. Coordinates and orientation of vectors used in describing the scattering by infinite cylinder. The "E" (or "H") case is that in which $\vec{E}$ (or $\vec{H}$), $\vec{k}$ and the cylinder axis are coplanar.

where

$$S = (la)^{-2} - (l_1 a)^{-2} \; ; \; R_n = J_n (la)/H_n (la)$$

$$A_n(\xi) = \frac{H'_n (la)}{laH_n (la)} - \xi \frac{J'_n (l_1 a)}{l_1 a J_n (l_1 a)} \; ;$$

$$B_n (\xi) = \frac{J'_n (la)}{la J_n (la)} - \xi \frac{J'_n (l_1 a)}{l_1 a J_n (l_1 a)}$$

The extinction efficiencies (using the optical theorem) and the scattering efficiencies obtained by integrating the differential scattering cross-section are given by

$$Q^E_{ext} = \frac{C^E_{ext}}{2a} = \frac{2}{ka} \operatorname{Re} \left\{ b^E_0 + 2 \sum_{n=1}^{\infty} b^E_n \right\} \tag{26}$$

$$Q^H_{ext} = \frac{C^H_{ext}}{2a} = \frac{2}{ka} \operatorname{Re} \left\{ a^H_0 + 2 \sum_{n=1}^{\infty} a^H_n \right\} \tag{27}$$

$$Q^E_{sca} = \frac{C^E_{sca}}{2a} = \frac{2}{ka} \left[|b^E_0|^2 + 2 \sum_{n=1}^{\infty} (|b^E_n|^2 + |a^E_n|^2) \right] \tag{28}$$

$$Q^H_{sca} = \frac{C^H_{sca}}{2a} = \frac{2}{ka} \left[|a^H_0|^2 + 2 \sum_{n=1}^{\infty} (|a^H_n|^2 + |b^H_n|^2) \right] \tag{29}$$

When the index of refraction is real $Q_{ext} = Q_{sca}$, all of the above (Eqs. 26 - 29) apply to unit length of cylinder.

The case of arbitrary orientation of the cylinder axis relative to the **k**, **E**, and **H** of an incident electromagnetic wave of arbitrary state of polarization can be made up of a linear superposition of the basic "E" case and "H" case solutions with appropriate amplitudes and phases (see Eq. (34)).

b. Numerical results for the tilted cylinder.

The calculations have been made for cylinders with real index of refraction m = 1.6 which corresponds to the index of refraction of lucite for microwaves. As a numerical check, Q_{ext} and Q_{sca} were independently evaluated.

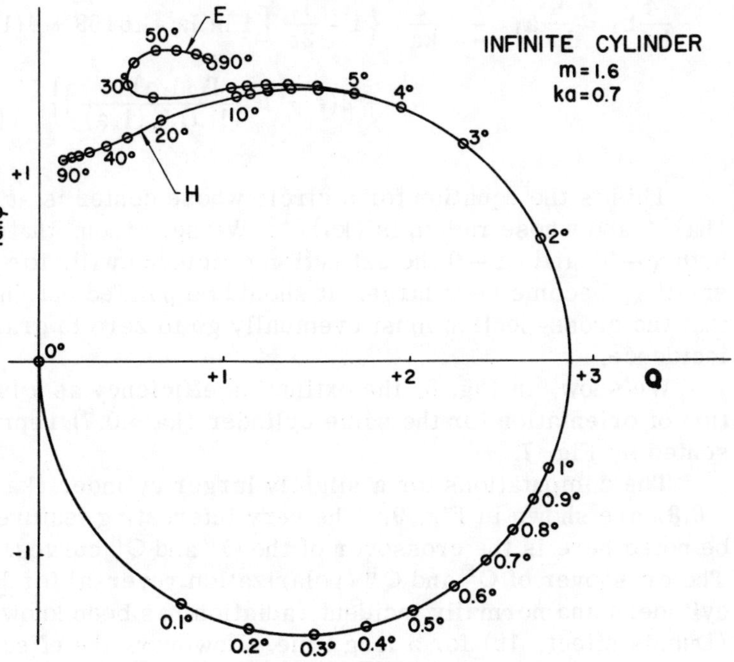

Fig. 7. Complex scattering efficiencies, Q^E and Q^H as a function of orientation angle χ denoted by circular points.

In Fig. 7 we have plotted the complex expressions

$$\frac{2}{ka}\left\{b_0^E + 2\sum_{n=1}^{\infty} b_n^E\right\} \quad \text{and} \quad \frac{2}{ka}\left\{a_0^H + 2\sum_{n=1}^{\infty} a_n^H\right\}$$

the projections on the real axis being the extinction efficiencies. The cylinder for which ka = 0.7 is rather thin and it is to be expected that for normal incidence only a few terms in the expansions are required. This is indeed the case. Furthermore as the propagation direction approaches the direction of the cylinder axis ($\chi \to 0°$, $\alpha \to 90°$), only the n = 1 terms for the "E" case and the "H" case are important. It can be shown that as $\chi \to 0°$

$$\frac{4}{ka} b_1 = \frac{4}{ka} a_1 \underset{\chi \to \infty}{\to} \frac{2}{ka} \left\{ 1 - \frac{i}{2\pi} \left[4 \ln la - .6159 + 4(l_1 a)^2 + 2(\epsilon + \mu \frac{J_1'(l_1 a)}{(l_1 a) J_1(l_1 a)} \right] \right\}^{-1} \quad (30)$$

This is the equation for a circle whose center is at $(ha)^{-1}$ and whose radius is $(ka)^{-1}$. We see, then, that as both $\chi \to 0°$ and $ka \to 0$ the extinction efficiency will, for some small χ, become very large. It should be pointed out, however, that the cross-section must eventually go to zero to grazing incidence.

We show, in Fig. 8, the extinction efficiency as a function of orientation for the same cylinder (ka = 0.7) represented by Fig. 7.

The computations for a slightly larger cylinder (ka = 0.8) are shown in Fig. 9. The very interesting feature to be noted here is the crossover of the Q^E and Q^H curves. The crossover of Q^E and Q^H (polarization reversal for large cylinders and normally incident radiation has been known (Dubois effect, 19) for a long time. However, the effect shown in Fig. 8 is quite different in that it shows up for small cylinders and is a function of their orientation.

As one increases the cylinder diameter, more and more terms are required in the expansion and, as a consequence, the n = 1 term is no longer dominant except for extremely small values of χ. This is shown in Fig. 10 where the circular form of the complex extinction has almost vanished. It can be seen in Fig. 11 that for ka > 1 the values of Q^E and Q^H become relatively insensitive to cylinder tilt angle and that also $Q^E - Q^H$ is fairly constant.

Finally in Fig. 12 we see some samples of the variations of the extinction Q^E with size for tilt angles $\chi = 1°$ and $\chi = 10°$. For normal incidence $\chi = 90°$) one obtains a curve which (except for a few wiggles) rises uniformly to a maximum at $2ka(m - 1) \approx 4$(ka = 3.3 in our case) then decreases for a rather considerable distance in ka.

A comment on angular scattering distribution is perhaps in order. It should be noted that the scattered radiation is confined to a cone whose half angle is the angle χ.

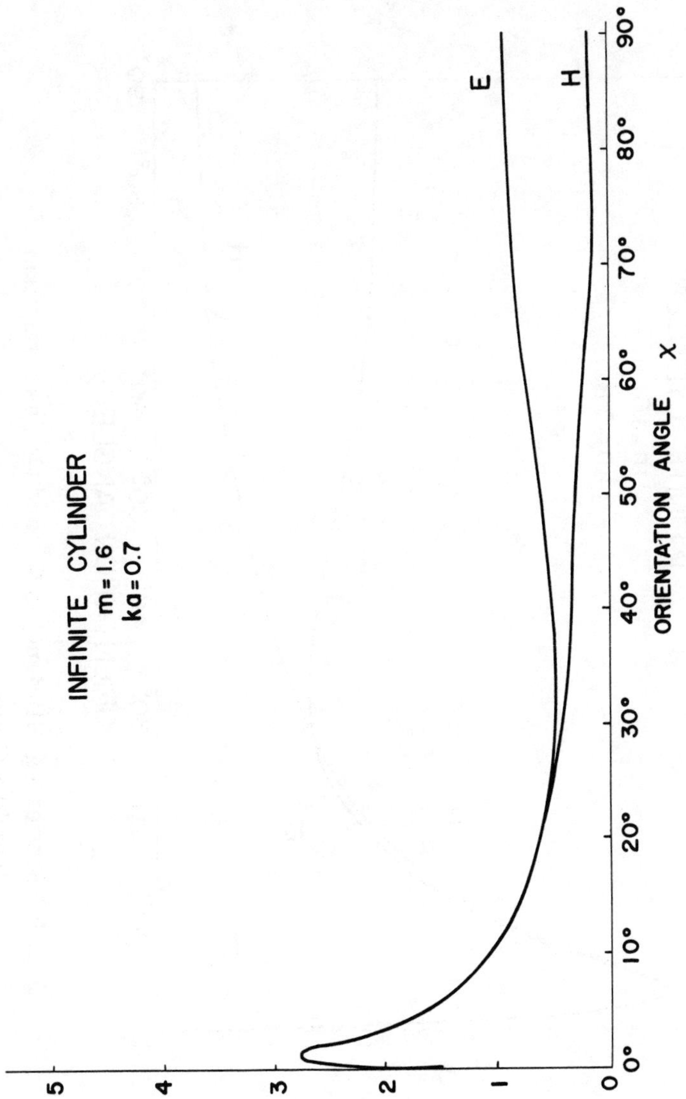

Fig. 8. Scattering efficiencies Q^E and Q^H as a function of orientation angle.

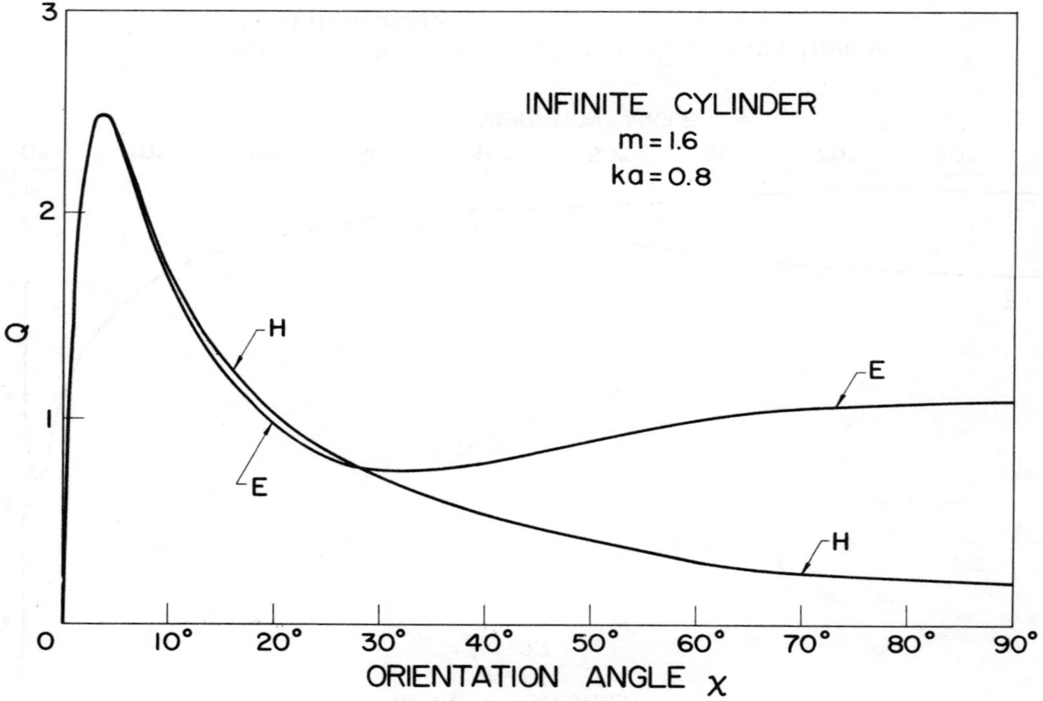

Fig. 9. Scattering efficiencies Q^E and Q^H as a function of orientation angle.

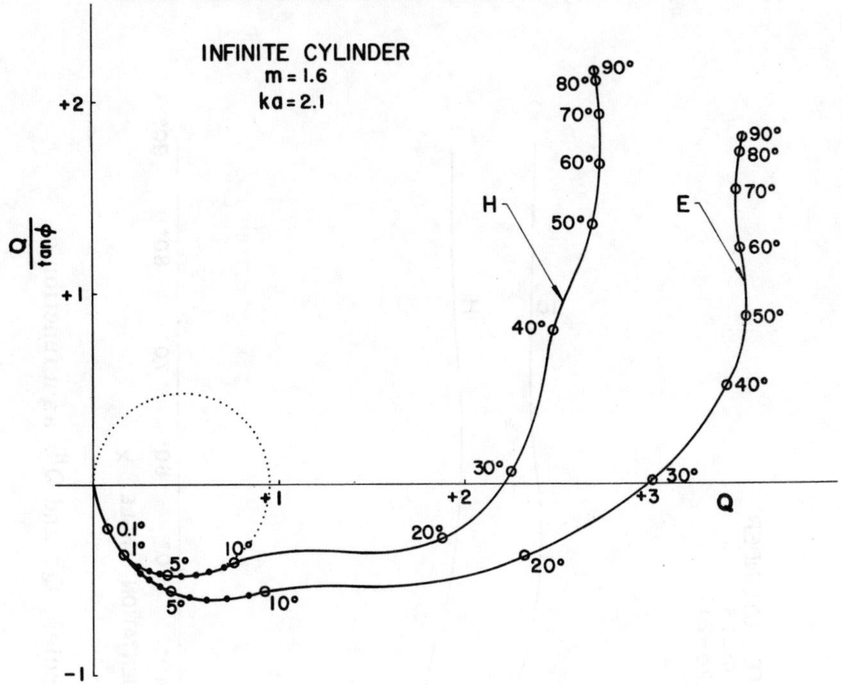

Fig. 10. Complex scattering efficiencies, Q^E and Q^H as a function of orientation angle χ denoted by circular points.

In other words, for the infinite cylinder there is no true back scattering even though there is radiation appearing at $\theta = 180°$.

IV. MICROWAVE SCATTERING

A preliminary account of this work which consists of a new and improved method for obtaining detailed information on the extinction cross sections for scattering of 3 cm microwaves by arbitrarily oriented particles has appeared elsewhere (7). More detailed exposition of the experimental method is being prepared for publication. We present here an enlarged abstract along with some of the results in

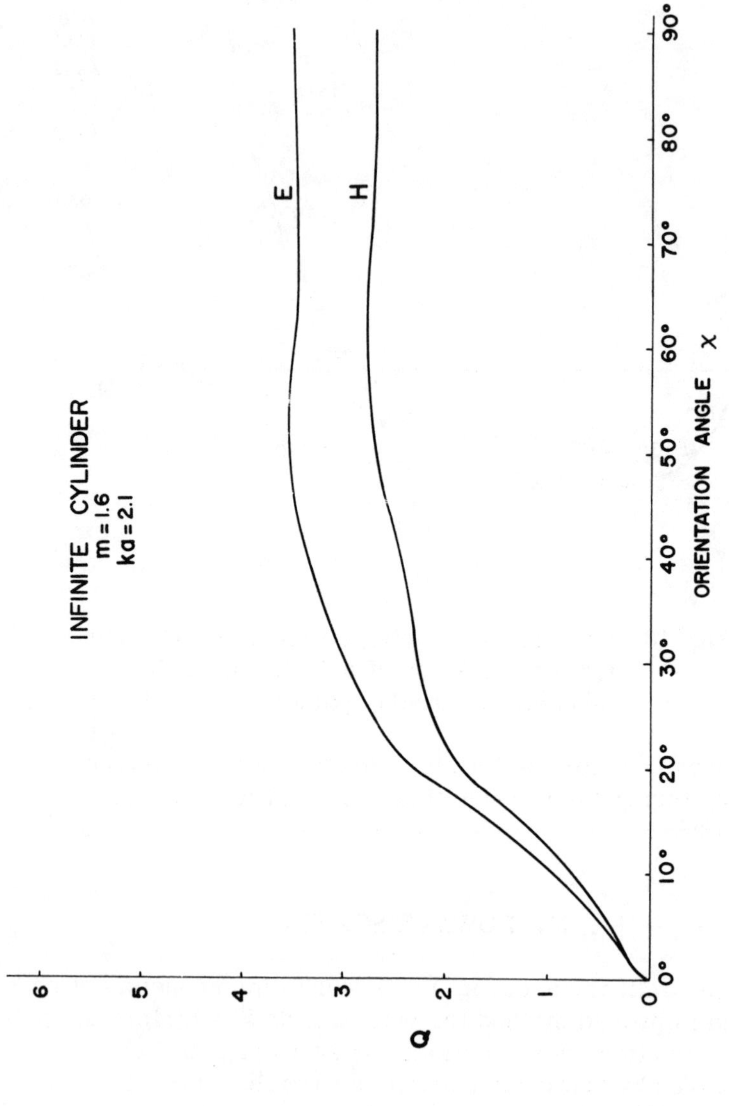

Fig. 11. Scattering efficiencies, Q^E and Q^H, as a function of orientation angle.

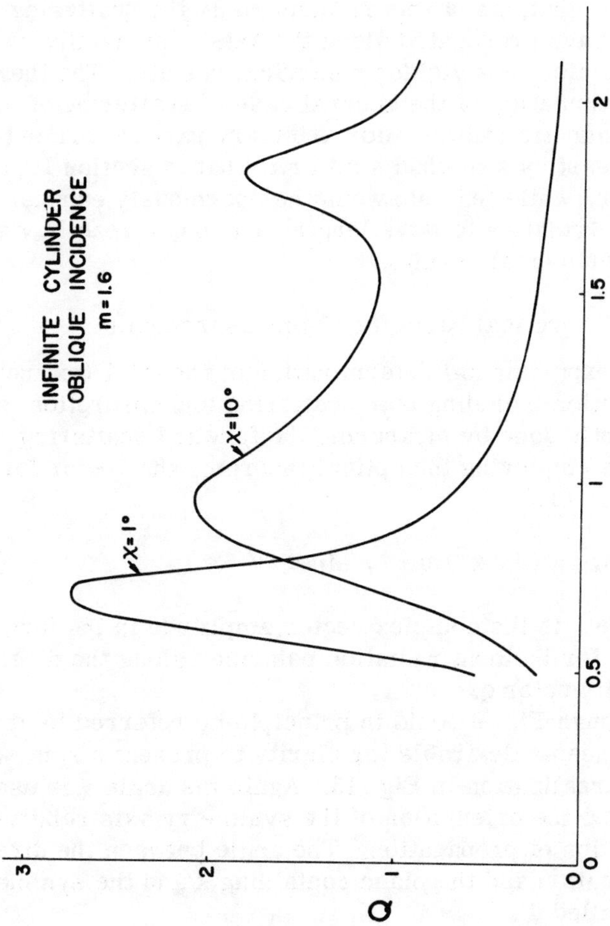

Fig. 12. Scattering efficiency Q^E as a function of ka showing increasing resonance for increasing tilt.

order to demonstrate the usefulness of the experimental approach to the scattering problem. It should be remembered that in practice the problems we are faced with can not entirely be solved by consideration of simple particle shapes and that, as of this moment, only the scattering of a scalar wave propogated along the axis of an axially symmetric particle has yielded numerical results. The theoretical calculation of the general case of scattering of electromagnetic radiation for arbitrary particle orientation, at least by a method similar to that in section II of this paper, while feasible would be enormously expensive for sizes (relative to wave length) which can readily yield good experimental results.

a. Theoretical basis for the measurements

The experimental determination of the total (extinction) cross section including both scattering and absorption is conveniently done by measuring the forward scattering amplitude employing the optical theorem, the vector form of which is (15):

$$C_{ext} = (4\pi/k^2)\ \mathbf{q}\cdot\mathbf{f_q}\ \sin\varphi \tag{31}$$

where $\mathbf{f_q}\, e^{i\varphi}$ is the complex vector amplitude in the forward direction for incident radiation polarized along the direction of the unit vector $\mathbf{q}$.

Although Fig. 6 could in principle be referred to at this point, it seems desirable for clarity to present a somewhat different realization in Fig. 13. Again the angle χ is used to describe the orientation of the symmetry axis relative to the direction of propagation. The angle between the direction of polarization and the plane containing $\mathbf{k}$ and the symmetry axis is called ψ.

We denote the forward scattering amplitude when $\psi = 0°$ as $f_E(\chi)$ and when $\psi = 90°$ as $f_H(\chi)$. Due to the symmetry of our scatterers it is necessary to know only the cross section in these two mutually perpendicular planes; i.e., the $\mathbf{E} - \mathbf{k}$ plane and the $\mathbf{H} - \mathbf{k}$ plane in order to fully describe the case for arbitrary orientation.

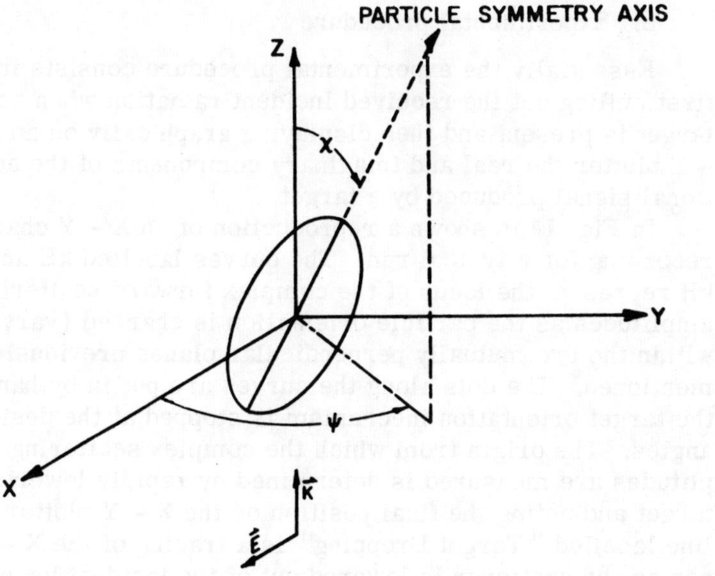

Fig. 13

The scattering amplitude for a particle oriented as in Fig. 13 is given by

$$f(\chi, \psi) = [f_E(\chi) \cos^2 \psi + f_H(\chi) \sin \psi]\, \mathbf{i} + [f_E(\chi) - f_H(\chi)] \sin \psi \cos \psi\, \mathbf{j} \tag{32}$$

where i and j are unit vectors along the x and y direction respectively. The optical theorem then gives

$$C_{ext}(\chi, \psi) = \frac{4\pi}{k^2} [f_E(\chi) \sin \varphi_E(\chi) \cos^2 \psi + f_H(\chi) \sin \varphi_H(\chi) \sin^2 \psi] \tag{33}$$

or, in the notation of section III for extinction efficiencies,

$$Q_{ext}(\chi, \psi) = Q^E(\chi) \cos^2 \psi + Q^H(\chi) \sin^2 \psi \tag{34}$$

b. Experimental procedure

Essentially the experimental procedure consists in first nulling out the received incident radiation when no target is present and then displaying graphically on an X - Y plotter the real and imaginary components of the additional signal produced by a target.

In Fig. 14 is shown a reproduction of an X - Y chart recording for a typical run. The curves labelled kE and kH represent the locus of the complex forward scattering amplitudes as the particle orientation is charged (vary χ) within the two mutually perpendicular planes previously mentioned. The dots along the curves are put in by hand as the target orientation mechanism is stopped at the designated angles. The origin from which the complex scattering amplitudes are measured is determined by rapidly lowering the target and noting the final position on the X - Y plotter. The line labelled " Target Dropping" is a tracing of the X - Y pen as the scatterer is lowered out of the incident beam. In order to normalize and orient the scattering amplitudes one experimentally locates the point which defines the complex scattering amplitude for a sphere of known size and index of refraction. A Mie theory calculation for the scattering by the sphere gives the phase (φ_{calc} in the figure) and the amplitude ($|f_{calc}|$). The phase, φ_{calc}, is used to orient the real and imaginary axes, and the amplitude $|f_{calc}|$, defines the absolute scale in the X - Y plane. In order to elimate the possibliities of systematic errors which could be introduced if a particular sphere is inaccurately manufactured, we perform the actual normalization by averaging over a set of "standard" spheres.

The repeatability and the internal consistency of the measurements have been quite good with deviations of less than 2 percent in the magnitude and 3° in phase of the forward scattering amplitude.

It can be seen that the experimental data appears naturally in exactly the same form as that which we have used in Figs. 7 and 10 for the theoretical results on the cross section of infinite cylinders. This manner of presentation of the raw data makes it possible to detect and measure subtle differences in scattering produced by orientation changes and is

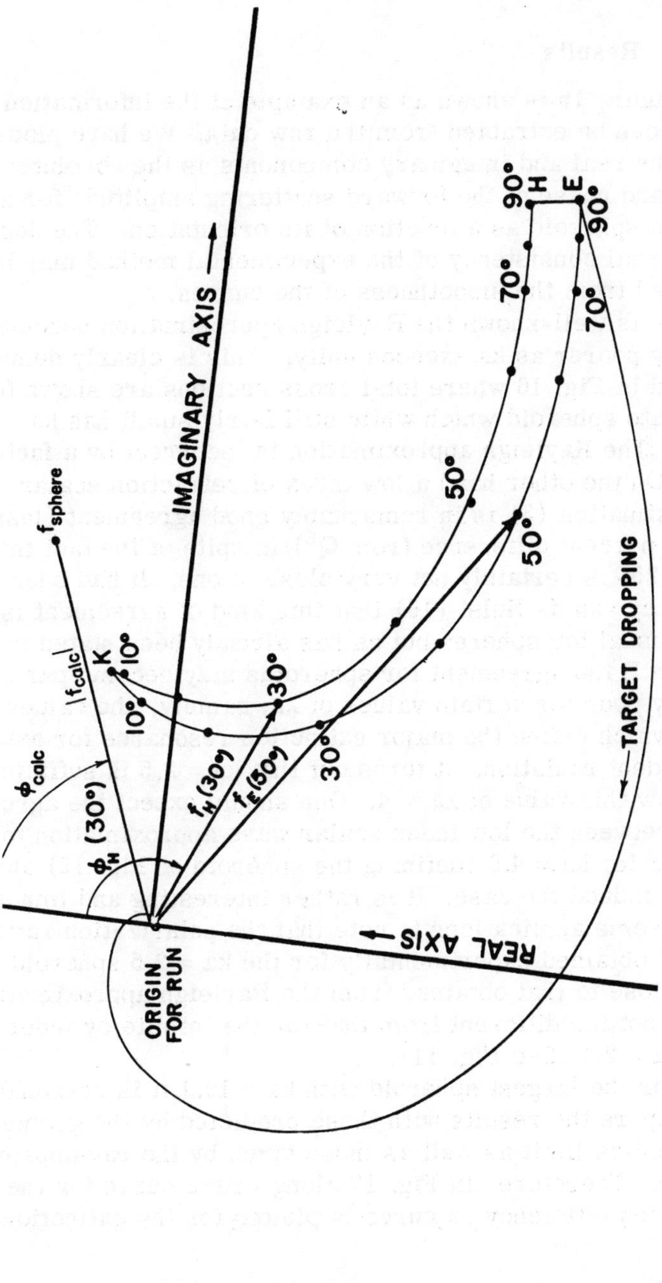

Fig. 14. Typical data run showing vector scattering amplitudes at various orientations.

perhaps the most important feature of our new experimental procedure.

c. Results

Figure 15 is shown as an example of the information which can be extracted from the raw data. We have plotted here the real and imaginary components as the absolute value and phase of the forward scattering amplitude for a prolate spheroid as a function of its orientation. The degree of internal consistency of the experimental method may be inferred from the smoothness of the curves.

As is well-known the Rayleigh approximation becomes rapidly poorer as ka exceeds unity. This is clearly demonstrated in Fig. 16 where total cross sections are shown for a prolate spheroid which while still fairly small has ka = 2.5. The Rayleigh approximation is incorrect by a factor of 5. On the other hand a low index of refraction scalar approximation (3) is in remarkably good agreement (less than 3 percent difference from Q^E) in spite of the fact that m = 1.255 is certainly not very close to one. It had been shown by van de Hulst (16) that this kind of agreement is not unusual for spheres but as has already been stated in section II the agreement for spheroids may become particularly poor for certain values of ka; namely, the values of ka which define the major extinction resonance for axially incident radiation. It turns out that ka = 2.5 is sufficiently below this value of ka ≈ 4. One should expect the agreement between the low index scalar wave approximation to be poor for ka = 4.6 (defining the spheroid of Fig. 15) and this is indeed the case. It is rather interesting and important in some applications to note that the polarization ratio Q^E/Q^H obtained experimentally for the ka = 2.5 spheroid is very close to that obtained from the Rayleigh approximation, and is not too different from that for the infinite cylinder with ka = 2.1 (See Fig. 11).

For the largest spheroid with ka = 10.1 it is reasonable to compare the results with those predicted by the geometrical optics limit as well as those given by the ray approximation. Therefore, in Fig. 17 along with a curve for the extinction efficiency, a curve is plotted for the extinction

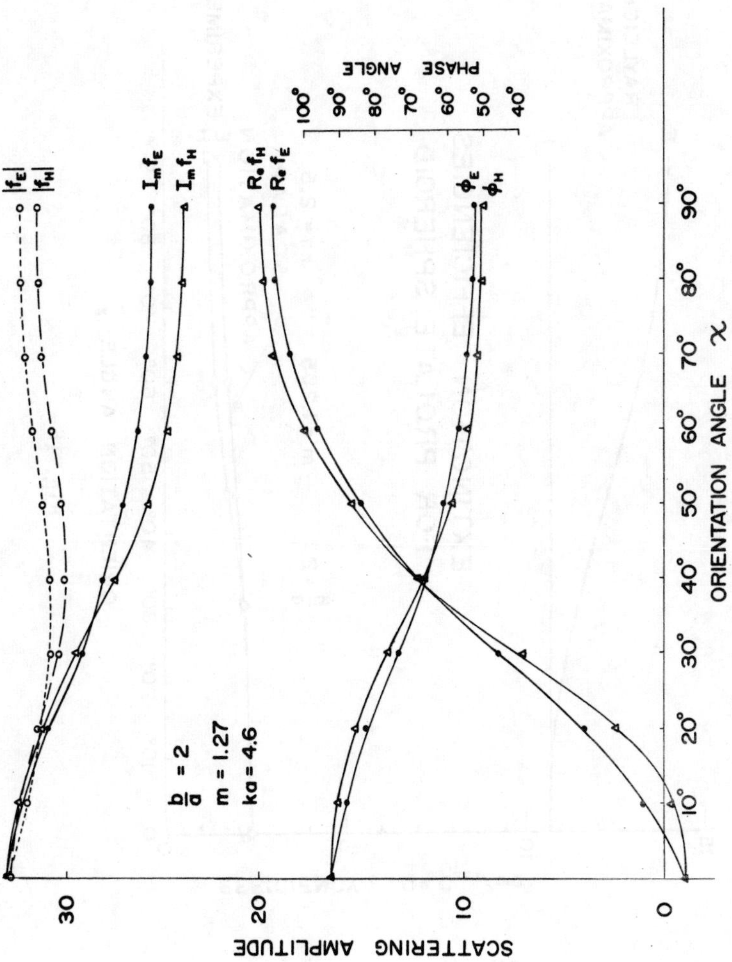

Fig. 15. Scattering amplitudes and phases for dielectric prolate spheroid.

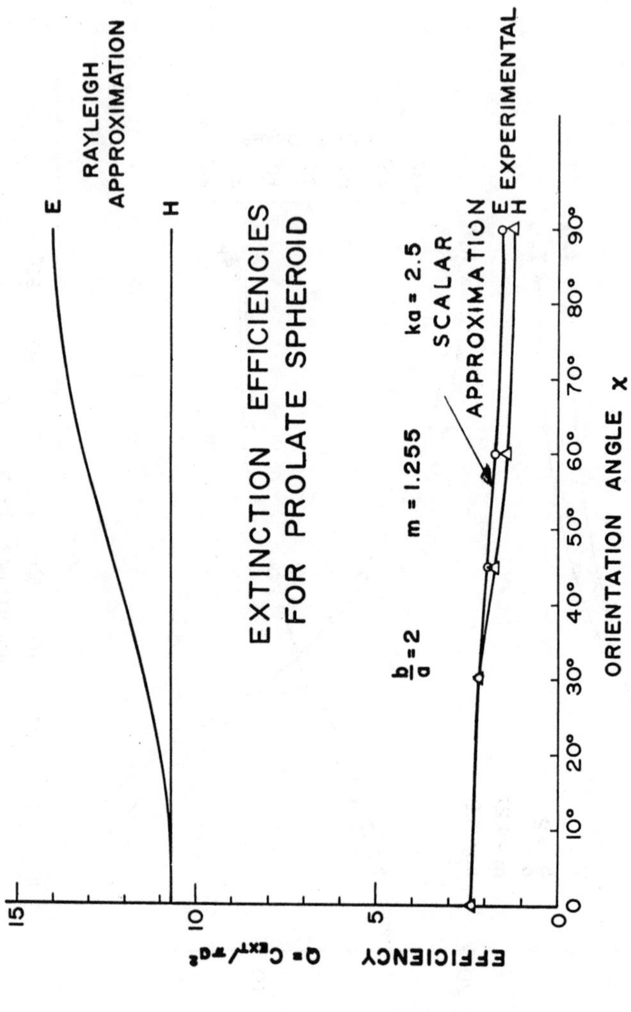
EXTINCTION EFFICIENCIES
FOR PROLATE SPHEROID
RAYLEIGH
APPROXIMATION
E
H
b/a = 2
m = 1.255
ka = 2.5
SCALAR
APPROXIMATION
EXPERIMENTAL
E
H
EFFICIENCY Q = C_EXT/πa²
15
10
5
0
0
10°
20°
30°
40°
50°
60°
70°
80°
90°
ORIENTATION ANGLE X

Fig. 16

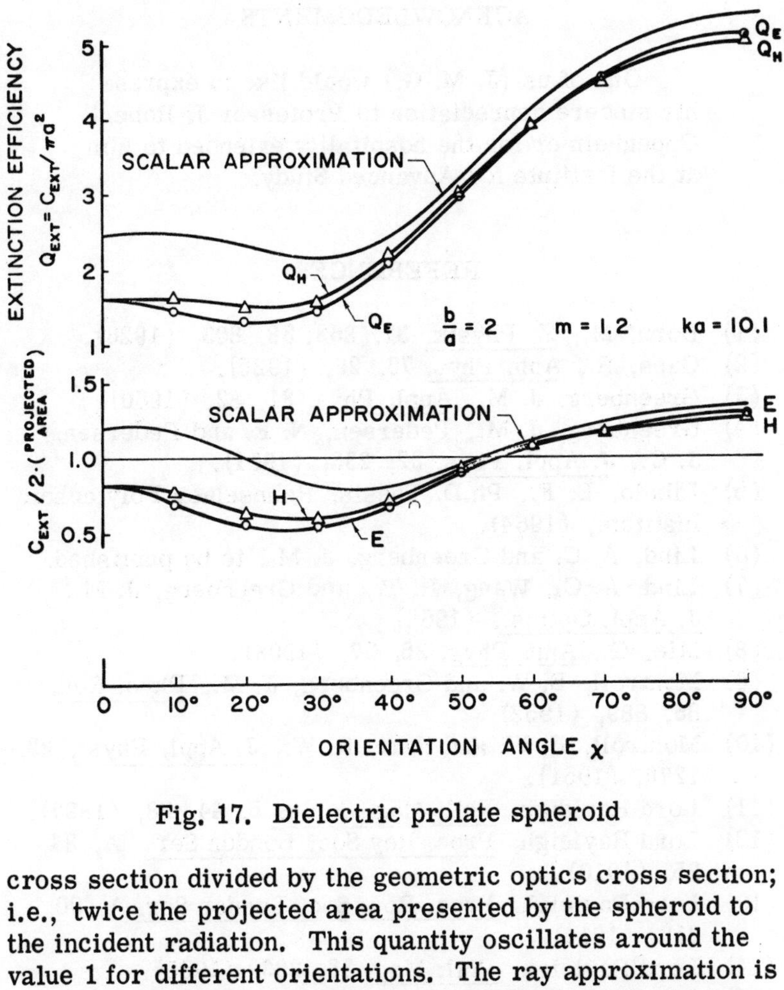

Fig. 17. Dielectric prolate spheroid

cross section divided by the geometric optics cross section; i.e., twice the projected area presented by the spheroid to the incident radiation. This quantity oscillates around the value 1 for different orientations. The ray approximation is in partial agreement with the experimental results for ka = 10.1 in that it gives a very similar dependence of cross section on orientation. The agreement is certainly not as good as that for ka = 2.5 although it is probably satisfactory for semi-quantitative calculations.

ACKNOWLEDGMENTS

One of us (J. M. G.) would like to express his sincere appreciation to Professor J. Robert Oppenheimer for the hospitality extended to him at the Institute for Advanced Study.

REFERENCES

(1) Born, M., Z. Physik, **37**, 863; **38**, 803, (1926).
(2) Gans, R., Ann. Phys. **76**, 29, (1925).
(3) Greenberg, J. M., Appl. Phys. **31**, 82, (1960).
(4) Greenberg, J. M., Pedersen, N. E. and Pedersen, J. C., J. Appl. Phys. **32**, 233, (1961).
(5) Libelo, L. F., Ph.D. Thesis, Rennselaer Polytechnic Institute, (1964).
(6) Lind, A. C. and Greenberg, J. M., to be published.
(7) Lind, A. C., Wang, R. T., and Greenberg, J. M., J. Appl. Optics., (1965).
(8) Mie, G., Ann. Phys. **25**, 37, (1908).
(9) Montroll, E. W. and Greenberg, J. M., Phys. Rev. **86**, 889, (1952).
(10) Montroll, E. W. and Hart, R. W., J. Appl. Phys., **22**, 1278, (1951).
(11) Lord Rayleigh, Phil. Mag. Series 5, **44**, 28, (1897).
(12) Lord Rayleigh, Proc. Roy Soc. London Ser. A, **84**, 25, (1910).
(13) Lord Rayleigh, Proc. Roy. Soc. London Ser. A, **90**, 219, (1914).
(14) Lord Rayleigh, Phil. Mag. **36**, 233, (1955).
(15) Saxon, D. S., Phys. Rev. **32**, 233, (1955).
(16) van de Hulst, H. C., Recherches astron Obs. d'Utrecht, **11**, part 1, (1946), **11** part 2, (1948).
(17) van de Hulst, H. C., Light Scattering by Small Particles, J. Wiley and Sons, Inc., New York, p. 132, (1957).
(18) Ref. 1. p. 297.
(19) Ibid, p. 322.
(20) Wait, J. R., Can. J. Phys., **33**, 189, (1955).

DISCUSSION FOLLOWING PAPER BY J. M. GREENBERG

R. B. Mack: How were particles suspended for measurements?

J. M. Greenberg: Particles were suspended by very thin nylon threads. Cotton, which twisted less, could be seen when no model was present because of its large absorption. The nylon threads were invisible.

V. Erma: In this method you described, which consists of matching boundary conditions at only certain points for a fixed number of points, have you looked at different geometrical distributions of these points, and if so, are the results sensitive to the distribution?

J. M. Greenberg: Yes, we tried different distributions of points and found the results to be quite insensitive.

V. Erma: In the actual results and calculations you reported, what was the distribution? Were the points equally spaced along the axis?

J. M. Greenberg: It has been about a year since these results were obtained and I do not remember this detail. I do remember that they were more or less equally distributed in angle, but we avoided the points at 0° and 90°.

V. Erma: What angles were used for the tabulated data?

L. Libelo (Collaborator with Greenberg): The table was produced from equal angular increments. We did not choose the forward direction for matching boundary conditions.

R. Stein: (a) Are your theoretical techniques extendable to particles having anisotropic refractive indices? (b) Can interaction effects be experimentally studied by using arrays of cylinders?

J. M. Greenberg: (a) Yes, the results are, of course, more difficult to obtain numerically. We are beginning an investigation of such particles both theoretically and experimentally. (b) Yes, but there are size limitations of overall array dimensions because of laboratory space limitations.

E. M. Kennaugh: In the approximate solution to scalar scattering by spheroids, were the boundary conditions satisfied at points other than the finite number chosen initially? That is, were the solutions obtained compared with regard to boundary values at other points? This test may serve as a verification of the approximation method.

J. M. Greenberg: This is good suggestion. It has not yet been done although, of course, we expect to do it.

D. S. Saxon: Your talk was devoted primarily to the estimation of total cross-sections or extinction coefficients. What can you say about the more difficult and sensitive question of differential cross-sections or angular distributions?

J. M. Greenberg: We are doing reflection nebulae calculations as well but in astronomy you know that the specification of the observed geometry is not easy so that the results are not as useful as those which will be described in later talks where the angular distribution is obtained from some reasonably specified situation.

Added comment by L. Libelo (Collaborator with Greenberg): For the sake of brevity and without losing any of the essential content of the method of approximation the discussion is confined within the frame work of the scattering of a scalar wave axially incident on a penetrable spheroid. It should be remembered that somewhat more general situations have been subjected to rather detailed analysis. To begin with the method takes as point of departure the usual partial wave approach. With this in mind two points require emphasis. First, for any given scatterer with dimensions comparable to the wavelength of the incident radiation only a finite number of the scattering coefficients (or expansion coefficients) are significant. Beyond this number the contribution of the remaining coefficients is quite negligible. Second, the approximation requires satisfying the conventional boundary conditions everywhere on a finite number of circles (normal to they symmetry axis). These circles, of course, were arbitrarily chosen in such a manner as to be more or less smoothly distributed over the boundary surface. With regard to the second point, successively higher order approximations very naturally lead to the choice of different sets of angles (which correspond to the circles) at which the boundary conditions are satisfied. Nevertheless, calculations were also carried out for different sets of such angles for the same order of approximation. The results obtained for the significant coefficients were found to be relatively insentitive to the choice of angles at which the boundary conditions were applied. This refers only to those coefficients which make a significant contribution and which an adquate order of approximation have established. The remaining coefficients are considerably more sensitive to the choice of the set of matching angles. (Again, this refers to the order of approximation which gives us reliable values for this significant coefficients.) Since they are negligible anyway, their erratic behavior does not significantly affect the predicted scattering properties. Finally, one can speculate that some variational approach may yield the best set of points at which to apply the boundary conditions. We did not make any attempt in this direction.

Light Scattering from Colloidal Spheres and Cylinders *

Milton Kerker
Department of Chemistry
and
Institute of Colloid and Surface Science
Clarkson College of Technology
Potsdam, New York

TABLE OF CONTENTS

---

*This investigation was supported in part by the U. S. Atomic Energy Commission, by the U. S. Army Electronics Research and Development Activity and by P. H. S. Research Grant AP-0048 from the Division of Air Pollution of the Public Health Service.

This paper has a twofold purpose. It is, first of all, to review broadly the subject of electromagnetic scattering by spheres and, secondly, to describe some recent light scattering work with colloidal spheres. We will also consider the closely related problem of scattering by infinitely long cylinders.

I. SCATTERING BY HOMOGENEOUS SPHERES

The subject is an old one; yet there is still considerable activity and there still remain important unsolved problems. Our concern is with the far field scattered radiation when an electromagnetic wave is incident upon a spherically or cylindrically symmetric object.

We will consider mainly "exact" solutions, i.e., those which obey Maxwell's equations without any assumptions regarding the size or optical properties of the particles. This, admittedly, eliminates the overwhelming preponderance of both theoretical and experimental work.

The case of the homogeneous circular cylinder at perpendicular incidence was solved by Lord Rayleigh (46) and that of the homogeneous sphere was worked out, apparently independently, by Lorenz (31), Love (32), Mie (38), and Bromwich (5). Bromwich claimed to have obtained his solution as early as 1899. Both Lorenz and Debye (8) provided extensions which facilitated numerical computations. The results are usually, if inappropriately, referred to as the Mie theory. The detailed treatment may be found in any one of a number of textbooks (Stratton, 57; van de Hulst, 21; Born and Wolf, 4). In the main, it consists of the solution of the scalar wave equation in a coordinate system appropriate to the geometry of the particle. The results for spheres may be expressed as follows:

$$I_1 = \frac{1}{k^2 r^2} \left| \sum_{n=1}^{\infty} \frac{2n+1}{n(n+1)} \{a_n \pi_n + b_n \tau_n\} \right|^2 \tag{1}$$

$$I_2 = \frac{1}{k^2 r^2} \left| \sum_{n=1}^{\infty} \frac{2n+1}{n(n+1)} \{b_n \pi_n + a_n \tau_n\} \right|^2 \tag{2}$$

$$Q_{SCA} = \frac{2}{\alpha^2} \sum_{n=1}^{\infty} (2n+1)\{ |a_n|^2 + |b_n|^2 \} \tag{3}$$

$$Q_{EXT} = \frac{2}{\alpha^2} \sum_{n=1}^{\infty} (2n+1) \, \mathrm{Re}(a_n + b_n) \tag{4}$$

I_1 and I_2 are the intensities of the radiation scattered in the direction θ when a particle is illuminated by parallel light of unit intensity with the electric vector polarized perpendicularly and parallel, respectively, to the scattering plane. The efficiencies for scattering and extinction, Q_{SCA} and Q_{EXT} are the ratios of the cross sections for scattering and extinction (scattering plus absorption) to the geometrical cross section. The distance from the center of the particle to the point of observation is r, k is the propagation constant in the medium $(2\pi/\lambda)$, α is the ratio of the particle circumference to the wavelength in the medium $(2\pi a/\lambda)$, π_n and τ_n are the functions of the scattering angle and a_n and b_n are the functions of α and the complex refractive index, m. involving spherical Bessel functions. This notation corresponds to that given by van de Hulst (21). It should be noted that these definitions of a_n and b_n are interchanged from those given by Stratton (57). The geometry is depicted in Fig. 1.

As pointed out by Gustav Mie (38), the scattering can be viewed physically as due to the superposition of the energy radiated by an array of electric and magnetic multipoles with arbitrary multipole moments, the terms containing the a_n's corresponding to the electric multipoles and those containing the b_n's to the magnetic multipoles. The series defined by the above equations converge more slowly with increasing α. In practice, it is sufficient to take only a few more terms than the magnitude of α. For dielectric materials, the magnetic terms converge somewhat more rapidly than the electric terms with the result that in the limit of small $\alpha(\alpha < .3)$ only the first electric term, corresponding to the Rayleigh or Thomson oscillating electric dipole, need be considered (Heller, 19).

The complexity of the scattering patterns of spheres is well known and indeed this has resulted in a preoccupation

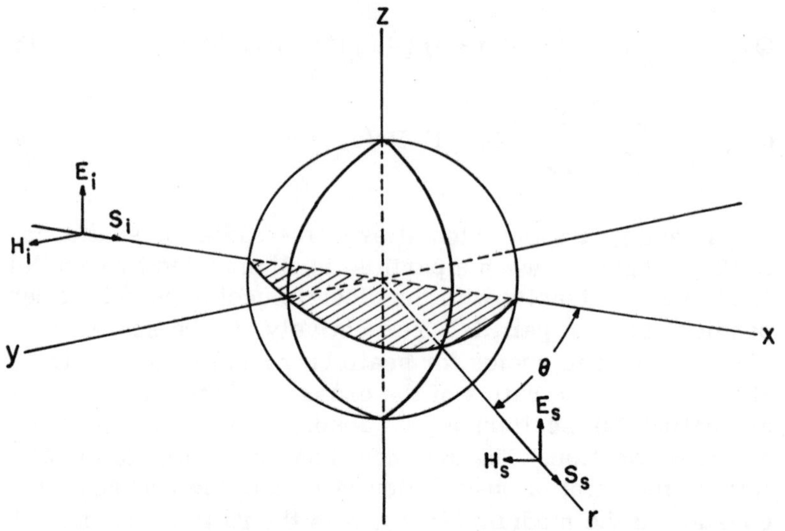

Fig. 1. Scattering geometry. Incident direction S_i, scattered direction S_s, scattering angle θ, field vectors E_i, H_i, E_s, H_s.

on the part of many workers with the cataloguing of numerical results with a view to discerning some underlying regularities. Actually, there are such regularities and they are already contained in Mie's physical analysis of the problem into contributions by multipoles. Mevel (37) and Metz and Dettmar (36) have related the scattering patterns in a detailed way to the properties of the individual scattering coefficients, a_n and b_n, which do vary regularly with the particle properties. These scattering coefficients represent the amplitudes of the electric and magnetic multipoles excited within the particle and it is their superposition which gives rise to the final scattering effect.

When α becomes large, an alternative physical view in terms of ray optics is sometimes convenient and possibly useful. The scattering can be envisaged as the Fraunhofer diffraction pattern due to the sphere, combined with the rays undergoing successive reflections and refractions upon impinging on the sphere. The various rays are depicted in Fig. 2. The incident ray divides into a reflected

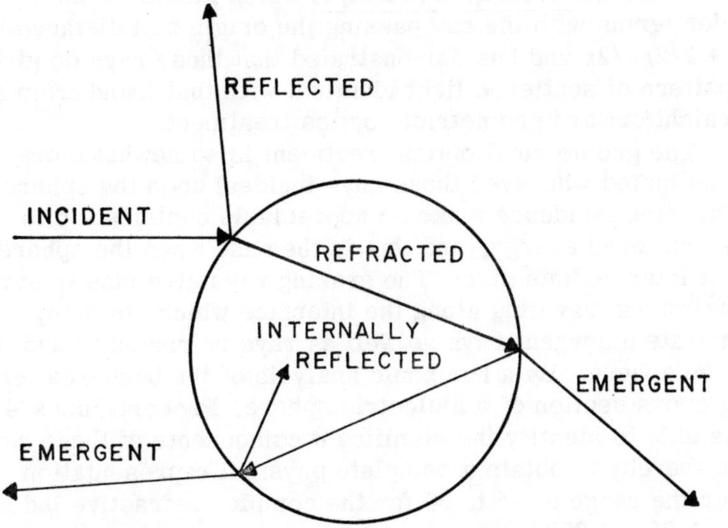

Fig. 2. Geometrical optics rays scattered by sphere.

and refracted ray; the latter, in turn, divides into an internally reflected and emergent ray, and for the internally reflected ray, the process continues. The direction of each of these rays is determined by the law of reflection and Snell's law. The intensity and phase are given by the Fresnel factors as well as by the divergence which measures the spreading of a tube of rays upon interaction with a curved surface. For each encounter, the two polarized components must be considered separately.

Van de Hulst (21) has noted that the coefficients, a_n and b_n, may be separated into two terms; one independent of the nature of the particle and one dependent on it as follows:

$$a_n = \frac{1}{2}\left[1 - \exp(-2i\alpha_n)\right]; \quad b_n = \frac{1}{2}\left[1 - \exp(-2i\beta_n)\right] \quad (5)$$

The first term gives the Fraunhofer diffraction pattern and the second the scattering by reflection and refraction. Indeed, for sufficiently large particles, van de Hulst has

enunciated a localization principle which identifies the nth order terms with the ray passing the origin at a distance $(n + 1/2) \lambda/2\pi$ and has demonstrated that these rays do give a pattern of scattered light identical with that found from a straightforward geometrical optics treatment.

The geometrical optics treatment is somewhat more complicated whenever those rays incident upon the sphere at grazing incidence make an appreciable contribution to the scattered energy, and this is the case when the sphere is of intermediate size. The grazing rays give rise to surface waves traveling along the interface which, in turn, generate emergent rays as well as rays refracted in and out of the sphere. By a harmonic analysis of the back-scattering cross section of a dielectric sphere, Probert-Jones (44) was able to identify the significant components of these rays and thereby to obtain a complete physical representation over the range $\alpha = 4$ to 30 for the complex refractive index, $m = 1.78 - 0.0024i$.

The validity and applicability of the geometrical optics method, particularly to back-scattering, has been explored in considerable detail by Kouyoumjian, Peters and Thomas (28) both for dielectric bodies ($m > 1$) and for plasmas ($m < 1$). The usual methods must be modified for two special kinds of rays. One of these emerges from an equivalent ring source located behind the illuminated surface of the object; the other passes through aspects in the neighborhood of the back-scattering direction. The results, which do not include the surface waves, agree quite well with the exact theory for $\alpha > 3$. An example for a plasma with dielectric permittivity $\epsilon_r = 0.50$ is shown in Fig. 3.

II. SCATTERING BY NON-HOMOGENEOUS SPHERES

A simple case of a non-homogeneous sphere is a homogeneous spherical core surrounded by any number of homogeneous concentric shells, each uniform but of different optical properties and thicknesses. The single shell case (Aden and Kerker, 1) can be easily generalized to an arbitrary number of shells (Kerker and Matijevic, 26), and calculations have been carried out for a sphere with as

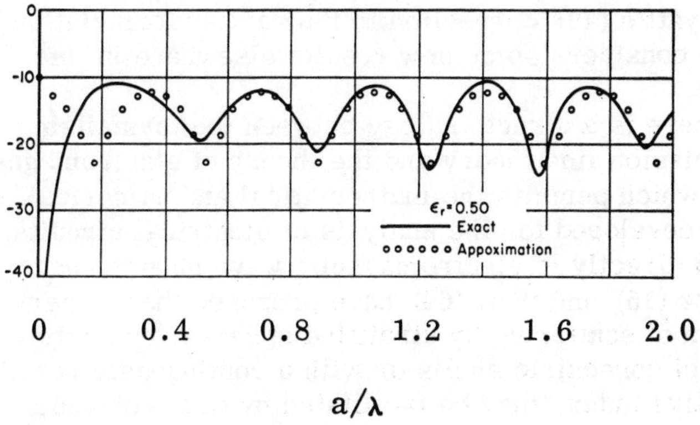

Fig. 3. Comparison of exact and approximate back scatter efficiency, $\sigma/\pi a^2$, of dielectric sphere for $m^2 = 0.50$. Reproduced with permission from Trans. I. E. E. E., **AP11**, 690 (1965).

many as 100 layers in an attempt to simulate an Eaton lens (Rheinstein, 47). The results are formally identical to Eqs. (1) to (4). The expressions for functions a_n and b_n become somewhat more complicated.

When the refractive index of the sphere varies continuously, but with radial symmetry, the expressions for a_n and b_n are formally similar to the homogeneous core but involve the functions S_n and T_n which are the solutions to two second order linear differential equations of the form

$$\frac{d^2 S_n}{dr^2} + \left[k^2 m^2 - \frac{n(n+1)}{r^2}\right] S_n = 0 \qquad (6)$$

$$m^2 \frac{d}{dr} \left[\frac{1}{m^2} \frac{dT_n}{dr}\right] + \left[k^2 m^2 - \frac{n(n+1)}{r^2}\right] T_n = 0 \qquad (7)$$

where m is the radially dependent refractive index and r is the radial distance. The solutions to these equations have been reported for a number of radial profiles by Nomura and Takaku (39), Tai (58) and Levine and Kerker (30). Various numerical results have been discussed by Garbacz (14) and Wyatt (76, 77, 78). (The reader is cautioned to note Wyatt's (79) correction to his earlier formulation.) Levine considers some new results elsewhere in this volume.

There is a direct analogy between the formalism of transmission line theory and the theory of electromagnetic waves which permits the mathematical and numerical techniques developed for the analysis of electrical circuits to be applied directly to electromagnetic wave phenomena. Garbacz (15) and Wait (64) have proposed that numerical solution of scattering by stratified spheres, consisting either of concentric shells or with a continuously variable refractive index, may be facilitated by this technique. Wait and Jackson (66) have presented extensive numerical results using the surface impedance boundary conditions.

III. COMPUTATIONS

A considerable effort has been expended in the computation of scattering functions during the past decade and many of these have been tabulated and analyzed. This work will not be reviewed here, but reference is made to the compilation of Penndorf (41) which catalogues these results. Mention will also be made, in addition, of some recent computations which have been selected because of their particular interest for some workers.

Rheinstein (48) has computed the backscatter cross section of perfectly conducting spheres with a radius to wavelength ratio (a/λ) varying from 0.01 to 19.00 at intervals of 0.01 or less. The same author (Rheinstein, 49) has made similar computations for a conducting sphere ($a/\lambda = 0.02$ to 10.0) with a dielectric coating ($m^2 = 2.56$, 4.0 or 6.0) whose thickness was 0.1 or 0.05 times the outer radius of the coated sphere.

Although the back-scatter cross section for a large partially absorbing sphere should approach the geometrical optics limit and thereby become equal to the reflectivity of the material at perpendicular incidence (McDonald, 35), the limiting value is not closely approached until the particle becomes very large. For plexiglas in the microwave region ($m = 1.61 - 0.0025\,i$), Atlas and Glover (3) have noted that the back-scatter cross section in the neighborhood of $\alpha = 50$ is still three orders of magnitude greater than the plane reflectivity value of 0.079. Querfeld (45) has made computations for the ranges of α: 0.01(0.01) 480.00; 9.000(0.001) 12.00; 500(0.01) 510.00; 520.00(0.01)570.00; 580.00(0.01)600.00; 620.00(0.01)630.00; 640.00(0.01)690.00. Even near $\alpha = 690$, there are minima and peaks in the back-scatter lying at 0.04 and 0.125, respectively.

IV. INFINITE CYLINDERS

The scattering theory for the infinite cylinder upon which the radiation falls at perpendicular incidence is quite analogous to that for the sphere. The equations corresponding to (1) - (4) are

$$I_1 = \frac{2}{\pi kr} \left| b_0 + 2 \sum_{n=1}^{\infty} b_n \cos(n\theta) \right|^2 \tag{8}$$

$$I_2 = \frac{2}{\pi kr} \left| a_0 + 2 \sum_{n=1}^{\infty} a_n \cos(n\theta) \right|^2 \tag{9}$$

$$Q_{1(SCA)} = \frac{2}{\alpha} \sum_{n=-\infty}^{\infty} |b_n|^2; \quad Q_{1(EXT)} = \frac{2}{\alpha} \sum_{n=-\infty}^{\infty} \mathrm{Re}\, b_n \tag{10}$$

$$Q_{2(SCA)} = \frac{2}{\alpha} \sum_{n=-\infty}^{\infty} |a_n|^2; \quad Q_{2(EXT)} = \frac{2}{\alpha} \sum_{n=-\infty}^{\infty} \mathrm{Re}\, a_n \tag{11}$$

The expressions of a_n and b_n differ from the spherical case only in replacement of the spherical Bessel functions by integral order Bessel and Hankel functions.

Scattering by radially stratified cylinders can be treated in a manner analogous to that for the case of spheres. Contributions to the case of a cylindrical core with coaxial cylindrical sheaths have been made by numerous workers (Thilo, 61; Adey, 2; Kerker and Matijevic, 26; Tang, 60; Plonus, 43). Just as for spheres, when the refractive index is variable with radial symmetry, the scattering coefficients involve functions which are solutions of two differential equations which are more general than Bessel's equation. This problem was treated originally by Keitel (23) and more recently by Yeh and Kapreilian (82) and Wait (65) in connection with plasma cylinders formed upon the entry of meteors and space vehicles into the atmosphere.

In connection with the current work on plasmas there has been particular interest in a cylindrical plasma confined in a constant magnetic field directed along the cylinder axis. Such plasmas, which are termed gyroelectric, correspond to media with a macroscopic dielectric constant in the form of a tensor where the tensor elements are functions of the density of the electrons and ions and the frequency of collision between them. Scattering at both perpendicular incidence (Platzman and Ozaki, 42; Wait, 63) and oblique incidence have been treated (Wilhelmsson, 74). The case of a conducting cylindrical core encased in a sheath of a gyroelectric medium has also been discussed (Ohba, 40; Seshadri, 51; Chen and Chang, 6). Numerical results have been obtained by Lee, Peters and Walter (29) and compared with a simplified optics treatment.

There is also a symmetric case in which there is magnetic anistropy formally analogous to the above. This occurs for certain ferromagnetic materials called ferrites and the condition is termed gyromagnetic. Tai and Chow (59) have investigated a single ferrite cylinder and Chow (7) has extended this to the case of two coaxial ferrite cylinders.

Kelly and Russek (24) have studied cylinders with anisotropic conductivity. Mention will also be made of the solution recently of scattering by an elliptic dielectric cylinder at both perpendicular and oblique incidence (Yeh 80, 81).

A few words are in order regarding scattering by an infinite cylinder at oblique incidence. Wait (62) and Wilhelmsson (71, 72) obtained the solution for the homogeneous cylinder, and this was extended to a dielectric-clad conducting cylinder and to a gyroelectric medium by Wilhelmsson (73, 74) and by Samaddar (50). The physical optics is depicted in Fig. 4. The incident ray which forms the angle ϕ with the cylinder gives rise to a cone of scattered radiation traveling along the conical surface. We are now planning experiments to observe the scattering along

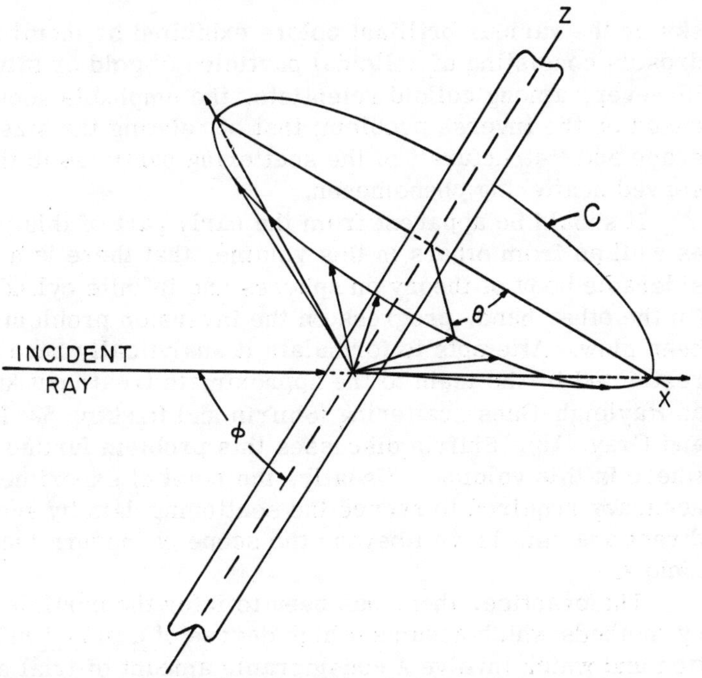

Fig. 4. Physical optics of scattering by a tilted cylinder. Scattered rays go out along surface of the cone.

the circular rim C. The incident radiation is thought of as being composed of a TM and a TE mode, for which the z-component of the magnetic and electric field, respectively, are zero. Each mode gives rise separately to both a TM and TE mode in the scattered waves. These will correspond to the components polarized tangentially and perpendicularly to the circular rim of observation.

V. THE INVERSION OF EXPERIMENTAL LIGHT SCATTERING DATA

The initial impetus for the development of the theory of light scattering arose from a desire to explain phenomena of nature and of the laboratory such as the blue of the sky or the various brilliant colors exhibited by metal hydrosols consisting of colloidal particles of gold or silver. However, among colloid scientists, the emphasis soon focused on the inverse problem; that of relating the size, shape and "structure" of the scattering particles to the observed scattering phenomenon.

It should be apparent from the early part of this paper, as well as from others in this volume, that there is a considerable body of theory on spheres and infinite cylinders. On the other hand, progress on the inversion problem has been slow. Attempts to formulate it analytically have been restricted in the main to the approximate treatment known as Rayleigh-Gans scattering (Shifrin and Raskin, 52; Hart and Gray, 18). Shifrin discusses this problem further elsewhere in this volume. Usually, the level of experimental accuracy required to reduce the scattering data by such direct analysis is well beyond the scope of modern techniques.

The practice, then, has been to infer the particle size by methods which assume a high degree of a priori information and which involve a considerable amount of trial and error. The refractive index of the particle is usually known as well as its shape and the general size range. Scattering patterns are calculated corresponding to the probable size distributions and the appropriate one is selected by comparison of the experimental with the theoretical results.

There are any number of possible measurable quantities that can be used in such work. Heller and his co-workers have utilized both the turbidity spectrum (Wallach, Heller and Stevenson, 70) and the spectrum of the scattering ratio at 90° (Stevenson, Heller and Wallach, 56). These techniques have been based upon an examination of the wavelength dependence of the turbidity and the scattering ratio. Recent experimental studies have been reported by Heller and Wallach (20), by Wallach and Heller (68, 69) and a number of other workers have reported somewhat similar experiments (Dettmar, Lode and Marre, 9; Gledhill, 16; Mailliet and Pouradier, 33; Wales, 67).

In our laboratory we have utilized the angular dependence of the polarization ratio. The polarization ratio, ρ, is the ratio of the intensity of the horizontal component (I_2) to that of the vertical component (I_1) of the scattered light. The practice has been to observe this quantity at either every 5° or every 2.5° over a broad angular range and to compare the observations with computed values.

VI. CYLINDER RADIUS BY THE POLARIZATION RATIO METHOD

The inversion of light scattering data by the polarization ratio method will be illustrated with some recent results obtained with submicron fibers which correspond to the infinite circular cylinder. A more complete discussion may be found elsewhere (Farone and Kerker, 13).

A typical scatterer is shown in Fig. 5, which is an electron micrograph of a silica fiber. Such fibers can be prepared by pulling out a rod in an oxygen-gas flame and, after some intricate manipulation, may be mounted in a light scattering photometer as shown in Fig. 6. The polarization ratio was measured every 2.5° over the range $\theta = 15$ to 130°. After determining the approximate radius from observation in the electron microscope, systematic computation of scattering functions was carried out using the known refractive index for fused silica. The size was determined by selecting that value for which the sum of the squares of the deviations between the experimental and theoretical values of the polarization ratio was a minimum.

The results obtained at the wavelength $\lambda = 546$ mμ are shown in Fig. 7. It is immediately apparent that m = 1.46 and $\alpha = 4.00$ give excellent concordance between the measured and computed values of the polarization ratio. We believe this represents a considerable advance in the technique of measurement of light scattering by a single particle in the colloidal range. Earlier reported measurements of scattering by single spheres in particle counters (Gucker and Rowell, 17) cannot compare with this either in terms of accuracy or of angular resolution of the data. Consider, for example, the other panels in Fig. 7. The discrepancy between experiment and theory for $\alpha = 3.98$ or $\alpha = 4.02$ at

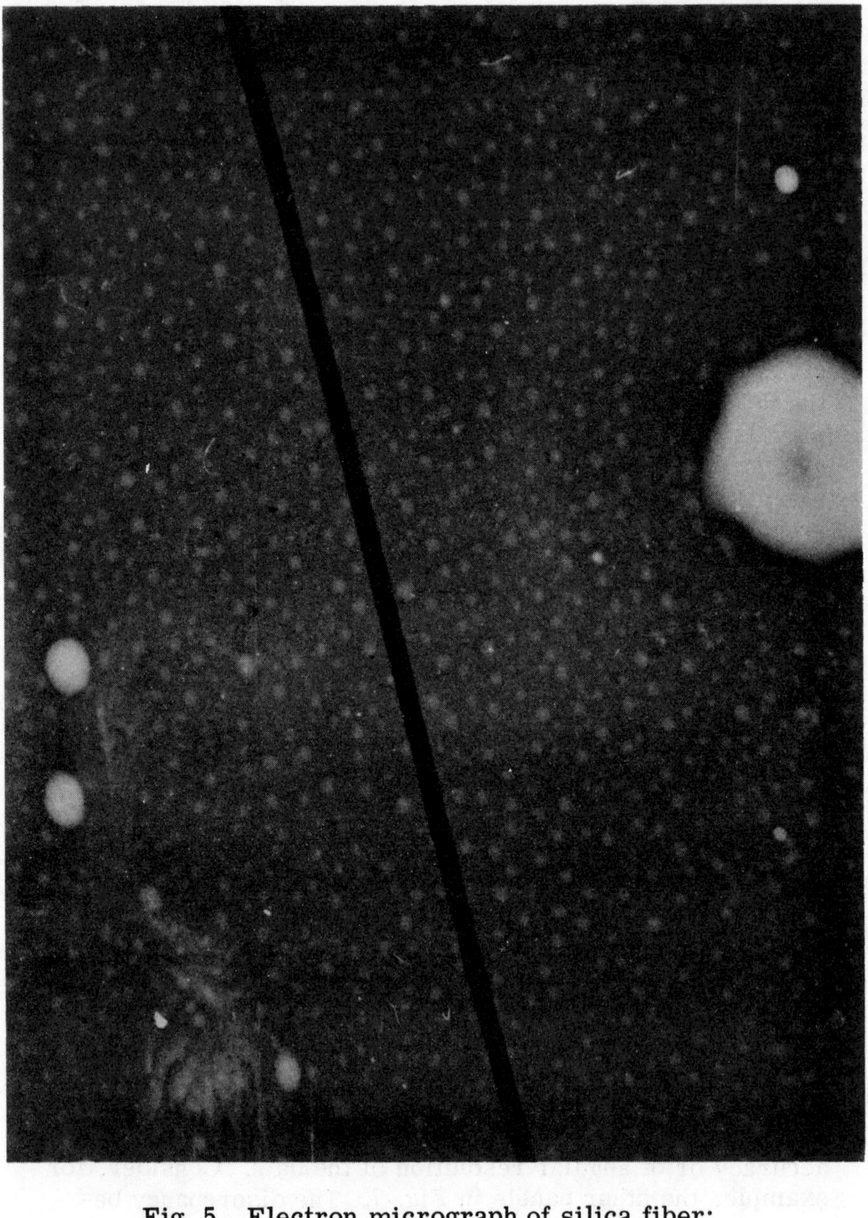

Fig. 5. Electron micrograph of silica fiber; magnification 1200X.

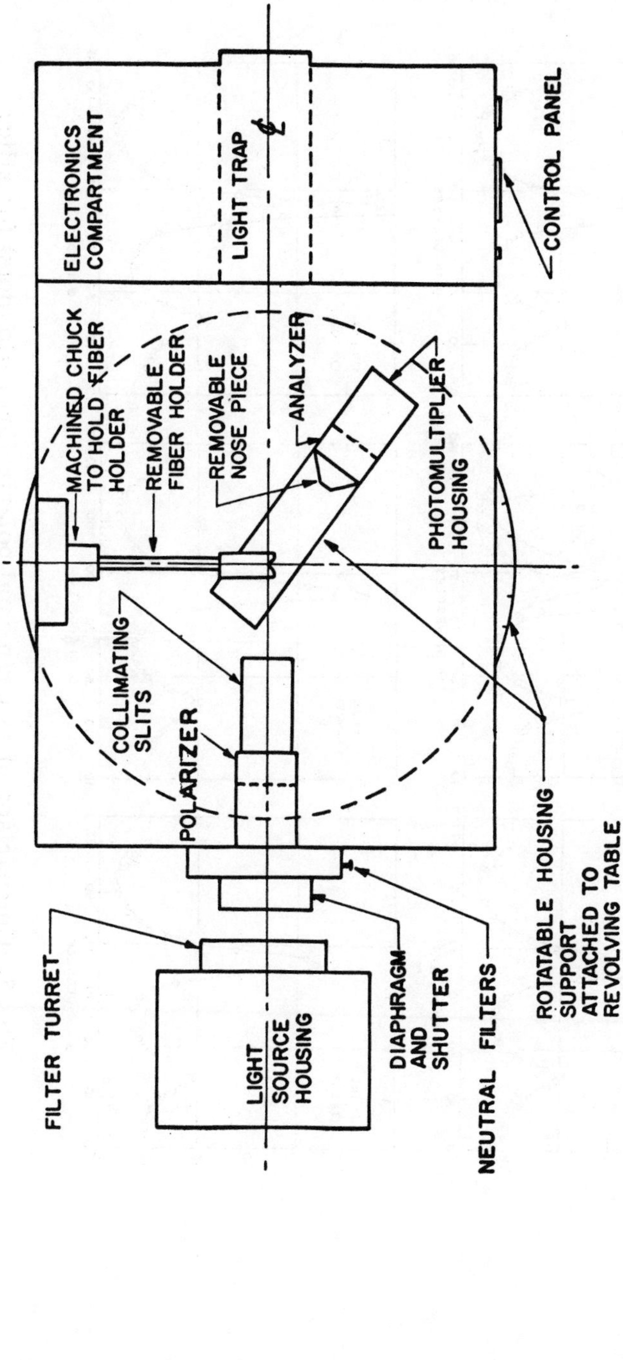

Fig. 6. Schematic diagram (top view) of the modified Brice-Phoenix Light Scattering Photometer.

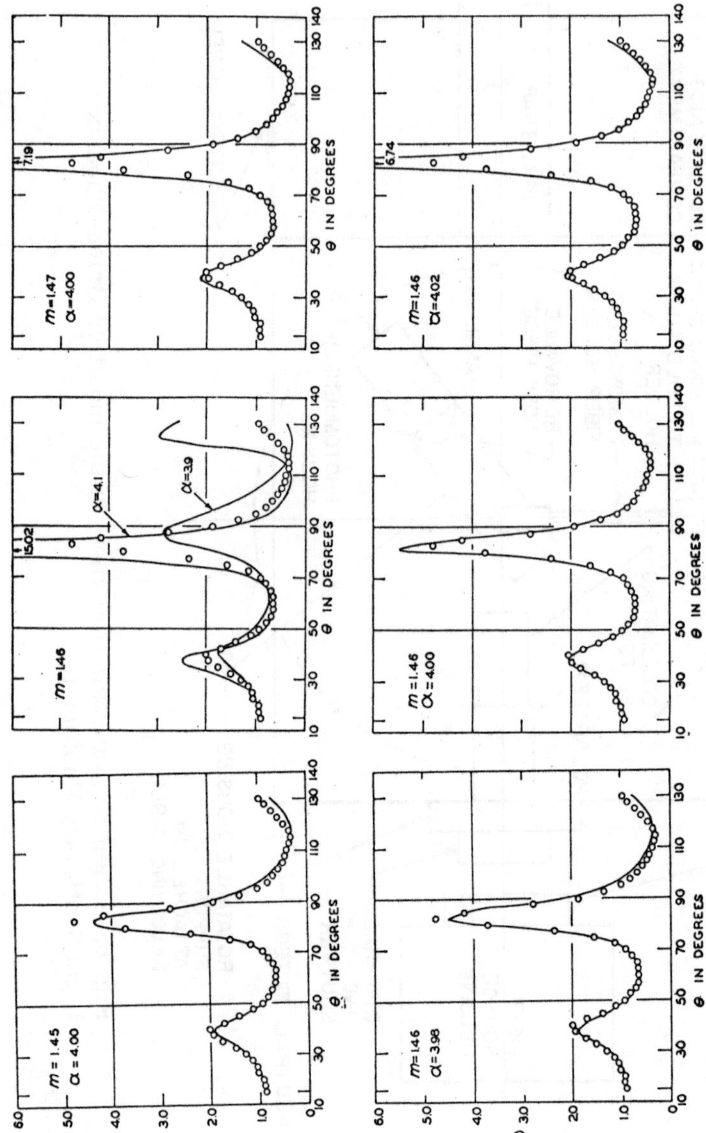

Fig. 7. Comparison of experimental polarization ratio (dots) for silica fiber λ = 546 mμ with theoretical results (smooth curves) corresponding to various refractive indices m and size parameters α.

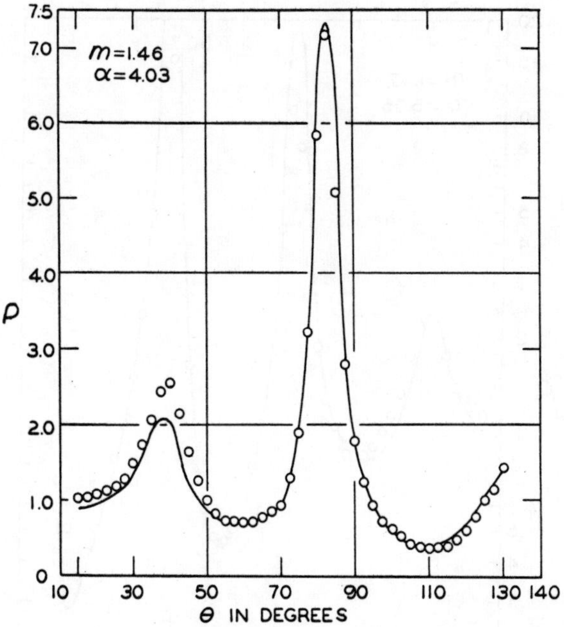

Fig. 8. Comparison of experimental polarization ratio (dots) for same silica fiber as Fig. 9 at λ = 546 mμ with theoretical result (smooth curve) for m = 1.46, α = 4.03.

m = 1.46 is obvious as is that for m = 1.45 and m = 1.47 at α = 4.00. Viewed from the point of view of the "inversion problem," the size of this particular fiber has been "determined" to within ±.25% and the refractive index to within ±0.01. This is a remarkable result when one considers that an accuracy of 5% by electron microscopy would be quite acceptable.

The results for another silica fiber examined at two wavelengths are shown in Figs. 8 and 9. For λ = 546 mμ, the best fit was obtained for α = 4.03, m = 1.46; for λ = 436 mμ, α = 5.05, m = 1.47. These results correspond to a radius of 7.01 mμ and 7.02 mμ, respectively. Although not every fiber examined gave results of such accuracy, it was generally possible to determine the particle radius to within at least 1%.

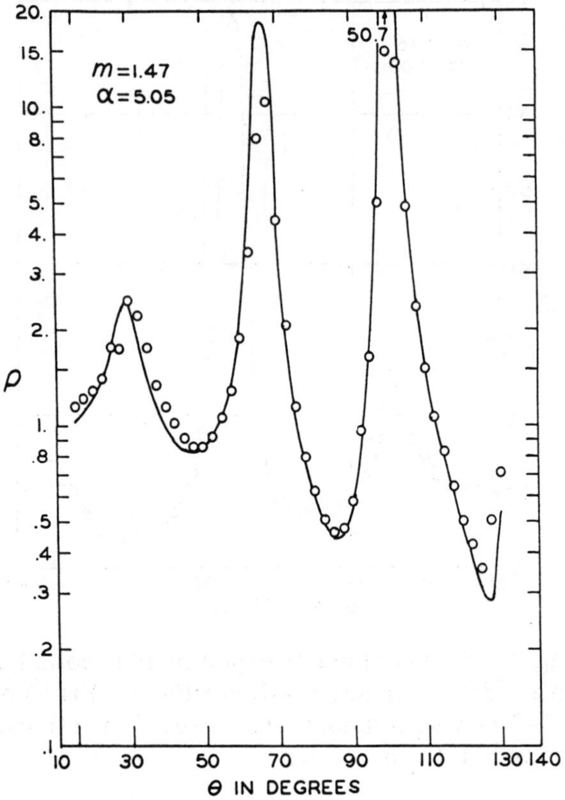

Fig. 9. Comparison of experimental polarization ratio (dots) for same silica fiber as Fig. 8 at λ = 436 mμ with theoretical result (smooth curve) for m = 1.47, α = 5.05.

In addition to fused silica fibers, the following systems were also studied: Pyrex, dacron (birefrigent), tungsten, platinum, Pyrex coated with gold, tungsten coated with paraffin. Except for the Pyrex, it was not possible to analyse the other materials with the same succses because the other fibers were somewhat larger ($r > 1\mu$) and in the case of metals, had complex refractive indices. The limitation imposed by these factors was the excessive amount of computer time necessary to obtain the calculated results. This work will be presented in detail elsewhere in due course.

VII. PARTICLE SIZE DISTRIBUTION BY THE POLARIZATION RATIO METHOD

The reduction of light scattering data from a single colloidal particle is a rather unique experience. The usual situation involves an array of particles. If these particles are randomly positioned so that the scattering is incoherent and if the concentration is sufficiently low so that there is no appreciable multiple scattering, the scattered intensity is obtained by addition of the intensity from each individual particle. In such a case, the polarization ratio is given by

$$\rho = \frac{\int p(\alpha)\, I_2\, d\alpha}{\int p(\alpha)\, I_1\, d\alpha} \qquad (12)$$

where $p(\alpha)$ is the distribution function. The inversion problem now consists in determining this distribution function, assuming the shape and refractive index of the particles are known. From hereon, the discussion applies to spherical particles.

We have chosen to represent the particle sizes by a positively skewed two parameter distribution defined by

$$p(\alpha) = \frac{\exp\left[-(\ln \alpha/\alpha_M)^2/2\sigma_0^2\right]}{\sqrt{2\pi}\,\sigma_0\,\alpha_M \exp(\sigma_0^2/2)} \qquad (13)$$

which has been called a zeroth-order logarithmic distribution (Espenscheid, Kerker and Matijević, 10). The two parameters are α_M, which is the modal value of the size parameter α, and σ_0, which is a measure of the width of the distribution. For narrow distributions, σ_0 approximates the coefficient of variance.

Our studies on a variety of colloidal dispersions consisting of spherical particles have been reported in the literature (Kerker et al. 25; Kerker et al. 27, Matijević et al. 34, Espenscheid, Matijević and Kerker, 11, Espenscheid et al. 12), and we will only present some of the salient features of the work here. The method consists, as above, in the matching of the measured polarization ratio

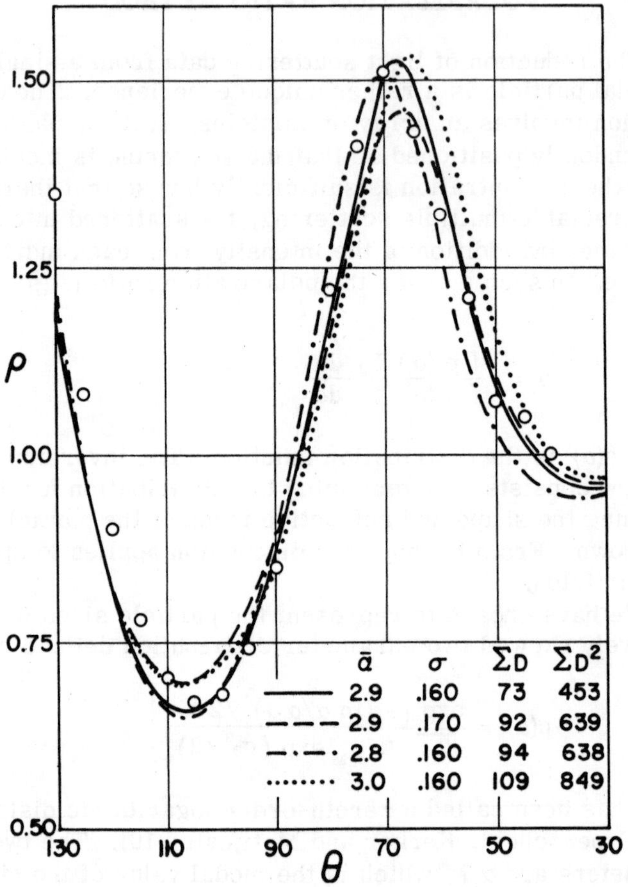

Fig. 10. Comparison of experimental values of $\rho(\theta)$ for an octanoic acid aerosol with the theoretical values for the four sets of distribution parameters which best fit. Here the agreement is is within 12% at each of the 19 angles $\theta = 40°(5°)$ 130°. Reproduced with permission from Journal of Colloid Science, 19, 223 (1965).

with the values calculated with the aid of Eq. (12). To this end, a huge library of computed results was accumulated and stored on punched cards, corresponding to the parameters of the distribution that might possibly be encountered and to the refractive indices of the material in question. Our library presently consists of $\alpha_M = 1.9(.1)\,15.0$, $\sigma = 0.005(.005).155; .16(.01).30$, $\theta = 30°(5°)\,130°$, and $m = 1.43, 1.51, 2.074$. These comprise 382,536 cases.

A typical result for an octanoic acid aerosol is shown in Fig. 10. The experimental points are denoted by circles and are compared with the curves corresponding to the four sets of distribution parameters which best fit. In each case, the agreement between experiment and theory is to within 12% at each of the 19 angles. The sum of the deviations, ΣD, and of the squares of the deviations ΣD^2 between experiment and theory are also given. The distribution $\alpha_M = 2.9$, $\sigma_0 = 0.160$ best agree with the data. The other results clearly indicate the high degree of accuracy.

In Fig. 11 the experimental data and those computed results best conforming to these are shown for the same aerosol at two different wavelengths, $\lambda = 436$ and 546 mμ. In this case, the particles consist of spheres of sodium chloride. Since the size parameter, α, is dependent upon the ratio of radius to wavelength, quite different results are obtained at the two wavelengths. However, when the values of α_M and σ_0 are converted into size distributions expressed as radii, the results shown in the inset to Fig. 11 are obtained. Clearly, the agreement at the two wavelengths is excellent.

A note of caution should be introduced at this point. The colloidal systems illustrated thus far have had a reasonably narrow size distribution ($\sigma_0 \simeq 0.1$) and the particle sizes have been comparable in magnitude to the wavelength, i.e., in the so-called resonance region. Under these conditions, the light scattering data are highly structured and nearly uniquely reflect the particular size distribution of the scattering system. However, as the distribution broadens, and possibly also as the size becomes appreciably larger than the wavelength, the structure just referred to is "washed-out," and the light scattering data are no

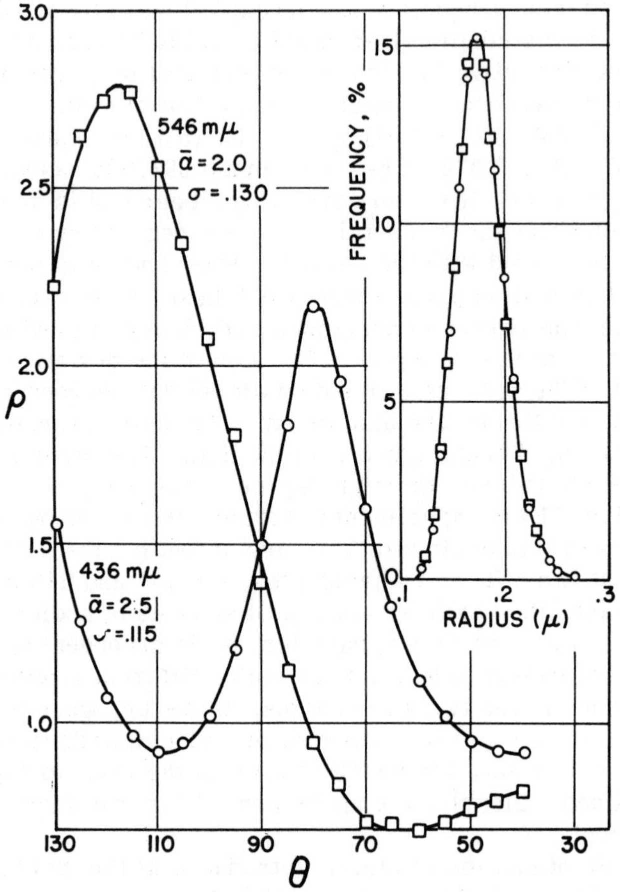

Fig. 11. Comparison of experimental values of $\rho(\theta)$ for a sodium chloride aerosol at λ = 546 mμ and 436 mμ with the theoretical values for the distribution parameters which best fit. The corresponding size distributions are in the inset. Reproduced with permission from the Journal of Physical Chemistry, 68, 2831 (1964).

longer uniquely related to a particular distribution. An illustration of this wash-out is shown in Fig. 12. Studies are now under way which attempt to determine the limits for both size range and width of size distribution over which practical results can be obtained.

VIII. AEROSOLS CONSISTING OF COATED SPHERES

We have recently explored the possibility of utilizing the above procedure to determine the size distribution of aerosols consisting of spheres of one material ($AgCl$, $m_1 = 2.105$) coated with a concentric spherical shell of a second material (linolenic acid, $m_2 = 1.482$) using the theory formulated by us a number of years ago (Aden and Kerker, 1).

For a system of concentric spheres, there are two distinct distribution functions to consider; one describes the distribution of core sizes, the other the distribution of the thicknesses of the spherical shell. A complete search for the four parameters of the two distributions would require an inordinate amount of computer time. Instead, the following procedure was used. The core aerosol ($AgCl$) was first prepared and the light scattering data were obtained and later analyzed by the procedure which has already been described. The coating was applied and similar light scattering data were obtained for the coated aerosol. Computations were then made for coated aerosols consisting of cores with the distribution as determined and with various thicknesses of coatings. The coatings were assumed to go on according to one of two models; either each core particle acquired a coating of the same thickness or each core particle acquired the same volume of coating material. The experimental data were then compared with the various calculated results, proceeding on a trial and error basis, until a fit was obtained. In some cases, the distribution of the cores was altered somewhat from that determined for the single spheres.

A typical experimental result is shown in Fig. 13. The solid lines are drawn through the experimental points. The

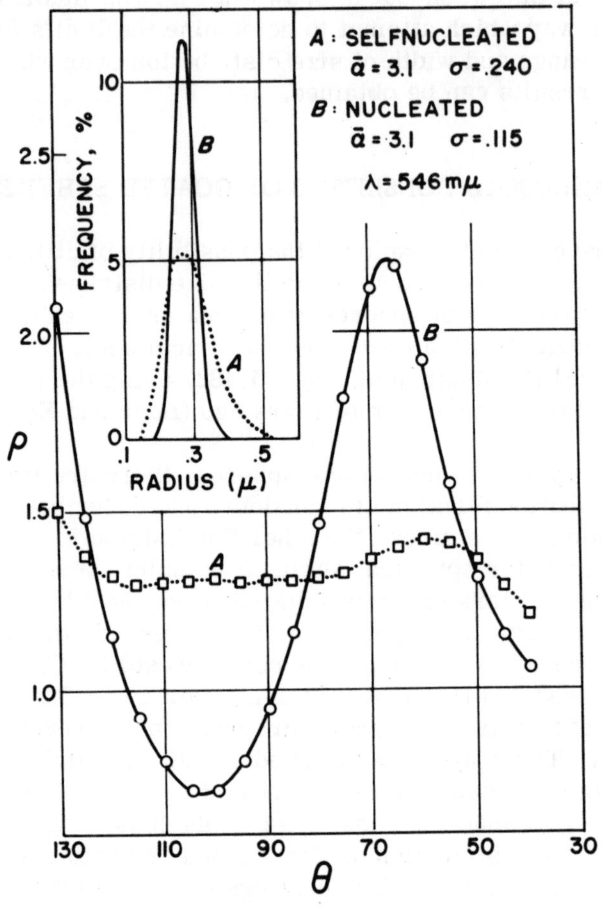

Fig. 12. Comparison of experimental values of $\rho(\theta)$ for two sodium chloride aerosols at $\lambda = 546$ mμ with the theoretical value for the distribution parameters which best fit. The self-nucleated is the broad distribution case; the nucleated is the narrow distribution case. Reproduced with permission from the Journal of Physical Chemistry, 68, 2831 (1964).

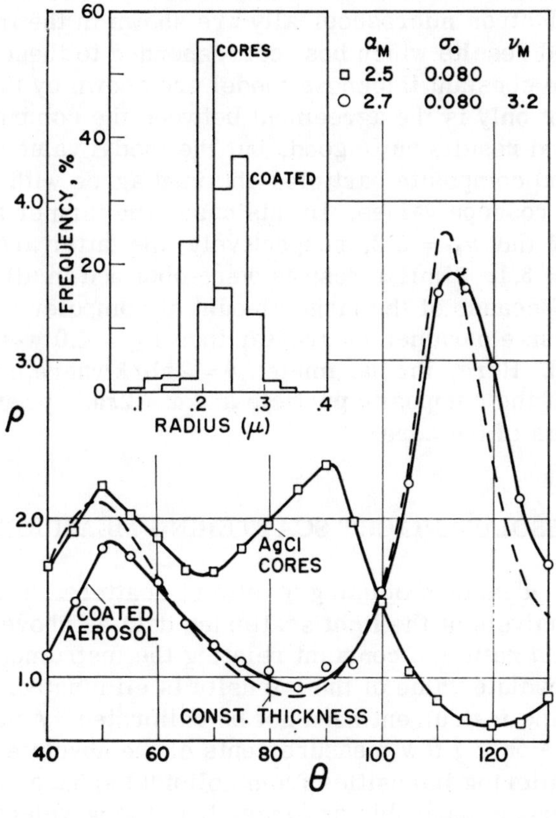

Fig. 13. Experimental values of $\rho(\theta)$ for cores consisting of silver chloride (squares) and concentric spheres consisting of silver chloride cores coated with linolenic acid at $\lambda = 546$ mμ. The dashed curve corresponds to the best theoretical fit using the constant thickness model. Size distribution parameters for core and coated particles in the upper right corner. Histograms in the inset obtained by electron microscopy. Reproduced with permission from Journal of Colloid Science, 20, 501 (1965).

effect of the coating upon these data is quite apparent. The size histograms for the core and coated aerosols as determined electron microscopically are shown in the inset. The computed results which best corresponded to these data using the constant thickness model are shown by the dashed line. Not only is the agreement between the computed and calculated results quite good, but the modal values of the cores and composite particles obtained agree with the electron microscope values. In this case, the former are $\alpha_M = 2.7$ and $\nu_M = 3.2$, respectively; the latter are $\alpha_M = 2.5$ and $\nu_M = 3.1$. Similar results were obtained in all other cases. Because of the large amount of computer time required, size parameters greater than $\nu_M = 4.0$ were not explored. Here, the parameter $\nu = 2\pi b/\lambda$ where b is the radius of the composite particle and $\alpha = 2\pi a/\lambda$ where a is the radius of the core.

IX. ABSOLUTE LIGHT SCATTERING MEASUREMENTS

The advantage of using a ratio of scattered intensities in the analysis of the light scattering data as above is that for such a ratio the constant relating the instrument signal to the absolute value of the intensity is eliminated. In other words, the instrument need not be calibrated. Actually, there are only a few measurements of the absolute angular light scattering intensities from colloidal spheres having dimensions comparable or larger than the wavelength and with refractive indices which necessitate exact computations rather than the Rayleigh-Gans approximation. These few measurements have been limited to 90° with varying degrees of success in the comparison of theoretical and experimental results.

Quite recently, Smart and Kratohvil (55) determined, over a wide angular range, the absolute intensities scattered by a polystyrene latex consisting of spheres with a narrow size distribution. A typical result is shown in Fig. 14. The solid curve is the computed value of i_2 for a normalized distribution of spheres with $\alpha_M = 9.8$, $\sigma_0 = 0.02$ where

$$i_2 = r^2 k^2 \int p(\alpha)\, I_2\, d\alpha \qquad (14)$$

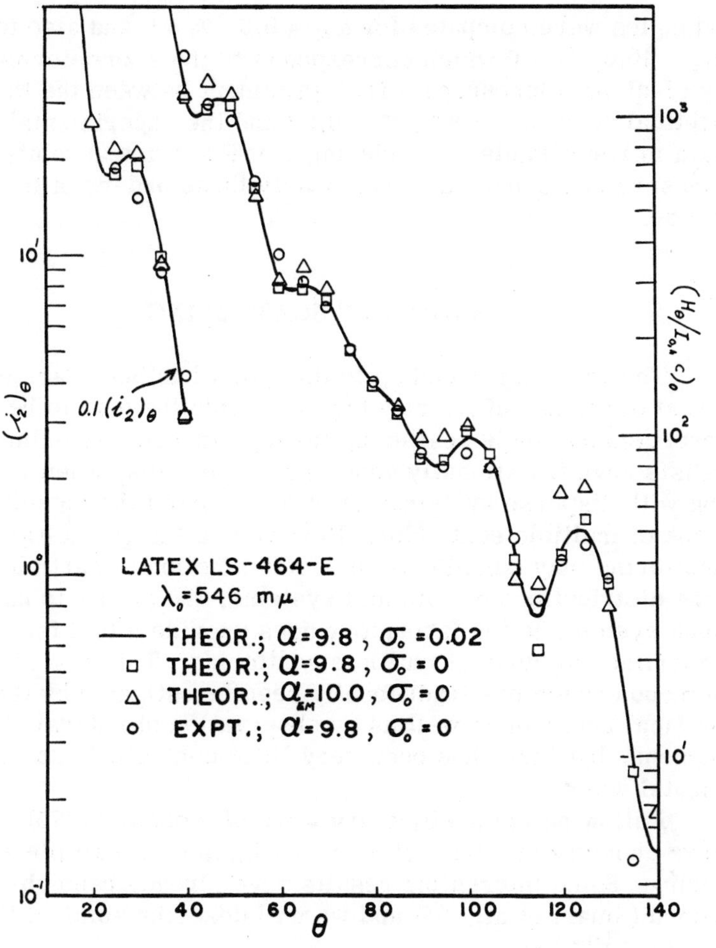

Fig. 14. Angular intensity i_2 for horizontally polarized component for Dow polystyrene lates at λ = 546 mμ. Reproduced from Journal of Colloid Science, 20, 875 (1965).

The distribution function, p(α), is defined by (12) and the subscript, 2, refers to the horizontal component of the scattered light. The points depicted by circles are values obtained from the light scattering data and the experimentally determined concentration. Those plotted as squares and triangles were computed for $\alpha_M = 9.8$, $\sigma_0 = 0$ and also for $\alpha_M = 10.0$, $\sigma_0 = 0$ which corresponds to the size determined by electron microscopy. The agreement between the theoretical curve $\alpha_M = 9.8$, $\sigma_0 = 0.02$ and the experimental data is remarkable, considering that these are absolute measurements and vary over nearly three orders of magnitude.

X. MULTIPLE SCATTERING

The work described up to this point has been carried out at dilutions sufficiently high to enable the data to be interpreted by single scattering theory. Indeed, experimentalists have traditionally gone to great lengths, when working with disperse systems, in order to avoid the complications of multiple scattering. However, although multiple scattering may complicate the determination of particle size distributions of colloidal systems, the ability to handle such systems in the laboratory does provide a tool for the experimental study of multiple scattering. This is a phenomenon which has traditionally been investigated by theoretical analysis as well as by observation of natural phenomena, but there has been very little controlled experimental work.

Following the preliminary work of Woodward (75), we have undertaken a laboratory investigation of multiple scattering. Some interesting results have already been obtained (Smart et al., 54) and we will describe some of these very briefly here.

The system studied is the polystyrene latex upon which the absolute angular scattering measurements just described were obtained. This hydrosol consists of spherical particles with $\alpha_M = 9.8$ for green light $\lambda = 546$ mμ and $\sigma_0 = 0.02$, corresponding to a modal diameter of 1.277μ.

The measurements were carried out in a special rectangular cell designed to correspond to the model of an infinite plane parallel slab. The optical path length of the cell could be varied by means of glass inserts so that path lengths of 3.00 mm, 1.83 mm and 0.89 mm were obtained.

The optical system is illustrated in Fig. 15 which shows the mercury arc (A), the monochromatic filter (B), the lens C, the light Stops D, E, H, the cell F, the cylindrical jacket G, and the photomultiplier H. The cylindrical jacket G was filled with Nujol, which has a refractive index close to that of glass. Not only does this eliminate most of the reflection at the outer surface of the cell, but it bends the emergent rays towards the forward direction because the effective refraction upon emergence from the cell is determined by the refraction at a water-Nujol interface. Thus, light scattered out of the ceil at 80° would be observed to emerge at 63°. This permits observation at higher angles than would be normally accessible for a cell of this shape.

Measurements were made in the forward scattering directions on seven concentrations of latex between 10^{-2} g/g and 10^{-5} g/g using vacuum wavelengths 546 and 436 mμ and two cell thicknesses. These corresponded to optical depths (turbidity $\times$ path length) varying from 0.0336 to 78.5. Only the case of perpendicular incidence was observed. The incident light was unpolarized.

A typical result is shown in Fig. 16 where the three cases correspond to optical depths of .0781, 0.798, and 2.40 in order of the increasing concentrations. The points plotted are the experimental values of the Rayleigh ratio, which is the intensity scattered per unit solid angle by a unit volume of the slab in the direction θ. The deviations at the lowest concentrations are probably due to the fact that the calculations are for a perfectly monodisperse system. The effect of polydispersity is to wash out the oscillations which in any case do wash out at the higher concentrations where there is more multiple scattering. At the higher concentrations, marked deviations are encountered in the lateral directions as shown in Fig. 17. This is not surprising and indicates that the light beam was not sufficiently wide to correspond to the model of an infinite slab which is completely illuminated. The experimental scattering is on the low side both because the entire field of view is not illuminated and also because the contribution from the scattering originating further in the slab, outside

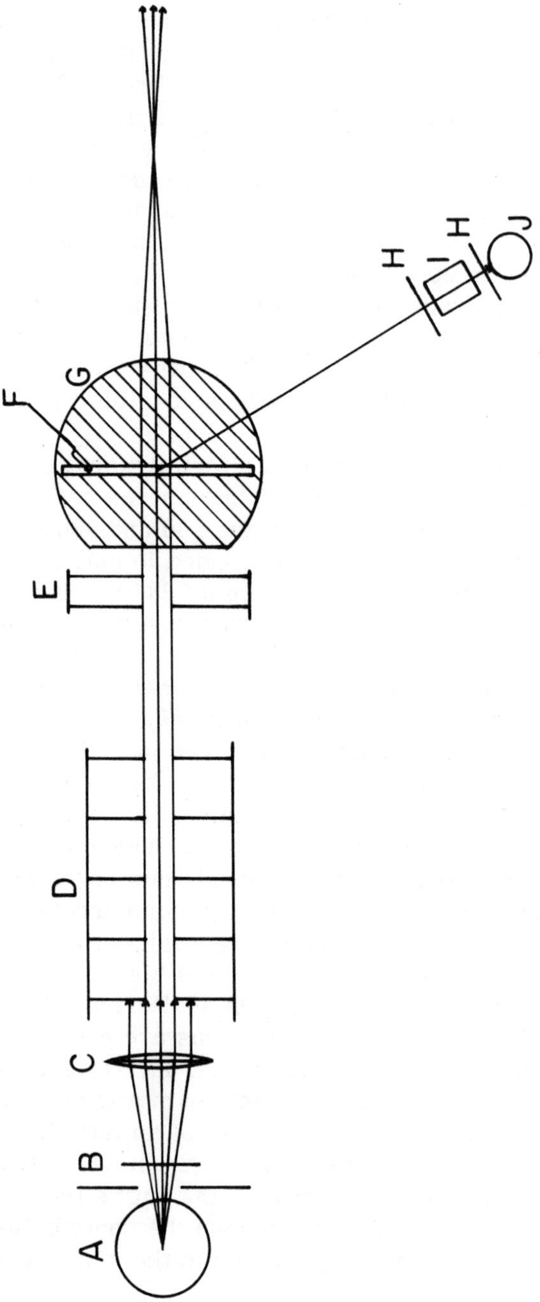

Fig. 15. Optical system for multiple scattering experiments A. Hg Arc, B. monochromatic filler, C. lens, D. light stops, E. light stops, F. cell, G. cylindrical jacket filled with Nujol, H. light stops, J. photomultiplier. Reproduced with permission from Journal of the Optical Society of America, **55**, 947 (1965).

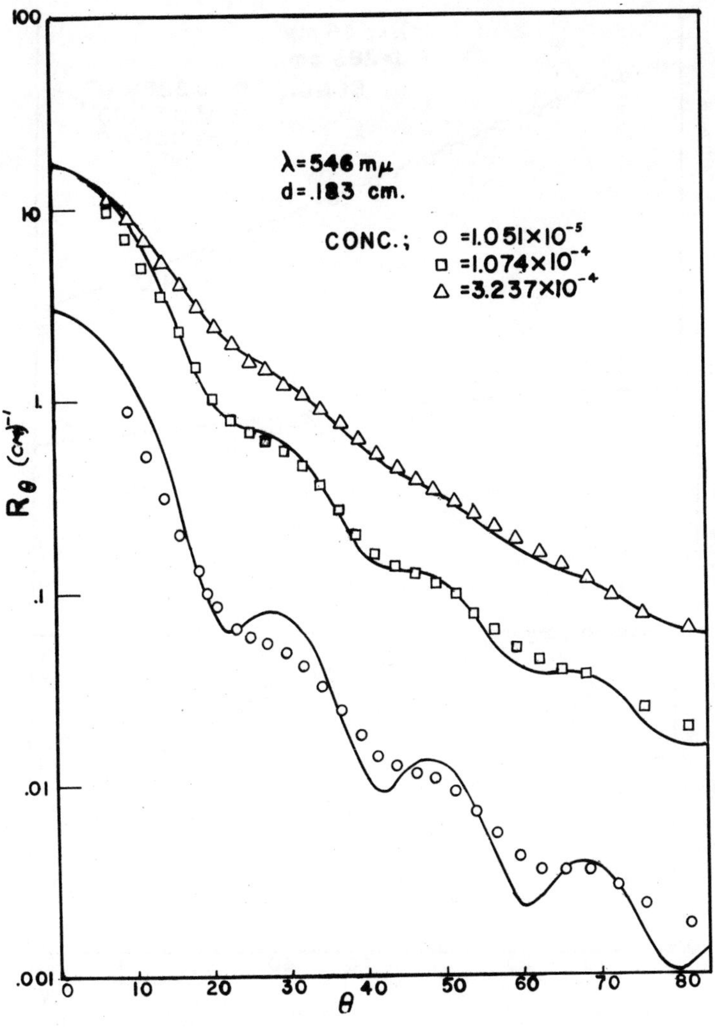

Fig. 16. Rayleigh ratio vs angle of observation for path length x = 0.183 cm and wavelength λ = 546 mμ. Concentrations are 1.051×10^{-5} g/g (circles), 1.074×10^{-4} (squares), and 3.237×10^{-4} (triangles). Reproduced with permission from Journal of the Optical Society of America, 55, 947 (1965).

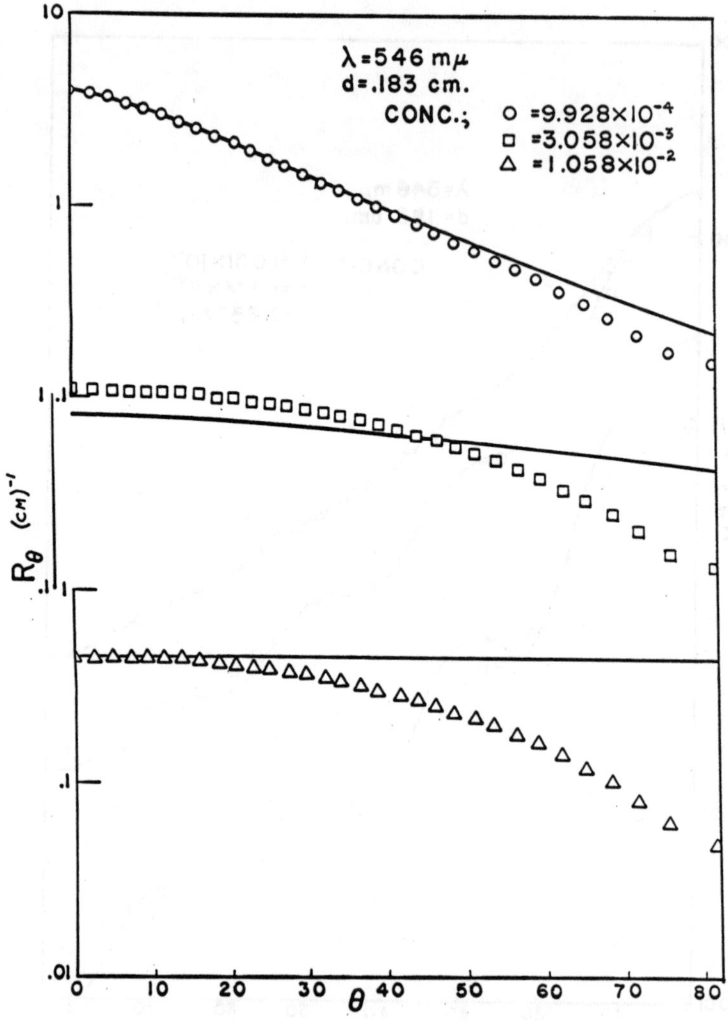

Fig. 17. Rayleigh ratio vs angle of observation for path length x = 0.183 cm and wavelength λ = 546 mμ. Concentrations are 9.928×10^{-4} g/g (circles), 3.058×10^{-3} (squares), and 1.058×10^{-2} (triangles). Reproduced with permission from Journal of the Optical Society of America, 55, 947(1965).

of the field of view, is missing. Further experiments are planned in which the beam will be broadened and in which observations will be made in the backward directions as well for oblique incidence.

XI. COLOR EFFECTS IN THE SCATTERING OF WHITE LIGHT

We would like to conclude, finally, by considering some recent computations on the color effects when spheres and cylinders are illuminated with white light. The phenomenon known as Higher Order Tyndall Spectra can be observed by illuminating a dilute suspension of polystyrene latex of narrow size distribution with a polychromatic beam such as that originating with an incandescent tungsten lamp. A similar effect may be observed when a submicronic glass fiber is illuminated in the same manner. It arises because the scattering pattern, which depends upon $\alpha = 2\pi a/\lambda$, varies sharply with α. Accordingly, in each particular direction each wavelength will be scattered quite differently and varying colors will be observed as a function of angle. Although this phenomenon has been used as the basis for a method of particle size estimation for many years (Sinclair and La Mer, 53), an exact calculation in order to deduce accurately the dependence of the color effects upon the properties of the particulate system has never been carried out.

The quantities required involve calculation of the tristimulus values (Judd and Wyszecki, 22) of the scattered light as given by

$$X_1 = k \int_\lambda \int_0^\infty P_\lambda \overline{X}_\lambda p(a)\, r^2 I_1 \, da\, d\lambda \tag{15}$$

$$Y_1 = k \int_\lambda \int_0^\infty P_\lambda \overline{Y}_\lambda p(a)\, r^2 I_1 \, da\, d\lambda \tag{16}$$

$$Z_1 = k \int_\lambda \int_0^\infty P_\lambda \overline{Z}_\lambda p(a)\, r^2 I_1 \, da\, d\lambda \tag{17}$$

Here, P_λ gives the spectral radiant flux of the source, and $\overline{X}_\lambda$, $\overline{Y}_\lambda$ and $\overline{Z}_\lambda$ are the tristimulus values of the equal energy spectrum. These latter correspond to the basic perceptions of color; hue, saturation and brightness. From these tristimulus values (viz., X_1, Y_1, Z_1) of the vertical component of the light scattered by a system having a particle radius distribution, p(a), the color may be represented by two chromaticity coordinates or, alternatively, by a principal wavelength and purity. The color is that obtained by mixing a fraction, equal to the purity, of the spectrally pure color of the dominant wavelength with the source.

For cylinders, calculations were carried out for each polarization (vertical, horizontal and unpolarized) for two sources (3200°K black body radiator and noon sunlight), two materials (ice, m = 1.31; glass, m = 1.46) eleven radii [a = 0.4 (0.1) 1.4 μ] and 73 angles [0°(2.5°) 180°]. Similar calculations for water spheres included only a single modal radius, $a_M = 0.4\ \mu$, but considered various size distributions, σ_0 = 0.01, 0.02, 0.05, 0.07, 0.10, (0.02) 0.18. These results are discussed in detail elsewhere (Kerker, Farone and Espenscheid, 25a), but some of the results for cylinders may be briefly considered here.

The scattered light may be considered to consist of alternating blue-green, yellow and orange-red bands or orders. In Table I, the centers of the angular positions of the orders are listed for the particular parameters given there. Thus, for a 0.4 μ, the first red order is at 30°, the first green one at 45°, the second red one at 70°, etc. At 102.5° there is a yellow order in place of the third red one. The pattern given here is quite typical. At first, the number of the orders increases with particle size, but then the colors in the backward directions become uniformly yellow, so that the alternation of colored orders at r = 1.4 is confined to $\theta \leq 45°$.

This means that the position and frequency of the orders can be used as a measure of particle size only over a limited range of size; in this case, possibly up to about a = 0.7 μ. Furthermore, the frequency and brilliance of orders does not necessarily provide a criterion of monodispersity. Thus, a monodisperse system of cylinders with a = 1.4 μ would appear "washed out" having only a few orders in the forward directions while a distribution of cylinders in the neighborhood of a = 0.5 μ might exhibit very brilliant Higher Order Tyndall Spectra.

TABLE 1

Angular Positions of Orders for Glass Cylinder (m = 1.46) with Vertically Polarized 3200°K Source

Radius (μ)	R-1	G-1	R-2	G-2	R-3	G-3	R-4	G-4	R-5	G-5	R-6	G-6	R-7	G-7
0.4	30	45	70	87.5	102.5Y	140	162.5							
0.5	20	35	50	70	82.5	100	115	130	145Y	152.5	170			
0.6	10	25	40	55	67.5	82.5	100	112.5	125	135	150Y	160	170	
0.7	blue-green		32.5	45	57.5	70	orange-yellow		→	122.5	130	142.5	155Y	165
0.8	blue-green		22.5	35	47.5	57.5	70	77.5	90	orange yellow		→		
0.9	green →		15Y	30	40	50	60	70	80	90	orange yellow →			
1.0	yellow →			25	32.5	42.5	52.5	orange-yellow →						
1.1	yellow →		10	20	25	35	45	orange-yellow						
1.2	purple →			15	25	30	40	47.5	*yellow orange →					
1.3	purple →			10	20	25	35	40	47.5	*orange yellow →				
1.4	green →				17.5	22.5	30	37.5	45	**yellow →				

* green at 157.5
** green at 147.5

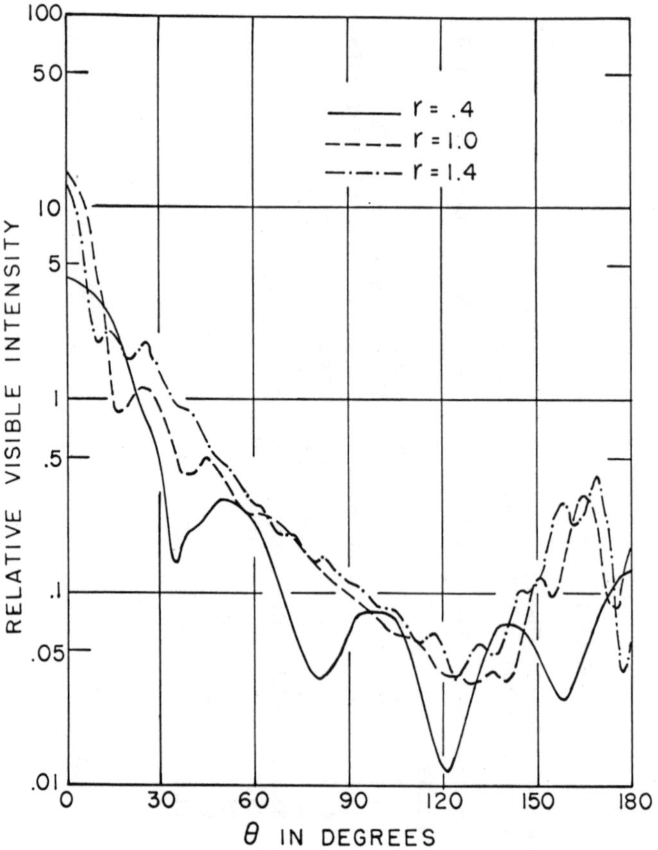

Fig. 18. Visible intensity of vertically polarized light scattered by a glass cylinder (m = 1.46) with radii a = 0.4, 1.0, 1.4 μ vs angle of observation.

The variation of the visible intensity of the scattered light with scattering angle is shown in Fig. 18 for a glass cylinder of three different radii (r = 0.4, 1.0 and 1.4 μ). Again, there is a very striking effect. For a = 0.4 μ, the visible intensity undergoes marked oscillation with angle. With increasing sizes, the frequency of the oscillations increases but the amplitude damps down until at a = 1.4 μ, there is only the diffraction lobe in the forward direction and a broad lobe in the backward direction which may be the beginning of the rainbow.

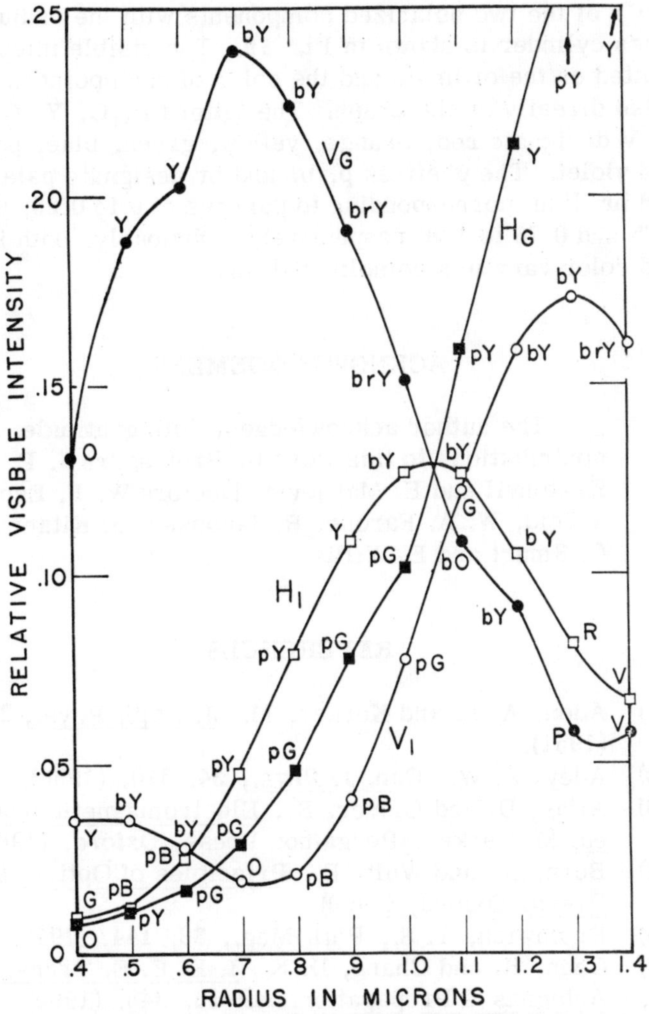

Fig. 19. Visible intensity and color of vertically and horizontally polarized light back scattered by glass and ice cylinders. Color designations as in text. Circles are for the vertical component; squares for the horizontal component. Open circles and squares are for ice; filled circles and squares for glass.

Finally, the variation of the back-scattered light (θ = 180°) of the two polarized components with the radius of the glass cylinder is shown in Fig. 19. The visible intensity is plotted on the ordinate and the color of each point is indicated directly on the graph. The letters R, O, Y, G, B, P, V designate red, orange, yellow, green, blue, purple and violet. The prefixes p, b, and br designate pale, bright and brilliant corresponding to purities of 0 to 0.25, 0.51 to 0.75 and 0.76 to 1.00 respectively. Obviously, both intensity and color vary in a complicated way.

ACKNOWLEDGEMENT

The author acknowledges, with gratitude, the contributions to this work by Professors J. P. Kratohvil and E. Matijević, Doctors W. F. Espenscheid, W. A. Farone, R. Jacobsen, S. Kitani, C. Smart and E. Willis.

REFERENCES

(1) Aden, A. L. and Kerker, M., J. Appl. Phys., **22**, 1242, (1951).
(2) Adey, A. W., Can. J. Phys., **34**, 510, (1956).
(3) Atlas, D. and Glover, K., Electromagnetic Scattering, ed. M. Kerker, Pergamon Press, Oxford, (1963).
(4) Born, M. and Wolf, E., Principles of Optics, Pergamon Press, Oxford, (1959).
(5) Bromwich, T. S., Phil. Mag., **38**, 144, (1919).
(6) Chen, H. and Chang, D. K., I. E. E. E. Trans. on Antennas & Propagation, **AP-12**, 348, (1964).
(7) Chow, Y., Appl. Sci. Res. **8B**, 290, (1960).
(8) Debye, P., Ann. Phys., **30**, 59, (1909).
(9) Dettmar, H. -K., Lode, W., and Marre, E., Kolloid-Z., **188**, 28 (1963).
(10) Espenscheid, W. F., Kerker, M. and Matijević, E., J. Phys. Chem., **68**, 3093, (1964).
(11) Espenscheid, W. F., Matijević, E. and Kerker, M., J. Phys. Chem., **68**, 2831, (1964).

(12) Espenscheid, W., Willis, E., Matijević, E. and Kerker, M., J. Colloid Sci., **20**, 501 (1965).
(13) Farone, W. A., and Kerker, M., J. Opt. Soc. Am., 56, 481 (1966).
(14) Garbacz, R. J., "Electromagnetic Scattering by Radially Inhomogeneous Spheres," Report 1223-3, Ohio State University Research Foundation, Columbus, Ohio, (1962).
(15) Garbacz, R. J., Phys. Rev., **133A**, 14, (1964).
(16) Gledhill, R. J., J. Chem. Phys., **66**, 458, (1962).
(17) Gucker, F. and Rowell, R. L., Discussions Faraday Soc., **30**, 185, (1960).
(18) Hart, R. W. and Gray, E. P., J. Appl. Phys., **35**, 1408, (1964).
(19) Heller, W., J. Chem. Physics, **42**, 1863, (1965).
(20) Heller, W. and Wallach, M. L., J. Phys. Chem., **68**, 931, (1964).
(21) Hulst, H. C. van de, Light Scattering by Small Particles, John Wiley, New York, (1957).
(22) Judd, D. B. and Wyszecki, G., Color in Business, Science and Industry, John Wiley and Sons, New York, (1963).
(23) Keitel, G. H., Proc. IRE, **43**, 1481 (1955).
(24) Kelly, R. F. and Russek, A., Nuovo Cimento, **16**, 594, (1960).
(25) Kerker, M., Daby, E., Cohen, G. L., Kratohvil, J. P. and Matijević, E., J. Phys. Chem., 67, 2105, (1963).
(25a) Kerker, M., Farone, W. A., and Espenscheid, W., J. Colloid Interface Sci. **21**, 459 (1966).
(26) Kerker, M. and Matijević, E., J. Opt. Soc. Am., **51**, 506, (1961).
(27) Kerker, M., Matijević, E., Espenscheid, W., Farone, W. A. and Kitani, S., J. Colloid Sci., **19**, 213, (1964).
(28) Kouyoumjian, R. G., Peters, L., Jr., and Thomas, D. T., Trans I. E. E. E., **AP11**, 690, (1965).
(29) Lee, W. C. Y., Peters, L. and Walter, W. H., J. Res. Natl. Bur. Std., **69D**, 227, (1965).
(30) Levine, S. and Kerker, M., Electromagnetic Scattering, ed. M. Kerker, Pergamon Press, Oxford, (1963).
(31) Lorenz, L., Vidensk. Selsk. Skr., **6**, 405, (1890); Oeuvres Sci., **I**, 405, Copenhagen, (1898).

(32) Love, A. E. H., Proc. London Math. Soc., **30**, 308, (1899).
(33) Mailliet, A. -M., and Pouradier, J., J. Chem. Phys., **58**, 7, (1961).
(34) Matijević, E., Kitani, S. and Kerker, M., J. Colloid Sci., **19**, 223, (1964).
(35) McDonald, J. E., Quart. J. Roy. Meteorol. Soc., **88**, 183, (1962).
(36) Metz, H. J. and Dettmar, H. -K., Kolloid-Z., **192**, 107, (1963).
(37) Mevel, J., J. Phys. Radium, **19**, 630, (1958).
(38) Mie, G., Ann. Physik, **25**, 377, (1908).
(39) Nomura, Y. and Takaku, K., Tohoku Research Institute, Res. Inst. Elec. Comm., **7B**, 107, (1955).
(40) Ohba, Y., Can. J. Phys., **41**, 881, (1963).
(41) Penndorf, R., Research on Aerosol Scattering in the Infra-Red, T. R. RAD-TR-63-26, AVCO Corporation, Wilmington, Mass, (1963).
(42) Platzman, P. M. and Ozaki, H. T., J. Appl. Phys., **31**, 1597, (1960).
(43) Plonus, M. A., Can. J. Phys., **38**, 1665, (1960).
(44) Probert-Jones, J. R., Electromagnetic Scattering, ed. M. Kerker, Pergamon, Oxford, (1963).
(45) Querfeld, Private communication, USAERDA, White Sands, New Mexico, (1963).
(46) Rayleigh, Lord, Phil. Mag., **12**, 81; Sci Papers, **I**, 518, (1881).
(47) Rheinstein, J., "Scattering of Electromagnetic Waves by an Eaton Lens," Lincoln Laboratory, T. R. No. 273, (1962).
(48) Rheinstein, J., "Tables of the Amplitude and Phase of the Backscatter from a Conducting Sphere," M. I. T. Lincoln Laboratory Report 22G-16, Lexington, Massachusetts, (1963).
(49) Rheinstein, J., I. E. E. E. Trans. Antennas and Propagation, **AP-12**, 334, (1964).
(50) Samaddar, S. N., Appl. Sci. Res., **10B**, 385, (1962).
(51) Seshadri, S. R., Can. J. Phys., **42**, 860, (1964).
(52) Shifrin, K. S. and Raskin, V. F., Optics and Spectroscopy, **11**, 141, (1961).

(53) Sinclair, D. and La Mer, V. K., Chem. Rev., **44**, 245, (1949).
(54) Smart, C., Jacobsen, R., Kerker, M., Kratohvil, J. P. and Matijević, E., J. Opt. Soc. Am., **55**, 947, (1965).
(55) Smart, C., and Kratohvil, J. P., J. Colloid Sci., **20**, 875, (1965).
(56) Stevenson, A. F., Heller, W., and Wallach, M. L., J. Chem. Phys., **34**, 1789, (1961).
(57) Stratton, J. A., Electromagnetic Theory, McGraw Hill, New York, (1941).
(58) Tai, C. T., J. Res. Natl. Bur. Std., **67D**, 199, (1963).
(59) Tai, C. T. and Chow, Y., ITA Engenharia **2**, 71, (1959).
(60) Tang, C. C. H., J. Appl. Phys., **28**, 628, (1957).
(61) Thilo, G., Ann. Physik, **62**, 531, (1920).
(62) Wait, J. R., Can. J. Phys., **33**, 189, (1955).
(63) Wait, J. R., J. Res. Natl. Bur. Std., **65B**, 137, (1961).
(64) Wait, J. R., Appl. Sci. Res., **10B**, 441, (1963).
(65) Wait, J. R., J. Res. Natl. Bur. Std., **69D**, 247, (1965).
(66) Wait, J. R. and Jackson, C. M., J. Res. Natl. Bur. Std., **69D**, 299, (1965).
(67) Wales, M., J. Phys. Chem., **66**, 1768, (1962).
(68) Wallach, M. L. and Heller, W., J. Phys. Chem., **67**, 2477, (1963).
(69) Wallach, M. L. and Heller, W., J. Phys. Chem., **68**, 925, (1964).
(70) Wallach, M. L., Heller, W. and Stevenson, A. F., J. Chem. Phys., **34**, 1796, (1961).
(71) Wilhelmsson, H., Trans. Chalmers Univ. Tech., No. **155**, (1954).
(72) Wilhelmsson, H., Trans. Chalmers Univ. Tech., No. **168**, (1955).
(73) Wilhelmsson, H., Arkiv för Fysik, **23**, 447, (1962).
(74) Wilhelmsson, H., J. Res. Natl. Bur. Std. **66D**, 439, (1962).
(75) Woodward, D. H., J. Opt. Soc. Am., **54**, 1325, (1964).
(76) Wyatt, P., Phys. Rev., **127**, 1837, (1962).
(77) Wyatt, P., Electromagnetic Scattering, ed. M. Kerker, Pergamon Press, Oxford, (1963).

(78) Wyatt, P., J. Appl. Phys., **34**, 2078, (1963).
(79) Wyatt, P., J. Appl. Phys., **35**, 1996; Phys. Rev., **134**, AB1, (1964).
(80) Yeh, C., J. Math. Phys., **4**, 65, (1963).
(81) Yeh, C., J. Opt. Soc. Am., **54**, 1227, (1964).
(82) Yeh, C., and Kaprielian, Z. A., Can. J. Phys., **41**, 143, (1963).

DISCUSSION FOLLOWING PAPER BY M. KERKER

J. A. Prins: Do your calculations and experiments only bear upon real indices of refraction or also upon complex values (absorption) ?

M. Kerker: None of these cases are restricted to real indices. Mr. Jacobsen is completing work now on aerosols of vanadium pentoxide which we didn't discuss here in which he is looking at the scattering at nine different wavelengths where the complex index of refraction varies from a dielectric material all the way to that of a metal. For complex refractive indices the calculations become more difficult and much of the structure "washes out" faster.

R. L. Rowell: I am pleased with your fine contribution particularly with the work on single mode distributions. Have you given any consideration to two narrow distribtutions spaced closely together with reference to the problems of separation and distinguishability from a single broader distribution?

M. Kerker: We currently have work under way with a variety of polystyrene latexes with narrow size distributions. These will be mixed in order to prepare synthetic distributions of various forms and among the possibilities we will definitely explore are bimodal distributions.

R. J. Clark: Would you comment on your method of scattering data inversion to obtain size and size-distribution of scattering particles, i.e., do you work in the scattering domain or in the real particle domain?

M. Kerker: We work in the scattering domain in that all calculations are in terms of the optical size, $\alpha = 2\pi a/\lambda$, rather than the physical size, a. The physical size can then be obtained if the wavelength is known.

R. Stein: Are there any special features that arise from birefringence of fibers?

M. Kerker: No, except that we have to carry out the search and make the calculations for two different refractive indices, one along the fiber axis and one perpendicular to it.

R. H. Marchessault: In the case on concentric spheres, if one knows all properties of the "core" what can be inferred about the "skin" from light scattering?

M. Kerker: This depends upon the amount of contrast in refractive index between that of the skin and the core on the one hand and the medium on the other hand. With sufficiently contrasting media a very thin skin, e.g. a thickness which is only 1% of the total radius, can exert an appreciable influence. See Kerker, Kratohvil and Matijevic, J. Opt. Soc. Am. **52**, 551, (1962).

Multiple Scattering from Particles in the Mie Region

Benjamin M. Herman
and
Douglas N. Yarger

Institute of Atmospheric Physics, The University of Arizona

ABSTRACT

A Numerical Method of solving the equation of radiative transfer for a plane parallel, horizontally homogeneous medium is presented. The method is applicable for problems with nonconservative scattering as well as for conservative scattering problems. Comparison of results for the reflected and transmitted radiation from this method with existing solutions for conservative Rayleigh scattering shows that, for optical depths up to 1.0, the present scheme is accurate to within 2 percent total intensity and 1 percent in polarization. Comparison of this scheme with the techniques of Sekera (10) and Dave (5) for non-conservative scattering show agreement to the same degree as above. Some preliminary results for multiple scattering by Mie particles are presented.

I. INTRODUCTION

In recent years an ever increasing array of problems in which multiple scattering is of importance has attracted the attention of atmospheric scientists. In many of these problems the range of sizes of the pertinent scatterers may cover several orders of magnitude so that the relevant laws governing the disposition of the incident radiation by a single particle will also vary widely.

The solution for a pure, plane-parallel, conservative Rayleigh atmosphere, valid for optical depths to about 1.0, has been set forth by Chandrasekhar (2). Recently the problem of a nonhomogeneous (in the vertical direction) imperfect scattering atmosphere, scattering according to Rayleigh's laws, has been solved by Sekera (10) and extended by Dave (5) in terms of the so-called auxiliary equations. These latter solutions are valuable not only because they permit solutions for atmospheres with varying amounts of absorbing material with height, but also because they are not limited by the restriction to optical depth inherent in the solution of Chandrasekhar.

The solutions above, however, have been worked out only for the specific scattering phase function appropriate for Rayleigh scattering. Presumably these techniques can be extended to the more complicated phase functions typical of the larger "Mie" particles. In doing so, however, the complexity of the solution increases rapidly. A limited extension of Chandrasekhar's solution to allow for more complex phase functions has been carried out by Churchill et al. (3). Other techniques allowing for more general types of phase functions have been or are being worked upon. One of these, the so-called invariant imbedding method essentially reformulates the problem into a form more amenable to digital computers. This method has been described by Bellman, et al. (1). Other approximate methods such as random walk models, diffusional models, etc., have also been used with varying degrees of success.

The present program consists essentially of a numerical integration of the formal solution to the equation of radiative transfer. The method is unrestricted as to: (1) form of the phase function: (2) vertical variations of any of the parameters; and (3) total optical depth. This latter quantity, however, is restricted in the sense that the computing time increases roughly in proportion to the square of the optical depth. As with any numerical scheme, the accuracy of the results is dependent upon the size of the finite difference increments utilized. As will be domonstrated, accuracies to within ± 2 percent may be obtained with a moderately dense grid network in the three independent variables of the problem.

The first part of this paper will outline the computing scheme, while the latter part will show results of the method compared to other techniques for Rayleigh scattering with and without absorption. Also some results for multiple Mie scattering which have been obtained to date are presented.

II. THE METHOD OF CALCULATION

The formal solution for the pth Stokes parameter, I_p, to the equation of radiative transfer for a plane-parallel, horizontally homogeneous non-absorbing atmosphere illuminated at the top by plane-parallel radiation travelling in the direction specified by μ_0, φ_0, is

$$I_p(\tau_2, \mu, \varphi) = I_p(\tau_1, \mu, \varphi) \exp\left[-\frac{(\tau_2 - \tau_1)}{\mu}\right] + \int_{\tau_1}^{\tau_2} \left[\frac{1}{K_T} \int_{\omega'} P_{pq}(\Theta) I_q(\tau', \mu', \varphi') d\omega'\right] \exp\left[-\frac{(\tau_2 - \tau')}{\mu}\right] \frac{d\tau'}{\mu} \quad (1)$$

$$+ \int_{\tau_1}^{\tau_2} \frac{1}{K_T} P_{pq}(\Theta) F_q(\tau, \mu_0, \varphi_0) \exp\left[-\frac{(\tau_2 - \tau')}{\mu}\right] \frac{d\tau'}{\mu} \qquad (\tau_2 > \tau_1, 0 < \mu \leq 1)$$

(1)

and

$$I_p(\tau_2, -\mu, \varphi) = I_p(\tau_3, -\mu, \varphi) \exp\left[-\frac{(\tau_3 - \tau_2)}{\mu}\right] + \int_{\tau_2}^{\tau_3} \left[\frac{1}{K_T} \int_{\omega'} P_{pq}(\Theta) I_q(\tau', \mu', \varphi')\, d\omega'\right] \exp\left[-\frac{(\tau' - \tau_2)}{\mu}\right] \frac{d\tau'}{\mu} + \int_{\tau_2}^{\tau_3} \frac{1}{K_T} P_{pq}(\Theta) F_q(\tau, \mu_0, \varphi_0) \exp\left[-\frac{(\tau' - \tau_2)}{\mu}\right] \frac{d\tau'}{\mu}$$

$$(\tau_3 > \tau_2,\ 0 < \mu \leq 1). \qquad (2)$$

In these expressions, $\mu = \cos\theta$, $-\theta$ being the angle between the direction of propagation of I_p and the z-axis which is oriented in the direction of the inward normal to the top of the atmosphere, φ is the azimuthal angle measured from an appropriately chosen x-axis (thus, beams travelling in the $+\mu$ direction are travelling towards the ground while $-\mu$ refers to beams travelling towards the top of the atmosphere), $d\omega'$ is a differential element of solid angle, and Θ is the angle between the incident and scattered intensities (see Fig. 1). The quantity τ is the optical depth, increasing downward, τ_T is the total optical depth, K_T is the total mass attenuation coefficient, and $F_q(\tau, \mu_0, \varphi_0)$ is the qth Stokes parameter of the incident plane-parallel radiation at the depth τ and is related to the incident radiation at the top of the atmosphere through the expression

$$F_q(\tau, \mu_0, \varphi_0) = F_q(0, \mu_0, \varphi_0) \exp\left(-\frac{\tau}{\mu_0}\right). \qquad (3)$$

The matrix P_{pq} is the scattering phase matrix and expresses the contribution to the beam travelling in the direction μ, φ, from scattering out of beams travelling in the directions μ', φ'. The most general form of the scattering matrix has been given by Sekera (9) as

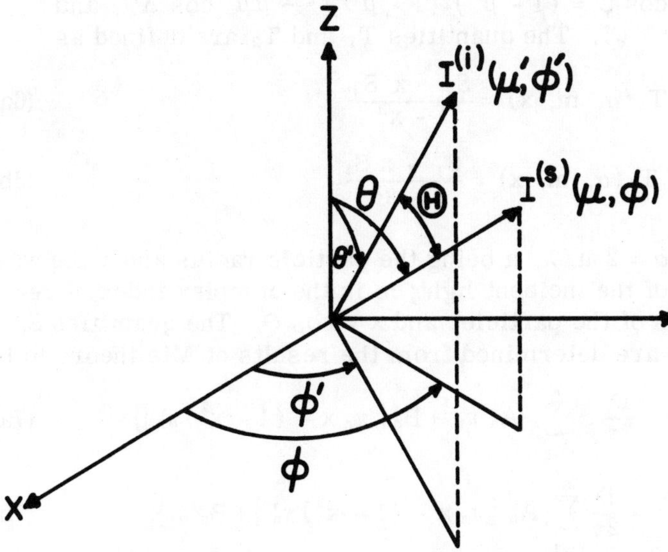

Fig. 1. Coordinate system and angles used in the transfer problem. The superscript (i) refers to the incident beam and (s) refers to the scattered beam, $\mu = \cos\theta$.

$$
P_{pq} = \begin{matrix}
A_{11}A_{11}^* & A_{12}A_{12}^* & R_e(A_{11}A_{12}^*) & -I_m(A_{11}A_{12}^*) \\
A_{21}A_{21}^* & A_{22}A_{22}^* & R_e(A_{21}A_{22}^*) & -I_m(A_{21}A_{22}^*) \\
2R_e(A_{11}A_{21}^*) & 2R_e(A_{12}A_{22}^*) & R_e(A_{12}^*A_{21} + A_{11}A_{22}^*) & -I_m(A_{21}A_{12}^* + A_{11}A_{22}^*) \\
2I_m(A_{11}A_{21}^*) & 2I_m(A_{12}A_{22}^*) & I_m(A_{11}A_{22}^* - A_{12}^*A_{21}) & R_e(A_{11}A_{22}^* - A_{21}A_{12}^*)
\end{matrix}
$$

where the asterisks denote the complex conjugate of the quantity, and R_e and I_m indicate real and imaginary parts, respectively. The quantities A_{mn} are given by

$$A_{11} = T_1 \cos\Delta\varphi + T_2 \cos\psi \tag{5a}$$

$$A_{12} = (\mu' T_1 + \mu T_2)\sin\Delta\varphi \tag{5b}$$

$$A_{21} = (\mu T_1 + \mu' T_2)\sin\Delta\varphi \tag{5c}$$

$$A_{22} = T_1 \cos\psi + T_2 \cos\Delta\varphi \tag{5d}$$

where $\cos \psi = (1 - \mu^2)^{\frac{1}{2}}(1 - \mu'^2)^{\frac{1}{2}} + \mu\mu' \cos \Delta\varphi$, and $\Delta\varphi = \varphi - \varphi'$. The quantities T_1 and T_2 are defined as

$$T_1(\alpha, m, x) = \frac{S_i - x S_j}{1 - x^2} \tag{6a}$$

$$T_2(\alpha, m, x) = \frac{S_j - x S_i}{1 - x^2} \tag{6b}$$

where $\alpha = 2\pi a/\lambda$, a being the particle radius and λ the wavelength of the incident light; m is the complex index of refraction of the particle, and $x = \cos \Theta$. The quantities S_i and S_j are determined from the results of Mie theory to be

$$S_i = \frac{i\lambda}{2\pi} \sum_{n=1}^{\infty} \{A_n \pi_n + B_n [\pi_n x - (1 - x^2)\pi_n']\} \tag{7a}$$

$$S_j = -\frac{i\lambda}{2\pi} \sum_{n=1}^{\infty} \{A_n [\pi_n x - (1 - x^2)\pi_n'] + B_n \pi_n\}. \tag{7b}$$

Here

$$\pi_n = -\frac{d}{d(\cos \Theta)} [P_n(\cos \Theta)] \tag{8a}$$

$$\pi_n' = \frac{d^2}{d(\cos \Theta)^2} [P_n(\cos \Theta)] \tag{8b}$$

where $P_n(\cos \Theta)$ is the Legendre polynomial of degree n and argument $\cos \Theta$ and

$$A_n = \frac{2n + 1}{n(n + 1)} a_n^s ; \qquad B_n = \frac{2n + 1}{n(n + 1)} b_n^s \tag{9}$$

a_n^s and b_n^s being the well-known Mie scattering coefficients defined by Stratton (12) and others. For the case of Rayleigh particles, Eqs. (7a) and (7b) become simply

$$S_i = \left(\frac{3}{8\pi}\right)^{\frac{1}{2}} \tag{10a}$$

$$S_j = \left(\frac{3}{8\pi}\right)^{\frac{1}{2}} \cos \Theta \tag{10b}$$

For a distribution of scatterers, each possessing a different set of values for S_i and S_j, the individual elements of the different scattering matrices may be simply summed over the entire distribution, so long as the individual particles are randomly spaced. Further, the quantity K_T must also be summed over the size distribution. It would appear that this assumption of incoherency is equally as valid for the aerosol problem as it is for a pure molecular atmosphere. It will suffice to say that, if the scattering from the aerosols were coherent, then the individual amplitudes. (i.e., the quantities S_i and S_j, or equivalently the quantities T_1 and T_2) would have to be summed first, and the scattering matrix formed from these quantities.

The formal solution to the equation of radiative transfer as represented by Eqs. (1) and (2) contains an integral over optical depth, τ, the evaluation of which requires a knowledge of $I_p(\tau, \mu, \varphi)$ for the entire range of optical depth over which the integral extends. Initially, only the Stokes parameters of the inward directed intensities at the bottom and top of the atmosphere are known (these being zero for most problems of practical interest).* The outward directed parameters at the level $\tau = 0$ and $\tau = \tau_T$ (those associated with the reflected and transmitted intensities, respectively) are unknown. In fact, we are primarily interested in solving for these values. We thus have a two-point boundary value problem and a straightforward numerical integration is not possible. However, the problem lends itself quite readily to the Gauss-Seidel iterative technique (Hildebrand, 7), the application of which we will now discuss.

Let us restrict ourselves for the time being to solutions for $I_p(\tau, +\mu, \varphi)$, and consider solutions for $\mu < 0$ later. Assume that initially I_p for all μ and φ at the level τ_n, denoted by $I_p^{(n)}(\mu, \varphi)$, are known (superscripts will be used to indicate the level). The values of $I_p(\mu, \varphi)$ at some level

*The inward directed intensities at the boundaries are not to be confused with the incident plane-parallel radiation which is illuminating the top of the atmosphere, and is not zero.

$\Delta\tau$ away from the nth level, which we will indicate as level n + 1, may be evaluated approximately by rewriting Eq. (1) as

$$I_p^{(n+1)}(\mu, \varphi) \approx \overline{J_p}(\mu, \varphi) \int_{\tau_n}^{\tau_n+\Delta\tau} \exp\left[-\frac{(\tau_n + \Delta\tau - \tau')}{\mu}\right] \frac{d\tau'}{\mu}$$
$$+ I_p^{(n)}(\mu, \varphi) \exp\left(-\frac{\Delta\tau}{\mu}\right) \tag{11}$$

where $\overline{J}$ is the average value of J over the interval $\Delta\tau$, and J the source function, is given by

$$J = \int_{\omega'} \frac{1}{K_T} P_{pq}(\Theta) I_q(\tau', \mu', \varphi') d\omega' + \frac{1}{K_T} P_{pq}(\Theta) F_q(\tau, \mu_0, \varphi_0) \tag{12}$$

The integral in Eq. (11) may now be evaluated yielding

$$I_p^{(n+1)}(\mu, \varphi) \approx \overline{J}_p(\mu, \varphi) \left[1 - \exp\left(\frac{\Delta\tau}{\mu}\right)\right] I_p^{(n)}(\mu, \varphi) \exp\left(-\frac{\Delta\tau}{\mu}\right) \tag{13}$$

Upon substituting for $\overline{J}$, using Eq. (12), this becomes

$$I_p^{(n+1)}(\mu, \varphi) \approx I_p^{(n)}(\mu, \varphi) \exp\left(-\frac{\Delta\tau}{\mu}\right)$$
$$+ \left[1 - \exp\left(-\frac{\Delta\tau}{\mu}\right)\right] \int_0^{\pi} \int_0^{2\pi} \frac{1}{K_T} P_{pq}(\mu, \varphi, \mu', \varphi')$$
$$\times \overline{I}_q(\mu', \varphi') \sin\theta', d\theta', d\varphi'$$
$$+ \frac{1}{K_T} P_{pq}(\mu, \varphi, \mu_0, \varphi_0) \overline{F}_q(\mu_0, \varphi_0) \left[1 - \exp\left(-\frac{\Delta\tau}{\mu}\right)\right] \tag{14}$$

where $\overline{I}_q(\mu', \varphi')$ and $\overline{F}_q(\mu_0, \varphi_0)$ are the average values of $I_q(\tau, \mu', \varphi')$ and $F_q(\tau, \mu_0, \varphi_0)$ over the interval $\Delta\tau$.*

*It should be noted that if the scattering matrix, P_{pq}, varies with height due to a varying distribution of particles in the vertical, then the average value of the products $P_{pq}I_q$ and $P_{pq}F_q$ must be extracted from the integration over τ.

These average values are taken to be the values of the variables at the midpoint of the interval $\Delta\tau$. In Eq. (14) it should be noted that the functional dependence of the scattering phase angle Θ has been replaced with a functional dependence upon the independent variables μ, φ, μ', φ' by virtue of the relationship

$$\cos\Theta = \mu\mu' + (1-\mu^2)^{\frac{1}{2}}(1-\mu'^2)^{\frac{1}{2}}\cos\Delta\varphi \quad (15)$$

Consider now the integral in Eq. (14), which may be written as

$$\int_{-1}^{1}\int_{0}^{2\pi} P_{pq}(\mu, \varphi, \mu', \varphi')\, I_q^{(n+\frac{1}{2})}(\mu', \varphi')\, d\mu'\, d\varphi'. \quad (16)$$

The evaluation of this integral is also performed numerically in steps, over which a mean value for

$$P_{pq}(\mu, \varphi, \mu', \varphi')\, I_q^{(n+\frac{1}{2})}(\mu', \varphi')$$

may be extracted from the integral giving

$$\overline{P_{pq}(\mu, \varphi, -1\to\mu'_1, 0\to\varphi'_1)\, I_q^{(n+\frac{1}{2})}(-1\to\mu'_1, 0\to\varphi'_1)} \times \int_{-1}^{\mu'_1}\int_{0}^{\varphi'_1} d\mu' d\varphi'$$

$$+ \overline{P_{pq}(\mu, \varphi, \mu'_j\to 1, \varphi'_k\to 2\pi)\, I_q^{(n+\frac{1}{2})}(\mu'_j\to 1, \varphi'_k\to 2\pi)} \int_{\mu'_j}^{1}\int_{\varphi'_k}^{2\pi} d\mu' d\varphi' \quad (17)$$

$$= \sum_{\Delta\mu'_j}\sum_{\Delta\varphi'_k} \{\overline{P_{pq}(\mu, \varphi, \Delta\mu'_j, \Delta\varphi'_k)\, I_q^{(n+\frac{1}{2})}(\Delta\mu'_j, \Delta\varphi'_k)}\}\, (\mu'_j - \mu'_{j-1})(\Delta\varphi'_k),$$

where the functional notation $-1\to\mu'_1$, $0\to\varphi'_1$, indicates the interval over which the mean of the variable is taken. The quantity

$$\overline{P_{pq}(\mu, \varphi, \Delta\mu'_j, \Delta\varphi'_k)\, I_q^{(n+\frac{1}{2})}(\Delta\mu'_j, \Delta\varphi'_k)}$$

is the mean value of the product

$$P_{pq}(\mu, \varphi, \mu', \varphi')\, I_q^{(n+\frac{1}{2})}(\mu', \varphi')$$

over the interval from μ'_j to μ'_{j-1}, and $\Delta\varphi'_k = (\varphi'_k - \varphi'_{k-1})$. In the actual calculations, this average was taken to be the value of the product at the midpoint of the interval $\Delta\mu'_j$ and $\Delta\varphi'_k$.

Rewriting Eq. (14), solving for I_p at the level n + 1 in terms of quantities at the levels n and n - 1, and using Eq. (17) for the integral, we get

$$I_p^{(n+1)}(\mu, \varphi) = I_p^{(n-1)}(\mu, \varphi) \exp\left(-\frac{2\Delta\tau}{\mu}\right)$$
$$+ \left[1 - \exp\left(-\frac{2\Delta\tau}{\mu}\right)\right] \sum_{\Delta\mu'_j} \sum_{\Delta\varphi'_k} \left\{\frac{1}{K_T} P_{pq}(\mu, \varphi, \Delta\mu'_j, \Delta\varphi'_k)\right.$$
$$\left.\times\, I_q^{(n)}(\Delta\mu'_j, \Delta\varphi'_k)\right\} \times (\mu'_j - \mu'_{j-1})(\Delta\varphi'_k) \tag{18}$$
$$+ \frac{1}{K_T} P_{pq}(\mu, \varphi, \mu_0, \varphi_0) F_q^{(n)}(\mu_0, \varphi_0) \left[1 - \exp\left(-\frac{2\Delta\tau}{\mu}\right)\right],$$
$$(p, q = 1, 2, 3, 4)$$

where the unscattered flux which penetrates to the nth level, $F_q^{(n)}$, is given by

$$F_q^{(n)}(\mu_0, \varphi_0) = F_q^{(0)} \exp\left(-\frac{n\Delta\tau}{\mu_0}\right) \tag{19}$$

by viture of Eq. (3).

The numerical procedure is started by solving for the Stokes parameters at the level n = 1 in terms of the parameters at the level n = 0 (i.e., at the level $\tau = 0$); that is, the computing equation is written in forward difference form. Thus, Eq. (18) for the level n = 1 in this form becomes

$$I_p^{(1)}(\mu, \varphi) = \left[1 - \exp\left(-\frac{\Delta\tau}{\mu}\right)\right] \sum_{\Delta\mu'_j} \sum_{\Delta\varphi'_k} \left\{\frac{1}{K_T} P_{pq}(\mu, \varphi, \Delta\mu'_j, \Delta\varphi'_k)\right.$$
$$\left.\times\, I_q^{(0)}(\Delta\mu'_j, \Delta\varphi'_k)\right\} (\mu'_j - \mu'_{j-1})(\Delta\varphi'_k)$$
$$+ \frac{1}{K_T} P_{pq}(\mu, \varphi, \mu_0, \varphi_0) F_q^{(0)}(\mu_0, \varphi_0) \left[1 - \exp\left(-\frac{\Delta\tau}{\mu}\right)\right] \tag{20}$$

where the first term on the right of Eq. (18) has been set equal to zero by virtue of conditions of zero incident intensity.* The only non-zero parameters at the level $\tau = 0$ are those associated with the outward directed intensities for which $\mu < 0$ (i.e., the reflected radiation) and the incident, parallel flux represented by $F_q^{(0)}$. However, the outward directed intensities are unknown initially, and thus, for the purpose of getting the solution started, they are assumed to be zero. This gives a first approximation to the parameters $I_p^{(1)}$. Equation (18) is then used to compute the parameters at the second and succeeding levels, for $\mu > 0$. Parameters for $\mu < 0$ are assumed to be zero for all of these initial calculations. At the top of the medium ($\tau = \tau_T$) initial calculations for all $I_p^{(n)}(\mu, \varphi)$, $\mu > 0$, have been made.

A pair of computing equations analogous to Eqs. (18) and (20) may be derived for the Stokes parameters for $\mu < 0$. Using the equations so obtained, these parameters are computed starting with the first level below τ_T and working back to the level $\tau = 0$. However, now values for the Stokes parameters for $\mu > 0$ have already been computed, and these values are used in the numerical evaluation of the source term. When the level $\tau = 0$ is reached, initial values for all of the unknowns have been computed, and the same process is now repeated, utilizing the previously calculated values for all unknowns appearing on the righthand side of the set of equations. Successive iterations performed in this manner may or may not converge to the solution of the set of equations. In general, experience with this technique has shown that convergence is likely if the coefficients of the unknowns on the right hand side are all smaller than that of the unknown on the left. It is not difficult to show that the coefficients of the unknowns appearing on the right hand side of Eqs. (18) and (20) are all smaller than unity (and

---

*If the ground reflectivity is to be considered, then the inward directed intensities at the ground level ($\tau = \tau_T$) will not be zero, and the term corresponding to the first term on the right of Eq. (18), but for $-\mu$ directions, will not be zero. However, for the remainder of this paper, the ground reflectivities will be assumed zero.

similarly for the corresponding equations for $\mu < 0$), and thus the above, rather empirical criterion is met.

The above iterative procedure is repeated, each time utilizing the most recently calculated values of the Stokes parameters on the right hand side of the computing equations, until successive values of the same variable agree to within some specified tolerance. For the case of conservative scattering, it was found that the best criterion to terminate the process was the value of the total emergent radiation. This value was computed by numerically integrating the calculated reflected and transmitted intensities over all solid angles. For conservative scattering, the resulting flux must, of course, equal the incoming flux. It was found that the first iteration results in too small a value for the emergent flux and that, with succeeding passes, this flux converges to a value of a few tenths of one percent greater than the incident flux. Succeeding iterations result in extremely small oscillations about the equilibrium value. Therefore the calculations were stopped at the end of the first pass for which the total emergent radiation was greater, by any amount, than the input radiation. For non-conservative scattering, the calculations are stopped when succeeding passes result in the emergent flux changing by less than any pre-specified amount.

Before going into a discussion of results, it is perhaps advisable to examine the computational stability of Eq. (18), as we have no guarantee, at this point, that the present scheme will not blow up for large values of τ. If we let $I_p^{(n\Delta\tau)}$ denote the solution to the finite difference equation at the level $n\,\Delta\tau$, and let $I_p(n\Delta\tau)$ represent the exact solution to the differential equation at the same level, then following Richtmeyer (8), the numerical solution is said to be stable if $I_p^{(n\Delta\tau)} - I_p(n\Delta\tau) < k$ as $n \to \infty$, where k is some constant. Another way of saying this is that the solution is stable if the error remains bounded as $n \to \infty$ (the error here is taken to be the difference between the finite difference solution and the true solution).

As is so often the case in practice, a stability analysis of the complete Eq. (18) is not possible. However, by resorting to a simplified form of the equation, an analysis may be performed, the results of which will then serve as a quide for the complete equation. Thus, let us rewrite Eq. (18) neglecting the last term on the right hand side, and further, let us assume that the scattering may occur only in the forward direction. This latter assumption then means that the second term on the right will not have to be summed over all solid angles, as only the parameter in the same direction as the unknown on the left hand side of the equation will contribute. Further, assume the scattering matrix to be diagonal, so that Eq. (18) becomes

$$I_p^{(2)} = I_p^{(0)}\exp\left(-\frac{2\Delta\tau}{\mu}\right) + \beta I_p^{(1)}\left[1 - \exp\left(-\frac{2\Delta\tau}{\mu}\right)\right] \tag{21}$$

where the functional dependencies have been omitted and $\beta = P_{pp}(\Theta)\Delta\omega'$. Eq. (21) is now homogeneous in I_p. Assuming a solution of the form

$$I_p^{(n)} = I_p^{(0)}\,\xi^n \tag{22}$$

substituting into Eq. (21) and solving for ξ results in

$$\xi = \frac{-\beta\left[1 - \exp\left(-\frac{2\Delta\tau}{\mu}\right)\right] \pm \sqrt{\beta^2\left[1 - \exp\left(-\frac{2\Delta\tau}{\mu}\right)\right]^2 + 4\exp\left(-\frac{2\Delta\tau}{\mu}\right)}}{2} \tag{23}$$

and therefore, from Eq. (22)

$$I_p^{(n)} = I_p^{(0)}\left\{\frac{-\beta\left[1 - \exp\left(-\frac{2\Delta\tau}{\mu}\right)\right] \pm \sqrt{\beta^2\left[1 - \exp\left(-\frac{2\Delta\tau}{\mu}\right)\right]^2 + 4\exp\left(-\frac{2\Delta\tau}{\mu}\right)}}{2}\right\}^n \tag{24}$$

Since $I_p^{(n)}$ must be positive for any n, we are forced to accept only the positive sign for the square root term in Eq. (24). From physical considerations, it is evident that the true solution must remain bounded as $n \to \infty$. It follows that for computational stability $\xi \leq 1$ or

$$0 \leq \frac{-\beta\left[1 - \exp\left(-\frac{2\Delta\tau}{\mu}\right)\right] \pm \sqrt{\beta^2\left[1 - \exp\left(\frac{2\Delta\tau}{\mu}\right)\right]^2 + 4\exp\left(\frac{2\Delta\tau}{\mu}\right)}}{2} \leq 1. \tag{25}$$

It is easy to show that Eq. (25) is always satisfied and therefore Eq. (21) is always stable for any $\Delta\tau$. A similar analysis for the expression for $-1 \leq \mu < 0$ yields identical results. The above results are strongly indicative that the numerical solutions will be stable and will not be limited, for stability reasons, to a maximum value of the optical depth, τ, for a given increment, $\Delta\tau$ of integration.

III. ACCURACY OF PROCEDURE

As in any finite difference scheme, the choice of proper values of the incremental sizes is of considerable importance. It has been shown that computations are likely to be stable for any value of $\Delta\tau$. However, the accuracy of the results deteriorates as the value of $\Delta\tau$ increases, with a similar situation existing with respect to the increments of μ and φ. It is, of course desirable to have these increments as large as possible, and still maintain acceptable accuracy in the results.

Fortunately, a check upon the accuracy of the current method is readily available for the case of pure Rayleigh scattering. For the conservative case, the tables of Coulson, et al., (4) provide a ready check for optical depths, τ_T, up to 1.0. For non-conservative, non-homogeneous Rayleigh scattering, the solution utilizing the auxiliary equation as derived by Sekera (10) was programmed, following the technique outlined by Dave (5). Since both of these methods are completely different from the present program, they offer essentially an independent check.

Considerable experimentation with incremental sizes has been performed with this program. Considering first the conservative scattering Rayleigh problem, values of $\Delta\tau = 0.020$ and $\Delta\varphi = 30°$ were decided upon. In addition, 24 unequal increments of μ were used, the midpoints of which, over the range from $\mu = 0.0$ to $\mu = 1.0$ are as follows: $\mu = 0.0375$, 0.100, 0.1625, 0.250, 0.350, 0.450, 0.550, 0650, 0.750, 0.850, 0.925, 0.975. The negative of these values was taken over the range from $\mu = 0.0$ to $\mu = -1.0$. Some results comparing the present method with the Coulson, et al., tables, using the above increments in τ, μ, φ, are shown in Figs. 2-5. In these figures the solid curves are drawn from the data of Coulson, et. al. (4), while the encircled points are calculated from the present work. Note that the Stokes parameter U(I_3 component) is shown on the curves for $\varphi = 60°$ but not on the curves for $\varphi = 0°$. At this latter azimuthal angle, U = 0 for all μ and μ_0. Further, for incident unpolarized light, the Rayleigh scatter matrix results in V(I_4) = 0 for all μ and φ regardless of the angle of incidence of the incident beam, and thus this parameter is not shown.

Examination of these results, and others for different optical depths and other values of μ_0, indicated that the values of the total intensity were in agreement with the results of Coulson, et al., to within 2 percent, while the polarization values were in agreement to within 1 percent, for the incremented sizes presented earlier. A finer grid network would undoubtedly reduce these errors.

A further test was made for a non-conservative Rayleigh scattering problem, and the results were compared with calculations made from the auxiliary equation. The particular test was at a wavelength $\lambda = 3112\text{Å}$, and the absorption was considered due to ozone, which, at this wavelength, has an exponential absorption coefficient of 2.464 cm^{-1}. The particular ozone distribution used was from a sounding taken at taken at Fort Collins, Colorado, on Feb. 6, 1963. The sounding terminated at 10 mb, above which a constant mixing ratio of ozone was assumed. Figures 6 and 7 show results from the two methods for the reflected and transmitted intensities and polarizations for $\varphi = 0$ and $\mu_0 = 0.10453$. As can be seen, the two methods are in excellent agreement. The maximum discrepancies in intensity between the two methods are again about 2 percent, while in polarization the agreement is to within 1 percent. These computations were performed at increments of $\Delta\tau = 0.005$ using the auxiliary equation, while the same incremental sizes as described earlier were used in the numerical integration.

IV. SOME PRELIMINARY RESULTS OF MULTIPLE MIE SCATTERING

To date, two rather simple calculations of multiple Mie scattering have been performed. In both of these applications, the radiation was assumed normally incident upon the scattering medium (i.e., $\mu_0 = 1.0$). For this case, it can be shown that the I_1 and I_2 Stokes parameters are independent of the I_3 and I_4 parameters. Since these latter two parameters were of no interest for the particular problems,

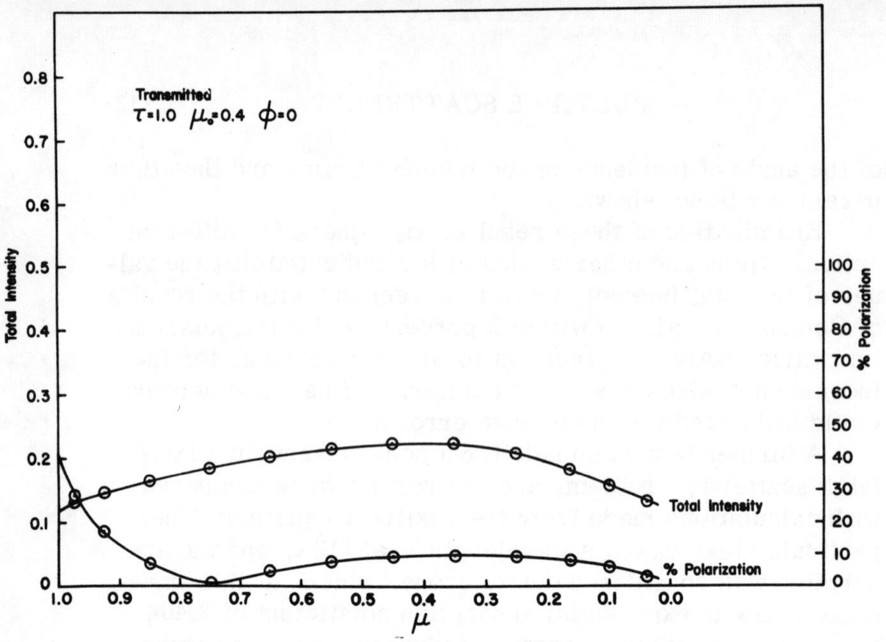

Fig. 2

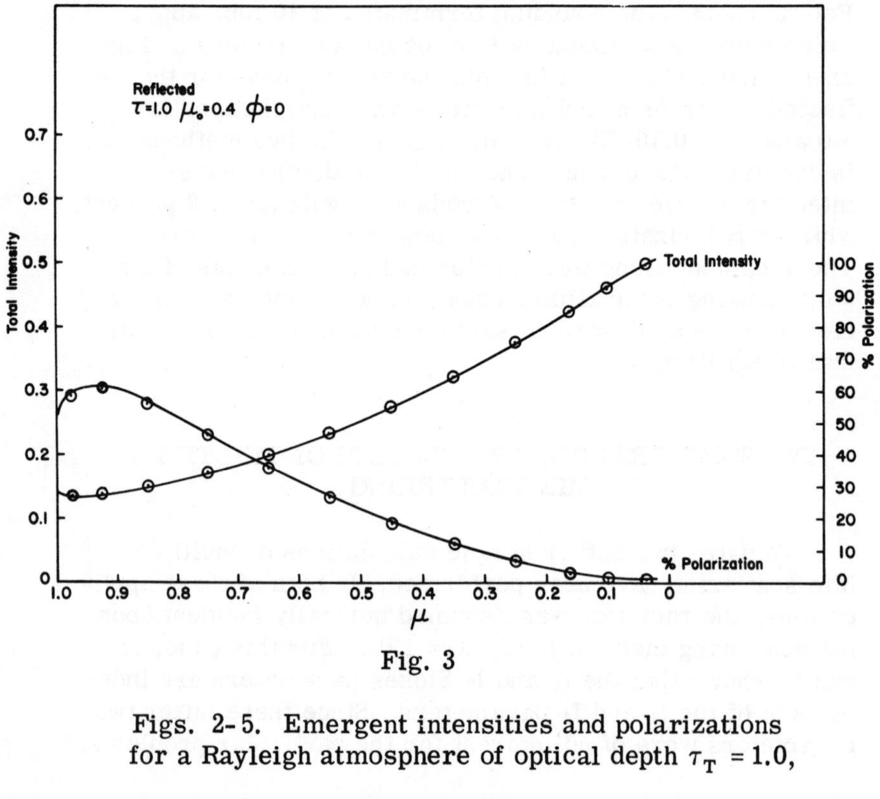

Fig. 3

Figs. 2-5. Emergent intensities and polarizations for a Rayleigh atmosphere of optical depth $\tau_T = 1.0$,

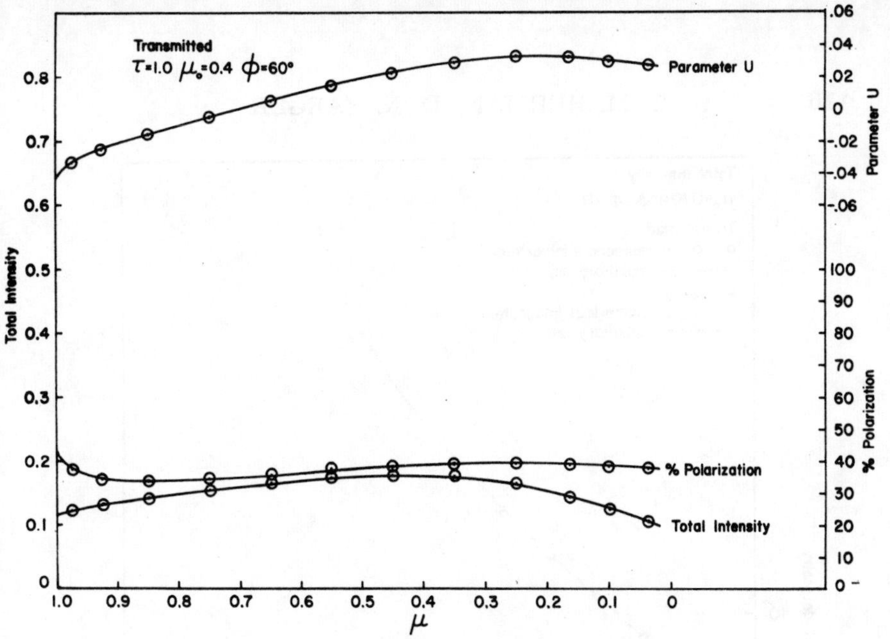

Fig. 4

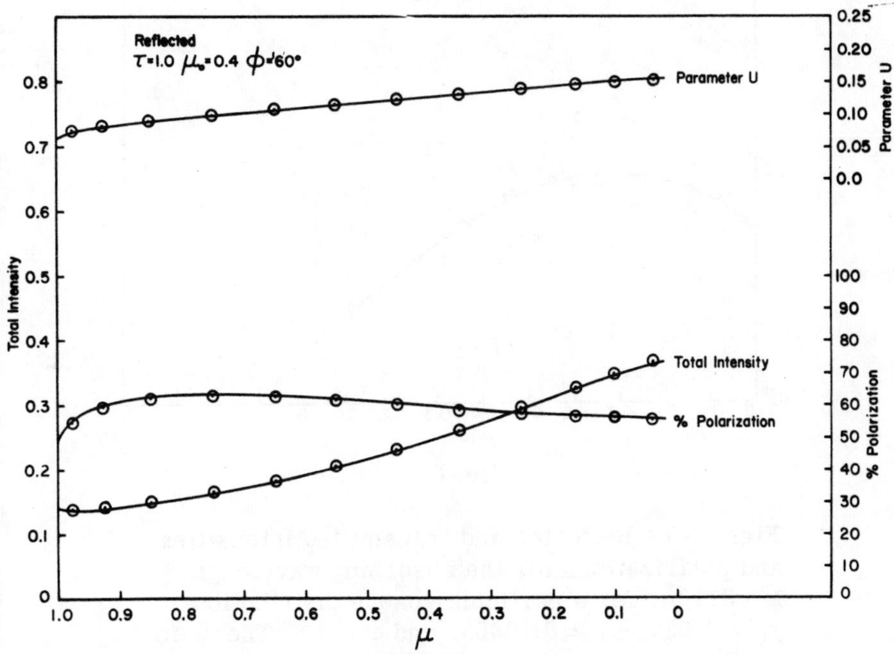

Fig. 5

$\mu_0 = 0.4$, $\varphi = 0°$ and $60°$. The solid lines are from the tables of Coulson, et al. (4), while the encircled points are from the present work.

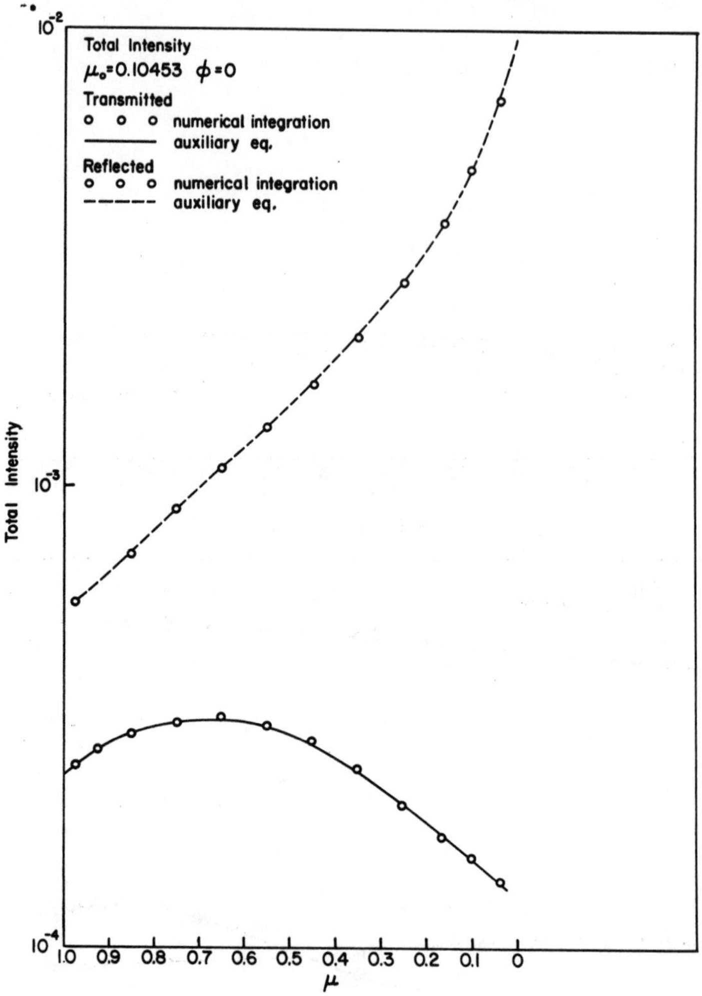

Fig. 6

Figs. 6-7. Reflected and transmitted intensities and polarizations for the absorbing wavelength λ = 3112Å, for a particular ozone distribution, τ_T = 1.537, μ_0 = 0.10453, and φ = 0°. The solid curves were computed from the auxiliary equation, while the encircled points are by the present numerical integration technique.

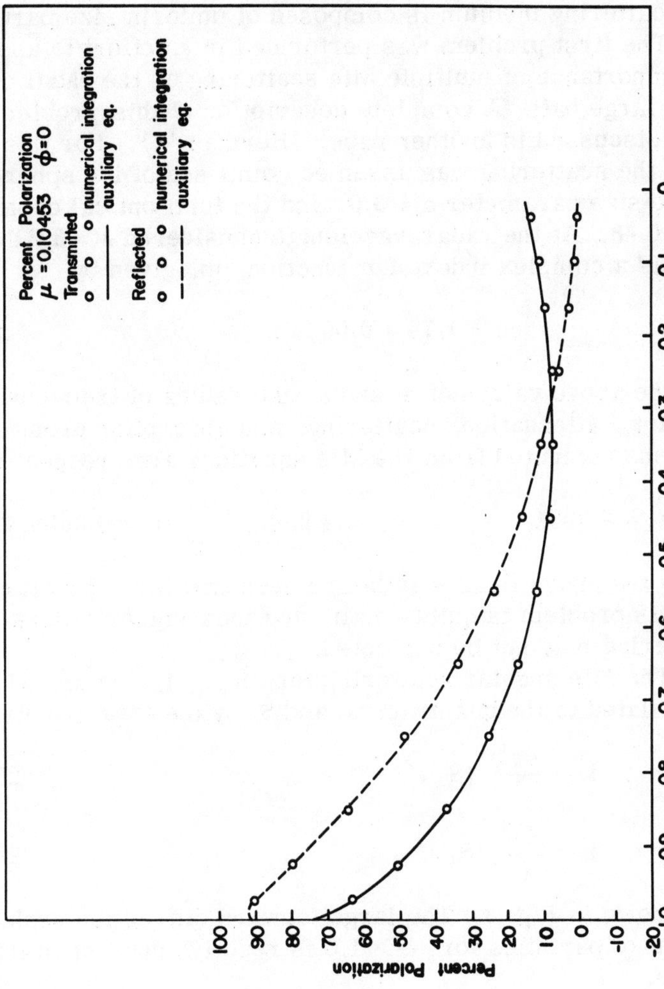
Percent Polarization
μ =0.10453 ϕ=0
Transmitted
o o o numerical integration
auxiliary eq.
Reflected
o o o numerical integration
auxiliary eq.
Percent Polarization
100
90
80
70
60
50
40
30
20
10
0
-10
-20
1.0
0.9
0.8
0.7
0.6
0.5
0.4
0.3
0.2
0.1
0
μ

Fig. 7

they were not computed, and only the results for the total intensi ty $I(= I_1 + I_2)$ will be shown. Further, in both cases, the scattering medium is composed of uniform size particles.

The first problem was performed in an effort to assess the importance of multiple Mie scattering on the radar return from large bail. A complete description of this problem has been discussed in another paper (Herman, 6). For this problem, the scattering was assumed composed of ice spheres whose size parameter $\alpha = 3.0$, and the total optical depth, $\tau_T = 0.48$. At the radar wavelength considered $\lambda = 3.21$ cm), ice has a complex index of refraction, m, given by

$$m = 1.74 - 0.0024\, i. \tag{26}$$

For the above values of m and α, the values of the normalized total attenuation, scattering, and absorption cross-sections computed from the Mie equations are, respectively,

$$\sigma_t = 4.8951, \qquad \sigma_s = 4.8342, \qquad \sigma_a = 0.0609. \tag{27}$$

From the above figures it can be seen that the absorption for this problem is quite small, and thus higher orders of scattering may not be neglected.

The Mie angular scattering functions, i_1 and 1_2, which are related to the quantities S_j and S_i by the expressions

$$i_1 = \frac{4\pi^2}{\lambda^2} |S_j|^2 \tag{28a}$$

$$i_2 = \frac{4\pi^2}{\lambda^2} |S_i|^2 \tag{28b}$$

are shown in Fig. 8. The large forward diffraction peak, typical of particles for $\alpha > 1.0$ is readily apparent in this figure.

Figures 9 and 10 show the reflected and transmitted total intensities $(I_1 + I_2)$ as a function of μ for $\varphi = 0°$, $30°$, $60°$ and $90°$, and for incident plane polarized radiation. (The dotted portions of the curves represent extrapolations to $\mu = \pm 1.0$.) This problem can be shown to possess $90°$ symmetry in φ, and therefore the intensities at the remaining azimuthal angles may be determined from the symmetry

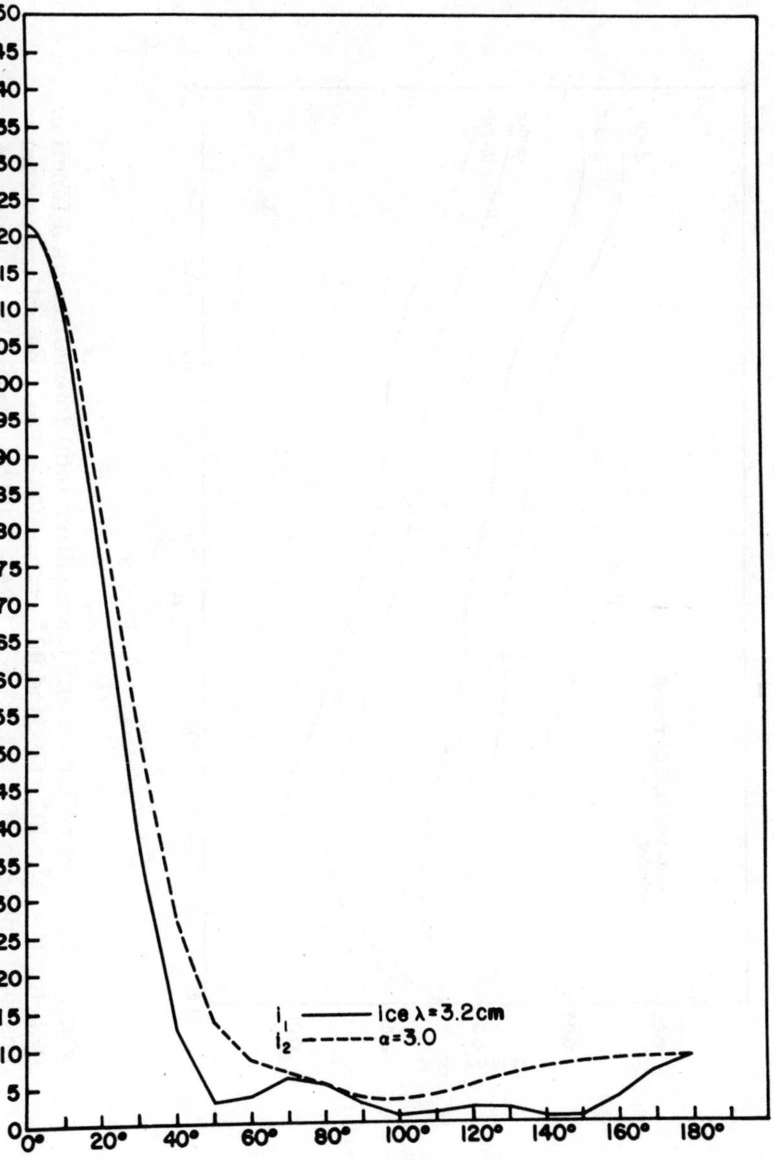

Fig. 8. The Mie angular scattering functions, i_1 and i_2, for $\alpha = 3.0$ and $m = 1.74 - 0.0024i$.

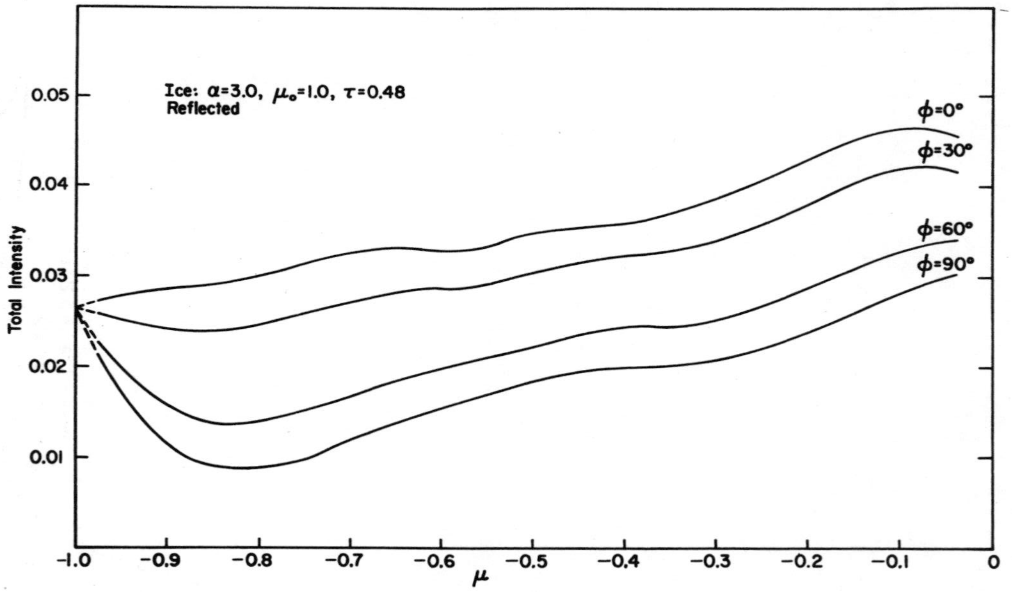

Fig. 9

Figs. 9-10. The reflected and transmitted total intensities as a function of μ for $\varphi = 0°$, $30°$, $60°$ and $90°$, $\tau_T = 0.48$. The atmosphere is composed of spheres of $\alpha = 3.0$, $m = 1.74 - 0.0024i$, normally illuminated by plane-parallel, linearly polarized radiation.

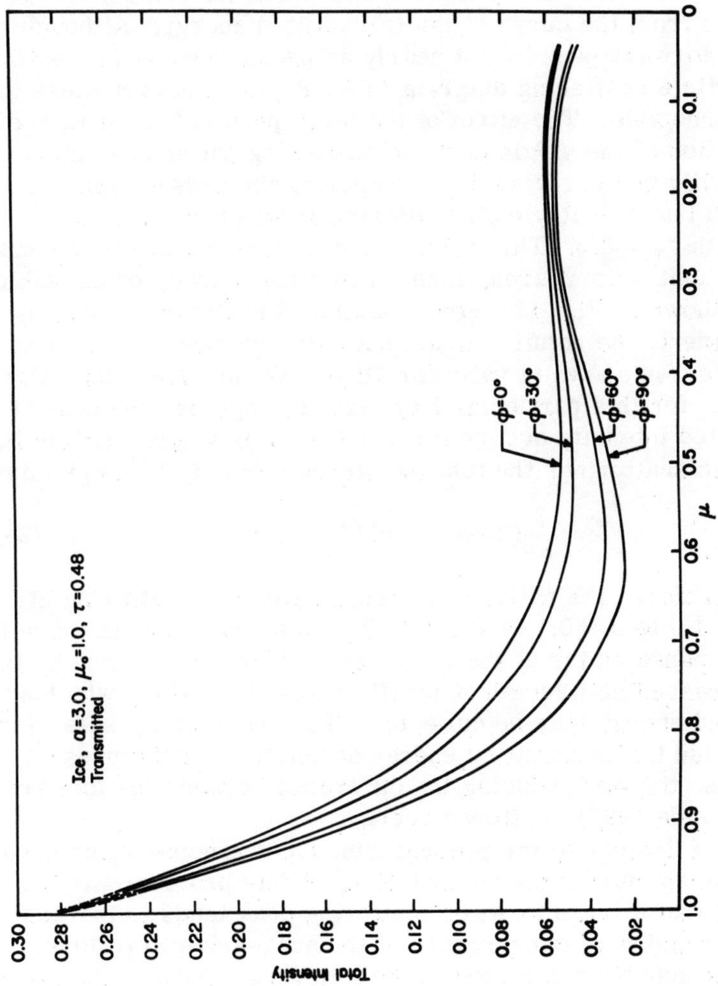
Ice, α=3.0, μ_0=1.0, τ=0.48
Transmitted
ϕ=0°
ϕ=30°
ϕ=60°
ϕ=90°
Total Intensity
μ
0.30 0.28 0.26 0.24 0.22 0.20 0.18 0.16 0.14 0.12 0.10 0.08 0.06 0.04 0.02
1.0 0.9 0.8 0.7 0.6 0.5 0.4 0.3 0.2 0.1 0

Fig. 10

relations. Thus, the intensity at $\varphi = 10°$ is identical to the intensity at $\varphi = 170°$, $\varphi = 190°$, and $\varphi = 350°$.

The effect of the large forward scatter can readily be seen from the curve of the transmitted energy. Although the forward peak is not nearly as pronounced as in the single particle scattering diagram (Fig. 8), it is nevertheless quite appreciable. The effect of the large peak in the forward direction of the single particle scattering pattern can more readily be appreciated by comparing the present solution with that of a Rayleigh scattering atmosphere of optical depth $\tau_T = 0.5$. This solution for an incident beam of π units per unit normal area, taken from the Coulson, et al. tables, is shown in Fig. 11. For unpolarized radiation, normally incident, the solution is azimuthally independent, and thus the curve shown is valid for all φ. We note from this curve that, for this particular Rayleigh atmosphere, the peak transmitted intensity occurs for $\mu \approx 0.1$. For single particle Rayleigh scattering, the total scattered intensity $I^{(s)}$ is given by

$$I^{(s)} = \frac{3}{8\pi}(1 + \cos^2 \theta) I^{(i)} \tag{29}$$

Therefore, the ration of the single particle scattering at $\mu = 1.0$ to $\mu = 0.1$ is about 1.98. This, however, is more than compensated for at the values of τ_T being considered by the increased path length at small values of μ, along which scattered energy may be collected. This same effect acts to increase the transmitted energy at small μ for the present case, thereby reducing the difference between the forward and side (90°) scattered energy.

A feature of the present numerical scheme which became apparent during the computations of this problem was the fact that a large forward scattering peak tends to increase the rapidity of convergence of the successive iterations. This may be understood in the following manner. During the first iteration over τ from $\tau = 0$ to $\tau = \tau_T$, all orders of scattered energy which always travel in a forward (i.e., $\mu > 0$) direction are accounted for (within the limits of finite differencing as opposed to actual integration). In integrating from τ_T to $\tau = 0$ the first time, all energy which is scattered out of the forward travelling beams ($\mu > 0$) into directions

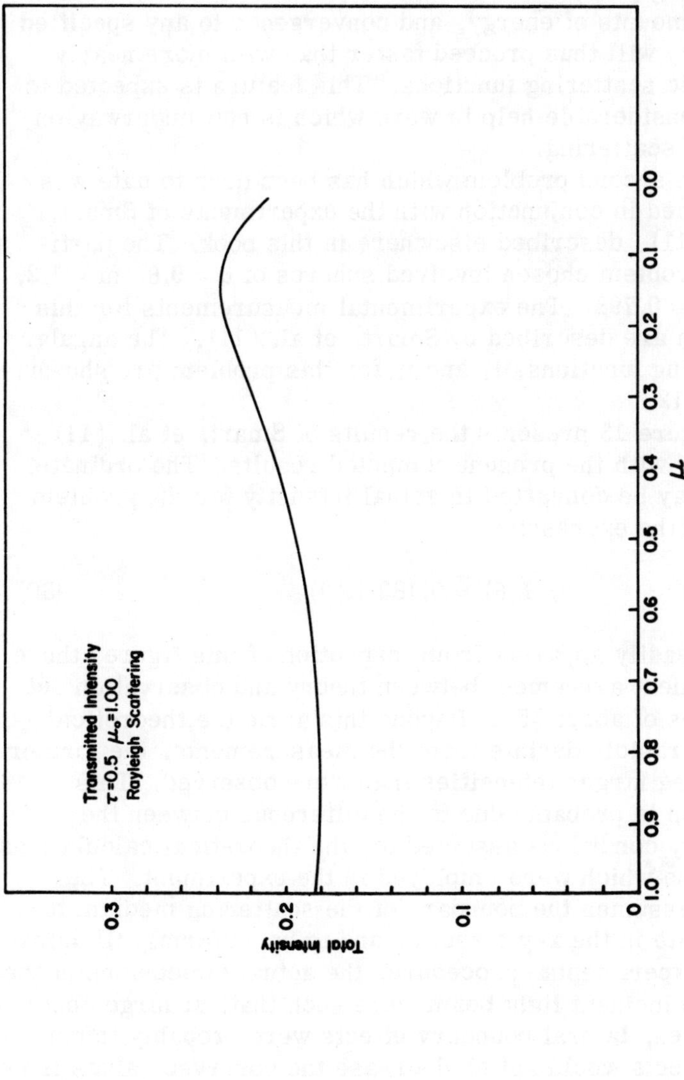

Fig. 11. Total intensity transmitted by a Rayleigh atmosphere, $\tau_T = 0.5$ illuminated normally.

which $\mu < 0$ is considered. Succeeding passes only add in scattering processes which cause a change in direction from $\mu > 0$ to $\mu < 0$, vice versa. Because of the large forward scattering peak, these changes in direction do not involve large amounts of energy, and convergence to any specified accuracy will thus proceed faster than with more nearly isotropic scattering functions. This feature is expected to be of considerable help in work which is now underway on aerosol scattering.

The second problem which has been done to date was performed in conjunction with the experiments of Smart, et al. (11), described elsewhere in this book. The particular problem chosen involved spheres of $\alpha = 9.8$, m - 1.2, and $\tau_T = 0.798$. The experimental measurements for this problem are described by Smart, et al. (11). The angular scattering functions, i_1 and i_2 for this problem are shown in Fig. 12.

Figure 13 presents the results of Smart, et al. (11) together with the present computed results. The ordinate, $R(\theta)$ may be converted to actual intensity for the problem through the expression

$$I(\theta) = 0.183\, R(\theta) \tag{30}$$

As is readily apparent from inspection of this figure, there is excellent agreement between theory and observation out to angles of about 35°. Beyond this angle the theoretical results rapidly deviate from the measurements, the former indicating larger intensities than were observed. This deviation is probably due to the difference between the boundary conditions assumed for the theoretical calculations and those which were employed in the experiment. The theory assumes the boundary of the scattering medium to be infinite in the x-y direction and to be uniformly illuminated. In the experimental procedure, the actual dimensions of the cell and incident light beam were such that, at large observing angles, lateral boundary effects were probably important. Such effects would act to decrease the observed values from those calculated, since there is no light input beyond the lateral boundaries of the incident beam. Further effort with Smart's group on these experiments is planned.

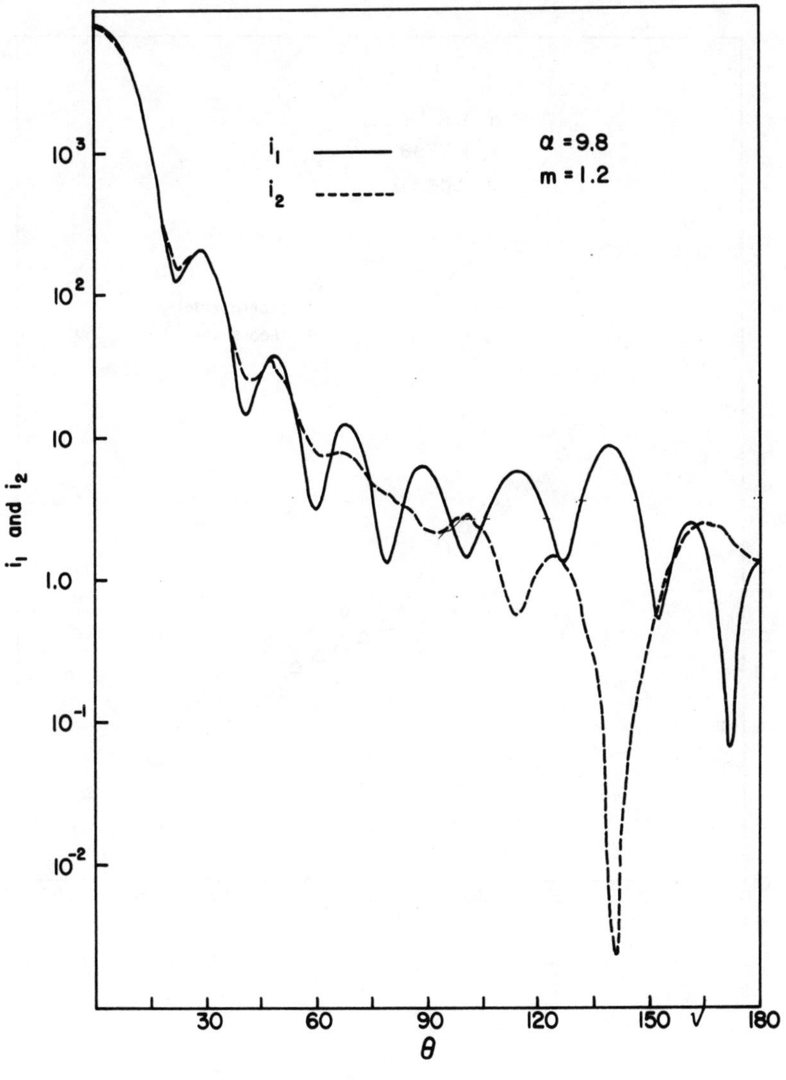

Fig. 12. The Mie angular scattering functions for α = 9.8, m = 1.2

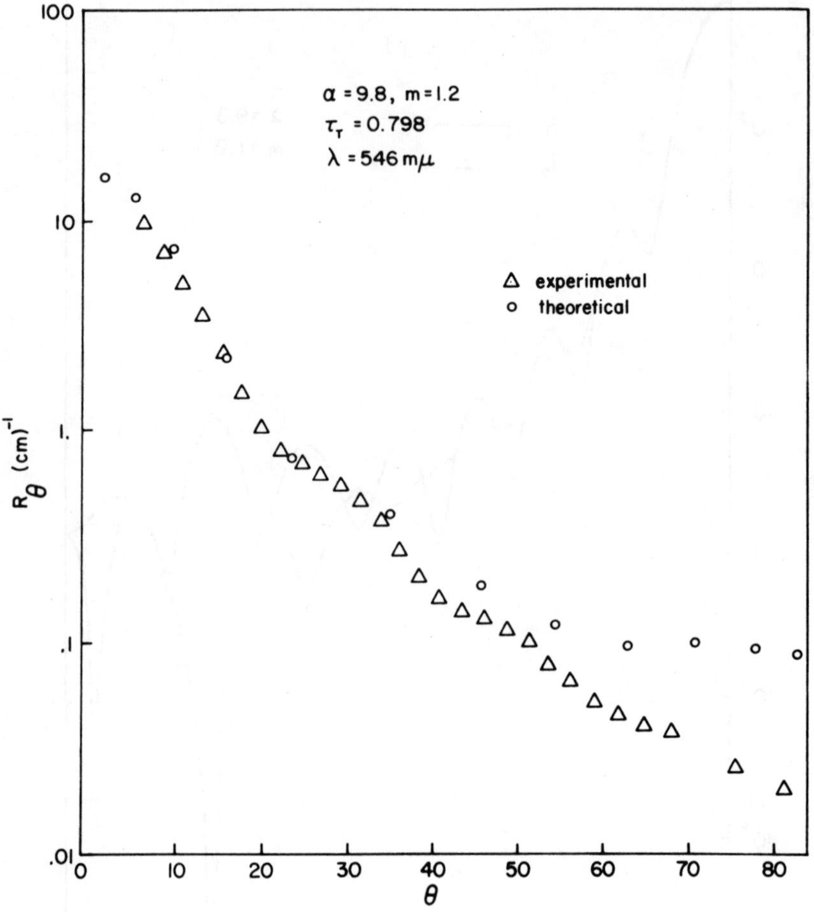

Fig. 13. Comparison of the experimental values o of Smart, et al. (11) with the present theoretical calculations. The quantity $R(\theta)$ is related to the total intensity by the expression $I(\theta) = 0.183 \times R(\theta)$.

As mentioned previously, the above set of calculations are all that have been completed to date. In addition to the work described above, research on the problem of atmospheric aerosol scattering is currently underway. Computations of the emergent intensities and polarizations of a Rayleigh atmosphere contaminated with various distributions and concentrations of aerosols will be performed. These computations will not treat Rayleigh effects and aerosol effects separately, but rather will allow for complete interaction between all particles. Further, the aerosol content will be allowed to vary in the vertical. This work will be reported on at a future date.

ACKNOWLEDGEMENTS

The numerical computations reported on this work were performed at the Numerical Analysis Laboratory of the University of Arizona. The authors are indebted to Gen. S. R. Browning (ret.) for his invaluable aid in preparing the relevant programs.

REFERENCES

(1) Bellman, R. Kalaba, R. and Weng, G. M., J. Math. Phys., 1, No. 4, 280 (1960).

(2) Chandrasekhar, S., Radiative Transfer, New York. Dover Publications (1950).

(3) Churchill, Chu, Evans, Tien and Pang, Exact Solutions for Anisotropic, Multiple Scattering by Parallel Plane Dispersions, Thermal Research Lab., Univ. of Michigan (1961).

(4) Coulson, K. L., Dave, J. V. and Sekera, Z., Tables Related to Radiation Emerging from a Planetary Atmosphere with Rayleigh Scattering, Berkeley and Los Angles, Univ. of California Press (1960).

(5) Dave. J. V., Astrophys. J., 140, 1292 (1964).

(6) Herman, B. M., J. Geophys. Res., 70, No. 5, 1215 (1965).

(7) Hildebrand, F. B., Introduction to Numerical Analysis, Chapt. 10, McGraw-Hill Book Company, New York, (1956).

(8) Richtmeyer, R. D., Difference Methods for Initial Value Problems, Chapt. I, Interscience Publishers, Inc., (1957).

(9) Sekera, Z., Scattering Matrix for Spherical Particles and its Transformation, in Investigation of Skylight Polarization, Final Rept., Contract AF 19(122)-239, Dept. Meteor., Univ. of California, Los Angles (1955).

(10) Sekera, Z., Radiative Transfer in a Planetary Atmosphere with Imperfect Scattering. Report No. R-413-PR, The Rand Corporation, June (1963).

(11) Smart, Jacobsen, Kerker, Kratohvil, and Matijević, J. Opt. Soc. Am., **4** (1965), (in press).

(12) Stratton, J., Electromagnetic Theory, Chapt. 9, McGraw-Hill Book Co., New York (1941).

DISCUSSION FOLLOWING PAPER BY B. HERMAN

W. Irvine: Have you made any calculations for Mie particles neglecting polarization (i.e., using a scalar equation of transfer and phase function) in order to see how good such a scalar approximation would be?

B. Herman: We have not performed computations to check the scalar equation against the vector equation. This would be a simple matter to do, but as yet, we have not done it.

Z. Sekera: Were you able to diagonalize the phse matrix for Rayleigh scattering? So far as I know this has not been done and I feel it can't be done. If this were possible, all problems of multiple scattering would be extremely simplified.

B. Herman: The phase matrix was assumed diagonal only for the purpose of simplifying the transfer equation in order to perform a stability analysis. However, this was not meant to imply that the matrix was in diagonalized form for the computations. Such was not the case.

M. Kerber: By combining a sol of Rayleigh scatters (Ludox) with a sol of Mie scatterer (polystyrene latex) we should be able to stimulate a Rayleigh atmosphere combined with Mie particles. Would multiple scattering experiments upon such a system be of interest to you?

B. Herman: Such an experiment would be of considerable interest, particularly if a size distribution of Mie particles similar to that of natural atmospheric aerosols could be assembled.

Inversion of Light Scattering Data for the Determination of Spherical Particle Spectrum *

K. S. Shifrin
and
A. Y. Perelman

Main Geophysical Observatory
Leningrad K-18 U. S. S. R.

ABSTRACT

The problem of determining the spherical particle spectrum by optical information is discussed. The difficulties of such inversion is analysed. The techniques considered are the small angle, spectral transparency and scattering pattern methods, which allow one to calculate the particle size distribution function in the range 0.01 μ - 100 μ. The asymptotic formula for optical characteristics of the system with narrow distribution is given here.

---

*The authors were unable to be present at the Conference. The paper was read by Professor William Farone, Department of Chemistry, Virginia State College, U. S. A.

I. INTRODUCTION

One of the most fundamental problems in physics is the determination of material properties by electromagnetic scattering. From the theoretical point of view differences in the kind of radiation are unimportant so that all formulations are valid for: photons, neutrons, α - particles etc. In all cases we deal with "direct" and "indirect" problems. In direct problems, characteristics of incident flux and substance are given and it is necessary to study the peculiarities of scattering. In indirect problems, properties of the flux before and after scattering are known and the task is to determine the properties of the scatterer. Of course both problems are closely associated, but from the theoretical point of view methods of solution differ. Moreover, direct problems always have in general a solution, which is not so for indirect problems.

It is a general peculiarity of indirect problems that in mathematical analysis very often we have to broaden the class of objects considered in order to secure existence of a solution. This method is unacceptable in physics. Here we have to divide problems into two groups: problems which have a solution and those which have not. In the latter group the scattered flux does not contain the necessary information on material properties we search for and, of course, which cannot be found by means of mathematical devices.

In other words the experiment is formulated incorrectly and the theorist's task is to indicate the correct statement and to formulate requirements for the accuracy of measurements.

In considering the optics of opaque media, beginning with classical works of Tyndall and Rayleigh, investigators have studied direct problems trying at the same time to solve indirect problems. As a result we have some outstanding achievements. For example, the well-known method of "corona" observation has led to a technique for estimating the mean particle size. The spectral variation of transparency or the extrema positions of scattering patterns are other developments.

It is easy to see that in all these methods we deal with different moments of particle size distribution and strictly speaking know nothing about the whole distribution.

However, in recent years, some methods of solution of indirect problems have been developed. These methods allow one to obtain the whole spectrum of particle size distribution from light scattering data only. The techniques considered are the small angle, spectral transparency, and scattering pattern methods. We have obtained in all three methods analytical solutions and simple calculational schemes for determination of the particle spectrum from the light scattering data. The experiments on light scattering appear to be very simple and the accuracy requirements of photometry are not high.

Thus using optical radiation one can include the range of radii of spherical particles from approximately 0.01 μ to 100 μ by means of all three methods.

In the present article the three above mentioned methods are studied. We shall not study calculational methods of inversion here.

II. GENERAL STATEMENT OF THE PROBLEM. FULL AND LIMITED PROBLEMS

In the case of "dilute" systems when it is possible to restrict oneself to examining single scattering, the problem is reduced to inversion of an integral equation of the first kind

$$\psi(x) = \int_0^\infty F(x, r)\ f^*(r)\ dr \qquad (1)$$

Here $f^*(r)$ is the particle size distribution curve; $F(x, r)$ is the kernel of equation known from the Mie or an approximate theory; $\psi(x)$ is the function determined experimentally. The kernel $F(x, r)$ may be, for example, the scattering pattern of a monodisperse system with particle radii r; in this case $\psi(x)$ would be the polydispersed scattering pattern describing scattering at the angle $\beta = x$. In all the cases the task of the inversion theory is to find a calculational method for determining the unknown distribution function $f^*(r)$ as a function of $F(x, r)$ and $\psi(x)$.

The inversion of Eq. (1) by means of substituting the algebraic system of equations results in difficulties characteristic of integral equations of the first kind. The resulting algebraic system is ill-conditioned and small inaccuracies in determining $\psi(x)$ and $F(x, r)$, inevitably arising due to errors of measurement and calculation, cause great errors in $f^*(r)$. The formal solution of the corresponding algebraic system contains negative roots which from the point of view of physics is nonsense.

The cause of these difficulties lies in the peculiarities of Eq. (1). Everything is determined by the kernel properties. For example, if the kernel is degenerating, i.e.,

$$F(x, r) = \sum_{i=1}^{n} a_i(x)\, b_i(r)$$

Eq. (1) either has no solutions or an infinite number. If, however, the kernel is of the form exp (ixr) –a Fourier kernel, a simple inversion is known. In general, if the kernel depends only upon the product of arguments

$$F(x, r) = F(xr) \tag{2}$$

the formal solution of Eq. (1) can be obtained with the help of Mellin's (32) or Titchmarsh's (32, 33) transformations.

Note that kernels of type (2) occur in the small angle, transparency, and scattering pattern methods. We shall have stable solutions of (1) if initial information on the system $\psi(x)$ known approximately, be introduced into the inversion obtained analytically. In this case the answer results from using the integral operator on the function $\psi(x)$.

Errors inevitably present in $\psi(x)$ make the inversion problem (1) incorrect (as in the well-known Hadamard's example). The solution $f^*(r)$ is determined accurate to an arbitrary function which is of the form $\Delta f^* = C \exp(i\omega r)$. This function will add

$$\Delta\psi = C \int_0^\infty F(x, r) \exp(i\omega r)\, dr$$

in the left part of Eq. (1).

If F(x, r) as function r changes slowly, $\Delta \psi$ being a Fourier coefficient, will decrease with enhancement of frequency ω. When ω has a large enough value, $\Delta \psi$ limits the fluctuation range of ψ which is defined by the errors of measurement. Thus both solution f* and f* + Δ f* appear to be indistinguishable whereas practically they can differ as much as possible by suitable choice of C. Absence of an exact result means that the information on the particle spectrum which the function $\psi(x)$ contains is not enough for general determination of f*(r). In this case we have to examine a limited problem instead of full one and be satisfied with separating characteristics of distributions obtained from (1). Thus, for example, measurements of light scattering in Rayleigh region gives

$$\int_0^\infty r^6 f^*(r)\, dr$$

only, i.e., the sixth initial moment of distribution; measurements of large particles gives the mean size particle surface, i.e., the second moment of distribution etc. The same is true in the above mentioned "corona", spectral transparency and extrema of scattering pattern methods.

It is of importance to emphasize that different methods determine different moments of the distribution and it is no wonder that in taking systems quasi-monodisperse we obtain different values for "mean" particle size from different methods. If, besides optical information described by Eq. (1), we have extra information on the nature of the unknown distribution f*(r), one can use the measurement of $\psi(x)$ to determine parameters of some distribution chosen beforehand. In many cases it is convenient to use an extended Γ-distribution

$$f^*(r) = Ar^{\mu} \exp(-\beta r^{\gamma}) \tag{3}$$

suggested in (8) or its particular form at $\gamma = 1$

$$f^*(r) = Ar^{\mu} \exp(-\beta r) \tag{4}$$

See detail in (9). A Junge distribution can also be used:

$$f^*(r) = \begin{cases} 0 & r < r_0 \\ Ar^{-n} & r \geq r_0 \end{cases} \qquad n = 4 \tag{5}$$

or other Junge types (n = 3, 5, 6, ...) or a logarithmic-normal distribution etc. In all the cases the amount of necessary experimental data must be not less than the number of parameters.

Let us note as an example the determination of drop distributions in precipitation by data on their intensity and transparency by means of distribution (3) at $\mu = 2$ (see (6)).

If it is possible to obtain extra data one can use them for decreasing the effect of measurements errors, determining the most probable values of distribution parameters by the method of least squares.

III. METHOD OF SMALL ANGLES

This method was developed in the USA by J. H. Chin, C. M. Sliepcevich and M. Tribus and quite independently in the USSR by one of the authors of the present paper with collaborators (7), (10, 11, 27-31, 2, 3, 4). Here we relate the content of the approach developed in the USSR.

A. Inversion formula

Let a parallel monochromatic light beam with wave length λ fall on a spherical particle of radius r. From the exact Mie formulae one can strictly derive the intensity of light scattered by a particle in the limiting case $\rho \to \infty$ ($\rho = 2\pi a/\lambda$), $\beta \to 0$ (β is the scattering angle)

$$J(\beta) = I_0 r^2 J_1^2 (\rho\beta)/\beta^2 \tag{1}$$

Here I_0 is the intensity of incident light and $J_1(x)$ is the first Bessel function.

It is of interest that formula (1) is valid for any sphere because of the disappearance of the refractive index m in the asymptotic formulae. See (7). If the light beam crosses a polydisperse volume then

$$\bar{J}\ (\beta) = (I_0/\beta^2) \int_0^\infty f^*(r)\, r^2\, J_1^2\ (\rho\beta)\ dr \qquad (2)$$

Formula (2) states that the integral transformation from the original distribution $f^*(r)\ r^2$ to the representation $\beta^2\ I_0^{-1} \bar{J}\ (\beta)$ takes place in the experiment with the help of kernel, $J_1^2\ (\rho\beta)$. Let us introduce

$$\psi\ (\beta) = \frac{d}{d\beta} \left[\frac{\bar{J}(\beta)}{I_0}\ J_1\, \beta^3 \left(\frac{2\pi}{\lambda} \right)^3 \right] \qquad (3)$$

and

$$F(x) = xJ_1(x) \quad Y_1(x), \quad x = \rho\beta \qquad (4)$$

where $Y_1(x)$ is the second Bessel function. Then according to a Titchmarsch inversion we shall obtain the following final formula. See (10).

$$f^*(\rho) = \frac{2}{\rho^2} \int_0^\infty F\ (\rho\,\beta)\,\psi(\beta)\ d\beta \qquad (5)$$

B. Direct problem

We shall assume formula (2) for f^* (r); the distribution of scattered light is given by

$$\psi_K^\gamma\ (\epsilon) = \int_0^\infty Z^K \exp\left(-\ \epsilon Z \gamma\right)\ J_1^2\ (Z)\ dZ,$$

$$K = \mu + 2,\ \epsilon = \lambda\ \mu/2n\,\beta \qquad (6)$$

For small and large β we have respectively

$$\psi_K^\gamma\ (\epsilon) = \frac{\Gamma((K+3)/\gamma)}{4\gamma}\ \ \epsilon - (K+3)/\gamma$$

$$\psi_K^\gamma(\epsilon) = \frac{\Gamma(K/\gamma)}{n\gamma}\ \epsilon - K/\gamma \qquad (7)$$

We have obtained for the functions $\psi_K^\gamma(\epsilon)$, series and explicit expressions by means of known tabulated functions (10, 31).

We shall restrict ourselves to the case of the Γ-distribution ($\gamma = 1$). The functions $\psi_K^1(\epsilon)$ can be represented as a product of polynomials and full elliptical functions K(x) and E(x) with the variable $x = 2(4 + \epsilon^2)^{-1/2}$.

For K = 0(1) 7 explicit expressions are given in (10, 31). For example, K = 4 (μ = 2) gives

$$\psi_4^1(\epsilon) = \frac{3x^5}{16\pi(1 - x^2)^2}\{(16x^6 - 40x^4 + 30x^2 - 4)\,E(x) + (1 - x^2)(8x^4 - 13x^2 + 4)\,K(x)\} \quad (8)$$

The method of calculating the functions $\psi_K^1(\epsilon)$ for fractional indices K has also been developed (31) (rapidly convergent series are obtained).

C. Inversion

The inversion procedure is reduced to two steps:
a) measurement of the scattered light distribution $\bar{J}(\beta)$;
b) calculation of $f^*(\rho)$ by means of formulae (3) and (5).

The measurement of $\bar{J}(\beta)$ is associated with overcoming the following difficulties: 1) a bright direct beam; 2) random particle distribution in illuminated volume; 3) parasitic light scattering in air, lenses etc.

To avoid difficulties 1 and 2 we have used narrow beams and carried out the measurements in the focal plane of the receiving lens. The dimension of the focal spot corresponded to scattering angles β = 10 - 13". All the measurements were made beyond this spot (Fig. 1). The function $\bar{J}(\beta)$ was determined by moving the photomultiplier tube in the focal plane from the centre to the edges. In (27) it was proved that in the limits of paraxial optics, each position of the multiplier tube corresponds to a strictly defined scattering angle which is the same for all particles. This angle does not depend on cross and longitudinal shifts in the illuminated volume. As for scattering, in the optical system it was assumed that the "zero" beam remains invariable both with and without particles. The beam was measured before the scatterers were introduced and then subtracted.

In Fig. 2 three typical examples of the distribution of

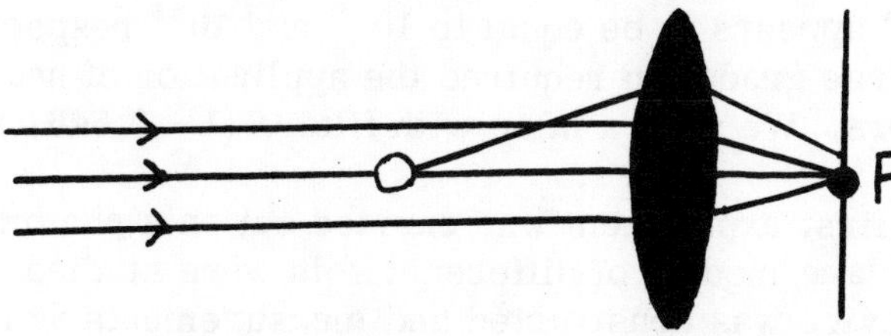

Fig. 1. Principal scheme of measurement $\bar{J}(\beta)$.

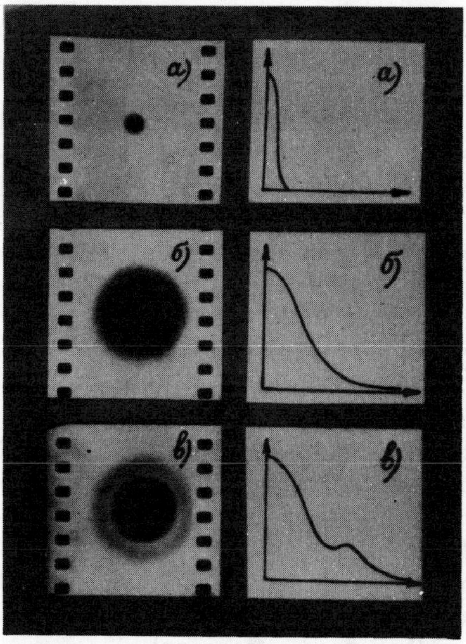

Fig. 2. Distribution of illumination in focal plane of receiving lens.

illumination in the focal plane are given: a) "zero" beam; a system with wide particle spectrum (ground fog); c) a system with narrow spectrum (licopodium powder).

When constructing the device it was necessary to make preliminary estimations of the illumination gradation at different β. We applied these to formulae (6) - (8). When $\mu = 2$ the relative illumination of the scattered beam for $\beta = 0°$,

3° and 5° appears to be equal to 10^{-3} and 10^{-5} respectively. Such a large gradation required the application of neutral attenuators. We used a lamp with filters ($\lambda = 0.546\,\mu$) as a source.

The first experiment was carried out on a photometric bench. Plane models of differenct sols were studied. Then a field device was constructed and measurements were made in ground fogs. b) The calculation of $f^*(\rho)$ can bring in errors since it is necessary to 1) use graphic or numerical differentiations and, 2) cut off the integral at definite β^* (formally it extends to infinity).

To estimate the error of differentiation and in the whole calculation scheme treatment we performed a calculational experiment. From formulae (6)-(8) we have determined the light distribution and then from (3)-(5) we have calculated $f^*(\rho)$. It turned out that in the studied range of radii (2-50μ) the error of the treatment did not exceed 10%. Also, calculations show that the error due to limitations of $\beta^* \leq 8°$ does not exceed 10% for radius range (2 - 50μ).

D. Accuracy, range of dimensions

The total accuracy of measuring $f^*(\rho)$ by direct comparison with microphotographic data is about 5% near the maximum of distributions and 20 - 25% at the extremes.

In Fig. 3 typical data are given; cases a) - d) refer to plane models of powders of different dimensions; the case e) refers to fog (two curves here correspond to two successive measurements).

We see rather good agreement.

The range of particle radii measured by the device is 2 - 50 μ and the minimum concentration is about 50 particles per cm^3.

IV. TRANSPARENCY METHOD

A. Formulation of the problem

The polydispersal scattering coefficient (transparency)

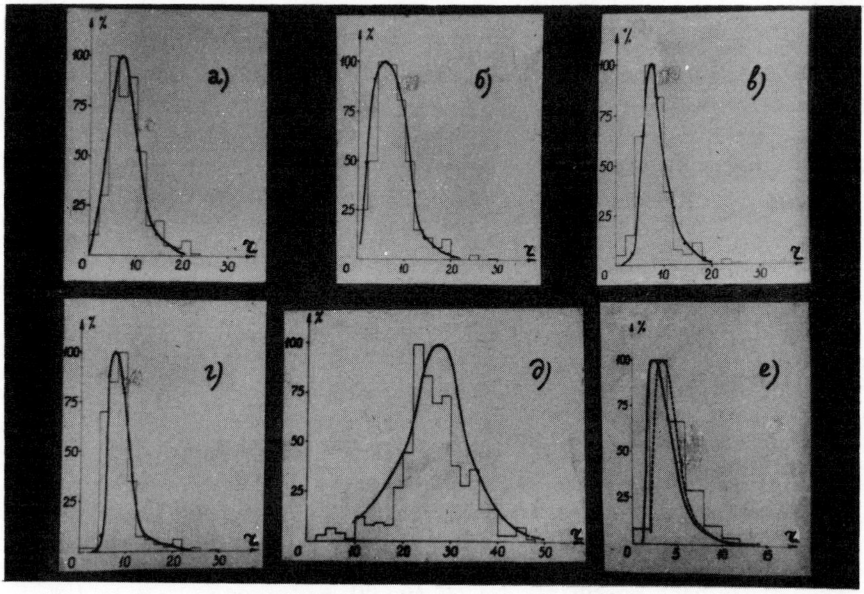

Fig. 3. Comparison of small angle and microphotometric methods.

$g^*(\nu)$ depends on a size distribution function $f^*(r)$ and scattering cross-section $K(r, \nu)$ (ν is the wave number) as follows

$$g^*(\nu) = \int_0^\infty K(r, \nu)\, \pi r^2 f^*(r)\, dr \tag{1}$$

Let us restrict ourselves by the case of "soft" scatterers. Then the cross-section is defined by Van de Hulst (5) as

$$K(r, \nu) = 2K(\delta) \tag{2}$$

$$K(\delta) = 1 - \frac{\sin 2\delta}{\delta} + 1 - \frac{\cos 2\delta}{2\delta^2} \tag{3}$$

Here $$\delta = (m - 1)\rho = \beta r \nu \tag{4}$$

$$\beta = 2\pi(m - 1), \quad \rho = \frac{2\pi r}{\lambda}, \quad \nu = \frac{1}{\lambda} \tag{5}$$

By Mellin's transformation and the measured transparency $g^*(\nu)$ one can find from (1) the unknown distribution function $f^*(r)$ (12).

Such computation of particle distribution functions $f^*(r)$ we shall call the transparency method. This method has been developed in references (12) through (20).

B. Accurate solution of the problem

Let us introduce the dimensionless variables

$$g(x/2) = r_0 g^*(\nu), \qquad x/2 = \beta r_0 \nu \tag{6}$$

$$f^*(r) = \frac{m(a)}{2\pi a^2 r_0^4} \qquad r = a r_0 \tag{7}$$

where r_0 is an arbitrary linear scale. Then (1) and (2) give

$$g(x/2) = \int_0^\infty K(xa/2)\, m(a)\, da \tag{8}$$

Accurate solution of integral Eq. (8) has the form (12)

$$\begin{cases} m(a) = -\frac{1}{\pi}\left\{\frac{1}{2\pi i}\int_{c-i\infty}^{c+i\infty}(1+P)\,\Gamma(P)\cos\frac{\pi P}{2}\,\gamma(P)\,a^{-P}\,dp\right\} \\ \qquad\qquad (-2 < c < 0) \qquad (9) \\ \gamma(P) = \int_0^\infty g(x/2)\,x^{-P}\,dx \quad (1 < \mathrm{Re}\,p < 3) \qquad (10) \end{cases}$$

The function $\gamma(P)$ under the contour integral sign in (9) is an analytic continuation of integral (10) to the band $-2 < \mathrm{Re}\,p < 0$ ($\mathrm{Re}\,p = c$).

Relations (8) and (9) - (10) determine a pair of reciprocal transformations for transparency and the particle distribution function. Direct check of these transformations is made for the Γ-particle distribution(13).

C. Use of tabulated information on transparency

For any particle distribution (12) we have

$$g(x/2) = 0\,(x^2),\ (x \to 0);\quad g(x/2) = 0\,(1),\ (x \to \infty) \qquad (11)$$

From the second relation in (11) one can write

$$g(x/2) = \sum_{n=0}^{\infty} \frac{c_n}{x^n} \simeq \sum_{n=0}^{K} \frac{c_n}{x^n} \quad (x \geq \tau) \qquad (12)$$

Let us denote the dimensional analog of the value τ by τ^*. Variation of x from 0 to τ corresponds to variation of ν from 0 to τ^*.

Taking into account (6) we obtain

$$\frac{\tau}{2} = \beta r_0 \tau^*, \quad \frac{x}{\nu} = \frac{\tau}{\tau^*} \qquad (13)$$

Suppose that dimensionless transparency g (x/2) is determined by some method in points $x = x_j$

$$0 < x_1 < \ldots < x_m < \tau \qquad (14)$$

and values c_0, $c_1 \ldots$, c_K from (12) are estimated.

The method of full use of this optical information for determination of disperse system spectrum is shown in (14). The inversion formula of integral Eq. (8) is valid and

$$\tilde{m}(a) = -\frac{1}{\pi}\left\{ \sum_{j=1}^{m} g\left(\frac{x_j}{2}\right) \omega(ax_j)\, \Delta x_j + \sum_{n=0}^{K} \frac{c_n}{\tau^{n-1}}\, \omega_n(a\tau) \right\},$$

$$\sum_{j=1}^{m} \Delta x_j = \tau \qquad (15)$$

Function $\tilde{m}$ (a) is the approximation to the true particle spectrum m (a). The accuracy of this approximation depends essentially upon successful choice of τ^*(16, 18).

A set of values $\Delta x_j > 0$ in (15) can be different depending on the type of quadrature formula used for deriving (15) from accurate expression (9). This set of values is determined by the requirements of avoiding absorption bands etc. (14).

The accuracy of inversion (15) increases with decreasing max Δx_j and increasing K. The problem of using different formulae of type (15) has been studied in (13, 14, 20). It turns out, for example, that all functions $\omega(y)$, $\omega_0(y)$, $\omega_1(y), \ldots, \omega_K(y)$ vary simultaneously from $K = 2l$ to $K = 2l + 1$ ($l = 1, 2, \ldots$). However the increase of l is, strictly speaking, not always admissible.

Only even powers x are often present in expansion (12) (14, 20). In (14) explicit expressions for $\omega(y)$, $\omega_{2n}(y)$ ($n = 0, 1 \ldots$) are obtained. They allow one to use inversions (15) with any $K = 2l$.

D. Calculation scheme of transparency method (for tabulated representation of optical information)

It is shown in (16, 15) that the spectrum m (a) of an arbitrary disperse system can be found by the following approximate formula

$$m(a) \simeq \tilde{m}(a) = -\frac{1}{\pi}\left\{ \Delta x \sum_{j=1}^{m} g\left(\frac{x_j}{2}\right) \omega(ax_j) + c_0 \tau \omega_0(a\tau) + c_2 \frac{\omega_2(a\tau)}{\tau} \right. \tag{16}$$

$$\Delta x = \frac{\tau}{m}, \quad x_j = (j - 0.5)\,\Delta x \tag{17}$$

where $\omega(y)$, $\omega_0(y)$, $\omega_2(y)$ in (16) are of the form

$$(y) = y \sin y + \cos y - 1; \quad \omega_0(y) = \cos y - 2\frac{\sin y}{y} + 1;$$
$$\omega_2(y) = \cos y - 1 \tag{18}$$

The functions (18) are tabulated in detail in (22).

The choice of values τ, m, c_0 and c_2 as in the general case (Sec. II) is completely determined by the asymptotic behaviour of g (x/2) when $x \to \infty$ (15, 20). Let us take the scale r_0 to be fixed. Denote the abscissas of all clear transparency extrema g (x/2) by $x^{(K)}$

$$0 < x^{(1)} < \ldots < x^{(n)} \tag{19}$$

and let the function g (x/2) reach its upper exact boundary at $x_M = x^{(K)}$

$$x^{g(x/2)} = g\,(x_M/2) \tag{20}$$

The value of τ has to meet requirements of (16)

$$\tau > x^{(n)} \tag{21}$$

and if n > 3 one practically can assume

$$\tau \simeq x^n \tag{22}$$

If also the transparency g (x/2) has the only extremum $x^{(1)}$ then according to (11) g (x/2) achieves the maximum value, i.e.,

$$x^{(1)} = x_M \quad . \tag{23}$$

In this case one can assume

$$\tau \simeq 2x_M \quad . \tag{24}$$

The main criterion for correct choice of τ results from the fundamental requirement for application of the transparency method which can be formulated as follows: experimental data on the transparency g (x/2) must provide a reliable estimation of the limit

$$\lim_{x \to \infty} g\,(x/2) = c_0 \tag{25}$$

The existence of asymptote c_0 for the function g(x/2) results from the second relation (11).

The value of τ must be so great as to satisfy the condition

$$|g\,(x/2) - c_0| \ll g\,(x_M/2)\,, \quad x > \tau \tag{26}$$

Numerous calculations (12-21) show that formula (16) gives adequate accuracy if τ is determined by relations (22), (24), (i.e., condition (26) is satisfied). It is advisable to take m in the range 10 to 20 (16, 24).

Calculational formula (16) is obtained from the supposition that

$$g(x/2) \simeq c_0 + \frac{c_2}{x^2} \qquad (x \geq \tau) \tag{27}$$

This representation is possible if the transparency g (x/2) monotonically tends to its asymptote (25) at $x \geq \tau$ (for sufficiently great τ.) The Γ-distribution family can be taken as an example (18). The constant c_2 is determined by the K ($K \approx 4$-5) values of g (x/2) at the part of its monotonous approximation to the asymptote c_0. Using, for example, the method of averages one obtains a linear equation versus c_2.

$$K c_0 + c_2 \sum_{i=1}^{K} \frac{1}{x_i^2} = \sum_{i=1}^{K} g(x_i/2), \tag{28}$$

with x_i ($i = 1, \ldots, K$) in (28) it is preferable to take values surpassing τ.

If the transparency g (x/2), when $x \to \infty$, fluctuates near the asymptote c_0, it is necessary to increase τ as much as possible (or change (27) to (12) at $K > 2$) in order to assume

$$g(x/2) = c_0, \quad c_2 = 0 \qquad (x \geq \tau) \tag{29}$$

so that (26) is fulfilled.

Then c_0 and c_2 are determined by (25) and (28) or (29).

The accuracy of the distribution function is determined by absolute error of calculation. Estimation of this error is obtained in (15). Taking into account the probability of error, calculations according to formula (16) are necessary to carry out for intervals $0 \leq a \leq a^*$, where at is the minimum value which satisfies conditions

$$\tilde{m}(a^*) < 0, \quad |m(a^*)| > (0.05 - 0.10)\ \tilde{m}(a_M) \tag{30}$$

$\tilde{m}(a_M)$ is the largest value of $\tilde{m}(a)$ (it is to the point here to use statistical estimation methods).

Thus the spectrum $\tilde{m}(a)$ is determined from (16) in the interval 0, a*. Then with the help of formula (7) we can find the dimensional particle distribution function f* (r) in the interval [0, r*],

$$r = a\, r_0, \qquad r^* = a^*\, r_0 \tag{31}$$

$$f^*(r) \simeq \tilde{f}^*(r) = \begin{cases} \dfrac{\tilde{m}(a)}{2\pi a^2 r_0^4}, & \text{if } \tilde{m}(a) > 0 \\ 0, & \text{if } \tilde{m}(a) \leq 0 \end{cases} \tag{32}$$

E. Supplement and examples

1) According to (5) and (13)

$$\tau = 4\pi\,(m - 1)\, r_0\, \tau^*, \tag{33}$$

The values of τ^* and m depend only on the physics of the problem. Dimensionless value of τ and the scale r_0 are related only by (33). In some cases it is convenient to fix r_0 (the check of the method on models) in others to fix τ (inversion of experimental transparency)(15, 21).

2) If transparency is measured accurate to 1% formula (16) gives an adequate result in the range

$$a^*\,\tau = 4\pi\,(m - 1)\, r^*\, \tau^* \lesssim 24 \tag{34}$$

This was taken into account in (22) when tables of functions (18) were made up. In all the examples (by inversion of both experimental and theoretical transparencies) it was chosen that the distribution curve $\tilde{f}^*(r)$ from (32) lies practically in the interval [0, r*] with r* determined from (34).

Otherwise it is necessary to raise the accuracy of the experiment and calculation and, perhaps, to use the more general formula (15).

3) In (13, 14, 18) the formulae for determining transparency of different Γ-structure are derived

$$m_\mu(a) = \gamma_0 \frac{\Delta \mu + 1}{\Gamma(\mu + 1)} \quad a^{\mu+2} e^{-\Delta a} \, {}_1 \; \gamma_0 = 2\pi N r_0^3 \tag{35}$$

where N is the volume concentration of particles.

One may treat single values of transparencies calculated with definite accuracy as experimental data (tabulated data). The utilization of (35) allows one to illustrate the mathematical correctness of the transparency method with concrete examples since the exact result is known here. In (15-20, 24) such checks were carried out with $\mu = 0, 2, 6, 100$ and different τ and m from (16). Example $\mu = 2$ in (24) illustrates the effect of the choice of different τ and m in (16). Results of these analyses coincide with the evaluation of the accuracy of formula (16) found in (15).

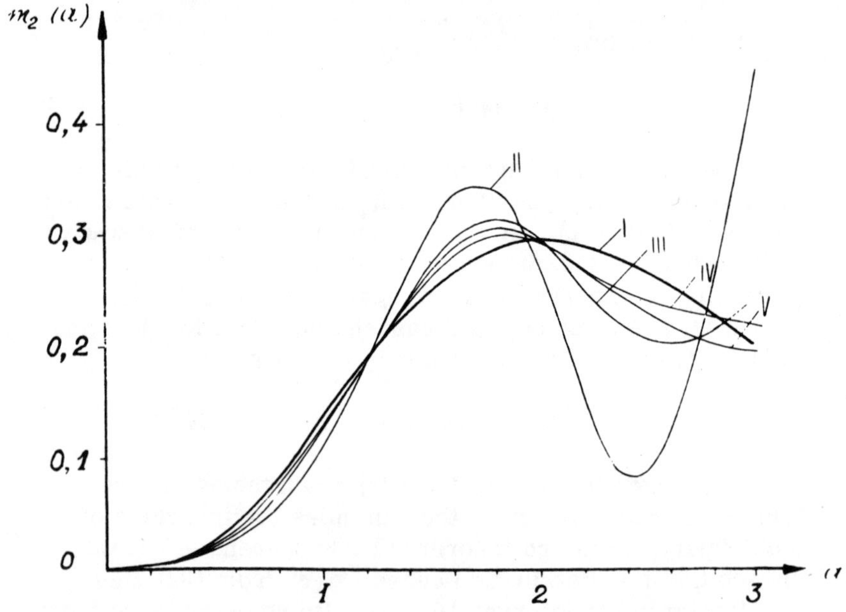

Fig. 4. Inversion of transparency at $\mu = 2$.

4) Let us give two examples of the transparency method check on Γ-distribution models. In Fig. 4 $\mu = 2$ is chosen for $r_0 = r_M$ (r_M is the mode of Γ-distribution). In

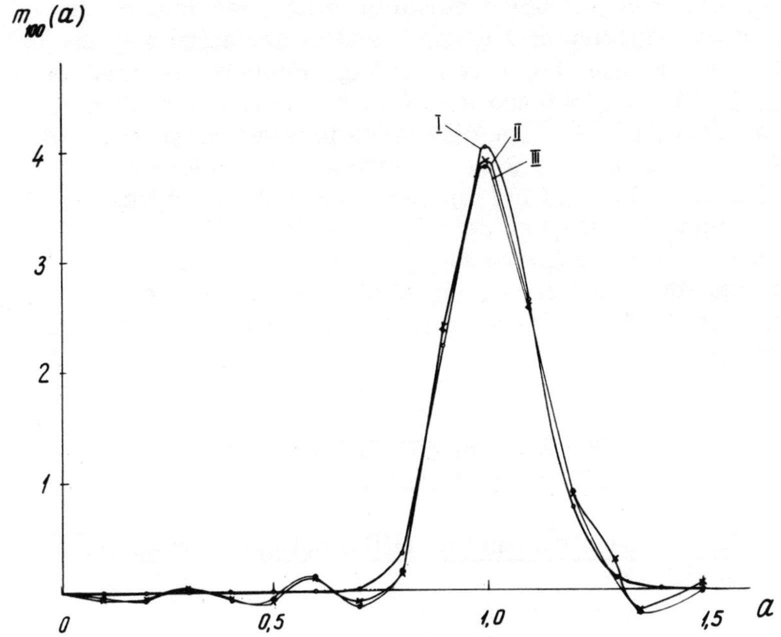

Fig. 5. Inversion on transparency at $\mu = 100$.

this case $\Delta = \mu = 2$ in (35) and Δ is assumed to be equal to 4 (16). We have used the following designation: I - the exact curve $a^4\ e^{-2a}$, curves II, III, IV and V - inversions according to the transparency method (accurate to constant factor $4\,\gamma_0$), when m = 5, 10, 20 and 40 respectively. The axis of the ordinate is designated by $m_2(a)$. Poor accuracy at m = 5 results from the fact that almost all wave numbers ν for which the transparency was taken fall in the region of geometric optics. This region maintains little information on a disperse system (24).

In Fig. 5 $\mu = 100$ is chosen for $r_0 = r_2$ (See Eqs. (1) and (2) of Section VI.) We have introduced the following designations there: curve I - the exact spectrum and curves II and III were obtained according to data on transparency, calculated accurate to 10^{-5} and 10^{-2} respectively. We assume $\tau = 20$, m = 20 and c_0 and c_2 are determined from Eq. (29) (τ is large enough). One can see that it is sufficient to measure transparency accurately to 1% when determining a particle spectrum. Curves II and III are calculated in (16). They differ from those of Fig. 5 only by the value of c_2. In Fig. 5 $c_2 = 0$ and in (16) c_2 has been determined from formula (28). The difference between curves is unimportant. When $a > 0.5$ they practically coincide; when $a < 0.5$ curves II and III in (16) give a more exact approximation—they almost coincide with the a-axis. The weak dependence of the transparency method (when τ is large enough) on c_2 is very essential since reliable determination of c_2 by the data of experimental transparency is often difficult.

V. EXPERIMENTAL CHECK OF TRANSPARENCY METHOD

A. General requirements on initial optical information (12-21, 24)

Initial optical information obtained experimentally can be given in tablular or graphic form. In (12) utilization of the transparency method for this case is shown. Let us formulate the conditions of application of the method arising from a mathematical analysis of the calculational scheme (See IV, D). There are two conditions: a) The transparency $g^*(\nu)$ must be measured in a sufficiently wide range of wavelength $\lambda_{min} < \lambda < \lambda_{max}$ $(\nu = \lambda^{-1})$ and b) the accuracy of the transparency measurements must be of the order of 1%.

Condition b is easy to fulfill. Let us dwell on condition a.

It is easy to show that determination of the particle distribution by the transparency method is impossible (independent of accuracy of measurements) when condition a is broken, (12-20). Let us give approximate estimations of λ_{min} and λ_{max}. Suppose

$$\lambda_{min} = \frac{4\pi(m - 1)\,\bar{r}}{\tau}, \qquad \lambda_{max} = \frac{4\pi(m - 1)\,\bar{r}}{\sigma} \tag{1}$$

where $\bar{r}$ is the mean particle size, m is the refractive index. Then from (15, 21)

$$\tau \simeq 4 - 8, \qquad \sigma \simeq 0.4 - 0.6 \tag{2}$$

If σ meets condition (2) the behaviour of the transparency in the Rayleigh region can be described accurately; however, it cannot be said that the estimation (2) for τ is universal. For example, τ can be considerably larger than 8 for a very narrow spectra of particles. The accuracy of the calculation depends on the correct choice of τ to no small degree. The main condition for application of the transparency method is to extend the measurements of $g^*(\nu)$ into the region of geometric optics. The corresponding numerical estimation of τ can be obtained according to the graphical shape of $g^*(\nu)$ (See IV, D).

B. Inversion scheme of experimental transparency (16, 21)

It is convenient (but not obligatory) first to estimate the interval $[\lambda_{min}, \lambda_{max}]$, where it is necessary to measure the transparency. This can be done by formulae (1) and (2), if an approximate estimation of $\bar{r}$ and m is known. Note, that one can manage to record by suitable devices the longwave region up to the necessary σ. Difficulties can arise in the shortwave region when approaching τ.

As shown in IV, D the experimental transparency $g^*(\nu)$ must enable one to graph $g^* = g^*(\nu)$ in the interval $0 < \nu < \tau^*$. If the graph of g^* has a single maximum ν_M then from Eqs. (13) and (24) of IV

$$\tau^* \simeq 2\,\nu_M \tag{3}$$

of the graph g^* has some extrema $\nu^{(1)} < \ldots < \nu^{(n)}$ then at $n > 3$ due to Eq. (22) of IV.

$$\tau^* \simeq \nu^{(n)} \tag{4}$$

Either τ or r_0 can be fixed arbitrarily (IV, E). Suppose τ

set equal to 4 (this choice to some degree is accidental). Then from Eq. (33) of IV

$$r_0 = \frac{1}{\pi(m - 1)\tau^*} \tag{5}$$

According to Eqs. (6) and (13) of IV we shall pass from $g^*(\nu)$ to the dimensionless transparency $g(x/2)$,

$$g(x/2) = r_0 g^*(\nu), \qquad x = \frac{4\nu^*}{\tau^*} \qquad (\tau = 4) \tag{6}$$

Let the value of m in Eq. (16) of IV be equal to 20 (16, 24). Then Eq. (16) of IV gives

$$\tilde{m}(a) = \frac{1}{\pi}\left\{ 0.2 \sum_{j=1}^{20} g(x_j/2)\,\omega(ax_j) + 4c_0\,\omega_0(4a) + \frac{c_2}{4}\,\omega_2(4a)\right\} \tag{7}$$

$$x_j = 0.2\,(j - 0.5) \tag{8}$$

The functions $\omega(y)$, $\omega_0(y)$ and $\omega_2(y)$ are determined from IV(18) and the coefficients c_0 and c_2 from IV (25) with consideration of IV (26) and IV (28). When calculating according to formula (7) above it is convenient to use tables of functions IV (18) from (15). The transition to dimensional distribution functions is carried out by IV (31) and IV (32).

C. Remarks

1) If the transparency $g(x/2)$ is known accurate to a constant factor, then the spectrum $\tilde{m}(a)$ from (7) is determined accurate to verticle scale and the distribution function $\tilde{f}^*(r)$ accurate to vertical and horizontal scales.

2) The following formula

$$m = 1 + \frac{1}{4\pi}\;\frac{\tau\,\tilde{a}}{\tau^*\,\tilde{r}} \tag{9}$$

is obtained in (16). In it $\tilde{a}$ and $\tilde{r}$ are the same parameters (for example modes) of curves $a^{-2}\,\tilde{m}(a)$ and $\tilde{f}^*(r)$.

Formula (9) allows one to estimate the refractive index m. Such a formula is used to find the nature of the dependence of the integral equation kernel IV (1) on δ (IV (3) - IV (4)).

D. Dimensional inversion formula

Often formulae which allow one to pass from dimensional transparency to dimensional particle spectrum without use of scale r_0 (for example calculations with variable τ^*) appear to be useful:

$$r^2 \tilde{f}^* (r) = -\frac{\beta}{\pi^2}\{ \Delta \nu \sum_{j=1}^{m} g^*(\nu_j)\, \omega(2\beta r \nu_j) + c_0^* \; \tau^* \, \omega_0(2\beta r \tau^*) + c_2^* \frac{\omega_2(2\beta r \tau^*)}{\tau^*} \tag{10}$$

$$\Delta \nu = \frac{\tau^*}{m}, \qquad \nu_j = \Delta \nu (j - 0.5) \tag{11}$$

$$c_0^* = \lim g^* (\;) \tag{12}$$

$$c_2^* = \frac{\sum_{i=1}^{K} g^*(\nu_i) - K c_0^*}{\sum_{i=1}^{K} \nu_i^{-2}} \qquad (\nu_K > \ldots > \nu_1 > \tau^*, \; K \simeq 4 - 5) \tag{13}$$

Here β is given by IV (5) and c_0^* and c_2^* are determined by the expression

$$g^*(\nu) \simeq c_0^* + \frac{c_2^*}{\nu^2} \quad (\nu \geq \tau^*) \tag{14}$$

E. Application of transparency method to real disperse systems (12-21)

The check of the transparency method verified the correctness of the calculational scheme and showed its stability to small errors of measurement and calculation. In the case of tabulated transparency data the main requirement of the necessary amount of initial optical information was formulated. Thus a mathematical ground of the method has been obtained. This ground, however, does not give any information on application of the suggested theory to real systems.

In fact, the theory contains a number of hypotheses of a physical nature: a) particles are spherical; b) scattering is 1) single and 2) incoherent; c) refractive index is 1) real 2) close to unity and 3) approximately constant at wavelength for which transparency is measured.

Strictly speaking none of the enumerated hypotheses are fulfilled for real objects. Analytical investigation of these limitations is rather difficult. Thus direct experimental measurements is the only way of verifying the method. The problem is to check the transparency method on aerosols calibrated beforehand; that is, to compare spectra obtained by the transparency method with direct microscope measurements. Hence the main aim of the experiment is to check if limitations a) - c) assumed in the theory of the transparency method are physically prohibitive. Otherwise the transparency method may give the particle spectrum with adequate accuracy. In accordance with this, experiments in (21) have been carried out so as to decrease the effects of limitations a) - c).

F. Experimental check of the theory (21)

Experiments were carried out for two models: a) spores of Calvatia (Fig. 6a); b) microcrystals of AgBr in gelatine (Fig. 6b). These spectral curves are given in Fig. 7a and 7b (respectively for models a and b). The intensity of light incident on the particle is given by $J_0 = J_0(\nu)$, the intensity of light passing the opaque medium by $J = J(\nu)$ and the transparency by $g^* = g^*(\nu)$. Intensitities J_0 and J were measured by the spectrophotometer and the transparency g^* was calculated by Bouguer-Lambert law for plane layer. In this case $g^*(\nu)$ is dimensionless and since all further calculations are carried out accurate to a constant factor one can suppose

$$g(x/2) = g^*(\nu) = \ln\frac{J_0}{J} \tag{15}$$

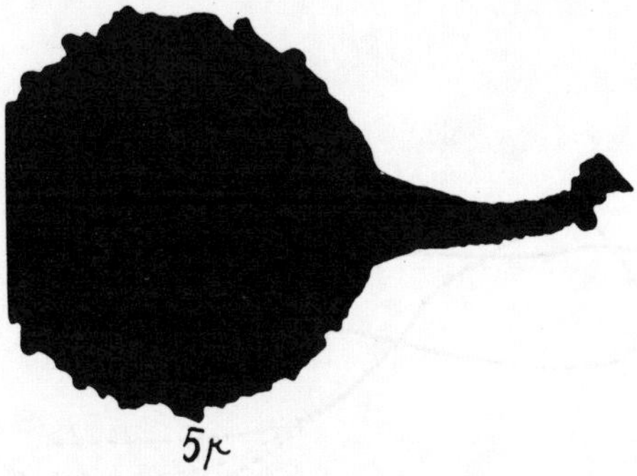

Fig. 6a. Photo of Calvatia spore.

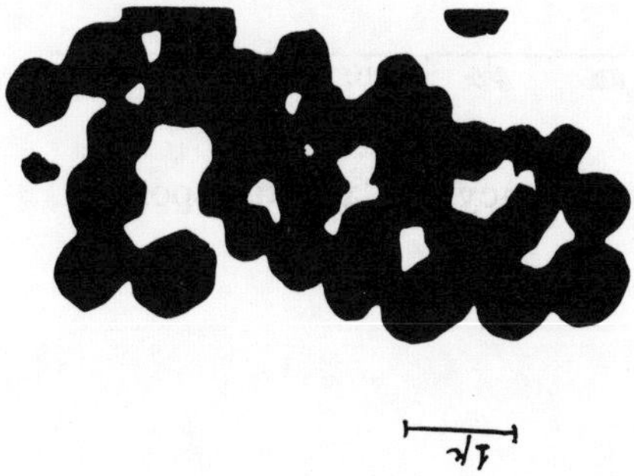

Fig. 6b. Photo of AgBr crystals.

The curves g* obtained from (15) are presented in Fig. 7a and 7b as full lines. For model a), experimental data in the shortwave region are not sufficient. In Fig. 7a the extrapolation of g* (ν) (at $\nu > 0.52_{\mu}^{-1}$) in the region considered practical is presented as dashed lines. Curve g* (model b) begins to raise at $\nu > 2.5_{\mu}^{-1}$. Here intensive absorption bands of AgBr are displayed at $\nu = 2.56_{\mu}^{-1}$, $\nu = 2.70_{\mu}^{-1}$, $\nu = 2.78_{\mu}^{-1}$. One of the most probably extrapolations of g* (ν) for $\nu > 2.5_{\mu}^{-1}$ is given by right dashed line. Also the curve of g* (ν) in Fig. 7b is extrapolated in Fig. 7b is extrapolated in the Rayleigh region (left dashed line). Extrapolation to the left results in an insignificant correction (15). The transparency method is used for the

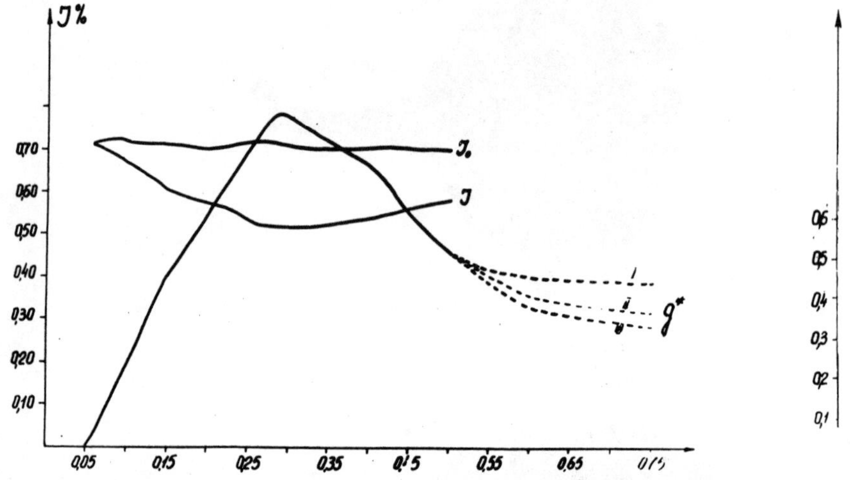

Fig. 7a. Transparency of Calvatia spores.

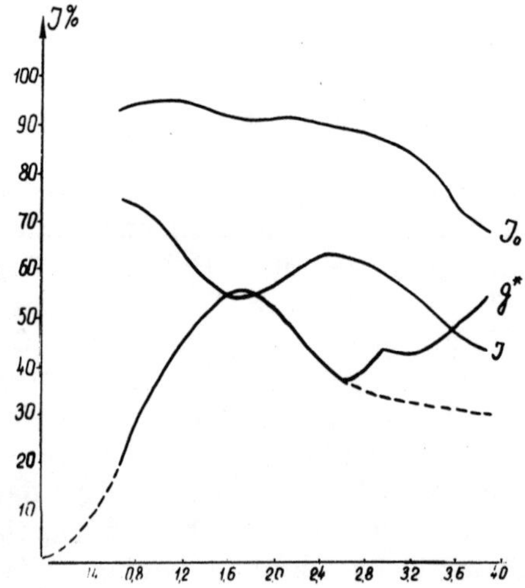

Fig. 7b. Transparency of AgBr crystals.

curves g* including extrapolated portions. Calculations were carried out by formulae of IV, B with consideration of Eq. (15).

The refractive index of model b (m = 1.47) was known beforehand (absolute refractive coefficient of AgBr and gelatin 2.253 and 1.53 respectively). The refractive index for model a was estimated from (9) as 1.44. In Fig. 8a and 8b (respectively for models a and b) dashed lines present spectrum obtained with the help of microscope; full lines present the spectrum determined by the transparency method. Curves I, II, III in Fig. 8a correspond to different extrapolations of the transparency (Fig. 7a) and illustrate the stability of the inversion method. All the spectra in Fig. 8a and 8b are normalized to unit area.

Particle spectra obtained microscopically and according to the transparency method are in good agreement.

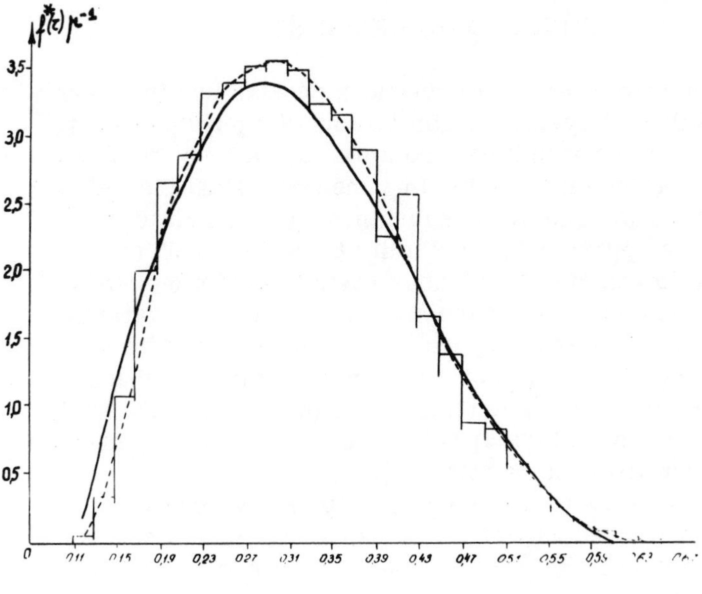

Fig. 8a. Spectra of Calvatia spores.

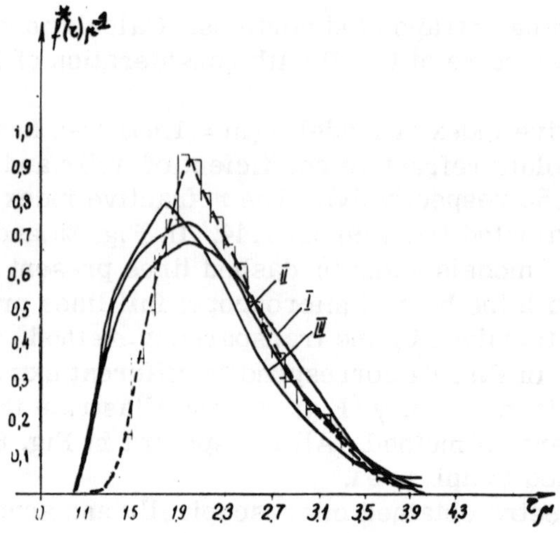

Fig. 8b. Spectra of AgBr crystals.

CONCLUDING REMARKS

The method of spectra transparency assumed in IV can be used with real systems. Limitations of a physical nature (12, 13, 14) are not critical and small deviations from them do not prevent one from using this method. Thus the method gives an adequate result for substances whose refractive index differs appreciably from unity (m ≃ 1.4 - 1.5) and allows one to examine substances having absorption bands.

The physical cause of the stability of the transparency method is associated with peculiarities of the scattering coefficient, its relatively poor sensitivity to particle shape, refractive index and other factors. In this respect the scattering coefficient differs greatly from angular scattering patterns or utilization of polarizations.

Let us note that the scheme of calculation for the method can be used as well for nonspherical particles. As a result we obtain the particle spectrum where r is an effective radius.

The transparency method is stable and this stability raises hopes of the practical use of this method in different problems.

IV. SCATTERING PATTERN METHOD

A. The formulation of the problem

The relation between the light scattering pattern of a single particle J (β, r), the particle distribution function f* (r) and the polydisperse scattering pattern $\bar{J}$ (β) is expressed by an integral equation of the first kind (See III) as

$$\bar{J}(\beta) = \int_0^\infty J(\beta, r)\, f^*(r)\, dr \qquad (1)$$

Let us consider optical properties of a particle system which differs very little from that of their environment, namely let

$$\rho = \frac{2\pi r}{\lambda}, \; \rho(m-1) < 1; \; \alpha = \frac{3}{4\pi}\, \frac{m^2-1}{m^2+2} \; |\alpha| \ll 1 \qquad (2)$$

In this case the monodisperse scattering pattern J(β, r) is expressed by a simple analytical formula (7):

$$J(\beta, r) = I_0\, \psi(\beta)\, K(q)\, r^2, \quad q = 2\rho \sin\frac{\beta}{2} \qquad (3)$$

$$\psi(\beta) = 2\pi^2 |\alpha|^2 \frac{(1+\cos^2\beta)}{(1-\cos\beta)^2}, \quad K(g) = \frac{(\sin q - q\cos q)^2}{q^2} \qquad (4)$$

By Mellin's transformation of (1), one can find an unknown distribution function f* (r) corresponding to a measured polydisperse scattering pattern $\bar{J}$ (β).

Such calculation of distribution functions f* (r) we shall call the scattering pattern method. This method is developed in Ref. (23, 24). The mathematical apparatus developed in Ref. (12, 14) is applied here.

B. Accurate solution of the problem

Let us pass to the dimensionless variables

$$x = \gamma \sin\frac{\beta}{2}, \quad \gamma = 4\rho_0^*, \quad \rho_0 = \frac{2\pi r_0}{\lambda}, \quad \tau = \gamma \sin\frac{\beta\ max}{2} \tag{5}$$

$$g(x/2) = \frac{r_0}{\psi\beta}\ \frac{\bar{J}(\beta)}{I_0} \tag{6}$$

$$r = ar_0, \quad f^*(r) = \frac{m(a)}{a^2 r_0^4} \tag{7}$$

$\beta = \beta_{max}$ is the largest angle ($0 < \beta_{max} \leq \pi$) for which the scattering pattern $J(\beta_1 r)$ is known and r_0 is an arbitrary linear scale. Then from (1) and (3) we have

$$g(x/2) = \int_0^\infty K\left(\frac{x}{2}a\right) m(a)\, da. \tag{8}$$

the function K (compare IV, b) is expressed by formula (4). Accurate solution of integral Eq. (8) is of the form (23)

$$m(a) = \frac{4}{\pi}\left\{ \frac{1}{2\pi i} \int_{c-i\infty}^{c+i\infty} \frac{P+1}{P-3} \cos\frac{\pi P}{2}\, \Gamma(P)\, \delta(P)\, a^{-P}\, dp, \right.$$

$$-2 < c < 0 \tag{9}$$

$$\delta(P) = \int_0^\infty g(x/2)\, x^{-P}\, dx, \quad 1 < \mathrm{Re}\,p < 5 \tag{10}$$

First, $\delta(P)$ is found from (10), then $\delta(P)$ is analytically continued to the band $-2 < \mathrm{Re}\,p < 0$ and last m (a) is calculated from (9).

C. Utilization of tabulated information on polydispersal scattering pattern

The inversion formula valid here is (23, 24).

$$m(a) \simeq \tilde{m}(a) = \frac{4}{\pi}\left\{ \sum_{j=1}^{m} g(x_j/2)\, \mathcal{H}(ax_j)\, \Delta x_j + c_0\, \tau\, \mathcal{H}_0(a\tau) \right.$$

$$+ c_2 \frac{\mathcal{H}_2(a\tau)}{\tau} \tag{11}$$

Where (compare IV, C)

$$\sum_{j=1}^{m} \Delta x_j = \tau \quad (\Delta x_j > 0) \ , \ g(x/2) \simeq c_0 + \frac{c_2}{x^2} \qquad (x \geq \tau) \qquad (12)$$

$$\mathcal{H}(y) = (1 - \frac{8}{y^2}) \cos y + (\frac{8}{y^3} - \frac{4}{y}) \sin y + \frac{1}{3} \qquad (13)$$

$$\mathcal{H}_0(y) = \frac{\mathcal{H}(y) - \omega_0(y)}{2} \ , \quad \mathcal{H}_2(y) = \frac{\mathcal{H}(y) - \omega_2(y)}{4} \qquad (14)$$

The functions $\mathcal{H}(y)$, $\mathcal{H}_0(y)$ and $\mathcal{H}_2(y)$ are tabulated in detail in Ref. (25) and expressions for $\omega_0(y)$ and $\omega_2(y)$ are written out in IV (18).

D. An example of inversion

The Γ-distribution IV (35) for $\mu = 0$ at $r_0 = \bar{r}$ ($\bar{r}$ - mean radius of particles, in this case $\Delta = \mu + 1$) is taken as a model. In Fig. 9 curve I is the exact spectrum obtained from:

$$\frac{m_0(a)}{\gamma} = a^2 e^{-a}, \quad \bar{\gamma} = N r^{-3} \qquad (15)$$

Curves II, III, IV and V are inversions of

$$\frac{\tilde{m}_0(a)}{\bar{\gamma}}$$

of the polydisperse scattering pattern calculated from formula (11) at $\tau = 2, 3, 4$ ($m = 10$) and $\tau = 4$ ($m = 20$) respectively, when $\Delta x_j = \Delta x$ ($j = 1, \ldots, m$).

The values of $g(x_j/2)$ used here are found with the help of formula (8) and (15). The ordinate axis in Fig. 9 is denoted $m_0(a)$. The shape of curves II, III, IV and V corresponds to the estimation obtained from (15). (See (24).) Note that in this example the scattering pattern $g(x/2)$ has a single maximum at $x_M = \sqrt{5}$.

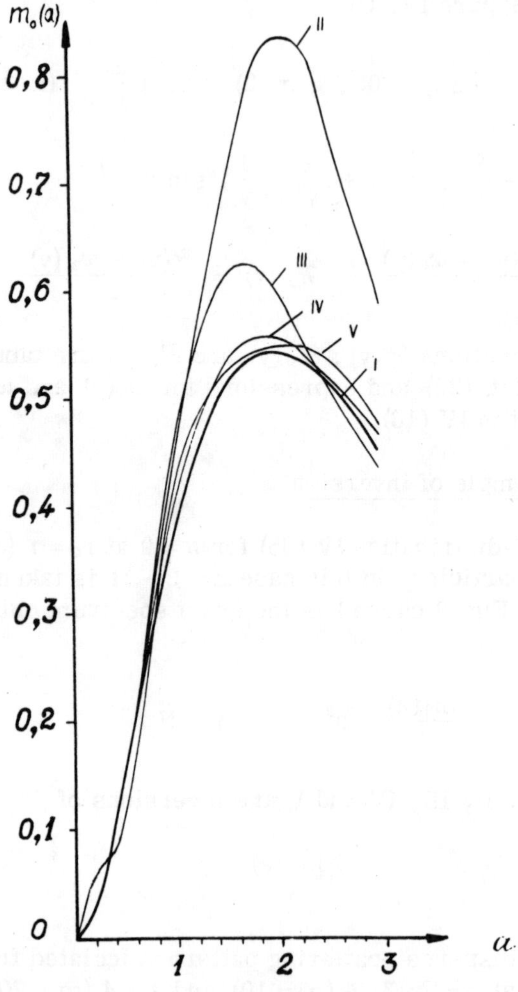

Fig. 9. Inversion of scattering pattern at $\mu = 0$.

E. General requirements to initial optical information

An analogy with the transparency method is valid here. If the scattering pattern g (x/2) has a single maximum, x_M, it is advisable to take

$$\bar{\rho} = \frac{2\pi \bar{r}}{\lambda} \simeq (0.4 - 0.5)\ x_M \qquad (16)$$

Calculation according to formula (11) is possible if $\bar{\rho}$ is large enough. Physically this means that the scattering pattern differs sufficiently from a Rayleigh one when $\bar{\rho}$ is large enough and only then is the inversion possible (See details in (23).).

VII. DETERMINATION OF OPTICAL CHARACTERISTICS OF DISPERSE SYSTEMS WITH NARROW DISTRIBUTION

As a model of the system with narrow distribution we shall take a Γ-structure

$$m_\mu (a) = \gamma \frac{\alpha^{\mu+1}}{\Gamma(\mu+1)} a^{\mu+2} e^{-\alpha a} \quad , \gamma = 2\pi N \bar{r}_2^3 \; (\mu \gg 1) \tag{1}$$

$$\alpha = \sqrt{(\mu+1)(\mu+2)}, \tag{2}$$

where the mean quadrature radius $\bar{r}^2$ is admitted as a scale r_0. At $\mu \to \infty$ function (1) is a δ-like succession (relative to a = 1). Thus at $\mu \gg 1$ spectrum (1) describes systems with arbitrarily narrow distributions.

Determination of the optical characteristics by the above mentioned methods reduces to calculation of an integral of the type

$$g_\mu (y) = \gamma \frac{\alpha^{\mu+1}}{\Gamma(\mu+1)} \int_0^\infty K(ay)\, a^{\mu+2} e^{-\alpha a}\, da, \tag{3}$$

where K (y) is a function of the definite type. In Ref. (19) integral (3) was examined for the case when K (y) is an arbitrary analytical function. We shall give the main result.

Function g_μ (y) from (3) can be written as a power series of y which converges absolutely for any case at

$$|y| < \frac{\alpha}{\lim\limits_{m\to\infty} \sqrt[m]{K^{(m)}(0)}} \tag{4}$$

This power series can be regrouped into power series in $1/\mu$ $(\mu > 1)$ and

$$\frac{g_\mu(y)}{\gamma} = K(y) + \frac{K_2(y) + 2K_{(1)}(y)}{2} \frac{1}{\mu} + \tag{5}$$

$$+ \frac{3K_{(4)}(y) + 8K_{(3)}(y) - 18K_{(2)}(y) - 44K_{(1)}(y)}{24} \frac{1}{\mu^2} + 0\left(\frac{1}{\mu^3}\right)$$

where

$$K_{(1)}(y) = y\,(y\ldots(y\,K'(y))'\ldots)' \qquad \text{(1 primes)} \tag{6}$$

(a prime denotes the derivative)

Expansion (5) has a definite meaning in region (4), since permutation of terms is admissible in an absolutely convergent series. Series (5) is conveniently used at $\mu \gg 1$. In the first approximation we suppose

$$\frac{g_\mu(y)}{\gamma} \simeq K(y) + \frac{K_{(2)}(y) + 2K_{(1)}(y)}{2} \frac{1}{\mu} \tag{7}$$

Let us utilize (7) for methods 1) small angle, (26); 2) transparency, (19); and 3) scattering pattern. We have ($\mu \gg 1$)

1) small angle method:

$$\frac{\alpha^{\mu+1}}{\Gamma(\mu+1)} \int_0^\infty a^{\mu+2} e^{-\alpha a} J_1^2(ay)\, da \simeq J_1^2(y) + \frac{y^2}{\mu} J_6^2(y) - $$

$$- J_1^2(y), \quad y = \frac{x}{2} \tag{8}$$

2) transparency method:

$$g_\mu(x/2) \simeq \gamma \left\{ 1 - 2\frac{\sin x}{x} + 2\frac{1-\cos x}{x^2} + \frac{x \sin x}{\mu} \right. \tag{9}$$

3) scattering pattern method:

$$g_\mu(x/2) \simeq \left\{ \frac{\left(2\sin\frac{x}{2} - x\cos\frac{x}{2}\right)^2}{x^2} + \frac{x\sin x - x^2\cos x}{4\mu} \right. \tag{10}$$

The calculations show that formulae (8) - (10) are parts of a power series in $1/\mu$, convergent in one and the same region.

$$|x| < \sqrt{(\mu + 1)(\mu + 2)} \tag{11}$$

Formulae (8) - (10) represent accuracy to 10% in the region

$$x < (0.10 - 0.20)\ \mu$$

In Ref. (19) it has been shown that the second approximation obtained from (5) improves the first insignificantly.

REFERENCES

(1) Chin, J. H., Sliepcevich, C. M., Tribus, M., J. Phys. Chem. 59, 841 (1955).

(2) Golikov, V. I., Trudy GGO, N 109 (1961).

(3) Golikov, V. I., Trudy GGO, N 118 (1961).

(4) Golikov, V. I., Trudy GGO, N 170 (1965).

(5) Van de Hulst, H. C., Light Scattering by Small Particles, J. Wiley and Sons, New York, (1957).

(6) Polyakova, E. A., Shifrin, K. S., Trudy GGO, N 42 (1953).

(7) Shifrin, K. S., Light scattering in opaque medium. (GITTL 1951).

(8) Shifrin, K. S., Trudy GGO, N 46 (1955).

(9) Shifrin, K. S., Trudy GGO, N 109 (1961).

(10) Shifrin, K. S., Trudy Wsesoyusnogo saochnogo lesotechnicheskogo instituta, N 2 (1956).

(11) Shifrin, K. S., Sbornic "Issledovanie oblakov, osadkov i grosovogo electrichestva" GIMIS, pp. 20 (1957).

(12) Shifrin, K. S., Perelman, A. Y., Opt. and Spectr. 15, N 4 (1963).

(13) Shifrin, K. S., Perelman, A. Y., Opt. and Spectr. 15, N 5 (1963).

(14) Shifrin, K. S., Perelman, A. Y., Opt. and Spectr. 15, N 6 (1963).

(15) Shifrin, K. S., Perelman, A. Y., Opt. and Spectr. **16**, N 1 (1964).

(16) Shifrin, K. S., Perelman, A. Y., Opt. and Spectr. **19**, N 5 (1965).

(17) Shifrin, K. S., Perelman, A. Y., DAN, **151** (1963).

(18) Shifrin, K. S., Perelman, A. Y., Trudy GGO, 1965, N **170**, 3.

(19) Shifrin, K. S., Perelman, A. Y., Trudy GGO, 1965, N **170**, 37.

(20) Shifrin, K. S., Perelman, A. Y., Pageoph **58**, 11 (Basel, 1964).

(21) Shifrin, K. S., Perelman, A. Y., and Bachtiyarov, W. G., Opt. and Spectr. **19**, N 6 (1965).

(22) Shifrin, K. S., Perelman, A. Y., and Potechina, L. K., Trudy GGO, N **152** (1964).

(23) Shifrin, K. S., Perelman, A. Y., DAN, **158**, 2 (1964).

(24) Shifrin, K. S. Perelman, A. Y., Isv. AN USSR ser. "Atm phys. and ocean", N **9** (1965).

(25) Shifrin, K. S., Perelman, A. Y., and Sagorovskaya, L. I., Trudy GGO, N **183** (1965).

(26) Shifrin, K. S., Perelman, A. Y., and Punina, V. A., Trudy GGO, N **183** (1965).

(27) Shifrin, K. S., Golikov, V. I., Sbornic "Issledovanie oblakov, osadkov i grosovogo electrichestva" AN USSR, pp 266 (1961).

(28) Shifrin, K. S., Golikov, V. I., Trudy Wsesoyusnogo nauchnogo meteorologicheskogo soveschania, **9**, 277 (1964).

(29) Shifrin, K. S., Golikov, V. I., Trudy GGO, N **152** (1964).

(30) Shifrin, K. S., Golikov, V. I., Trudy GGO, N **170** (1965).

(31) Shifrin, K. S. Novoselcev. E. P., Trudy GGO, N **100** (1960).

(32) Titchmarsh, Introduction to The Theory of Fourier Integrals, New York (1937).

(33) Titchmarsh, Proc. London Math. Soc. **23**, N 7 (1925).

DISCUSSION FOLLOWING PAPER BY K. S. SHIFRIN AND A. Y. PERELMAN (COMMUNICATED BY W. FARONE)

R. H. Marchessault: What precautions are taken to ensure that transmission does not include a large contribution from small angle scattering?

W. Farone: The specifications of the experimental apparatus was not given in this paper but could be found from previous publications of Shifrin et. al. I do not have copies of manuscripts of all this work and only several reprints none of which include this information.

W. Prins: This morning Dr. Kerker said that particle size distributions could not be obtained reliably for anything with a fairly wide distribution. You say that it is possible. Isn't that a controversy?

W. Farone: There is no real controversy as the techniques used and ranges of validity are entirely different. Dr. Kerker's method, based on the angular scattering patterns, is much more sensitive for narrower distributions but the information is "washed out" by broader ones. In the transmission measurements of Shifrin and Perelman use is made of the relative insensitivity of the scattering cross-section to shape and refractive index to obtain the distribution.

R. Fenn: Do the authors give values for the errors $\Delta \phi (x)$ for which they can derive solutions?

W. Farone: Based on their analysis an error of 1% in the data is sufficiently low to insure results in the size distribution of at least like accuracy.

J. M. Greenberg: Unless one knows rather well a considerable portion of the properties, kind of size distribution, shapes and optics of particles, the answer is far from unique. As a matter of fact in accounting for interstellar extinction one has very little direct information and the more data one puts on, the more ridiculous is the size distribution.

Use of Small Angle X-Ray Scattering to Determine the Distribution of Particle Diameters in Polydisperse Colloidal Samples*

Paul W. Schmidt
Physics Dept., University of Missouri, Columbia, Mo.

and

Orville L. Brill
Physics Dept., Kansas State College, Pittsburg, Kansas

ABSTRACT

The distribution of particle diameters in a polydisperse colloidal sample composed of independent randomly oriented particles with uniform electron density and with the same shape is shown to be expressible as an integral transform of the experimental small angle x-ray scattering intensity. Some properties of the diameter distribution function are discussed. While a final evaluation of the usefulness of the method cannot be made until it has been applied to a number of experimental scattering curves, preliminary tests suggest that this technique may develop into a useful procedure for analyzing small angle x-ray scattering data, especially scattering curves from samples composed of spherical particles.

---

*Work supported by the National Science Foundation.

INTRODUCTION

Small angle x-ray scattering is widely used in studying the structure of colloids. A very complete and general description of a colloidal sample can often be obtained from the small angle x-ray scattering data from samples containing independent, randomly oriented identical particles. The interpretation of the scattering curves is much more difficult, however, when the sample is polydisperse—that is, when the particles in the sample are not identical.

Several authors have studied the scattering from polydisperse samples. Shull and Roess (16), Roess and Shull (12), and Hosemann (6), after making some reasonable assumptions about the form of the scattering curve and about the distribution of particle dimensions, computed the scattering curves that would be expected for these conditions and developed procedures for interpreting experimental curves. Although in many colloidal systems the necessary assumptions are often satisfied, in principle a procedure not requiring these assumptions would be preferable.

Roess (11) considered the general problem of obtaining the distribution of particle diameters from the scattering curve for an assembly of non-interacting particles with different diameters but with the same shape. After outlining an integral transform procedure by which the diameter distribution could be obtained from the scattering curve, he developed detailed equations for finding the distribution of particle diameters from the scattering data from polydisperse samples composed of spherical particles. Riseman (10) independently obtained equivalent relations for polydisperse systems of spheres. Luzzati (9) described an integral transform method for finding the diameter distribution from the small angle x-ray scattering data from polydisperse samples containing particles with the same shape but with different diameters. His results, which apply to particles of any shape, are stated in terms of Fourier transforms which are essentially equivalent to the Mellin transforms given by Roess. None of these three authors applied his equations to experimental scattering data.

When integral transform methods are used to obtain diameter distribution functions, care must be taken to ensure that all integrals converge. The convergence is affected by the behavior of the scattered intensity in the outer part of the scattering curve. At the time of Roess's and Riseman's investigations, the form of the scattering curve in this angular region was not known, and as a result, Riseman's integral for the diameter distribution will not converge for experimental small angle x-ray scattering curves. In order to obtain convergent integrals for the diameter distribution function for polydisperse samples of spherical particles, Roess was obliged to express the diameter distribution as the derivative of an integral transform of the scattered intensity. For analysis of experimental data, an expression not requiring numerical differentiation would be preferable.

We have recently examined the theory of the scattering from polydisperse samples of non-interacting particles, in an attempt to determine whether a practical method might be developed for interpreting the scattering from polydisperse samples composed of independent particles of a given shape. In this investigation we have expressed the equations describing the properties of the scattered intensity from polydisperse samples in a form resembling the corresponding equations for systems of identical particles. We have shown that the distribution of particle diameters is obtainable from an integral transform of the scattered intensity, and the conditions of convergence of this transform have been investigated. For systems of spherical particles, some properties of the transform and the diameter distribution function have been treated in more detail.

SOME PROPERTIES OF THE SCATTERING FROM POLYDISPERSE SYSTEMS

The small angle x-ray scattering from a single randomly oriented particle with uniform electron density and maximum diameter a can be expressed in terms of a function $\gamma_0(r/a)$ which is called the characteristic function (2). This function contains all the information about the particle size and shape which is obtainable from scattering experiments.

For a polydisperse assembly of independent, randomly-oriented particles with uniform electron density, an average characteristic function $\gamma(r)$ can be defined for a particle of the polydisperse system. When the scattered intensity is expressed in terms of $\gamma(r)$, the equations describing the scattering can be put into a form similar to that used for systems of identical particles.

The average particle structure factor $\overline{F_0^2(h, a)}$ for a single, randomly-oriented particle with uniform electron density is given by (2)

$$\overline{F_0^2(h, a)} = 4\pi\rho^2 V \int_0^a dr\, r^2 \gamma_0(r/a) \frac{\sin hr}{hr} \quad (1)$$

where $h = 4\pi\lambda^{-1} \sin(\phi/2)$; ϕ is the scattering angle; λ is the x-ray wavelength; ρ is the difference between the particle electron density and the constant electron density of the medium in which the particle is assumed to be suspended; a is the maximum diameter of the particle—that is, the length, of the longest straight line that can be contained in the particle; V is the particle volume; and $\gamma_0(r/a)$ is the characteristic function.

The polydisperse sample will be assumed to consist of particles which vary in size, but have the same shape. Then, although the maximum diameter a may vary from particle to particle, the characteristic function $\gamma_0(r/a)$ will be the same for all particles of the same, and the intensity scattered by a particle will be proportional to $\overline{F_0^2(h, a)}$. The dimensionless parameter $V_0 = a^{-3} V$ is the same for all particles.

The diameter distribution function $\rho(a)$ will be defined to have the property that $\rho(a)\, da$ represents the probability that the radiation is being scattered by a particle with a maximum diameter between the values a and (a + da). In most cases, $\rho(a)$ will be assumed to satisfy the normalization relation

$$\int_0^\infty da\, \rho(a) = 1$$

Also, all derivatives of $\rho(a)$ will be assumed to be continuous for $0 \leq a < \infty$, and

$$\int_0^\infty da\, a^\alpha \rho(a)$$

will be assumed to exist for all $\alpha > -1$.

By use of Eq. 1, for the polydisperse sample, the average structure factor $\overline{F^2(h)}$ can be expressed

$$\overline{F^2(h)} = \int_0^\infty da\, \rho(a)\, \overline{F_0^2(h, a)}$$

$$= 4\pi \rho^2 \overline{V} \int^\infty dr\, r^2 \gamma(r)\, \frac{\sin hr}{hr} \qquad (2)$$

where

$$\gamma(r) = \frac{V_0}{\overline{V}} \int_r^\infty da\, a^3 \rho(a)\, \gamma_0\left(\frac{r}{a}\right) \qquad (3)$$

and

$$\overline{V} = V_0 \int_0^\infty da\, a^3\, \rho(a).$$

The function $\gamma(r)$, which can be considered to be the average characteristic function for the polydisperse system, has been defined to have properties similar to those of the characteristic function $\gamma_0\ (r/a)$ for a particle of maximum diameter a. For example (3), for small r,

$$\gamma_0 (r/a) = 1 - \frac{S_0}{4V_0}\frac{r}{a} + \ldots$$

where $S_0 = S/a^2$, and S is the surface area of a particle with maximum diameter a. The quantity S_0 is independent of a, since all particles have the same shape. For small r, $\gamma(r)$ can be written

$$\gamma(r) = 1 - \frac{\overline{S}}{4\overline{V}}\, r + \ldots \qquad (4)$$

where

$$\overline{S} = S_0 \int_0^\infty da\, a^2\, \rho(a)$$

Thus, for small r, $\gamma(r)$ and $\gamma_0 (r/a)$ can be approximated by similar series expansions.

The quantities $\overline{S}$ and $\overline{V}$ represent, respectively, the values of the particle surface area and volume, averaged over the polydisperse system.

For $\gamma(r)$ there are no directly analogous properties to the relations (4)

$$\gamma_0(1) = 0 \qquad \gamma_0'(1) = 0 \tag{5}$$

since, because of the assumed properties of $\rho(a)$, $\gamma(r)$ will be different from zero for all r.

By Fourier inversion, $\gamma(r)$ can be obtained from $\overline{F^2(h)}$ by the relation

$$\gamma(r) = \frac{1}{2\pi^2\rho^2\overline{V}} \int_0^\infty dh\, h^2\, \overline{F^2(h)}\, \frac{\sin hr}{hr} \tag{6}$$

For small h, the limiting form of $\overline{F^2(h)}$ is

$$\overline{F^2(h)} = \overline{F^2(0)} \left[1 - \frac{h^2\,\overline{R^2}}{3} + \dots\right]$$

where $(\overline{R^2})^{1/2}$, the average radius of gyration, is given by

$$(\overline{R^2})^{1/2} = \left[\frac{\int_0^\infty da\, a^6 \rho(a)\, R_0^2(a)}{\int_0^\infty da\, a^6 \rho(a)}\right]^{1/2}$$

and where $R_0(a)$ is the radius of gyration of a particle with maximum diameter a. The average radius of gyration $(\overline{R^2})^{1/2}$ strongly emphasizes large particles.

For large h, by three partial integrations, $\overline{F^2(h)}$ can be shown to have the approximate form

$$\overline{F^2(h)} \approx -8\pi\rho^2\,\overline{V}\,\gamma'(0)\,h^{-4}$$

Therefore

$$\overline{F^2(h)} \approx 2\pi\rho^2\overline{S}\,h^{-4}$$

At large h, $\overline{F^2(h)}$ for the polydisperse system thus is similar to the particle structure factor for identical particles (15).

DETERMINATION OF THE DIAMETER DISTRIBUTION FUNCTION $\rho(a)$

If experimental values of $\overline{F^2(h)}$ are available with sufficient accuracy and over a large enough range of h, the diameter distribution function $\rho(a)$ can in principle be computed.

From Eqs. 1, 2, and 5, after three partial integrations one can obtain the relation

$$f(h) = 4\pi \rho^2 V_0 \int_0^\infty da\, a^2 \rho(a)\; m(ha) \tag{7}$$

where, in the equations below, the t_j denote the points at which $\gamma_0''(t)$ or any higher derivatives of $\gamma_0(t)$ are discontinuous, and

$$f(h) = h^4 \overline{F^2(h)} - c_4$$

$$c_4 = \lim_{h\to\infty} h^4\, \overline{F^2(h)} = -\, 8\pi\rho^2\, V_0 \int_0^\infty da\, a^2\, \rho(a) \gamma_0'(0)$$

$$m(ha) = -\sum_{j=1}^{n} g(hat_j)\, t_j\, \Delta_j^2 - \int_0^1 dt\, g(hat)\, t\, \gamma_0'''(t)$$

$$g(x) = \cos x - (3/x) \sin x$$

$$\Delta_j^2 = \lim_{\substack{\epsilon > 0 \\ \epsilon > 0}} \left[\gamma_0''(t_j + \epsilon) - \gamma_0''(t_j - \epsilon)\right]$$

Then for a complex number z such that $0 < \mathrm{Re}(z) < 1$,

$$R_m(z) = \int_0^\infty da\, a^{z-1} a^2 \rho(a) = N(z) F(1 - z)$$

where

$$F(z) = \int_0^\infty dh\, h^{z-1} f(h)$$

$$N(z) = (z - 1)\, N_1(z)$$

$$N_1(z) = \frac{G_2(z)}{G_3(z)}$$

$$G_2(z) = \frac{2^{z-3}\Gamma\left(\frac{z}{2}+1\right)}{\pi^{3/2} V_0 \rho^2 \Gamma\left(\frac{5-z}{2}\right)}$$

$$G_3(z) = -\sum_{j=1}^{n} (t_j)^z \Delta_j^2 - \int_0^1 dt\, t^z \gamma_0'''(t)$$

By partial integration of $F(1-z)$, $R_m(z)$ can be expressed

$$R_m(z) = N_1(z)\ F_1(1-z)$$

where

$$F_1(z) = \int_0^\infty zh^{z-1}[\,hf'(h)\,]$$

As $R_m(z)$ is the Mellin transform of $a^2\rho(a)$, the diameter distribution function can be found from the inverse Mellin transform of the quantity $N_1(z)\ F_1(1-z)$. The values of $Re(z)$ for which the inverse Mellin transform will converge (17) to $a^2\rho(a)$ include the interval $0 < Re(z) < 1$.

By the Parseval formula for Mellin transforms (18),

$$\rho(a) = a^{-2} \int_0^\infty dh\ h\ f'(h)\ n_1(ha)$$

where $n_1(h)$ is the inverse Mellin transform of $N_1(z)$. Thus

$$\rho(a) = -a^{-2} \int_0^\infty dh\ f(h) \frac{d}{d\,ha}[\,ha\ n_1(ha)\,] \qquad (8)$$

Application of the Parseval formula requires that $N_1(z)$ and $f_1(h) = hf'(h)$ satisfy certain conditions (18), which for $f_1(h)$ will always be fulfilled because of the physical properties of the scattered intensity. However, $N_1(z)$ will not automatically have the necessary properties. For Eq. 8 to hold,

$$\int_{-\infty}^{\infty} dy\,|N_1(x+iy)| < \infty \qquad (9)$$

By use of Stirling's approximation for $\Gamma(z)$ for large z, $|G_2(x+iy)|$ can be shown to be proportional to $|y|^{x-3/2}$ when $|y|$ is large. Thus, when $0 < x < 1/2$, the behavior of $|G_3(x+iy)|$ for large $|y|$ determines whether or not Eq. 9 is satisfied. If at least one of the Δ_j^2 is not zero, $|G_3(x+iy)|$ approaches a constant value when $|y|$ is large, and therefore Eq. 9 will hold.

When all the Δ_j^2 are zero,

$$G_3(x+iy) = \sum_{j=1}^{n} G_{3j}(x+iy)$$

where

$$G_{3j}(z) = \int_{t_{j-1}}^{t_j} dt\, t^z \gamma_0'''(t)$$

All available information about the properties of $\gamma_0(t)$ indicates that the $G_{3j}(x+iy)$ ordinarily can be written

$$G_{3j}(x+iy) = \int_{t_{j-1}}^{t_j} dt\, t^{x+iy} (t - t_{j-1})^{\alpha_j - 1} (t_j - t)^{\beta_j - 1} l_j(t)$$

where $0 < \alpha_j < 1$, $0 < \beta_j < 1$, and $l_j(t)$ can be differentiated an arbitrary number of times. By a change of variables

$$G_{3j}(x+iy) = \sum_{j=1}^{n} \int_{s_j}^{s_{j-1}} ds\, e^{iys} L_j(s)(s - s_j)^{\alpha_j - 1}(s_{j-1} - s)^{\beta_j - 1}$$

where

$$s_j = -\log t_j$$

$$L_j(s) = e^{(x-1)s} l_j(e^{-s}) \left[\frac{s - s_j}{e^{-s_j} - e^{-s}}\right]^{1-\alpha_j} \left[\frac{s_{j-1} - s}{e^{-s} - e^{-s_{j-1}}}\right]^{1-\beta_j}$$

Thus, each $G_{3j}(x+iy)$ is expressed as a Fourier integral, and the behavior of $|G_3(x+iy)|$ can be obtained from the asymptotic expansions of these Fourier integrals (1). If δ is the smallest value of any of the α_j and β_j, then when $|y|$ is large, $|G_{3j}(x+iy)|$ is proportional to $|y|^{-\delta}$, and $|N_1(x+iy)|$ is proportional to $|y|^{x-3/2+\delta}$. Therefore Inequality 9 will hold if $0 < \delta < (1/2 - x)$. This condition can be satisfied only when $0 < \delta < 1/2$.

If $\delta \geq 1/2$, one could in principle use a modified and more complicated procedure to find $\rho(a)$, although there is no assurance that the resulting expression would be practical for analysis of experimental data.

For spheres (5) and for most generalized cylinders (13), at least one of the Δ_j^2 does not vanish, and therefore Eq. 8 can be applied to samples consisting of particles with these shapes.

For ellipsoids of revolution (14), all the Δ_j^2 vanish and $\delta = 1/2$, and Eq. 8 cannot be used.

Often it is convenient to express the derivatives of $\gamma(r)$ at $r = 0$ in terms of $\overline{F^2(h)}$. As differentiation under the integral sign in Eq. 6 is not possible, a different procedure must be developed.

Because of the conditions which $\rho(a)$ has been assumed to satisfy, when h is large $\overline{F^2(h)}$ will have the asymptotic expansion

$$\overline{F^2(h)} = c_4 h^{-4} + c_6 h^{-6} + c_8 h^{-8} + \ldots$$

Since $\overline{F^2(h)}$ has this form for large h, by induction $\gamma(r)$ can be expressed

$$\gamma(r) = \frac{1}{4\pi\rho^2 V} \sum_{k=0}^{2n+1} \frac{a_k r^k}{(k+1)!} + Q_{n+1}(r) \tag{10}$$

where

$$a_{2k} = (-1)^k (2/\pi) \int_0^\infty dh T_k(h)$$

$$a_{2k+1} = (-1)^{k+1} C_{2k+4}$$

$$T_0(h) = h^2 \overline{F^2(h)}$$

$$S_0(x) = x^{-1} \sin x$$

$$Q_n(r) = \frac{r^{2n}}{2\pi^2\rho^2 V} \int_0^\infty dh\, T_n(h)\, S_n(hr)$$

and where for $n \geq 1$

$$S_n(x) = x^{-2n-1} \left[\sin x - \sum_{k=0}^{n-1} \frac{(-1)^k x^{2k+1}}{(2k+1)!} \right]$$

$$I_n(h) = h^{2n+2} \left[\overline{F^2(h)} - \sum_{k=0}^{n-1} C_{2k+4} h^{-2k-4} \right]$$

As the first 2n - 1 derivatives of $Q_n(r)$ are zero at r = 0, Eq. 10 can be differentiated 2n + 1 times to give the first 2n + 1 derivatives of $\gamma(r)$ at r = 0, with n being zero or any positive integer

From Eqs. 3 and 10,

$$\gamma''(0) = \frac{V_0}{\overline{V}} \gamma_0''(0) \int_0^\infty da\, a\rho(a) = -\frac{1}{6\pi^2\rho^2\overline{V}} \int_0^\infty dh[h^4\overline{F^2(h)} - c_4]$$

$$\gamma'''(0) = \frac{V_0}{\overline{V}} \gamma_0'''(0) = \frac{c_6}{16\pi\rho^2\overline{V}}$$

Thus

$$\int_0^\infty dh[h^4\overline{F^2(h)} - c_4] = -6\pi^2\rho^2 V_0 \gamma_0''(0) \int_0^\infty da\, a\rho(a) \tag{11}$$

and

$$c_6 = 16\pi\rho^2 V_0 \gamma_0'''(0) \tag{12}$$

According to Eq. 11, for any particle shape for which $\gamma_0''(0) = 0$,

$$\int_0^\infty dh[h^4\overline{F^2(h)} - c_4] = 0 \tag{13}$$

For particles with a smooth boundary surface (i.e., a surface with no sharp corners) (7), $\gamma_0''(0) = 0$, and also $\gamma_0'''(0) > 0$, and thus

$$c_6 > 0 \tag{14}$$

Note that Eq. 12 and Inequality 14 do not depend on the form of the diameter distribution function $\rho(r)$.

SPHERICAL-PARTICLES

For spheres (5)

$$\gamma_0(t) = 1 - (3/2)t + (1/2)t^3 \tag{15}$$

Let

$$n(y) = - \frac{d}{dy} [y n_1 (y)]$$

Then

$$n(y) = [\pi^3 \rho^2]^{-1} \left[(1 - \frac{8}{y^2}) \cos y - 4 (1 - \frac{2}{y^2}) \frac{\sin y}{y}\right] \quad (16)$$

From Eqs. 15 and 3

$$\rho(r) = - \frac{\overline{V}}{3V_0} \frac{d}{dr} \left[\frac{\gamma''(r)}{r}\right]$$

Thus, from Eq. 10

$$\left.\frac{d^n \rho}{dr^n}\right|_{r=0} = - \frac{a_{n+4}}{2\pi^2 \rho^2 (n + 2)(n + 5)} \quad (17)$$

From Eq. 15, $\gamma_0'''(0) = 0$ for spheres, and thus Eq. 13 is true for polydisperse assemblies of independent spherical particles.

DISCUSSION

Before Eq. 8 can be used to find the diameter distribution function $\rho(r)$, the shape of the particles must be known, so that $\gamma_0(r/a)$ and $n_1(ha)$ can be computed. Usually sufficient information is available to permit a reasonable choice of particle shape.

The diameter distribution calculated from Eq. 8 is the distribution that would produce the observed scattering for a sample composed of independent, randomly oriented particles with uniform electron density and with the shape that has been chosen. If the sample particles do not have this shape, or if some of the other assumptions about the sample are not satisfied, the calculated $\rho(r)$ may not represent the actual distribution of particle diameters in the sample. As calculations have shown (16, 12) that in certain cases, at least, the scattering pattern is relatively insensitive to large changes in the form of $\rho(r)$, one might expect that relatively small changes in particle shape might sometimes cause large variations in the calculated diameter distribution.

Although the restrictions which were imposed in order to obtain Eq. 8 are sufficient, they may not always be necessary, and in some cases this equation may hold under weaker assumptions. Whenever $\rho(r)$ is expressed as an integral transform of the scattered intensity, however, the transform must converge.

Letcher and Schmidt (8) have recently made a number of tests of Eq. 8 for samples composed of spherical particles. Theoretical scattering curves were used which permitted evaluation of the transform integral both analytically and numerically. Errors in $\overline{F^2(h)}$ were deliberately introduced in order to determine the sensitivity of $\rho(r)$ to errors in the scattering data. The tests indicated that meaningful calculations of $\rho(r)$ can be made when the experimental scattering data are known with an accuracy of at least a few per cent.

The experimental data which are used in Eq. 8 are known only for a certain range of h, which will be denoted by $h_{min} \leq h \leq h_{max}$. Values of the intensity outside this interval of h can be estimated by extrapolation.

The data ordinarily extend to small enough angles to permit a reasonably reliable determination of the radius of gyration. If a linear radius of gyration plot is obtained, the plot can be extrapolated to estimate the scattered intensity for $0 \leq h \leq h_{min}$. Because of the values of $\overline{F^2(h)}$ are multiplied by the factor h^4, for $h \leq h_{min}$ they make a relatively small contribution to the integral and thus need not be known as accurately as the intensity at larger scattering angles.

The form of the outer part of the scattering curve can be estimated by assuming that

$$h^4 \overline{F^2(h)} = c_4 + h^{-2} c_6 + h^{-4} c_8 \qquad (18)$$

for $h \geq h_{max}$. Two conditions for determining the three constants in Eq. 18 are provided by requiring that $\overline{F^2(h)}$ and the slope of $\overline{F^2(h)}$ must both be continuous at $h = h_{max}$. For samples composed of particles for which $\gamma''_0(0) = 0$, Eq. 13

can provide the third relation necessary for finding the three constants. .n c_4, c_6, and c_8.

The scattering curves for any polydisperse system of spherical particles must satisfy Eq. 13. If this relation does not hold, the sample cannot be composed of independent spherical particles with uniform electron density.

Also, since Inequality 14 is satisfied for most particles, if a negative value is obtained for c_6 when an experimental curve is extrapolated, possibly the experimental data may be in error, or the sample may not satisfy some of the assumptions used to derive Eq. 8. While the computed $\rho(r)$ will not automatically be a poor representation of the diameter distribution in the experimental sample when a negative value is found for c_6, some caution must still be used in drawing conclusions from these diameter distributions.

It should be emphasized that Eq. 8 assumes that the scattered intensity is known exactly at all scattering angles. Experimental data never fulfill these conditions, since scattering data ordinarily are accurate within only about one per cent, even under favorable conditions, and the range of accessible scattering angles is limited by the experimental apparatus. Further investigations and tests will be necessary to determine whether use of Eq. 8 is practical for analysis of small angle x-ray scattering data. This method probably should be tested on systems of spherical particles before it is tried with particles with more complex shapes.

Equation 8 has been used with theoretical spherical-particle intensity functions for which the integral in Eq. 8 can be evaluated both analytically and numerically (8). These tests and further tests now in progress indicate that reliable values of $\rho(r)$ can easily be obtained with scattered intensities accurate to 7 significant figures. However, when the error in the intensity data approaches the error likely to be present in experimental scattering curves, the values of $\rho(r)$ near $r = 0$ become unreliable. Nevertheless, the outer part of the $\rho(r)$ curve can still be determined. Attempts are being made to give a relatively precise criterion for determining when the computed $\rho(r)$ curve can be considered reliable.

Since tests of Eq. 8 gave inconclusive results when applied to experimental data from colloidal silica samples containing spherical particles (8), a more extensive series of tests is now under way, in which $\rho(r)$ in several colloidal silica sols will be determined both by Eq. 8 and by electron microscopy.

While a final evaluation of the usefulness of Eq. 8 for finding $\rho(r)$ cannot be made until the method has been tested on a large number of experimental scattering curves, the preliminary results indicate that Eq. 8 may be able to provide a practical method for analyzing small angle x-ray scattering data, especially scattering curves from polydisperse samples of spherical particles.

ACKNOWLEDGEMENTS

The authors would like to thank D. E. Amos, J. E. Thomas, and J. H. Letcher for helpful advice during the course of this investigation. They are also grateful for the computer facilities provided by the Computer Centers of the University of Missouri and Kansas State College of Pittsburg.

REFERENCES

(1) Erdélyi, A., Asymptotic Expansions, Dover Publications, Inc., New York (1956), p. 49.
(2) Guinier, A., Fournet, G., Walker, C. B., and Yudowitch, K. L., Small Angle Scattering of X-Rays, J. Wiley and Sons, Inc., New York (1955), p. 12, eq. (21).
(3) Ref. 2, p. 15.
(4) These results are consequence of Eq. (23), p. 13, of Ref. 2.
(5) Ref. 2, p. 16.
(6) Hosemann, R., Kolloid-Z. 117, 13 (1950).
(7) Kirste, R., and Porod, G., Kolloid-Z. 184, 1 (1962).
(8) Letcher, J. H. and Schmidt, P. W., J. Appl. Phys. 37, 649 (1966)

(9) Luzzati, V., Acta Cryst. **10**, 33 (1957).
(10) Riseman, J., Acta Cryst. **5**, 193 (1952).
(11) Roess, L. C., J. Chem. Phys. **14**, 695 (1946).
(12) Roess, L. C., and Shull, C. G., J. Appl. Phys. **18**, 308 (1947).
(13) Schmidt, P. W., J. Math. Phys. **6**, 426 (1965).
(14) Schmidt, P. W., unpublished research.
(15) Schmidt, P. W., and Hight, R., Jr., J. Appl. Phys. **30**, 866 (1959).
(16) Shull, C. G., and Roess, L. C., J. Appl. Phys. **18**, 295 (1947).
(17) Titchmarsh, E. C., Introduction to the Theory of Fourier Integrals, 2nd Ed., Oxford University Press, London (1948), p. 46, Theorem 28.
(18) Reference 17, p. 60, Theorem 42.

DISCUSSION FOLLOWING PAPER BY O. L. BRILL AND P. W. SCHMIDT

G. Porod: Is there any chance of extending the method to variation in particle shape, too; that is, by representing $\delta_0(r)$ in terms of a distribution of simpler particles? (ellipsoids in terms of spheres?)

P. Schmidt: One could assume that the sample was composed of particles of several shapes. The n_1 (ha) function would then be a linear combination of n_1 (ha) functions for single particles. After the n_1 (ha) function was constructed in this way, the computation of $\rho(r)$ could be computed as outlined in the paper. To represent ellipsoids of revolution as a sum of the scattering from spheres of different diameters, one must use a discontinuous distribution function. [This function is not $\rho(r)$]. Because of this discontinuity, one probably would have convergence problems in computing $\rho(r)$ by our method. In fact, the reason that we encounter convergence problems in ellipsoids of revolution may be connected with this discontinuity.

W. Farone: There appears to be an incorrect mathematical interpretation of the physical situation. It should be realized that a perfect (i.e., errorless) instrument has been assumed and as soon as one tries to account in the analysis for error (which is always present to some degree) not only cannot a unique distribution [$\rho(a)$] be found but an infinite number can be constructed. This is fundamental of this type of analysis and Shifrin points out that there can be only little significance, at best, placed on this type of data treatment. There is no certain connection between the calculated $\rho(a)$ and the physically real ones. This led K.S. Shifrin and A. Y. Perelman to assume the necessary a priori knowledge of the "shape" of the distribution and then calculate the parameters of such a distribution by inversion with known uncertainty. It should be noted that the situation here is somewhat different than that of the analysis used in crystal x-ray work. Here additional constraints are applied and interpretation of results lies in independent experimental checks.

P. W. Schmidt: I don't think Shifrin and Perelman say that Mellin transform methods can never give reliable results.

They merely say that sometimes they won't work. In fact, in their method of small angles, they use a Mellin transform very analogous to ours, and they give figures showing that their results are reasonably reliable. Thus, their paper states, and provides supporting evidence, that methods like theirs and ours can give reliable values for the diameter distribution function.

W. D. Ross: In a crystalline sample, those crystals which are at a Bragg angle to the incident beam will reflect strongly, and therefore appear relatively opaque to the transmitted beam, while the rest will scatter weakly, and will appear relatively transparent. Will this complicate the analysis?

P. W. Schmidt: While this effect may often cause problems in electron diffraction, for x-rays the scattering cross-section is so small that there would be no difficulty.

Scattering of Ruby Laser Light by Spherically Symmetric Gas Molecules*

T. V. George
Gaseous Electronics Laboratory
University of Illinois
Champaign, Illinois

It is well known that when a beam of light passes through a transparent medium, the molecules of the medium interact with the incident beam and scatters light in all directions. Perhaps the simplest of all such phenomena is the scattering of light by particles of extremely small sizes for which a theory was developed by Lord Rayleigh as early as 1872 and almost half a century later it was demonstrated by a laboratory experiment by Cabnnes. In his experiments, as well as in those done by many investigators who followed him, observation was made at right angles to the incident beam. The main problem since then has been suppressing the stray light, spuriously scattered by the walls of the apparatus in directions other than just 90° to permit observation of light scattering by gases at NTP at different angles. In spite of the many modifications which have been on Cabanne's original apparatus, the problem has remained unsolved till recently (1). I would like to present here the principle and the design of an experimental configuration in which such a study was carried out.

---

*This work was supported by U. S. Air Force Cambridge Research Laboratory and the U. S. Army Signal Corps.

In order to acquire a better feeling of the experimental problem, let me go through the classical theory of scattering by spherically symmetric particles having dimensions very small compared to the wavelength of the incident beam. If we have a plane wave polarized in the z-direction incident along the x-axis upon a gas molecule located at the origin, as shown in Fig. 1, the intensity of the scattered radiation per unit incident intensity is obtained as

$$\frac{I}{I_0} \; \frac{k^4\alpha^2}{r^2} \sin^2\theta$$

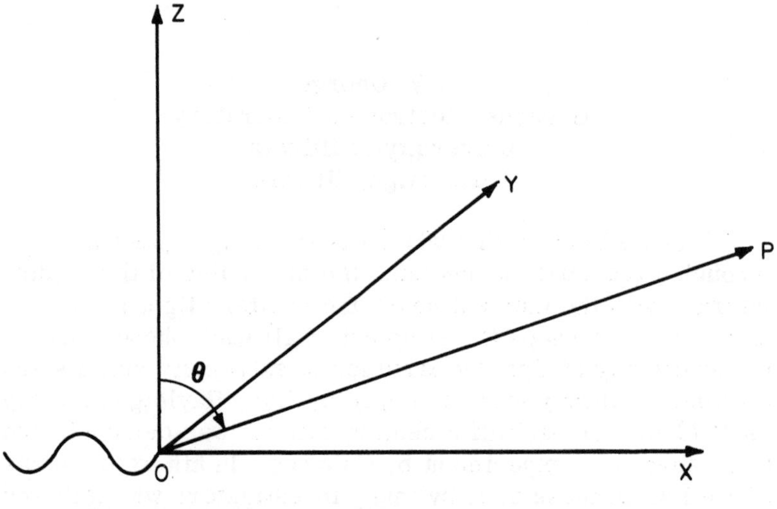

Fig. 1. The coordinate system to which the problems in scattering are referred.

The quantity $k^4\alpha^2 \sin^2\theta$ is known as the differential scattering cross section denoted by $(d\sigma/d\Omega)$. Here k is the magnitude of the wave vector and α the polarizability of the molecule. α is a scalar only if the molecule is spherically symmetric. r is the distance between the scatterer and the observer and θ is the angle between the secondary wave and the direction of polarization. If the molecules of a gas do not interact and if they are randomly distributed in space the light scattered by a large number of molecules would be completely incoherent and the total scattered intensity due to N number of molecules would be N times that of one molecule. For a gas such as argon at NTP if the volume of observation is about 1/10 of a c.c. and if the observation is made about 10 cm from the scatterers the value of this intensity ratio would be of the order of 10^{-12}; whereas the stray light primarily due to the scattering from the entrance window could be as large as 10^{-6} of the incident light. In the present experimental configuration the detectable stray light was reduced to about 10^{-12} of the incident light over a range of 45° to 135° of scattering angle.

The low levels of the scattered radiation which presented problems in detection baffled the experimentalists till the development of lasers and sensitive photomultipliers. In the present experiment, a pulsed ruby laser with the duration of lasering about 200 μsec and total output of 0.1 joule per pulse was employed. Indeed the monochromatic nature of the laser light is an added advantage which the previous experimentalists did not have in studying the absolute scattering cross section of gas molecules.

Careful studies of beam divergence of a ruby laser showed, as seen in Fig. 2, that the intensity of the laser light emitted by the ruby even at an angle of 80° with the forward beam is reduced only by a factor of 10^{-5}. Keeping this fact in mind, the optical system was designed. The next figure (Fig. 3) shows how an iris placed in front of the ruby produces a well defined beam of light. This diverging beam is incident on a lens having a long focal length and emerges as a slowly converging beam. The beam attains its smallest dimension at the plane where the image of the ruby's front surface is formed and the beam diverges thereafter. An iris (Iris 2) placed in between the lens and the image plane shadows the region of observation from the forward scattering of the lens. The exit window is placed at the Brewster angle to maximize the transmission. The backward scattering of the exit window is shadowed over the region of observation by a third iris. Light reflected from the exit window, primarily due to the cross polarized component, is allowed to escape through another window. These are illustrated in Figs. 3, 4 and 5.

Figure 6 shows the complete optical design. The ruby holder is rigidly attached to the brass cylinder-1 which

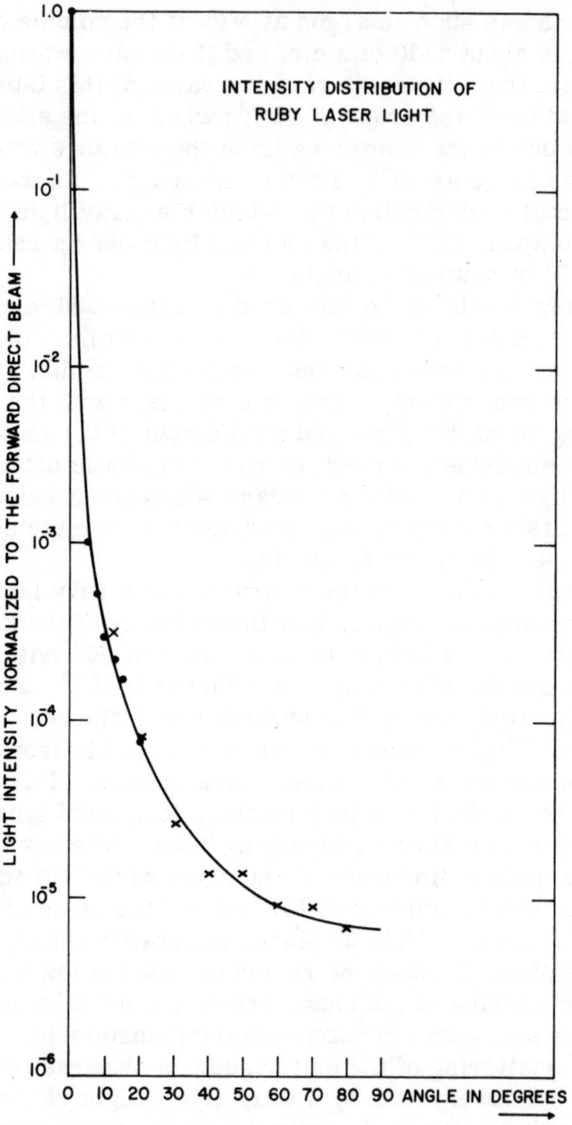

Fig. 2. The intensity distribution of the laser beam normalized to the intensity of the forward direct beam.

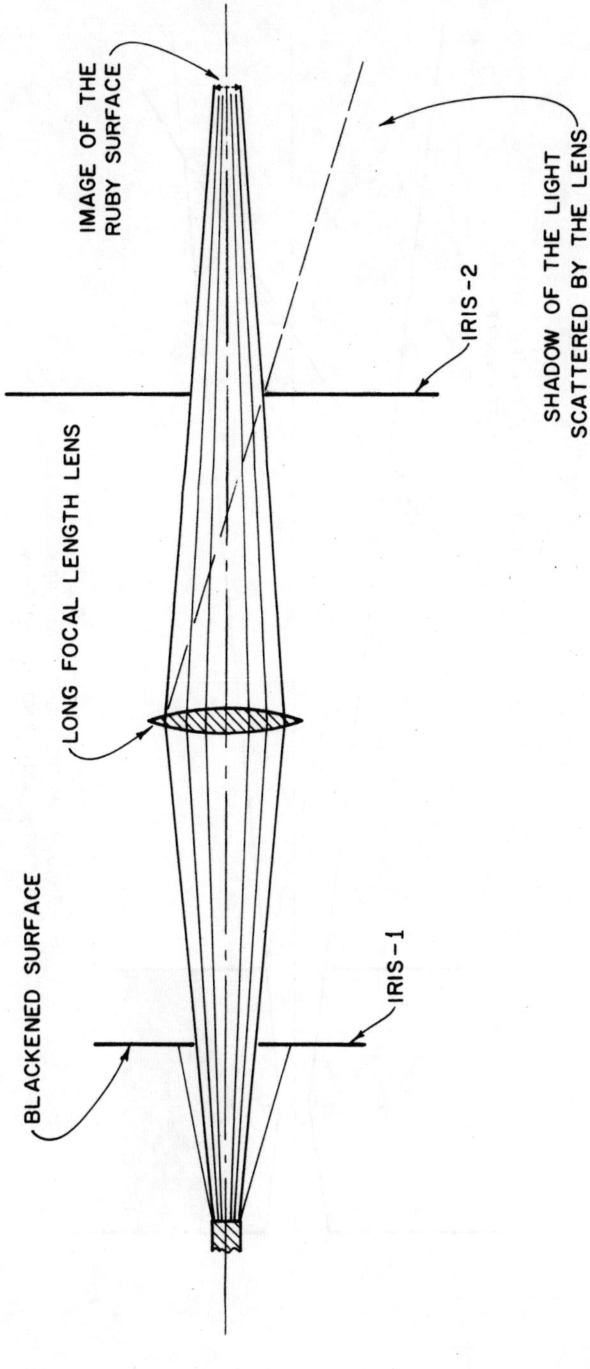

Fig. 3. The formation of shadow due to the forward scattering of the lens.

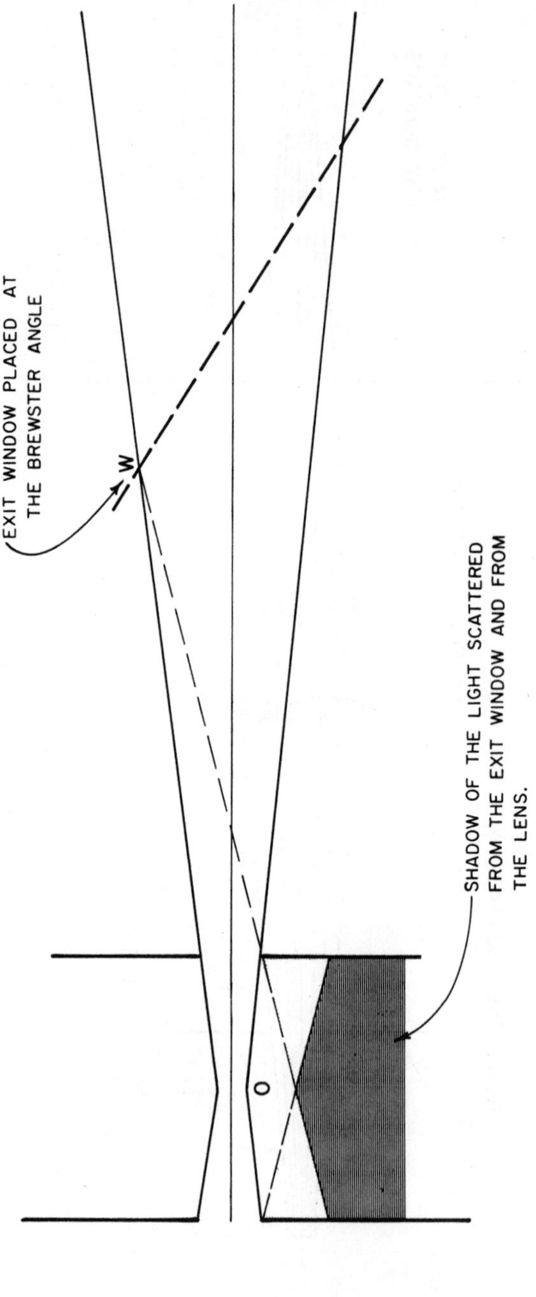

Fig. 4. The formation of shadow due to the backward scattering of the exit window.

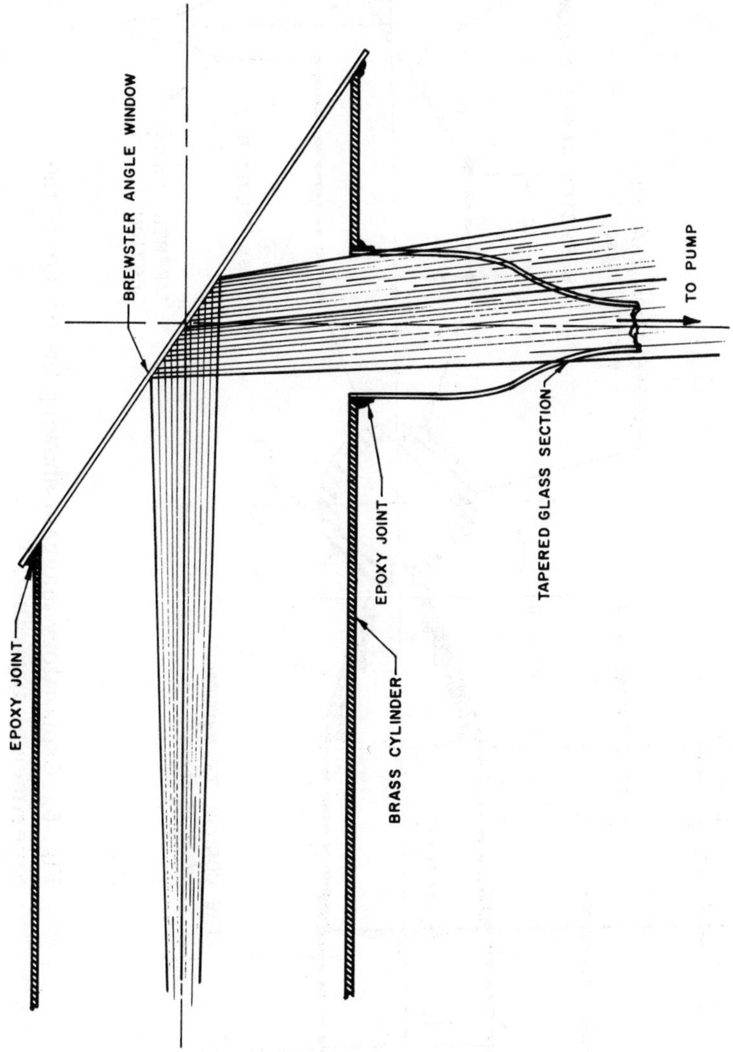

Fig. 5. Illustration of the function of the tapered glass section.

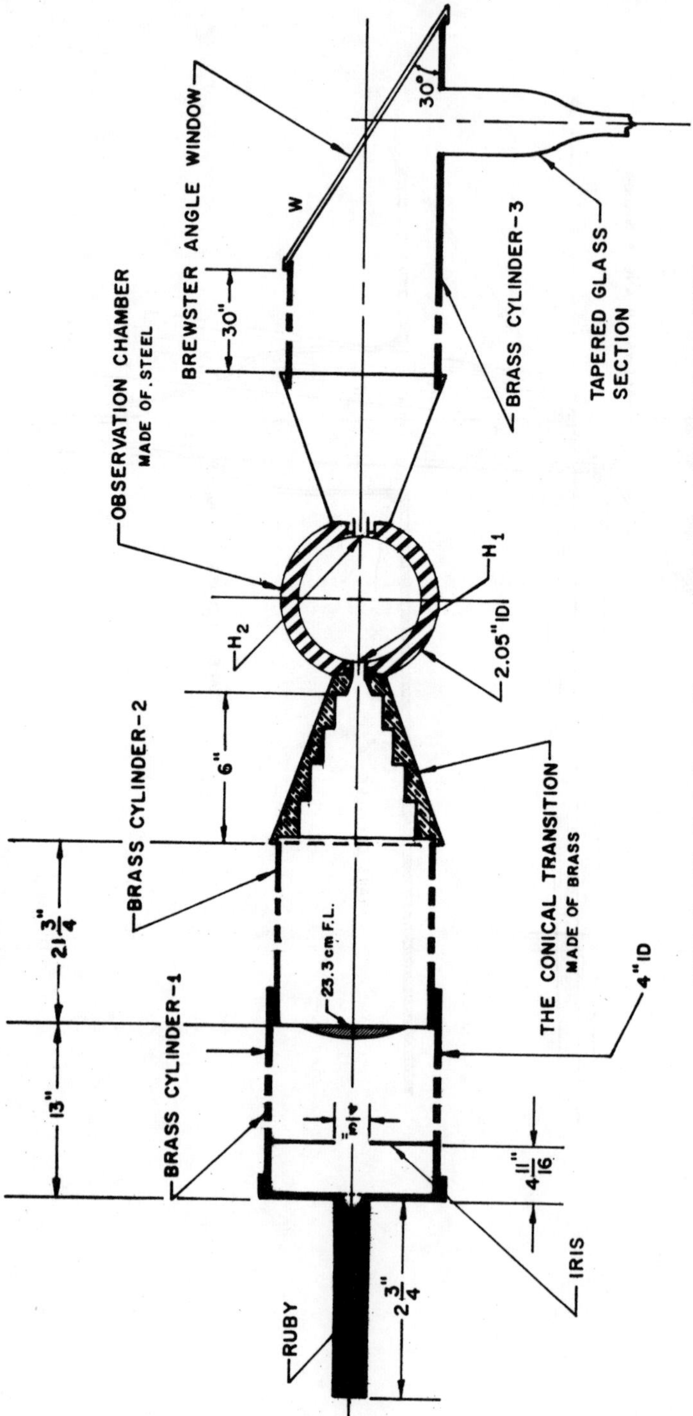

Fig. 6. Explanatory diagram showing the design of the experimental apparatus.

slides over another brass cylinder. An iris of 3/4" diameter is located in cylinder 1, and a lens of 23.3 cm focal length is epoxied on to the end of cylinder 2. Cylinder 2 is connected to the observation chamber through a specially designed connical transition. The inside of the transition is made in steps to minimize the wall scattered light entering the observation chamber. On the diametrically opposite side of the chamber, a similar transition is connected, which in turn is joined to a third cylinder, the end of which is cut approximately at the Brewster angle. A glass window is epoxied on the end and a tapered glass is cemented onto the hole through which the reflected light escapes. The tapered section is connected to the vacuum pump and containers of various gases under investigation. The part of the system from the lens to the exit window can be evacuated. A slight displacement of cylinder 1 with respect to cylinder 2 is possible and was made use of in obtaining proper optical alignment. The most delicate part of this system is perhaps the scattering chamber. The structure of the chamber can be better understood from Fig. 7. Holes are drilled in the walls of the chamber every 15°, where metal tubes of 1/10" in diameter and of equal lengths are welded in. Glass windows are epoxied on to the ends of these tubes. The entire system is mounted rigidly above a circular aluminum table with the observation chamber at the center as shown in Fig. 8. Corresponding to each observation window, a set of two slots is provided on the aluminum table which are used as guides in positioning a photomultiplier. The height of the photomultiplier assembly was so chosen that when it was pushed against the observation window, the orientation of the observation tube was unchanged. RCA 7102 photomultipliers equipped with interference filters centered around 6943 Å were used to monitor the incident beam power and the intensity of the scattered light. The angular distribution of the intensity of the scattered light was studied by moving this photomultiplier from window over the aluminum table.

The capacitors for the xenon flash tubes were charged to an energy corresponding to twice the energy at the threshold of lasering. The experiment was carried out by triggering the laser every sixty seconds.

Fig. 7. The scattering chamber.

Fig. 8. The experimental arrangement illustrating the mounting of the scattering chamber.

The experimental procedure was essentially this. Evacuate the chamber and observe the level of stray light. Then introduce gas at the proper pressure and observe the increase in scattered power normalized to the total incident energy. The particular characteristics of the ruby laser light might suggest that this normalization can be done in two ways. The laser output consists of a large number of random light pulses. Normalization can be performed on each of these individual pulses. The photomultiplier which monitors the incident beam can be operated with a low enough power supply voltage so that the noise at its output is negligible. Due to the low level of the scattered light, we were forced to operate the other photomultiplier in the most sensitive manner; therefore, the output of this photomultiplier possessed noise pulses some of which even resembled pulses. But by comparing the amplitude of only those pulses which were coincident in time, the contribution of noise pulses could be eliminated. The second approach is to integrate the photomultiplier output during the entire duration of lasering and then determine their ratios. The use of an electronic integrator and subsequent normalization were found to be much simpler. So this technique was utilized in the present experiment.

In spite of the great care taken in the construction of the scattering chamber, it was considered well worth the effort to check the alignment of the scattering chamber. This was done by studying the light scattered from a glass rod placed in the scattering chamber so that it was colinear with the laser beam. An ordinary light source was used to illuminate the glass rod by sending light through one of the ends. The results are shown in Fig. 9. The solid line shows the angular dependence of the intensity of the scattered light when the incident light flux was in the same direction as that of the laser beam and the dotted line when the incident light flux was in the reverse direction. It was found that the windows of the chamber did not transmit light equally and therefore a prior experiment had to be done to determine the correction factors. This variation was indeed taken into account in plotting these curves. The symmetry of the curves with respect to 90° (angle measured from the forward direction

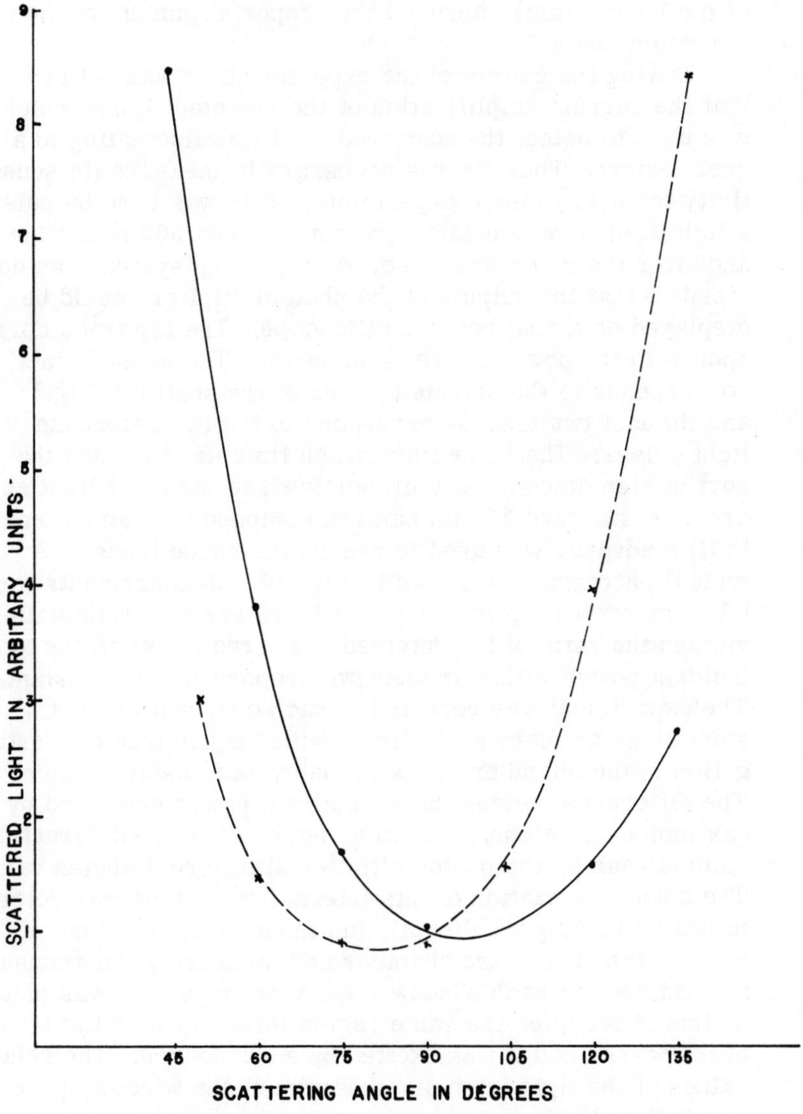

Fig. 9. Angular distribution of light scattered from a glass rod with incident beam in the same direction as the laser beam (solid line) and with the incident beam reversed (dotted line).

of the laser beam), assured the proper alignment of the observation tubes.

During the course of the experiment, it was noticed that the current amplification of the photomultiplier which was used to detect the scattered light was fluctuating to a great extent. Thus, it was necessary to measure its sensitivity for every single experiment. This was done by pulsing a light source of constant light output about 300 m sec before and after the laser was fired. A triggering system was devised so that the outputs of the photomultipliers could be displayed on a dual beam oscilloscope. The top trace corresponds to the power in the laser beam. The second trace corresponds to the detected power of the scattered light and the last two traces correspond to the two reference light pulses. The large integration time used yielded the sort of step discontinuity proportional to the input light energy. A standard 35 mm camera equipped with an automatic film advance was used to record the scope traces. A typical photograph is shown in Fig. 10. Measurements were taken by projecting the film on a large screen. Calculations yielded the ratio of the detected scattered power to the total incident power within an unknown proportionality constant. The experiment was repeated at each observation port, sometimes as many as 15 times with the gas under investigation in the chamber and with the system under vacuum. The difference yielded the normalized power scattered by gas molecules alone. It is to be noticed that the interaction volume seen by the photomultiplier at different angles varies. The angular variation of this interaction volume was determined by placing a uniformly luminous discharge tube of 4 mm in diameter in the chamber and measuring the amount of light seen at each window. The discharge tube was placed so that it occupied the same region through which the laser beam passed and it was excited by a DC source. The relative values of the light intensity observed at the windows gave the correction due to the variation of scattering volume and light transmission through the windows at different angles. Taking into account all these corrections the angular variations of differential scattering cross sections for argon and xenon were determined.

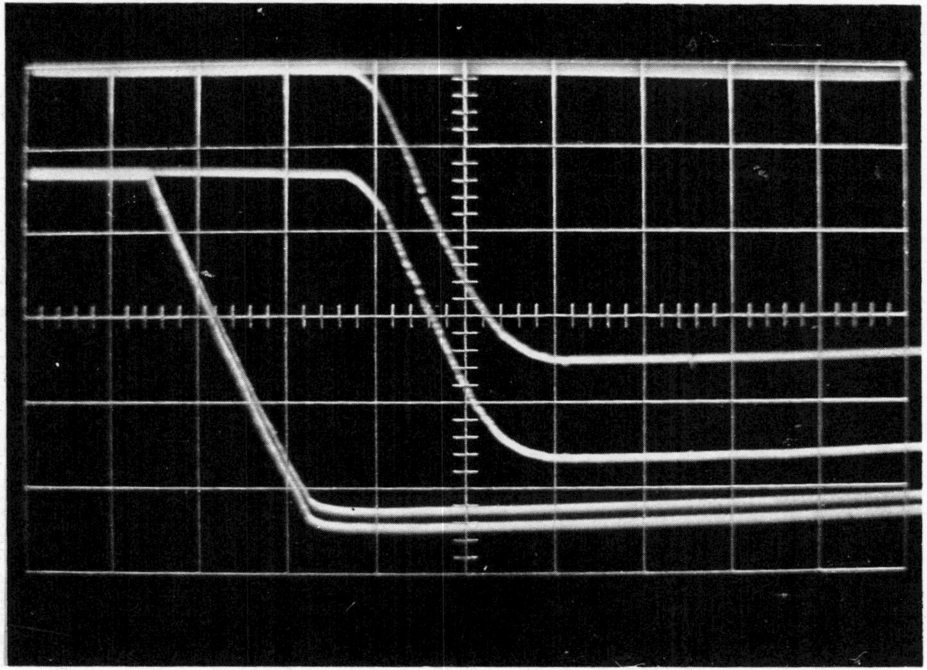

Fig. 10. Oscilloscope traces of the photomultiplier outputs. The deflection of the top two traces correspond to the total power in the laser beam and the detected power of the scattered light respectively. The bottom two traces are the responses of the photomultiplier to the "standard" light source.

The elementary theory outlined earlier predicts that the angular variation of the intensity of the scattered light will be proportional to $\sin^2\theta$ where θ is the angle between the direction of the secondary ray and the direction of polarization. That would mean, if the observation is performed in the plane of polarization and χ is the scattering angle, then the differential scattering cross section would vary as $\cos^2\chi$. On the contrary, if the observation is made in the plane perpendicular to the plane of polarization, the value of θ would be 90° for all scattering angles and the differential scattering cross section should remain constant.

Figure 11 shows the angular distribution of observed scattered power per unit volume normalized to the value at 90° scattering angle for argon at one atmosphere, when the laser was vertically polarized and the observation was done in the horizontal plane. The large uncertainities were mainly due to fluctuations in photomultiplier amplification factor. The study indicated that the experimental results did not agree with the theory. Similarly the study in xenon at 135 mm Hg pressure (Fig. 14) indicated that there was an enhancement of differential scattering cross section in the forward direction. The studies were conducted with the horizontally polarized beam and again the observation made in the horizontal plane in these two gases yielded the results given in Fig. 12 and Fig. 13. The vertical bar corresponds to the product of the values obtained in the experiment with the vertically polarized beam and the square of the respective scattering angle. The solid line is a theoretical line which agrees with the prediction in the other polarization. The measured values are shown without their associated uncertainties for clarity. It is seen that the measured values can very well agree with either of the two curves.

If there was any positional correlation between the scatterers (2) it should show up in a study of the variation of scattered power with pressure, since the interparticle distance varies as the cube root of pressure. Figure 15 shows the variation of scattered power at the scattering angle of 135° in argon up to one atmosphere. The next figure (Fig. 16) shows the same as 45° in SF_6 also up to one atmosphere. The linear variation of scattered power with pressure can

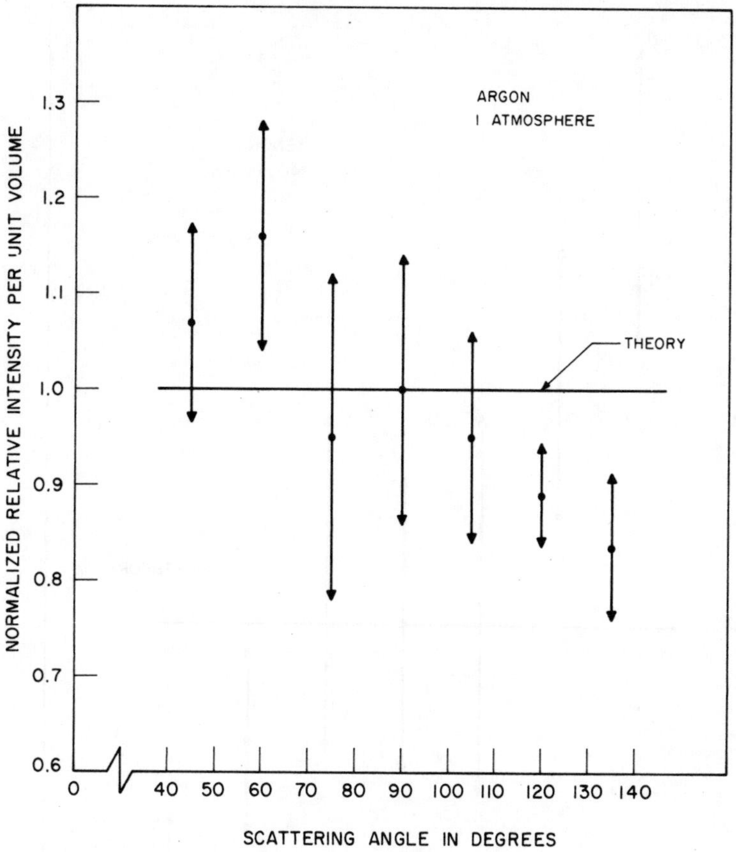

Fig. 11. Angular distribution of the intensity of scattered light for vertically polarized incident beam in argon at 1 atm.

rule out the effects due to positional correlation of scatters at these pressures. The determination of the differential scattering cross section of gases was done essentially by calibrating the two photomultipliers with respect to each other, determining the field of view of the photomultiplier, detecting the scattered radiation and measuring the solid angle each scatterer subtends at the detector. The first

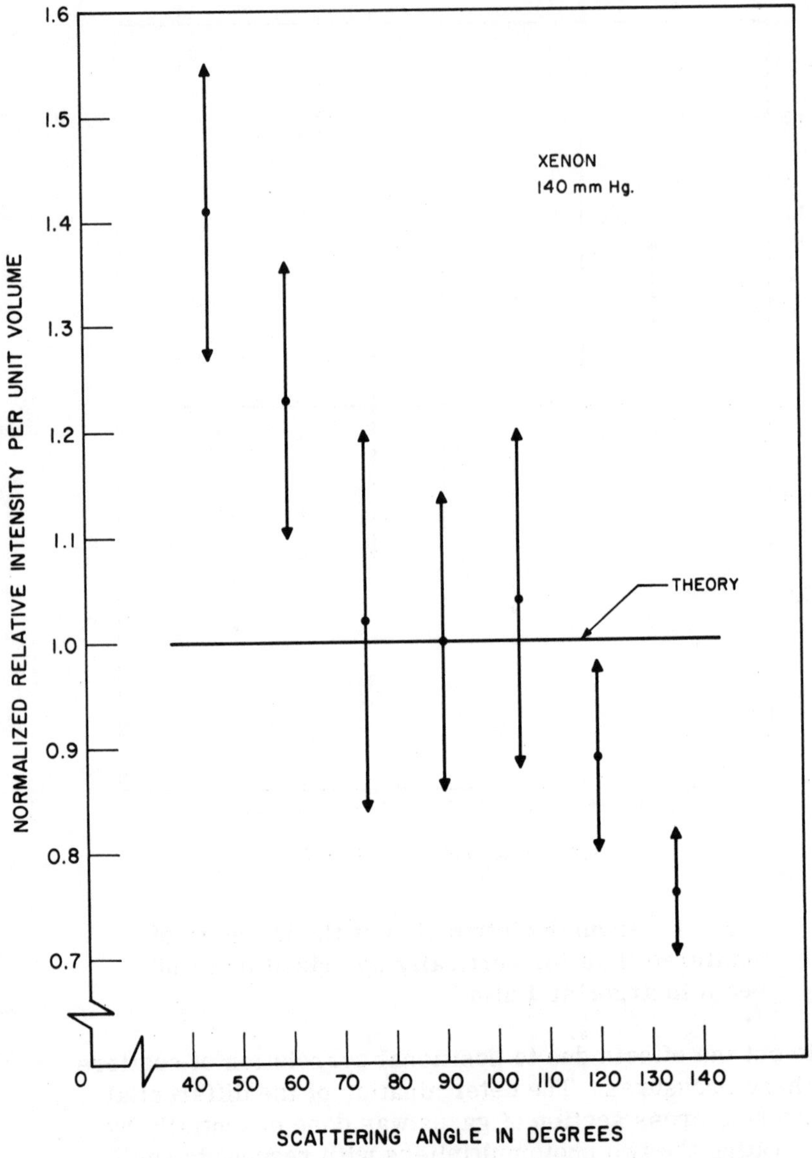

Fig. 12. Angular distribution of the intensity of scattered light for vertically polarized incident beam in xenon at 140 mm Hg.

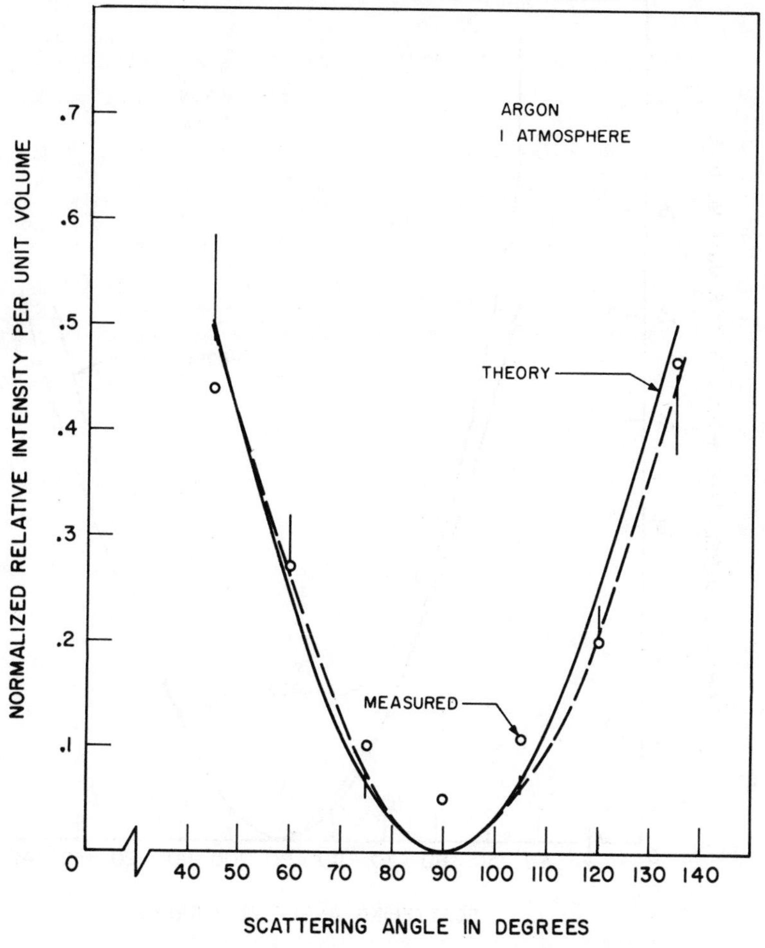

Fig. 13. Angular distribution of the intensity of scattered light for horizontally polarized incident beam in argon at 1 atm.

aspect was performed by the experimental system shown in Fig. 17. The laser beam was deflected downwards and was passed through a saturated solution of copper sulphate of known thickness. The emerging beam was focussed on the photocathode of the same photomultiplier used to detect

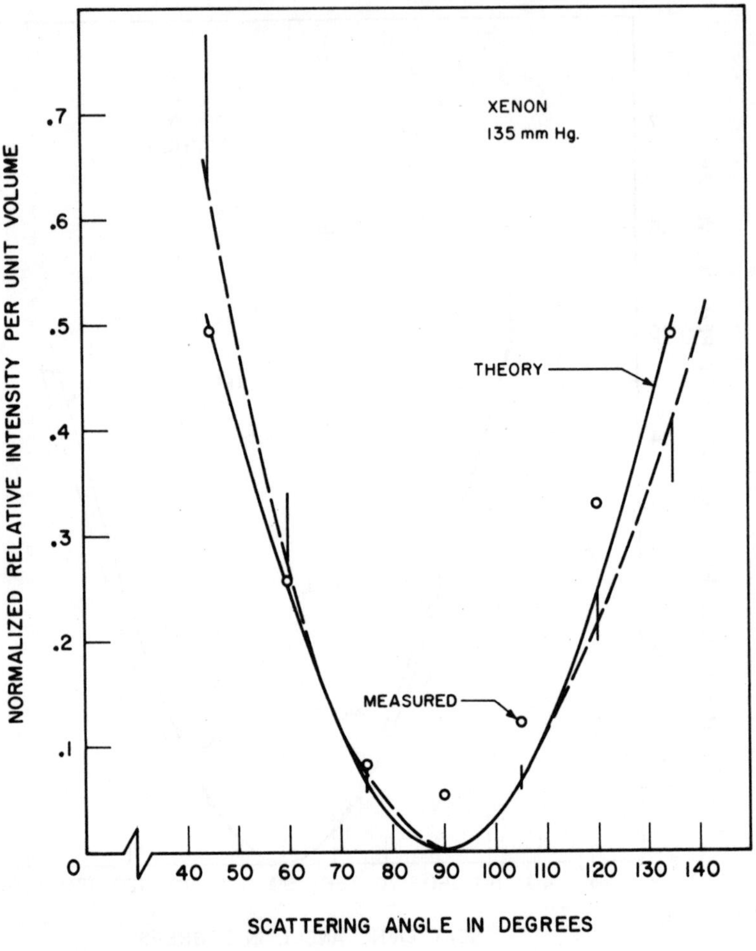

Fig. 14. Angular distribution of the intensity of scattered light for horizontally polarized incident beam in xenon at 135 mm Hg.

scattered light, operated in the identical manner. The ratio of the photomulitplier outputs were determined as a function of the height of the copper sulphate solution. Figure 18 shows the ratio plotted on a semilog scale. The value of this ratio as the height of copper sulphate solution tends to

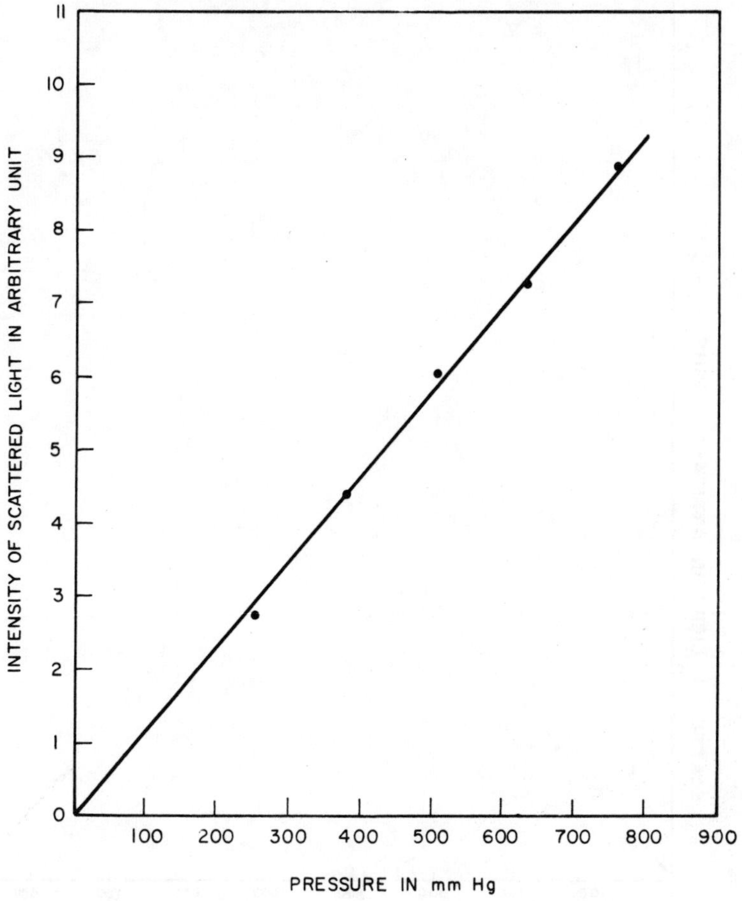

Fig. 15. Pressure dependence of the intensity of scattered light at 135° with the incident beam in argon at room temperature.

zero, which was calculated by the method of least mean square error, corresponds to the total intensity of the incident beam on the scale by which the scattered radiation was measured. For the next part, ideally a point source should be moved along the path of the laser beam inside the chamber.

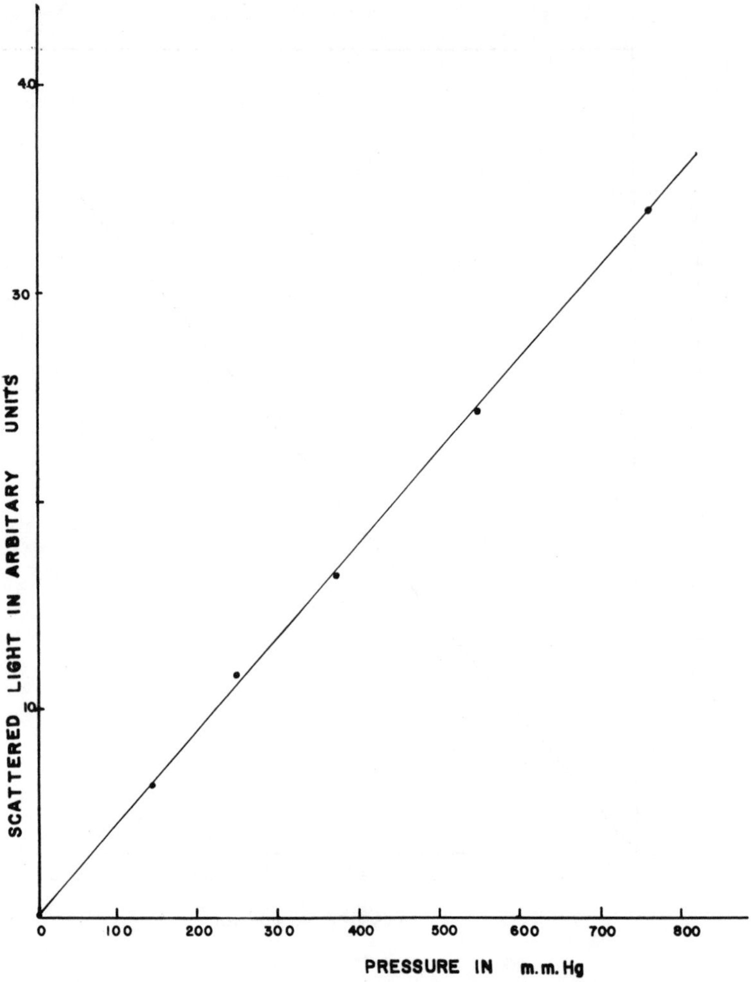

Fig. 16. Pressure dependence of the intensity of scattered light at 45° with the incident beam in sulphurhexafluoride at room temperature.

Due to practical difficulties, however, the field of view determination was done outside the chamber. An identical tube was used in the same manner and a source of 1/3 mm diameter was moved across and along the dotted line as shown in Fig. 19. Figure 20 shows the relative response

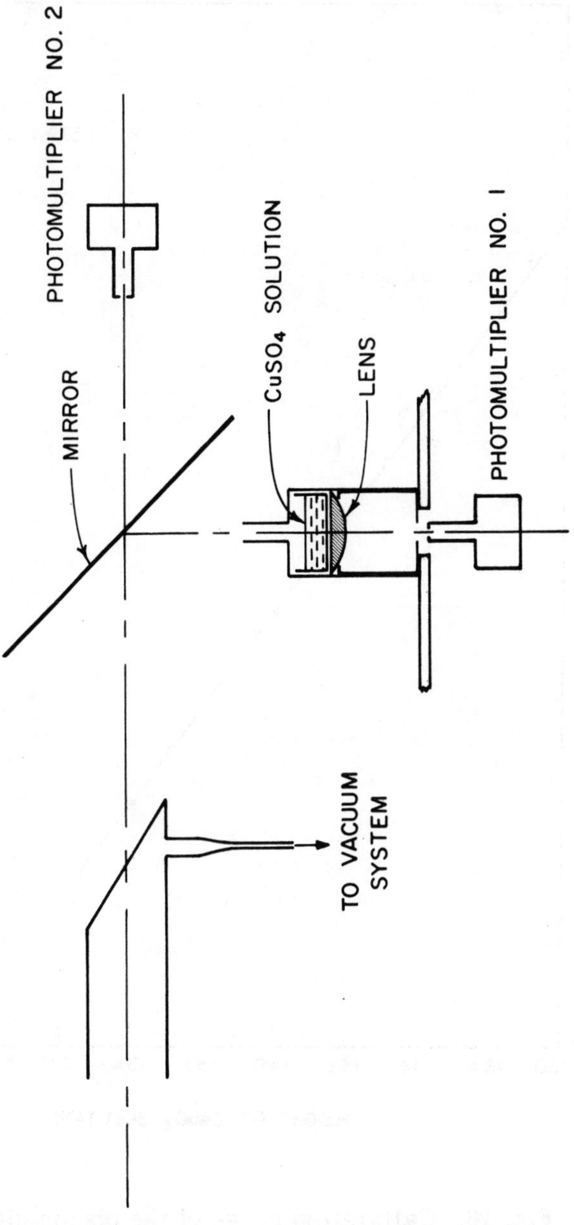

Fig. 17. Experimental setup for the calibration of the photomultiplier.

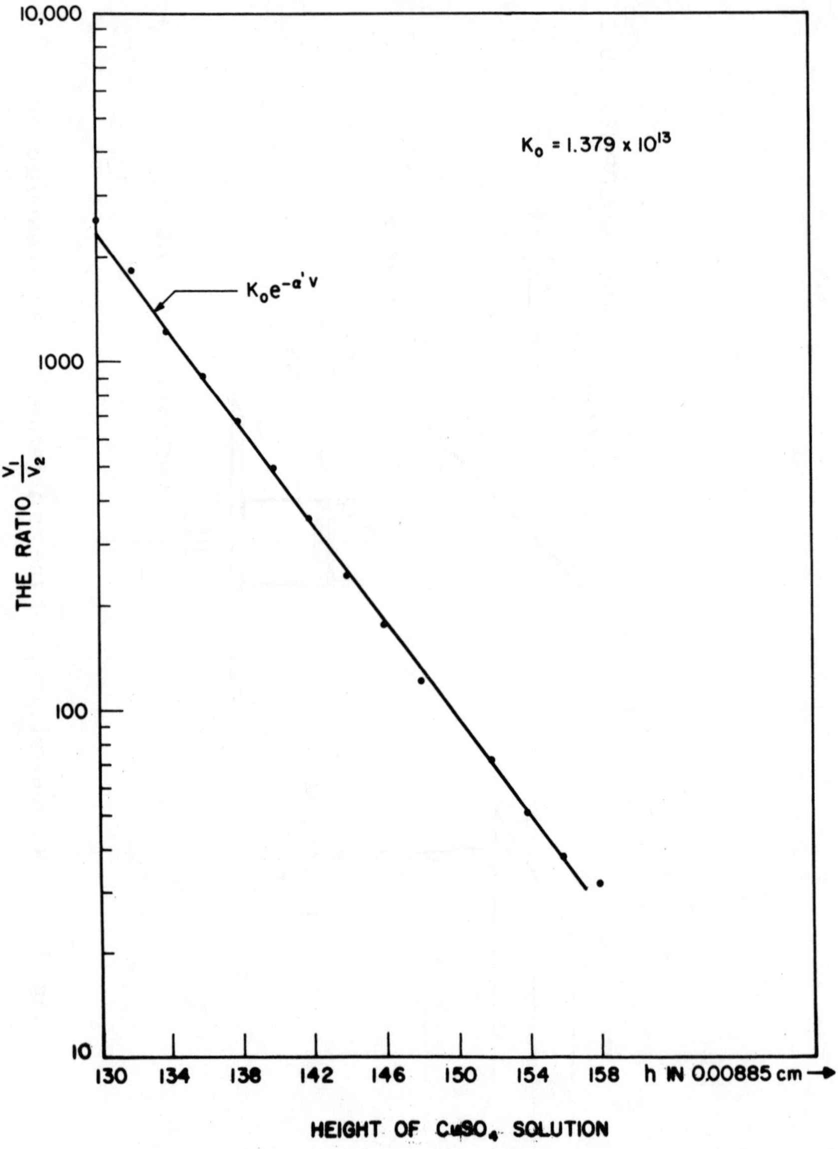

Fig. 18. Calibration curve of the photomultiplier.

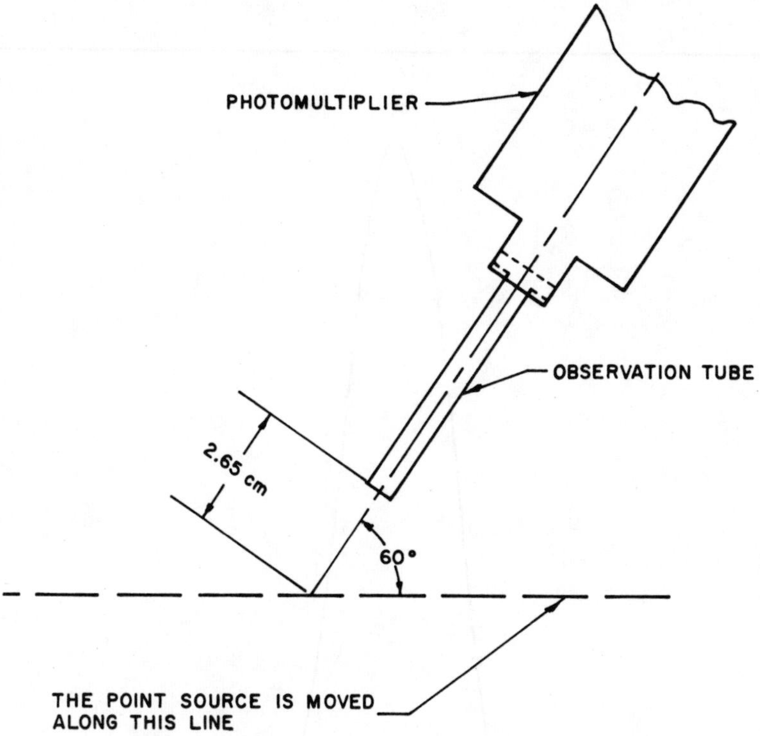

Fig. 19. Experimental arrangement for the determination of the field of view of the photomultiplier.

of the photomultiplier. Indeed scattered radiation detected from a molecule located slightly away from the center will be of a different angle than that at the center. These were taken into account and a graphical integration was employed to determine the differential scattering cross section of various gases at the scattering angle of 60° with the incident beam polarized in the plane of observation. The results are shown in Table 1. Values of α, the scalar polarizability, were calculated using the Clausius Mossotti equation for noble gases and the obtained theoretical values are shown here along with the experimental values. The experimental

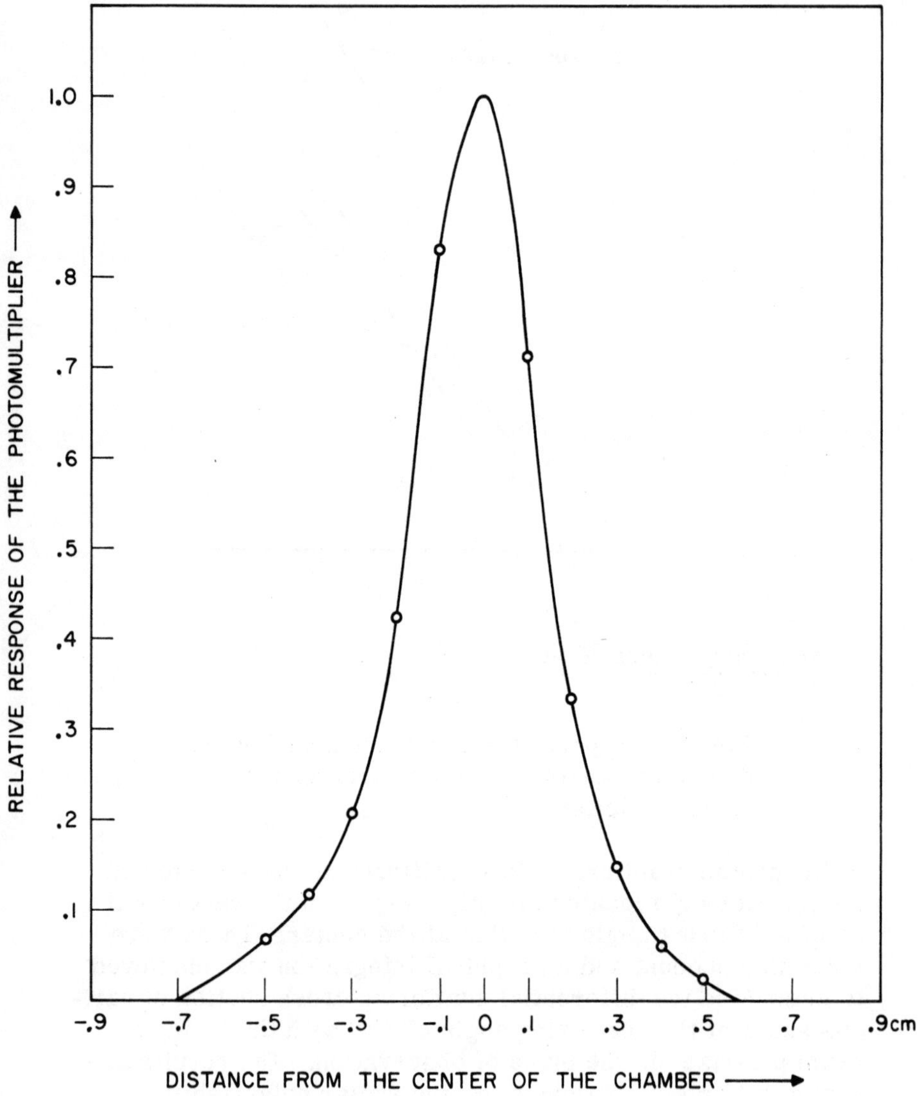

Fig. 20. Molecular scattering of ruby laser light.

TABLE 1

Differential Scattering Cross Section for Various Gases

Gases	Ne	Ar	Xe	O_2	N_2	Air	CO_2	SF_6	C_3H_8
Experimental values in 10^{-28} cm^2	0.048	0.843	5.71	0.90	1.04	1.03	2.76	6.08	19.6
Theoretical values in 10^{-28} cm^2	0.027	0.47	2.88						

values. The experimental errors should not be greater than 35 per cent. Hence there seem to be discrepancies between the values which are not accounted for so far.

For the first time we have conducted a systematic study of Rayleigh's theory under experimental circumstances which perhaps are not the best possible but certainly the best available; and an established theory doesn't quite agree with the experimental results. I would assume you will agree with me if I ask the question, not 'what is wrong with the theory?' but what are the possible errors?' The first is the presence of dust in the gas under investigation. To study the effect of dust, a pair of electrodes of about 2 cm in diameter were placed in the chamber approximately 2 cm apart, one above and the other below the laser beam. A high voltage supply which could go as high as 5 KV was connected to these electrodes. Dust was artifically produced by striking an arc between the electrodes. Immediately following that, the voltage was reduced to zero and then increased to, say 1500 volts so that the dust particles, if they are charge would be swept away. If there were some uncharged dust particles, in order that the electric field may act upon them, a strong source of radioactive material was placed directly below the scattering chamber and the observation of scattered light was done for extended periods of time. The scattered intensity steadily decreased form the time of the arc. The experiment showed that the influence of dust was negligible within a few hours. So also, observed ratios of differential scattering cross sections of different noble gases agreed within a few per cent with the theoretical values. If the contribution of dust had been substantial such an agreement would not be possible. Perhaps the next question would be whether we are causing some nonlinearities to show up with an intense laser beam. This was tested on a pulse by pulse normalization basis explained earlier and it was found that a sevenfold increase in the intensity of the incident laser pulses showed substantially no change in the cross section. In the noble gases, depolarization, if there was any, was negligible. In order that the ruby would emit light of the same wavelength every time, the laser was uniformly cooled and triggered. The study of the angular dependence was made with the laser operated by an electric timer. In the event that the frequency broadening of scattered signal would correspond to more than 50 Å and was angularly dependent, it would show up in the angular intensity distribution. Careful study showed that the broadening was far less than 50 Å which was the bandwidth of the interference filters used in the experiment.

In spite of the availability of lasers and sensitive photomultipliers, there still remained the problem of designing an optical system in which the stray light was reduced to a tolerable level over a wide angular range to put Rayleigh's theory into test for the first time. Adequate improvements of the experimental system and additional experiments on the topic will have to be done before fully establishing the reason for the observed discrepancies between the experimental results presented here and an established theory of Rayleigh.

REFERENCES

(1) George, T. V., Goldstein, L., Slama, L. and Yokoyama, M., Phys. Rev., 137, A369 (1965).
(2) Theimer, O., Phys. Rev. Letters, 13, 622 (1964).

DISCUSSION FOLLOWING PAPER BY T. V. GEORGE

R. T. Jacobson: How were the pre- and post-laser calibration flashes conducted to the photomultiplier? The above question was asked in view of the extreme sensitivity of photomultiplier output with respect to the position on the photo cathode at which the radiation is incident. This is especially important for small diameter beams. In this experimental set up the replacement of the photomultiplier housing for each angle would necessitate rather strict precautions in this respect.

T. V. George: The standard light source was placed at the window directly opposite to the one where the photomultiplier was located. This would assure that the light from the source falls almost within the region of the surface of the photo cathode illuminated by the scattered light from the chamber. The areas of illumination would also be concentric. The beam diameter falling on the photo cathode was slightly larger than 1/10" in diameter. Of course a better photomultipler assembly can be made in which one can be sure that these problems are fully taken care of.

R. Stein: I'd like to suggest using the technique of Buckingham in which a CW gas laser is used with the scattering chamber within the laser cavity. This has been used successfully for 90° measurements and should be extendable to measurements at other angles.

T. V. George: For the study of the angular distribution of scattered light, it is necessary that this incident light flux be unidirectional. In an ordinary gas laser this condition is not satisfied if the chamber is placed in the cavity. However, a special gas laser using more than one discharge tube and an optical uniline can be constructed for this purpose.

L. Oppenheimer: Will the use of an optical system in front of the laser not defeat the advantages of using a laser as the light source?

T. V. George: The use of a laser was not to make use of the coherence properties of the light beam. The laser was simply looked upon as an intense source of radiation producing a monochromatic parallel beam of light.

F. S. Harris, Jr: Did I understand that you claimed to have reduced the scattered light in your system by 10^{-13} ?

T. V. George: Yes. The scattered light observed when the system was evacuated was of the order of 10^{-13} times the power in the incident beam.

W. Irvine: Did you attempt to reduce the intensity of the incident laser beam in order to see if this would reduce presumed non-linear effects?

T. V. George: The only study that was performed in which the laser intensity was varied was on the value of differential scattering cross section at a specified angle. The intensity was varied by a factor of seven and no substantial variation in the value of the cross-section was observed.

M. Kerker: Can you be certain that spurious reflections arising from the primary scattered radiation being reflected from the equipment may not be important?

T. V. George: If such reflections from the primary scattered radiation occur, it should be observed both in the forward and the backward direction. One might expect the effect to be more noticable in the backward direction since the distance between the chamber and the exit window is about 28". This would imply a further enhancement of scattering in the forward direction. The inside of the apparatus was painted black. This should be sufficient to suppress such reflections to a level far below the level of the observed scattered light due to gas alone. Hence, I believe such reflections can be ignored.

C. A. Plint: For liquid benzene we find that the vertical component of scattered light is independent of scattering angle from 45° to 135° and that the horizontal components varies as the cosine squared. We have always used incoherent sources. What is your comment? Would you comment on Theimers criticism of an earlier experiment of the type described in your talk?

T. V. George: Other experiments on Rayleigh scattering from low-turbidity molecular liquids also agree with your results (R.C.C. Leite, et al., Phys. Rev. Letters, **14**, 7 (1965)). Dr. Theimer showed that coherence can produce deviations from Rayleigh's theory under certain conditions (O. Theimer, Phys. Rev. Letters, **13**, 622 (1964)). In our experiment we have not been able to conclusively verify his theory.

The Impulse Response Concept in Single-Body Scattering *

Edward M. Kennaugh
Antenna Laboratory, Ohio State University, Columbus, Ohio

ABSTRACT

A time-dependent response or signature is defined for a scattering object as the waveform observed at a fixed scattering angle when the object is illuminated by an impulsive plane wave. The physical properties of the scatterer are related to its signature, using spheres and other simple shapes as examples. The effect of illuminating signal waveform upon scattering can be determined from the impulse response, and the relation between response waveform and physical properties of a scatterer is discussed.

INTRODUCTION

It has been customary to classify scientists, as well as theoretical techniques in electromagnetic scattering, according

---

*The work reported in this paper was supported in part by Contract AF 19(628)-4002 between The Ohio State University Research Foundation and Air Force Cambridge Research Laboratories, Office of Aerospace Research.

to which end of the spectrum they are applied. To remove some of these artificial boundaries between radio physics and optics, we suggest a common approach to analyses of single-body scattering which embraces the whole spectrum. In this approach, one seeks a relation between the physical shape of an object and its electromagnetic scattering properties for transient or aperiodic incident plane waves. A typical interrogating waveform is the Dirac delta-function, corresponding to an impulsive source; step function and ramp function sources may also be employed. If the scattered field at a distant point is now determined, its waveform contains the complete spectral "signature" of the object. Using convolution, the scattered signal for arbitrary incident waveforms can then be determined. We imply, of course, a fixed spatial relation between source, observer and scatterer; different response waveforms are obtained for different orientations.

In this paper, we shall describe the transient scattering concept, present a few specific results for special scatterer shapes, and suggest possible applications for its future use. Further details of theory and its applications will be found in the literature (5, 6).

SCATTERING OF TRANSIENT PLANE WAVES BY A FINITE OBJECT

Adopting the body-fixed coordinate system of Fig. 1, an incident plane wave travels in the positive z-direction with an x-directed electric field intensity. The scattered field intensity $\mathbf{E}^s$ at a large distance from the origin is observed. If f (t) denotes the variation of E^i_x at the plane $z = 0$:

$$\mathbf{E}^i = f(t - z/c)\hat{\mathbf{x}},$$

and at a sufficiently large distance r from the origin,

$$\mathbf{E}^s = (1/r)\left[V_\theta(\theta, \phi; t - r/c)\hat{\theta} + V_\phi(\theta, \phi; t - r/c)\hat{\phi}\right].$$

In a particular scattering direction (θ_0, ϕ_0), selecting a

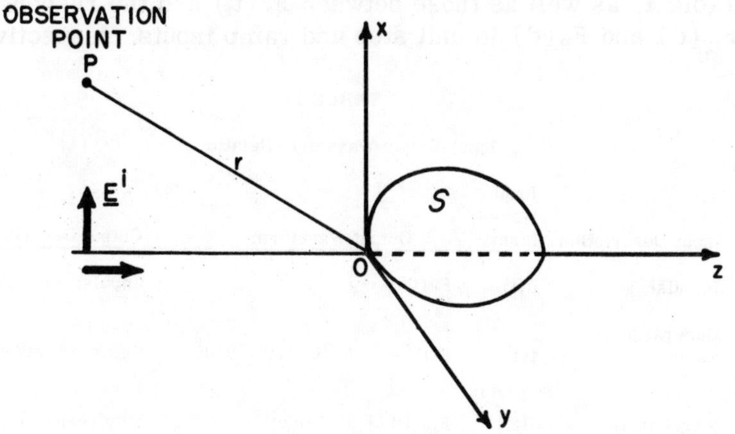

Fig. 1. Coordinate system

transverse component of $\mathbf{E}^s$, a response waveform $F(t - r/c)$ is defined:

$$F(t - r/c) = \lim_{r\to\infty} (2r/c)\ (\mathbf{E}^s \cdot \hat{\xi}),$$

where $\hat{\xi}$ is the unit transverse vector. The relation between $F(t - r/c)$ and $f(t)$ is that of output and input, respectively, in a one-dimensional linear system. The time delay r/c is characteristic of a distributed constant system. We shall include this delay implicitly, using a time scale $t' = t - r/c$ for the output waveform.

Let us assume an impulsive incident plane wave, for which $f(t)$ has the form of a Dirac delta-function:

$$\mathbf{E}^i = \delta(t - z/c)\hat{\mathbf{x}},$$

$$f(t) = \delta(t).$$

The corresponding output waveform is called the impulse response waveform $F_I(t')$, which is the complete spectral signature of the scatterer for the orientation and wave polarization selected. It is "complete" because the scattered waveform for any input waveform $f(t)$ can be determined through convolution with $F_I(t')$. These relations are summarized in

Table 1, as well as those between $F_I(t')$ and the responses $F_U(t')$ and $F_R(t')$ to unit step and ramp inputs, respectively.

TABLE 1

Input-Output Waveform Relations

Input Description	Input Wave-form	Output Waveform	Output Description
Impulse	$\delta(t)$	$F_I(t')$	Impulse response
General plane wave	$f(t)$	$F(t') = \int_{-\infty}^{\infty} F_I(u)\, f(t' - u)\, du$	Response waveform
Step Function	$U(t)$	$F_U(t') = \int_{-\infty}^{t'} F_I(u)\, du$	Step response
Ramp Function	$tU(t)$	$F_R(t') = \int_{-\infty}^{t'} F_U(u)\, du$	Ramp response
Monochromatic Plane Wave	$\cos \omega t$	$G(j\omega) = c \int_{-\infty}^{\infty} F_I(u)\, e^{-j\omega u}\, du$	Phasor response

The phasor response $G(j\omega)$ of Table 1 is the complex amplitude of the monochromatic scattered field, related to the differential scattering cross section σ by:

$$\sigma = \pi |G(j\omega)|^2 .$$

It is usually convenient to choose a coordinate system such that the first reflection from the scattering object arrives after $t' = 0$, insuring that the impulse response waveform is identically zero for $t' < 0$. In this case, the lower limit on integrals for output waveforms in Table 1 may be set to zero; $G(s)$ and $cF_I(t')$ then are a (single-sided) Laplace transform pair.

Since $G(j\omega)$ and $F_I(t')$ are equivalent forms for the description of scattering properties, one may ask whether the proposed use of $F_I(t')$ has any advantage over the conventional formulation, which employs $G(j\omega)$. This question may best be resolved by means of an example for which both $G(j\omega)$ and $F_I(t')$ can be evaluated and compared. The perfectly conducting spherical scatterer is an ideal example for this purpose. Using the classical formulation of Mie and modern, high-speed digital computers, it is possible to calculate values of $G(j\omega)$ for arbitrary scattering angles and for wide ranges of electrical size (7). A typical plot of $|G(j\omega)|$ for back scattering is presented in Fig. 2. It is difficult to relate the oscillations of Fig. 2 to the spherical shape, except to note a fairly regular interference between a constant component and one which diminishes with increasing source frequency. The equivalent impulse response waveform $F_I(t')$ is presented in Fig. 3, as a function of t'/t_0, where t_0 represents the transit time for one sphere diameter. At $t' = 0$, a negative impulse of magnitude $t_0/2$ is indicated by an arrow. This corresponds to a specularly reflected replica of the incident wavefront. There is also a discontinuous jump of 1/2 at $t' = 0$, following the specular impulse and characteristic of all conducting spherical surfaces. The waveform varies smoothly for $0 < t' < 2.57t_0$, as currents induced on the spherical surface by the incident wavefront produce radiation in the back scattering direction. At $t' \doteq 2.6t_0$, radiation produced by currents associated with a traveling wave reaches a sharp maximum. This corresponds closely to the time of arrival of a wave which has traveled along the surface of the sphere in the shadow region at the free-space velocity c. The radiation diminishes rapidly after $t' = 2.7t_0$, leaving a slowly decaying component which is quite small for $t' > 5t_0$. We see that the impulse response waveform of Fig. 3, while equivalent to the graph of Fig. 2, is more directly related to the geometrical form of the scatterer. Further, the innate simplicity of the waveform suggests that simpler methods than the Mie formulation may be found to obtain $F_I(t')$, or a good approximation, in many cases.

Another comparison between $G(j\omega)$ and $F_I(t')$ may be made at a scattering angle of 30° from the back scattering direction, in the plane of the incident electric field vector. The graph of $|G(j\omega)|$, shown in Fig. 4 for this case, is less regular than that of Fig. 2, and even more difficult to interpret. The graph of $F_I(t')$ in Fig. 5, however, shows that the traveling wave maximum is now split into two peaks, which occur at $t' \doteq 2.38t_0$ and $t' = 2.85t_0$. These correspond to waves

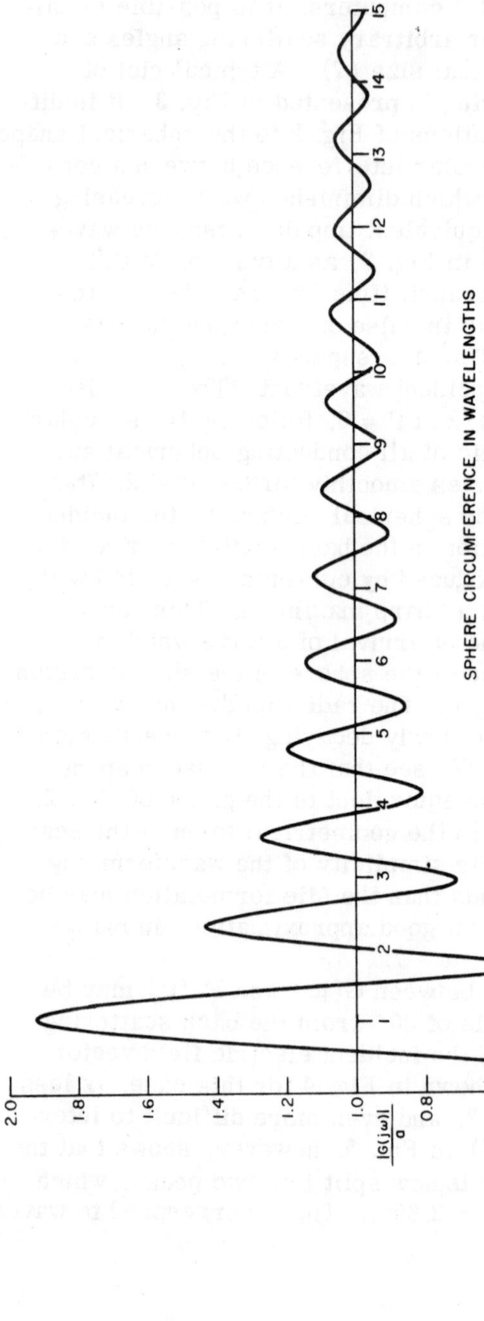

Fig. 2. Magnitude of phasor response versus circumference in wavelengths, backscattering by conducting sphere of radius a.

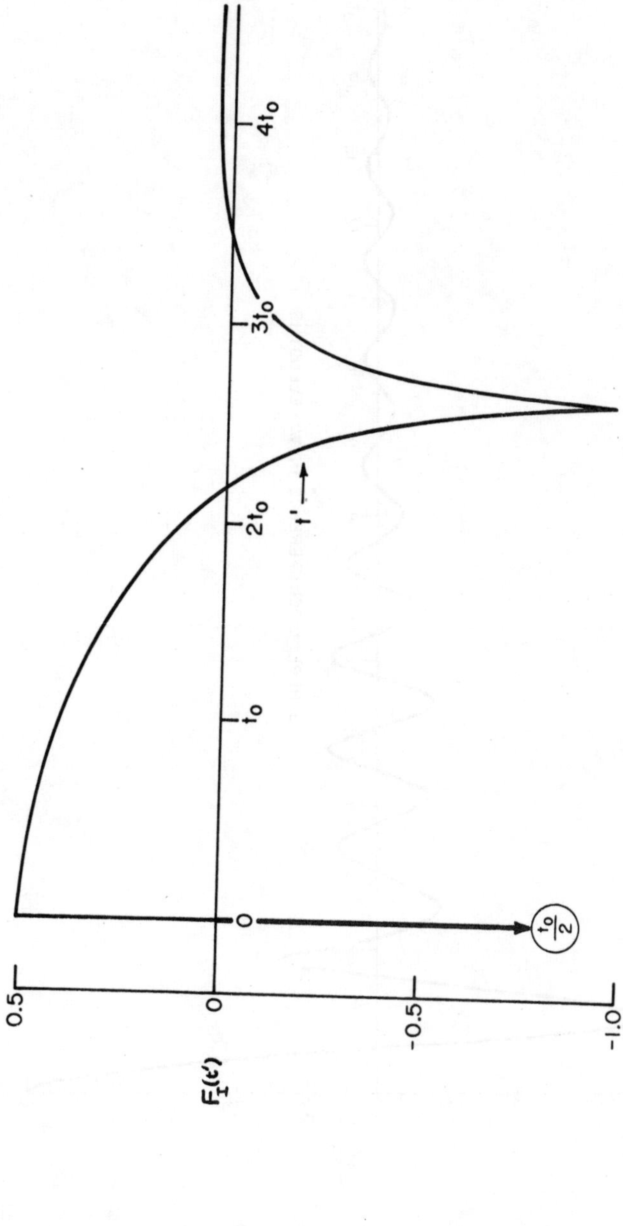

Fig. 3. Backscattered impulse response waveform, conducting sphere.

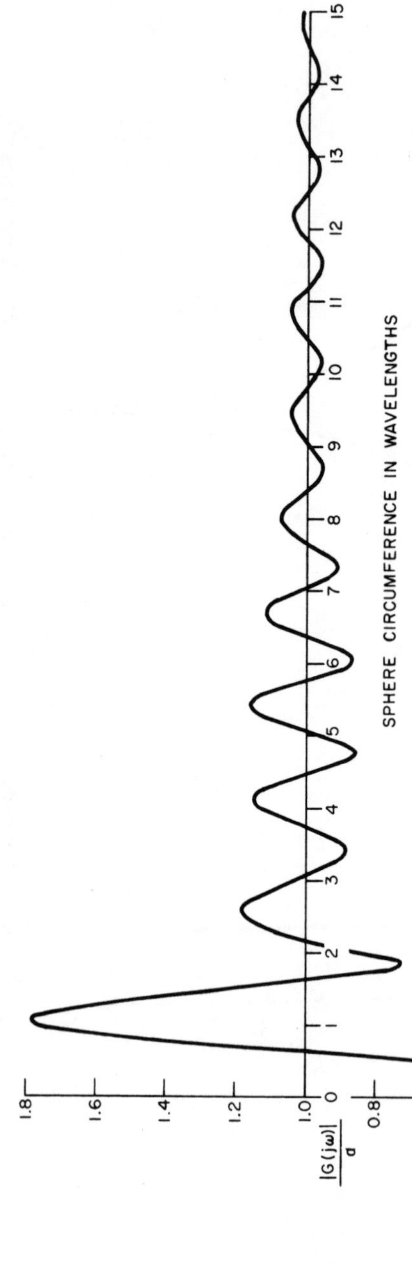

Fig. 4. Magnitude of phasor response versus circumference in wavelengths, E-plane at 30° from backscattering direction, conducting sphere of radius a.

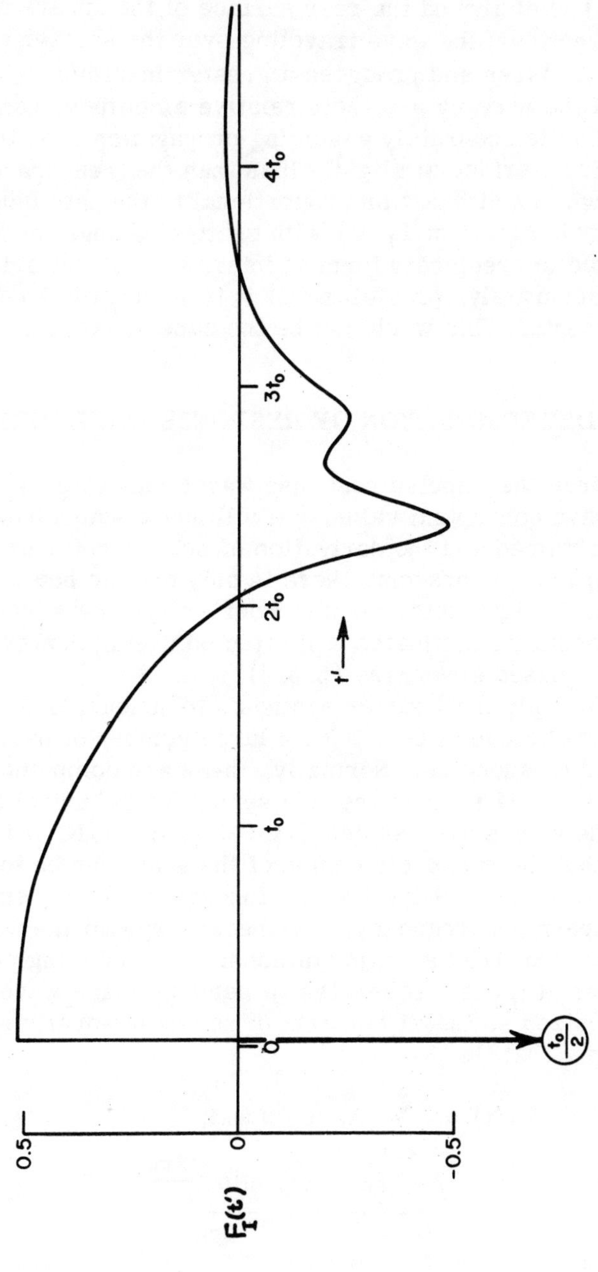

Fig. 5. Impulse response waveform at 30° from backscattered direction in E-plane, conducting sphere.

which travel around the rear surface of the sphere in different directions; the wave traveling over the shorter path is attenuated less and produces a greater maximum. The location of the maxima and their relative amplitudes can be predicted quite accurately assuming propagation over the rear spherical surface at slightly less than the free-space velocity, with an attenuation proportional to the path length. The regular behavior of $F_I(t')$ with scattering angle makes it possible to predict its form at intermediate scattering angles quite accurately, providing that it is accurately known at 30° increments. This would not be the case, however, for $G(j\omega)$.

DETERMINATION OF RESPONSE WAVEFORMS

Since the impulse response waveforms of Figs. 3 and 5 may have conceptual value, we will now discuss how these were obtained and the derivation of such waveforms for other scatterers. At present, there is only one method which yields results of high accuracy: the Fourier synthesis technique. Less accurate estimates will often be useful, however, and are discussed elsewhere (5, 6, 4).

To apply the Fourier synthesis technique, one requires accurate values of $G(j\omega)$ for a large number of harmonically related frequencies. Normally, these are computed from an exact formula such as the Mie series for spherical scatterers. If these values are denoted $G(jn\omega_0)$, $n = 1(1)N$, it is necessary that the major dimension of the scatterer be less than 1/10 wavelength at the lowest (fundamental) frequency. At the uppermost frequency, it is necessary that the wavelength be less than 1/5 the major dimension. Combining plane wave sources at these frequencies, a periodic plane waveform is synthesized so that it consists of series of equally spaced short pulses. That is,

$$f(t) = \sum_{n=1}^{N} A_n \cos n\,\omega_0 t,$$

$$A_n = \left(\frac{N^3}{N^2 - 4n^2}\right) \frac{\sin\left(\frac{2\pi n}{N}\right)}{2\pi n}$$

In the limit, as $N \to \infty$, this periodic waveform approaches a series of unit impulses, spaced at intervals of $2\pi/\omega_0 = \Delta t$. Since Δt exceeds $10t_0$, where t_0 is the transit time for the major scattering dimension, the response waveform will usually decay to zero between successive impulses, and each cycle of the periodic response waveform will approach the impulse response waveform, as $N \to \infty$. The effect of finite N is similar to that produced if the impulse response waveform were passed through a low-pass filter: some distortion of impulses in the output waveform and a finite rise time for step-type discontinuities. Fortunately, these can be corrected if the high frequency scattering properties are known. Thus, the impulse response waveform of Fig. 3 was obtained using N = 475, while that of Fig. 5 was obtained using N = 64, making minor corrections in the neighborhood of impulse and step discontinuities.

In Fig. 6, the form of the impulse response function for other scattering directions in the two principal scattering planes is shown (3). These waveforms include the low-pass filter distortion of impulses and step discontinuities, corresponding to N = 64. Note the absence of traveling wave effects in the plane of the incident magnetic field vector. More than 64 harmonics would be required to completely resolve the detail near the forward scattering direction.

While accurate values of $G(j\omega)$ at a large number of frequencies are required to obtain accurate impulse response waveforms using Fourier synthesis, ramp response waveforms can be obtained more easily and with less input data.

A sawtooth waveform is in fact a periodic succession of ramp functions of alternating polarity. Providing that the spacing Δt is significantly larger than the duration of a ramp response waveform, the ramp response can then be determined from the response to such a waveform. In Fig. 7, the back-scattered ramp responses for a number of different objects are shown as calculated by this technique. The sawtooth waveform for the incident field was approximated by combining 5 frequencies in harmonic ratio 1:3:5:7:9; calculated values for $G(j\omega)$ for only five frequencies were required. The ratio of maximum dimension to fundamental wavelength ranged from 0.08 to 0.20; in some instances a lower fundamental

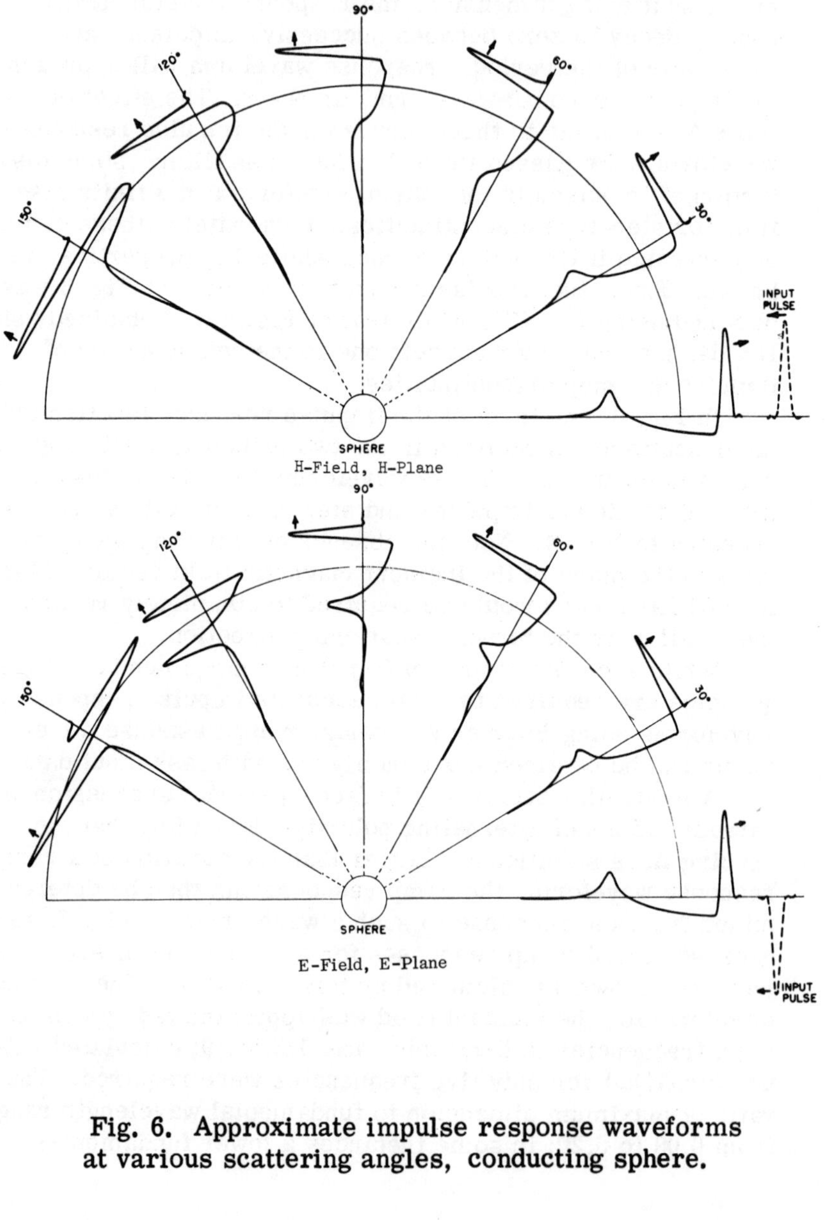

Fig. 6. Approximate impulse response waveforms at various scattering angles, conducting sphere.

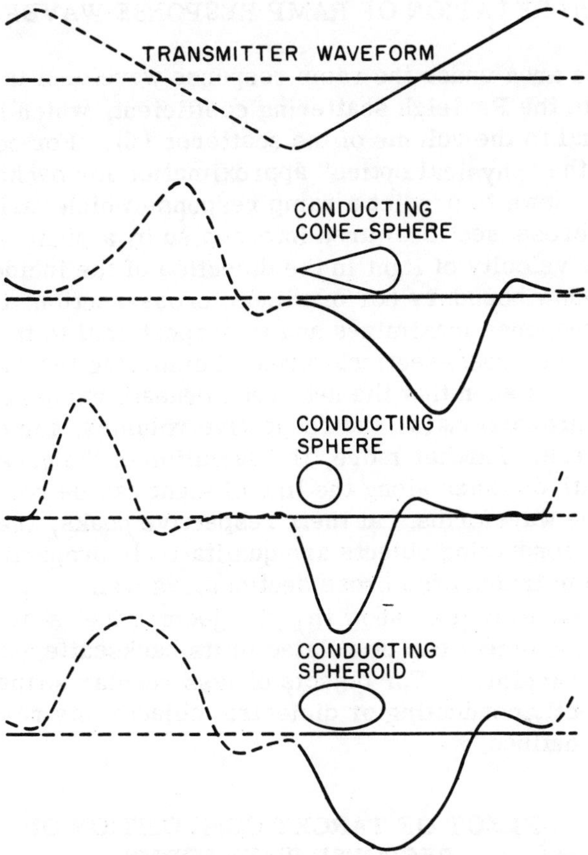

Fig. 7. Approximate ramp response waveforms backscattered by conducting objects.

frequency would be advantageous. A comparison of the exact backscattered ramp response waveform for the conducting sphere and one half-cycle of the waveform shown in Fig. 7 shows only minor differences. Since reasonable approximations to the ramp response can be obtained from relatively few values of G(jω), one might attempt to synthesize the ramp response from experimental data. The backscattered ramp response of an object may also be related to its physical shape and composition, as we shall now discuss.

INTERPRETATION OF RAMP RESPONSE WAVEFORMS

The area under the ramp response waveform is proportional to the Rayleigh scattering coefficient, which in turn is proportional to the volume of the scatterer (6). For conducting objects, the "physical optics" approximation for backscattering can be shown to predict a ramp response which varies with time as the cross-sectional area intercepted by a plane moving at one-half the velocity of light in the direction of the incident wave.* At the shadow boundary (or maximum cross-section) the predicted ramp response maximizes and is proportional to the maximum transverse cross-sectional area. Comparing the waveforms of Fig. 7, it is seen that the net areas beneath ramp responses are indeed proportional to the respective volumes, for conducting scatterers. Further more, the variation of the cross-sectional area with distance along the line of sight can be roughly estimated from the waveforms. At their respective peaks, the ramp responses for conducting objects are qualitatively proportional to the maximum transverse cross sections, as well.

These examples show that the geometrical shape of smooth conducting object can be related to its backscattered ramp response waveform. For objects of less regular shape, or for imperfectly conducting or dielectric objects this relation is less clearly defined.

EFFECT OF TARGET COMPOSITION ON RESPONSE WAVEFORMS

If a backscattered impulse response waveform is synthesized for a dielectric sphere, in a manner similar to that by which Fig. 2 was obtained, some rather unusual results are obtained. In Fig. 8, the response waveform for a sphere with a refractive index $n = 1.486$ is shown as obtained using values of $G(j\omega)$ for 64 harmonics. Note that the initial portion of the waveform, for $0 < t' < 2t_0$ is similar to that for

*Actually, a silhouette area function rather than a cross-sectional area is defined if the perimeter of the moving section is partially shadowed.

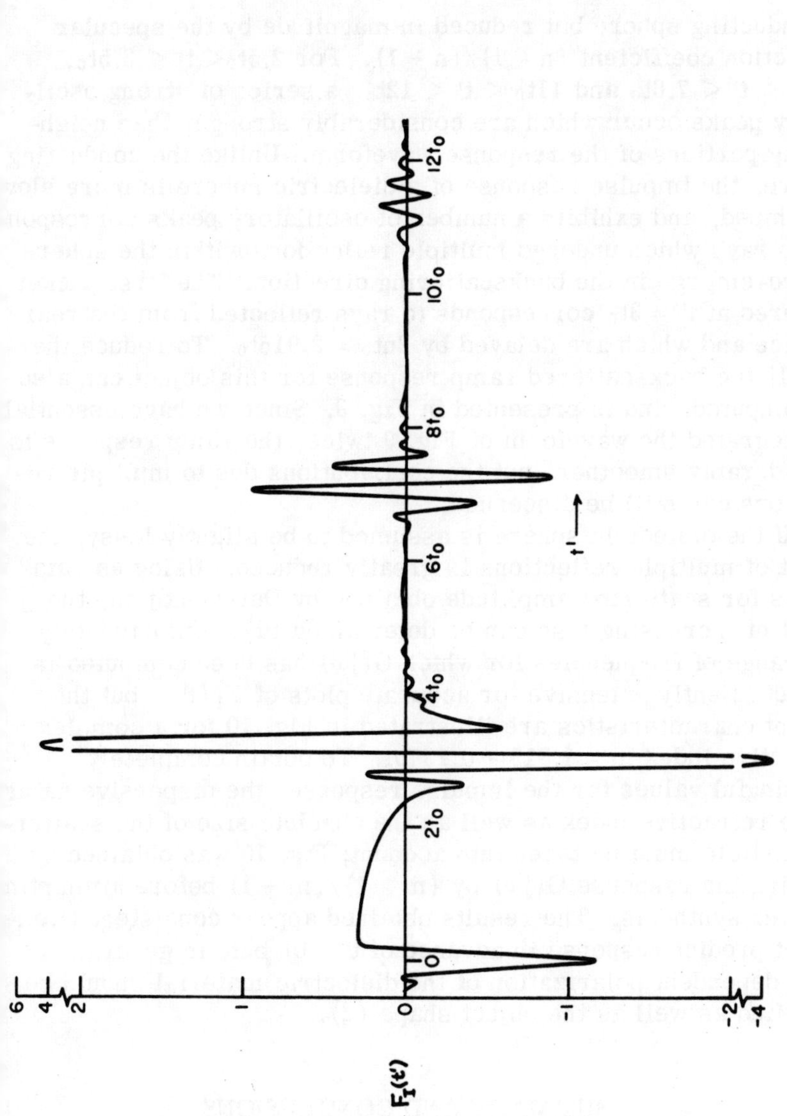

Fig. 8. Approximate impulse response backscattering by a dielectric sphere of refractive index 1.458.

a conducting sphere but reduced in magnitude by the specular reflection coefficient $(n - 1)/(n + 1)$. For $2.5t_0 < t' < 3.5t_0$, $6.5t_0 < t' < 7.6t_0$ and $11t_0 < t' < 12t_0$, a series of strong oscillatory peaks occur which are considerably stronger than neighboring portions of the response waveform. Unlike the conducting sphere, the impulse response of a dielectric sphere is more slowly damped, and exhibits a number of oscillatory peaks corresponding to rays which undergo multiple reflections within the sphere and re-emerge in the backscattering direction. The first packet centered at $t' = 3t_0$ corresponds to rays reflected from the rear surface and which are delayed by $2nt_0 = 2.916t_0$. To reduce the detail, the backscattered ramp response for this object can also be computed, and is presented in Fig. 9. Since we have essentially integrated the waveform of Fig. 9 twice, the ramp response is considerably smoother, but the contributions due to multiple reflections can still be discerned.

If the dielectric sphere is assumed to be slightly lossy, the effect of multiple reflections is greatly reduced. Using as data values for scattering amplitude obtained by Deirmendjian, the effect of increasing loss can be determined (1). Unfortunately the range of frequencies for which $G(j\omega)$ has been computed is not sufficiently extensive for accurate plots of $F_I(t')$, but the salient characteristics are illustrated in Fig. 10 for a complex refractive index $m = 1.315 - 0.1370i$. To obtain completely meaningful values for the impulse response, the dispersive nature of the refractive index as well as the absolute size of the scattering particle must be taken into account; Fig. 10 was obtained by dividing the response $G(j\omega)$ by $(m - 1)/(m + 1)$ before attempting Fourier synthesis. The results obtained appear consistent (i.e., do not predict response in advance of $t' = 0$) but, in general, a time-dependent polarization of the dielectric material should be specified as well as the object shape (2).

SUMMARY AND CONCLUSIONS

The use of transient response waveforms to describe the scattering properties of objects offers certain advantages over conventional descriptions. The geometrical properties of the scatterer may be related to certain features of the backscattered

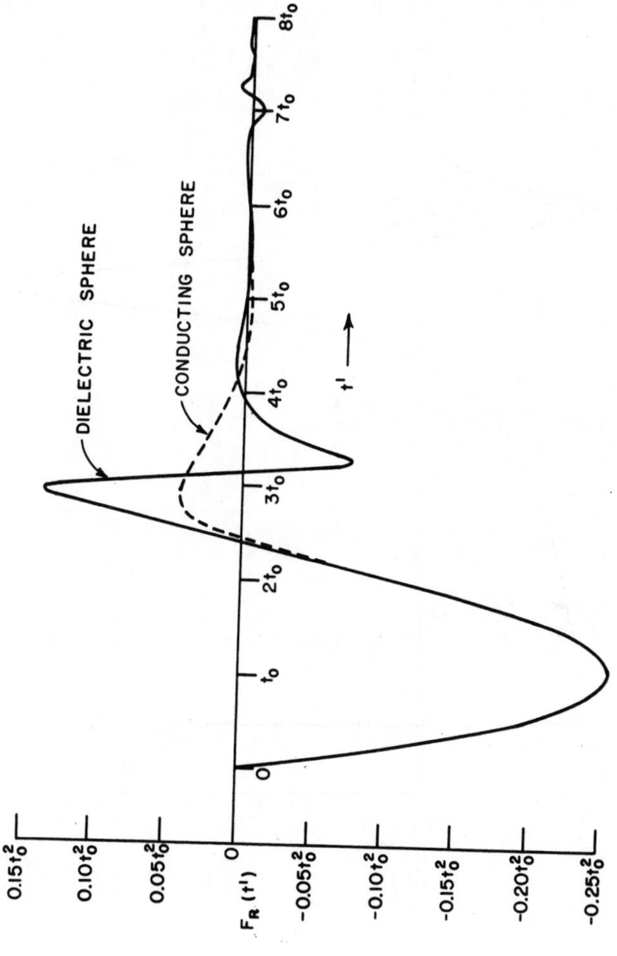

Fig. 9. Backscattered ramp responses for conducting and dielectric ($n = 1.458$) spheres.

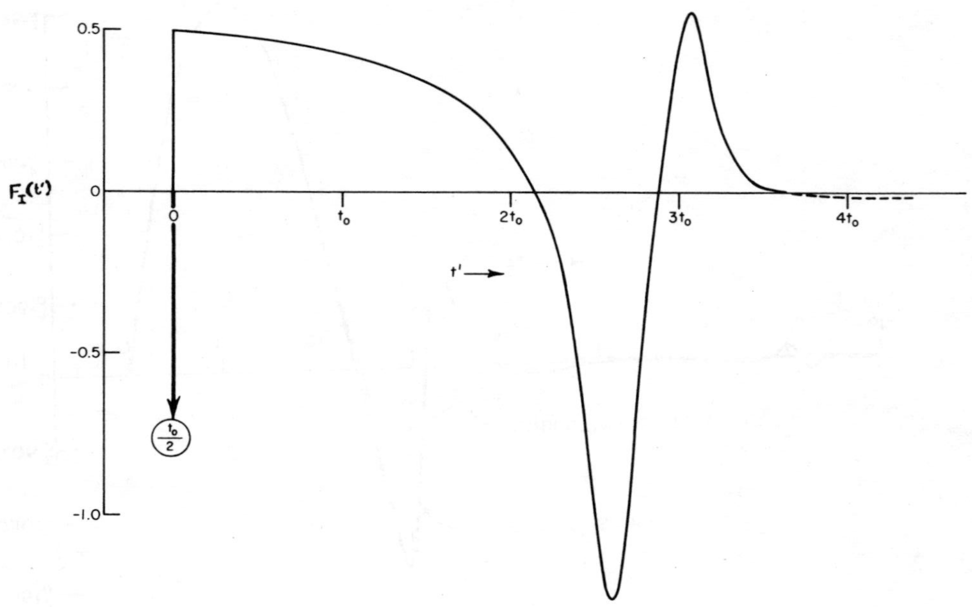

Fig. 10. Approximate impulse response, backscattering by a lossy dielectric (m = 1.315 - 0.137i) sphere.

waveform, and simple waveforms are obtained for smooth conducting objects. While response waveforms cannot now be accurately determined except through calculation of monochromatic solutions and Fourier synthesis involving many frequencies, it is possible to predict and interpret these waveforms qualitatively. It is suggested that scientists studying electromagnetic scattering at different ends of the spectrum might consolidate their findings and theoretical approaches in this unified concept of single-body scattering.

REFERENCES

(1) Deirmendjian, D., "Tables of Mie Scattering Cross Sections and Amplitudes," Rand Corporation, Report R-407-PR (1963).

(2) Frohlich, H., Theory of Dielectrics, Dielectric Constant and Dielectric Loss, Oxford University Press, Amen House, London E. C. 4, Second Edition (1958).

(3) Kennaugh, E. M., "The Scattering of Short Electromagnetic Pulses by a Conducting Sphere," Proc. IRE (Correspondence), Vol. **49**, 380 (1961).

(4) Kennaugh, E. M. and Cosgriff, R. L., "The Use of Impulse Response in Electromagnetic Scattering Problems," 1958 National Convention IRE Record, Pt. 1, 72-77.

(5) Kennaugh, E. M. and Moffatt, D. L., "Transient and Impulse Response Approximations," Proc. IEEE, **53**, No. **8**, 893-901 (1965).

(6) Moffatt, D. L. and Kennaugh, E. M., "The Axial Echo Area of a Perfectly Conducting Prolate Spheroid," IEEE Trans. on Antennas and Propagation, Vol. **AP-13**, 401-405 (1965).

(7) Rheinstein, J., "Tables of the Amplitude and Phase of the Backscatter from a Conducting Sphere," Massachusetts Institute of Technology, Lincoln Laboratory, Report 22G-10 (1963).

DISCUSSION FOLLOWING PAPER BY E. M. KENNAUGH

M. Kerker: How precisely can the time arrival of the creeping wave be determined? Is the wave displaced from the geometrical interface?

E. M. Kennaugh: The exact form of the creeping wave maximum cannot be directly determined from our calculations, in which a small, but non-zero, pulse width is simulated. However, the peak is sufficiently sharp (using a pulse train containing 475 harmonics) to fix the time of arrival within a few percent. It is slightly greater than that which would obtain for propagation at the free-space velocity around the shadowed surface, so that we might say the wave appears to travel a very small distance from the surface. I doubt that this is the correct interpretation of this delay, however. I think it more naturally arises from the variation of attenuation constant and phase constant with frequency in creeping wave propagation.

Electromagnetic Scattering by a Spherically Symmetric Inhomogeneous Particle

G. O. Olaofe and S. Levine*

Department of Mathematics,
University of Manchester, Manchester, England
and
Department of Chemistry,
Clarkson College of Technology, Potsdam, New York.

ABSTRACT

The scattering of a plane, plane-polarized, harmonic, electromagnetic wave by a non-absorbing spherical particle, having a spherically symmetric inhomogeneous refractive index, is considered. Maxwell's equations are solved exactly and the angular dependence of the 'perpendicularly polarized' intensity and of the polarization ratio are obtained for a refractive index varying radially according to a 'Cauchy' distribution law. The radial part of the scalar potential functions defining the characteristic modes of the transverse magnetic and transverse electric fields are expressed in

*One of us (S. L.) is pleased to acknowledge a visiting appointment at Clarkson College of Technology during the summer of 1964. This was supported by U. S. Atomic Energy Commission Grant No. AT(30-1) - 1801.

terms of hypergeometric functions. The corresponding scattering properties of a parabolic radial distribution for the square of the refractive index are also obtained. The Cauchy distribution and parabolic distribution are generalizations of the 'Maxwell fish eye' and spherical Luneberg lens respectively, both of which were originally investigated by C. T. Tai. At ICES I, Levine and Kerker examined the problem of scattering from two concentric spheres, when the outer shell has a variable refractive index described by an inverse power law with respect to radial distance. The particular cases where the refractive index of the outer shell is uniform or diminishes as the first or second power of distance are considered here.

Assuming the same particle radius a and the same total amount of refractive material the angular scattering intensity and polarization of these various types of inhomogeneous particles are compared for the two values $x = 2\pi a/\lambda = 5$ and 10. The forward scattering is found to be the least dependent on the form of the refractive index distribution, whereas the back-scattering is very sensitive to changes in this distribution. The scattering intensity and polarization ratio show considerable differences between the different types of inhomogeneities at the larger angles. A drop in the refractive index below that of the surrounding medium near the particle boundary leads to much more pronounced back-scattering and enhances the scattering intensity in general.

A preliminary comparison between Rayleigh-Gans (R. G.) theory and the exact 'Mie' theory is made for inhomogeneous particles. It is found that for small x, the R. G. scattering intensity is generally an overestimate, amounting to about 10 percent at $x = 1$. When x is larger and the intensity is highest in the forward direction, the R. G. theory continues to be satisfactory in this direction, but becomes extremely poor at the back-angles. The occurrence of the highest intensity for the vertically polarized component at some scattering angle different from zero, and in particular at back angles (excess back-scattering) is predicted by both the R. G. and Mie theories.

I. INTRODUCTION

The scattering of plane electromagnetic waves by a spherical particle having a spherically symmetric inhomogeneous refractive index has been considered by many authors. For a few types of distributions which describe the dependence of the refractive index n(r) on the distance r from the center of the particle, it is possible to obtain exact analytical solutions of Maxwell's equations in terms of known transcendental functions. The simplest model of an inhomogeneous sphere consists of two concentric spheres, i.e., of a uniform core surrounded by a uniform shell of different refractive index, and the exact scattering functions for this case have been obtained by Aden and Kerker (1) and Güttler (11). Special cases of this general solution for two concentric spheres have been considered by Scharfman (28) and Plonus (24) and more recent numerical computations are given by Kerker, Matijevic and Kratohvil (15) and by Espenscheid, Willis, Matijevic and Kerker (5). Wait (32) has shown how the more general problem of a sphere composed of any number of homogeneous concentric regions can be treated by introducing impedances and admittances for each shell. Rheinstein (25) computed the scattering for such a multi-layered spherical dielectric lens in the particular case where it approximates to the so-called Eaton-Lippmann lens ($n^2(r) = (2 - r)/r$ where $0 \leq r \leq 1$). Computations of the back-scattering cross-section for the radially-stratified sphere have been done by Mikulski and Murphy (22), who also considered approximations to the Eaton-Lippmann and spherical Luneberg lens ($n^2(r) = 2 - r^2$, $0 \leq r \leq 1$). Recently Murphy (28) has considered spherical single and multi-layered models to describe backscatter from a plasma-clad conducting body.

The solution of Maxwell's equations in terms of two scalar potential functions u and v which describe respectively transverse magnetic (T. M.) and transverse electric (T. E.) fields were derived by Bremmer (4), Marcuvitz (19) and Friedman (6) for the case where the refractive index n (r) is a function of radial distance r only, but where dependence on azimuthal angle is absent. Nomura and Takaku (1955) rederived independently the rotationally symmetric equations of these authors and obtained analytical expressions for the scalar potentials in terms of Bessel functions when n(r) is some power law of r. Another simple dependence for n(r) which can be solved exactly in terms of known functions (in this case hypergeometric functions) is known as the Maxwell fish eye $(n(r) = 2/(1 + r^2),\ 0 \leq r \leq 1)$. Tai (29b) showed very briefly how this type of inhomogeneous particle can be treated and the present authors have found independently the exact solution for a more general form which may be called the Cauchy distribution and will be described below. A third form of continuously varying spherically symmetric inhomogeneity which has been solved analytically by Tai (29a) is the spherical Luneberg lens. Tai showed that the scalar potential u for the T. M. field can be expressed in terms of 'generalized' confluent hypergeometric functions which are not simply related to standard functions but involve a four-term recurrence relation when expanded as a series. The scalar potential v for the T. E. field, however, is expressible in terms of confluent hypergeometric functions. Again a slightly more general case of Tai's solution will be considered by the authors under the form of a parabolic law for $n^2(r)$ and alternative methods of expanding the potential for the T. M. field are examined. Tai (29c) has also investigated a bilinear distribution, $(n^2(r) = (r + r_1)/(r + r_2))$ which involves new functions for both T. M. and T. E. modes. Recently, Gould and Burman (10) have shown that if $1/n(r)$ has the form $a + br$ where a and b are constants, then the radial part of the two scalar functions u and v satisfy the same differential equation, whose solution can be expressed in terms of hypergeometric functions (see discussion below on work of Arnush). They also consider the profile $n^2(r) = a + br^2 + c/r^2$ for which the radial part of the T. E. function v can be written in terms of confluent hypergeometric functions. We shall not examine these cases in the present paper.

Independently of the earlier authors, Sayasov (27) and Wyatt (35a, b, c) have re-derived the solutions of Maxwell's equations in terms of the two scalar functions. Wyatt solved numerically the differential equations satisfied by the radial part of these potentials for an inhomogeneous sphere with a particular form for n(r). He introduced a wrong factor, (which was subsequently corrected (35d, e)) in one of his scalar potentials but fortunately this did not affect his numerical results. Levine and Kerker (17) applied Wyatt's general results to the case of a central core of uniform refractive index surrounded by a spherical shell with varying index n(r) governed by a power law. The same error as in Wyatt's paper was made, but in the present paper we correct these results and also present some numerical computations. Friedman (6) also obtained expressions for the T. M. and T. E. fields but did not carry the solution to its completion. Garbacz (8) has transformed the second-order linear differentail equations for the radial part of the two scalar functions into first-order non-linear Riccati equations with a view to facilitating numerical integration and has considered scattering from the Luneberg lens and the Eaton-Lippmann lens.

Arnush (3) has expressed the solutions of Maxwell's equations, which describe scattering by an inhomogeneous sphere, in a manner somewhat different from (but equivalent to) that of previous authors. The guiding principle is to write the time-independent wave equations satisfied by the scalar potential functions u and v in forms similar to the Schrödinger wave-equation in the problem of scattering of particles by a central field of force. These functions are shown to obey the Schrödinger-type equation $\nabla^2\psi + (k^2 - U(r))\psi = 0$ where $\psi = v$ if the potential energy term $U(r) = U_1(r) = k^2(n^2(r) - 1)$ and $\psi = n(r)v$ if $U(r) = U_1(r) + n(r)d^2(1/n(r))/dr^2$, k being the wave number of the incident plane wave. Differences from the wave mechanical scattering problem occur in the asymptotic forms of u and v at infinity and in the boundary conditions satisfied by u and v at discontinuities in n(r) and dn(r)/dr. In the expansion for the scattering amplitude in terms of the wave modes, the coefficients involve two sets of phase angles (or phase shifts) corresponding to u and

v, instead of the one set in wave mechanics. Van de Hulst (31) has discussed the properties of phase angles in the particular case of a non-absorbing uniform sphere, and has pointed out certain advantages in their use. This approach was used by Margulies and Scarf (20) and Lynch (18), as well as by Arnush, all of whom were concerned with the particular case where $n^2(r)$ varies with r according to an inverse square law. Margulies and Scarf have computed the back scattering cross-section for the form $n^2(r) = 1 - \gamma/k^2r^2$, which is chosen to represent a plasma expanding into a vacuum. If the plasma source around the origin $r = 0$ is neglected and the above expression for $n^2(r)$ is assumed to hold for all $r \geq 0$, then the phase angles corresponding to the potential u are known exactly (Mott and Massey, 1949) and these angles were used by Margulies and Scarf (20). However, in order to satisfy the condition of continuity in the tangental component of the electric field at $r = r_0$, where $r_0 = \sqrt{\gamma}/k$ is the zero of $n(r)$, they assume that the spherical region $r < r_0$ is effectively a perfect conductor. This implies that $n^2(r) = \infty$ for $r < r_0$ and consequently the phase angles in the potential u would be altered. It appears therefore that the solution of Margulies and Scarf is not self-consistent.

An interesting feature of the refractive index for the plasma is that the inhomogeneous medium extends to infinite distances where $n(r) \to 1$. Assuming proper boundary conditions to account for the plasma source, this would provide an example of a two layer concentric system in which the solution of Maxwell's equations in the outer infinite inhomogeneous layer automatically includes the incident and scattered waves, a technique which avoids the necessity of satisfying boundary conditions at two separate radii. In their formulation of this approach to the inhomogeneous medium, Arnush, Margulies and Scarf and Lynch were guided by the analogous problem in quantum mechanical scattering problems. Sayasov (27) has similarly constructed the solution of Maxwell's equations for the case of a perfectly conducting sphere embedded in an infinite inhomogeneous medium for which $n(r) \to 1$ as $r \to \infty$. We are indebted to Prof. M. Kerker for suggesting the possibility of developing further such a method and we hope to report later on this matter.

The exact theory of scattering from an inhomogeneous sphere is very complex and also presents computational problems partly due to the slow convergence of the series representing the intensities. This has motivated various approximate methods, among which may be mentioned the Rayleigh-Gans theory, the vector Born approximation (Albini (2)), the Saxon-Schiff theory (Saxon (26b), Uberall (30)), the scalar approximation (Arnush, Margulies and Scarf), the treatment of 'soft' obstacles (Hart and Montroll (13)) and the W. K. B. method (Sayasov, Lynch (18)). Certain inadequacies exist in some of this work. Margulies and Scarf find for their model of a plasma that the scalar approximation to the back scatter cross-section can be in error by several orders of magnitude. However, this conclusion is based on comparison with their 'exact' solution which seems incorrect, as indicated above. In section V of this paper we shall raise certain objections to the way in which Albini introduces the vector Born approximation. We have adapted the Hart and Montroll method of summing the series for the scattering intensity functions to a soft particle with refractive index described by a Cauchy distribution. However, details will not be given here since we find that unless the refractive index of the particle remains very close to that of the surrounding medium, this method gives poor results, being inferior, for example, to the Rayleigh-Gans approximation. Each of the approximate methods, when properly applied, is applicable within its own characteristic limited range, the extent of validity depending on the scattering property calculated. The forward and total scattering cross-sections are much less sensitive to the form of the particle inhomogeneity than the scattering at large angles. Our results indicate that in the determination of scattering intensities at large angles, current approximate methods are quite inadequate over a wide range of the relevant parameters describing the physical system (in particular when wave-length and particle size are comparable or when the refractive index changes rapidly with position). In the present paper we shall compare the exact theory for particular inhomogeneous spheres with the Rayleigh-Gans theory and also with a certain form of 'soft obstacle' theory.

Although we shall only consider particles with real refractive index, the general analysis also applies to the case of complex refractive index.

II. SPHERICAL PARTICLE WITH REFRACTIVE INDEX GOVERNED BY CAUCHY DISTRIBUTION LAW

Consider a spherical particle having a spherically symmetric inhomogeneous refractive index given by the Cauchy distribution

$$n = n(r) = m/(1 + \epsilon\, r^2/a^2). \tag{2.1}$$

Here r is the radial distance from the center of the sphere of radius a, n is the ratio of the refractive index of the sphere to that of the surrounding infinite homogeneous medium and m and ϵ are constants which we assume to be real (and positive). If $m = 2$ and $\epsilon = 1$ then (2.1) reduces to the so-called Maxwell fish-eye which was treated by Tai (29a, b). Suppose that a plane, plane-polarized harmonic electromagnetic wave of wave-number $k = 2\pi/\lambda$ propagated in the positive z-direction, is incident on the particles. Let $s = kr$ and (assuming unit magnetic permeability), $k_2 = i\omega/c$ where c is the velocity of light and ω the angular frequency of the electromagnetic wave. We shall equate the refractive index of the medium outside the sphere to unity, so that $\omega = ck$. (We use Gaussian units.) Introducing spherical polar co-ordinates r, θ, ϕ, with origin at the center of the sphere, the two scalar functions $u^{(2)}$ and $v^{(2)}$ defining the transverse magnetic and transverse electric fields respectively at any position inside the sphere, are expressed as expansions in terms of the wave modes, namely

$$ru^{(2)} = \frac{1}{k_2} \exp(-i\omega t) \sum_{l=1}^{\infty} A_l\, i^{l-1} \frac{(2l+1)}{l(l+1)} W_l(s) P_l^1(\cos\theta) \cos\phi, \tag{2.2}$$

$$rv^{(2)} = \frac{1}{k} \exp(-i\omega t) \sum_{l=1}^{\infty} B_l\, i^{l} \frac{(2l+1)}{l(l+1)} G_l(s) P_l^1(\cos\theta) \sin\phi. \tag{2.3}$$

Here A_l and B_l are the coefficients of transmission and the functions $W_l(s)$ and $G_l(s)$ satisfy respectively the differential equations

$$\frac{d^2W_l}{ds^2} - \frac{2}{n}\frac{dn}{ds}\frac{dW_l}{ds} + \left(n^2 - \frac{l(l+1)}{s^2}\right) W_l = 0 \tag{2.4}$$

$$\frac{d^2 G_l}{ds^2} + (n^2 - \frac{l(l+1)}{s^2} \quad G_l = 0 \tag{2.5}$$

By writing $W_l = nV_l(s)$ the middle term of (2.4) is eliminated to yield

$$\frac{d^2 V_l}{ds^2} + \left[n^2 - \left(\frac{n'}{n}\right)^2 + \left(\frac{n'}{n}\right)' - \frac{l(l+1)}{s^2} \right] V_l = 0 \tag{2.6}$$

where the dash denotes differentiation with respect to s. The second and third terms inside the square brackets in (2.6) can also be written as $-n\, d^2(1/n)/ds^2$. The differential equation (2.5) and (2.6) for the radial parts of the lth wave mode now have the same form as in the formulation by Arnush, described in the introduction. To solve (2.5) and (2.6) when n is given by (2.1), we write $x = ka$, $z = -\epsilon s^2/x^2 = -\epsilon r^2/a^2$ and make the substitutions

$$V_l(s) = \frac{mz^{-1/4}}{(1-z)} U_l(z), \qquad G_l(s) = \frac{mz^{-1/4}}{(1-z)} F_l(z) \tag{2.7}$$

Then U_l and F_l satisfy equations of the same form, namely

$$4z^2(z-1)^2 \frac{d^2 y_l(z)}{dz^2} + (b z^2 + cz + d) y_l(z) = 0 \tag{2.8}$$

where, if $\alpha_0 = 2$ in the equation for U_l and $\alpha_0 = 0$ in that for F_l,

$$b = \frac{3}{4} - l(l+1) - \alpha_0, \quad c = \alpha_0 + 2l(l+1) - \frac{3}{4} - \frac{m^2x^2}{\epsilon},$$
$$d = \frac{3}{4} - l(l+1) \tag{2.9}$$

The further substitution

$$y_l(z) = z^p (z-1)^q \; Y_l(z)$$

reduces (2.8) to a hypergeometric equation

$$4z(z-1)\frac{d^2Y_l}{dz^2} + 8[(p+q)z - p]\frac{dY_l}{dz} + [8pq - c - 2d]Y_l(z) = 0 \tag{2.10}$$

provided

$$4p(p-1) + d = 0 \quad \text{and} \quad 4q(q-1) + b + c + d = 0. \tag{2.11}$$

From (2.9) and (2.11) the root of the first equation in (2.11) which gives a well-behaved solution at the origin $s = 0$ is

$$2p = 1 + 3/2. \tag{2.12}$$

The second relation in (2.11) yields

$$2q = 1 \pm \nu, \quad \nu^2 = 1 + m^2x^2/\epsilon \tag{2.13}$$

and we may choose either sign; the positive sign will be used here. It follows that the solutions of (2.4) and (2.5) can be written as

$$W_1(s) = s^{1+1}[n(s)]^{(\frac{1-\nu}{2})}\,{}_2F_1\left(\alpha_2, \beta_2; 1 + \frac{3}{2}; -\epsilon\frac{s^2}{x^2}\right) \tag{2.14}$$

and

$$G_1(s) = s^{1+1}[n(s)]^{-(\frac{1+\nu}{2})}\,{}_2F_1\left(\alpha_1, \beta_1; 1 + \frac{3}{2}; -\epsilon\frac{s^2}{x^2}\right) \tag{2.15}$$

where ${}_2F_1$ is the hypergeometric function given by the series

$${}_2F_1(\alpha, \beta; \gamma; \xi) = 1 + \sum_{\lambda=1}^{\infty} \frac{(\alpha)_\lambda (\beta)_\lambda}{(\gamma)_\lambda \lambda!}\xi^\lambda \tag{2.16}$$

where $(\chi)_\lambda = \chi(\chi + 1) \ldots (\chi + \lambda - 1)$, and the parameters are

$$2\alpha_1 = 1 + \nu, \quad 2\beta_1 = 2 + 21 + \nu, \quad \begin{matrix}2\alpha_2\\ 2\beta_2\end{matrix} = 1 + \frac{3}{2} + \nu \pm \left(1^2 + 1 + \frac{9}{4}\right)^{1/2} \tag{2.17}$$

It is easily verified from the standard transformation properties of the hypergeometric function that the root $2q = 1 - \nu$ of the second relation in (2.11) gives expressions for $W_1(s)$ and $G_1(s)$ which are equivalent to (2.14) and (2.15). Since the series (2.16) converges for $|z| < 1$ it can be used for $\epsilon \leq 1$, but when $\epsilon > 1$ we shall require an analytic continuation which is an expansion in inverse powers of z.

The refractive index $n(r)$ has a maximum or minimum at the origin of the particle according as $\epsilon < 0$ or $\epsilon > 0$; we shall only consider the case $\epsilon > 0$. In the range $0 < \epsilon < m - 1$, $n(r)$ has a discontinuous drop at the particle boundary. When $\epsilon > m - 1$, $n(r)$ is again discontinuous at the boundary and indeed is less than 1 just inside the particle. This could apply to an inhomogeneous particle suspended in a solvent of high refractive index. At $\epsilon = m - 1$, $n(r)$ is continuous at $r = a$ (or $s = x$). When $\epsilon = 1$ and $m = 2$ then our solutions become identical with those briefly outlined by Tai (29b). Also when $\epsilon = 1$, the series (2.16) is conditionally convergent at $s = x$ and can still be used in numerical computations.

The two scalar functions $u^{(1)}$ and $v^{(1)}$, which correspond to $u^{(2)}$ and $v^{(2)}$ and describe the scattered electromagnetic field outside the particle, take forms similar to (2.2) and (2.3). The quantities $A_l W_l(s)$ and $B_l G_l(s)$ in (2.2) and (2.3) respectively are replaced by $- c_l \zeta_l'(s)$ and $-d_l \zeta_l(s)$ where c_l and d_l are the scattering amplitude coefficients and $\zeta_l(s) = (\pi s/2)^{1/2} H^{(1)}_{l+1/2}(s)$, $H^{(1)}_{l+1/2}(s)$ being the first Hankel function. Applying the usual conditions that the tan– gential components of the electric and magnetic fields be continuous at the boundary $s = x$ of the particle, we obtain

$$c_l = \frac{\psi_l(x) M_l(x) - \dfrac{m^2 x}{(1+\epsilon)^2} \psi_l'(x)}{\zeta_l(x) M_l(x) - \dfrac{m^2 x}{(1+\epsilon)^2} \zeta_l'(x)}, \tag{2.18}$$

$$d_l = \frac{\psi_l(x) N_l(x) - x\psi_l'(x)}{\zeta_l(x) N_l(x) - x\zeta_l'(x)}, \tag{2.19}$$

where the dash denotes differentiation, $\psi_l(x) = (\pi x/2)^{1/2} J_{l+1/2}(x)$ is the Hankel Bessel function and if

$$F_{ii} = \frac{2\epsilon \alpha_i \beta_i}{\left(1 + \frac{3}{2}\right)} \cdot \frac{{}_2F_1(\alpha_i + 1, \beta_i + 1; 1 + \frac{5}{2}; -\epsilon)}{{}_2F_1(\alpha_i, \beta_i; 1 + \frac{3}{2}; -\epsilon)} \tag{2.20}$$

then

$$M_l(x) = 1 + 1 - \frac{\epsilon}{(1+\epsilon)} + \frac{(\epsilon^2 + m^2 x^2 \epsilon^2)^{1/2}}{(1+\epsilon)} - F_{22} \tag{2.21}$$

and

$$N_l(x) = 1 + 1 + \frac{\epsilon}{(1+\epsilon)} + \frac{(\epsilon^2 + m^2 x^2 \epsilon^2)^{1/2}}{(1+\epsilon)} - F_{11}. \tag{2.22}$$

The intensity of light scattered at an angle θ for polarizations perpendicular ($I_\perp$) and parallel ($I_\parallel$) to the plane of scattering (described in radio physics in terms of bistatic scattering cross-sections $\sigma_E(\theta)$, $\sigma_H(\theta)$ for the E-plane and H-plane) are

$$i_1(\theta) = s^2 I_\perp(\theta) = \frac{k^2}{4\pi}\sigma_E(\theta) = \left| \sum_{l=1}^{\infty} \frac{(2l+1)}{l(l+1)} (c_l \pi_l + d_l \tau_l) \right|^2, \tag{2.23}$$

$$i_2(\theta) = s^2 I_\parallel(\theta) = \frac{k^2}{4\pi}\sigma_H(\theta) = \left| \sum_{l=1}^{\infty} \frac{(2l+1)}{l(l+1)} (c_l \tau_l + d_l \pi_l) \right|^2, \tag{2.24}$$

where

$$\pi_l = \pi_l(\theta) = \frac{P_l^1(\cos\theta)}{\sin\theta}, \quad \tau_l = \tau_l(\theta) = \frac{d}{d\theta} P_l^1(\cos\theta) \tag{2.25}$$

The total scattering coefficient (or scattering efficiency factor) is

$$\frac{C_{sca}}{\pi a^2} = \frac{2}{x^2} \sum_{l=1}^{\infty} (2l+1)(|c_l|^2 + |d_l|^2) \tag{2.26}$$

and the back-scattering coefficient (or normalized back-scattering or radar cross-section) is

$$\frac{\sigma}{\pi a^2} = \frac{1}{x^2} \left|\sum_{l=1}^{\infty} (-1)^l (2l+1)(c_l - d_l)\right|^2 \tag{2.27}$$

The general term in the corresponding series for the forward scattering coefficient is $(2l+1)(c_l + d_l)$. Since $|c_l| \leq 1$ and $|d_l| \leq 1$ we may replace c_l and d_l by

$$\frac{1}{2}[\exp(2i\delta_l) - 1] \quad \text{and} \quad \frac{1}{2}[\exp(2i\eta_l) - 1]$$

where δ_l and η_l are the phase angles defined by the lth mode of the T. M. and T. E. waves respectively, to which we referred in the introduction.

III. PARABOLIC FORM FOR SQUARE OF THE REFRACTIVE INDEX

Consider the form

$$n^2(r) = m^2(1 - 2\epsilon\, r^2/a^2) \tag{3.1}$$

for the refractive index as a function of radius. This reduces to the Luneberg lens if $m^2 = 2$ and $\epsilon = 1/4$, which Tai* (29b) has treated and we shall employ similar techniques to find the scattering from the more general form (3.1). Introducing (3.1) into (2.5) and making the further substitution

$$\rho = \frac{m(2\epsilon)^{1/2}s^2}{x}, \quad G_l(s) = \rho^{-1/4} F_l(\rho) \tag{3.2}$$

we obtain

$$\frac{d^2F_l}{d\rho^2} + \left[-\frac{1}{4} + \frac{mx}{4(2\epsilon)^{1/2}}\,\frac{1}{\rho} + \frac{\frac{3}{16} - \frac{l(l+1)}{4}}{\rho^2}\right] F_l = 0, \tag{3.3}$$

which is Whittaker's normalized from of Kummer's confluent hypergeometric function. The solution of (2.5) which is finite at the origin is therefore

$$G_l(s) = s^{l+1} \cdot \exp\left[-\frac{ms^2}{x}\left(\frac{\epsilon}{2}\right)^{1/2}\right]$$

$$\times\, {}_1F_1\left(\frac{l}{2} + \frac{3}{4} - \frac{mx}{8}\left(\frac{2}{\epsilon}\right)^{1/2};\ l + \frac{3}{2};\ \frac{ms^2}{x}(2\epsilon)^{1/2}\right) \tag{3.4}$$

where

$${}_1F_1(\alpha;\gamma;\xi) = \sum_{\lambda=1}^{\infty} \frac{(\alpha)_\lambda}{(\gamma)_\lambda}\,\frac{\xi^\lambda}{\lambda!} \tag{3.5}$$

is the confluent hypergeometric function. The solution of (2.4), which takes the form

*Our equation (3.10) is identical in form to Tai's equation (44), in which there are two misprints.

$$\frac{d^2W_l}{ds^2} + \frac{4\epsilon s/x^2}{(1 - 2\epsilon s^2/x^2)} \frac{dW_l}{ds} + \left(m^2 - \frac{2\epsilon m^2 s^2}{x^2} - \frac{l(l+1)}{s^2}\right) W_l = 0, \tag{3.6}$$

cannot be expressed in terms of any well-known functions. For the Luneberg lens, Tai (29b) obtained a solution of (3.6) which involves a 'generalized' confluent hypergeometric function and this is readily applied to the more general refractive index (3.1). Introducing

$$\gamma = l + \frac{3}{2}, \quad a_2 = \frac{mx}{(2\epsilon)^{1/2}} \quad \alpha_1 = \frac{1}{2}\left(\gamma - \frac{a_2}{2} + \frac{1}{2a_2}\right), \tag{3.7}$$

$$\alpha_2 = -\frac{1}{8a_2}, \qquad \alpha_3 = 3\alpha_2, \qquad z = s^2/x,$$

we find that

$$W_l(s) = s^{l+1} \cdot \exp\left[-\frac{m}{x}\left(\frac{\epsilon}{2}\right)^{1/2} s^2\right] \cdot n(s) \cdot \sum_{\lambda=0}^{\infty} h_\lambda z^\lambda, \tag{3.8}$$

where

$$h_0 = 1, \quad h_1 = \frac{\alpha_1}{\gamma}, \quad h_2 = \frac{\alpha_1(\alpha_1+1)}{2\gamma(\gamma+1)} - \frac{(\alpha_2+\alpha_3)}{a_2(\gamma+1)},$$

$$h_3 = \frac{\alpha_1(\alpha_1+1)(\alpha_1+2)}{3!\gamma(\gamma+1)(\gamma+2)} - \frac{1}{3(\gamma+2)}$$

$$\left[\frac{(\alpha_1+2)(\alpha_2+\alpha_3)}{a_2(\gamma+1)} + \frac{2\alpha_1(\alpha_2+\alpha_3)}{\gamma a_2} + \frac{2(\alpha_2+2\alpha_3)}{a_2^2}\right] \tag{3.9}$$

and for $\lambda \geq 3$, we have the following four-term recurrence relation

$$a_2^2(\lambda+1)(\lambda+\gamma)\, h_{\lambda+1} - a_2\left[a_2(\alpha_1+\lambda) + 2\lambda(\gamma+\lambda-1)\right] h_\lambda$$

$$+\left[2a_2(\alpha_1+\alpha_2+\alpha_3+\lambda-1) + (\lambda-1)(\lambda+\gamma-2)\right] h_{\lambda-1}$$

$$-(\alpha_1+2\alpha_2+\lambda-2)\, h_{\lambda-2} = 0 \tag{3.10}$$

An alternative form for the solution which is finite at the origin and leads to a somewhat simpler recurrence relation is

$$W_l(s) = \sum_{\lambda=0}^{\infty} a_{2\lambda} s^{2\lambda+\sigma} \tag{3.11}$$

where choosing $a_0 = 1$,

$$a_2 = -\frac{m^2 + 4\epsilon(l+1)/x^2}{2^2(l+\frac{3}{2})}, \quad a_4 = \frac{m^4 - 16\epsilon^2 l(l+1)/x^4 + 4\epsilon/x^2}{2^4 \cdot 1 \cdot 2 \cdot (l+\frac{3}{2})(l+\frac{5}{2})} + \frac{\epsilon/x^2}{2(l+\frac{5}{2})} \tag{3.12}$$

and for $\lambda \geq 3$ again we have a four-term recurrence relation

$$2\lambda(2\lambda+2l+1)a_{2\lambda} + \left[m^2 + \frac{4\epsilon}{x^2}(l+2\lambda-1) - \frac{2\epsilon}{x^2}(2\lambda-2)(2l+2\lambda-1)\right]a_{2\lambda-2} - \frac{4\epsilon m^2}{x^2}a_{2\lambda-4} + \frac{4\epsilon^2 m^2}{x^4}a_{2\lambda-6} = 0 \tag{3.13}$$

At small ϵ and large x, it is possible to obtain a good approximation to $W_l(s)$ which is expressed in terms of confluent hypergeometric function. Substituting (3.1) into (2.6) and introducing $z = -2\epsilon s^2/x^2$ we have

$$\frac{d^2V_l}{dz^2} + \frac{1}{z}\frac{dV_l}{dz} + \left[\frac{m^2x^2(1-Z)}{8\epsilon z} - \frac{l(l+1)}{4z^2} - \frac{(3Z^2-Z+1)}{4z(1-z)^2}\right]V_l = 0 \tag{3.14}$$

Since $|Z| \leq 2\epsilon$, for small ϵ the three terms in the coefficient of V_l are of order $(x/\epsilon)^2$, $(l/\epsilon)^2$ and $1/\epsilon$ respectively. Substituting $U_l = Z^{1/4}V_l$, U_l now satisfies the differential equation

$$\frac{d^2U_l}{dz^2} + \left\{-\frac{m^2x^2}{8\epsilon} - 1 + \frac{1}{z}\left(\frac{1}{4} - \frac{m^2x^2}{8\epsilon}\right) - \frac{l(l+1)/4 - 3/16}{z^2}\right\}U_l = 0 \tag{3.15}$$

neglecting terms of order ϵ. This last equation is now in a convenient form as we readily find that

$$W_l(s) = n(s)\, s^{l+1}\exp\left(-\frac{\epsilon s^2}{\kappa x^2}\right)\cdot {}_1F_1\left(\frac{1}{2}+\frac{3}{4} - \frac{\kappa}{4}\left(\frac{m^2x^2}{2\epsilon} - 1\right); 1+\frac{3}{2}; \frac{\epsilon s^2}{\kappa x^2}\right)$$

where $\kappa^2 = 2\epsilon/(m^2x^2 + 8\epsilon)$ (3.16)

Since the n th terms of (3.8) and (3.11) are respectively proportional to $x^{2n}/n!$ and $x^n/n!$ the former series is more suitable for numerical work in the region of small x, whereas for larger x, (3.11) is to be preferred. However, when x becomes very large, both cases should be replaced by their equivalent asymptotic expansions. At such large x, (3.16) is particularly convenient when ϵ is small since the asymptotic expansions of confluent hypergeometric functions are well-known.

IV. SCATTERING FROM TWO CONCENTRIC SPHERES WITH POWER LAW DEPENDENCE IN THE OUTER SHELL

The profiles chosen for n(r) in the preceding sections do not readily cover the case where we have a small gradient in the index near the centre of the sphere but a rapid drop near its boundary. Such a dependence on radial distance is conveniently represented by the model of a uniform inner core surrounded by a spherically symmetric inhomogeneous outer coat for which n(r) varies with r according to a suitable power law; this was considered by Levine and Kerker (17).*

---

*In this paper (to be referred to as L.K.), the equation corresponding to (2.4) (i.e., L.K. (6)) was identical with the incorrect expression used by Wyatt (35a, b, c) and should therefore have the factor $1/n_2$ deleted. As a consequence, the following corrections should be made (i) the factor $1/n_2$ is removed from the left-hand sides of (L.K. 32) and (L.K. 35), (ii) the exponent $(2 - m)/(2m + 1))$ of X in the right-hand member of (L.K. 33) is replaced by $(2 + m)/(2(m + 1))$; (iii) the common exponent $- m/2(m + 1)$ of X_r, X_a and X_b in (L.K. 35), (L.K. 41) and (L.K. 42) respectively becomes $+ m/2(m + 1)$. The same corrections should also be made in the exponent $- m/2(m + 1)$ of X_a and X_b in the determinant (L.K. 48); and (iv) equation (L.K. 34) should read

$$S = (m + 1)K_3^{1/2}\left(\frac{A}{m + 1}\right)^{1/(2m+1)}$$

Let the inner core have a radius a_0 and the refractive index be given by

$$n(s) = \begin{cases} m & , \quad 0 \leq s \leq x_0 \\ \delta s^{\tau} & , \quad x_0 \leq s \leq x \end{cases} \tag{4.1}$$

where τ, δ, m are (real) constants and $x_0 = ka_0$. The radial functions which correspond to $W_1(s)$ and $G_1(s)$ in the solutions (2.3) and (2.4) respectively of Maxwell's equations, were originally obtained for a power law dependence of the refractive index by Nomura and Takaku (1955). The linear combinations of these functions appropriate to the outer shell will be written in the forms

$$W_1(s) = A_1\, T_1(s) + B_1\, U_1(s), \quad G_1(s) = C_1 \Phi_1(s) + D_1\, \Psi_1(s) \tag{4.2}$$

where A_1, B_1, C_1 and D_1 are constants determined by the boundary conditions. When $\tau \neq -1$

$$T_1(s) = s^{1/2} n(s)\, J_{\kappa}(\chi_s), \quad U_1(s) = s^{1/2} n(s)\, J_{\kappa}(\chi_s)$$

$$\Phi_1(s) = s^{1/2} J_{\mu}(\chi_s), \quad \Psi_1(s) = s^{1/2} J_{\mu}(\chi_s) \tag{4.3}$$

where

$$\chi_s = \frac{ns}{(1+\tau)}, \quad \kappa = \frac{(1^2 + 1 + (\tau - \frac{1}{2})^2)^{1/2}}{(1+\tau)}, \quad \mu = \frac{(1 + 1/2)}{(1+\tau)} \tag{4.4}$$

In the particular case $\tau = -1$, (2.5) and (2.6) reduce to Euler's homogeneous equation and on introducing

$$\eta = [(1 + 1/2)^2 - \delta^2]^{1/2},$$

(4.3) is replaced by

$$T_1(s) = s^{\eta - \frac{1}{2}}, \quad U_1(s) = s^{-\eta - \frac{1}{2}}, \quad \Phi_1(s) = s^{\eta + \frac{1}{2}}, \quad \Psi_1(s) = s^{-\eta + \frac{1}{2}} \tag{4.5}$$

provided $1 + 1/2 > \delta$. If $1 + 1/2 < \delta$ then

$$T_1(s) = s^{-1/2} \cos(\eta_1 \ln s), \quad U_1(s) = s^{-1/2} \sin(\eta_1 \ln s),$$

$$\Phi_1(s) = sT_1(s), \quad \Psi_1(s) = sU_1(s) \tag{4.6}$$

where $\eta_1^2 = -\eta^2$. If $l + 1/2 = \delta$, then we may write

$$T_l(s) = \Phi_l(s) = 1\ , \quad U_l(s) = s^{-1}\ , \quad \Psi_l(s) = s \tag{4.7}$$

Tai (29a) also observed the simplified form of the solution of (2.5) and (2.6) when $\tau = -1$.

The solutions (L.K. 47) and (L.K. 48), which express the scattering amplitude coefficients as ratios of two determinants, are similar to the formulae of Aden and Kerker (1), who considered the more special case of a uniform outer shell. These scattering amplitude coefficients are more conveniently written as

$$c_l = \frac{\psi_l(x)\,[U_l'(x) - c_{lo}T_l'(x)] - n^2(x)\,\psi_l'(x)\,[U_l(x) - c_{lo}T_l(x)]}{\zeta_l(x)\,[U_l'(x) - c_{lo}T_l'(x)] - n^2(x)\,\zeta_l'(x)\,[U_l(x) - c_{lo}T_l(x)]} \tag{4.8}$$

$$d_l = \frac{\psi_l(x)\,[\Phi_l'(x) - d_{lo}\Psi_l'(x)] - \psi_l'(x)\,[\Phi_l'(x) - d_{lo}\Psi_l(x)]}{\zeta_l(x)\,[\Phi_l'(x) - d_{lo}\Psi_l'(x)] - \zeta_l'(x)\,[\Phi_l(x) - d_{lo}\Psi_l(x)]} \tag{4.9}$$

where, denoting the refractive index at the inner boundary of the outer shell by $n(x_0^+)$,

$$c_{lo} = \frac{n^2(x_0^+)\,U_l(x_0)\,\psi_l'(mx_0) - m\,U_l'(x_0)\,\psi_l(m\,x_0)}{n^2(x_0^+)\,T_l(x_0)\,\psi_l'(mx_0) - m\,T_l'(x_0)\,\psi_l(m\,x_0)}\,, \tag{4.10}$$

$$d_{lo} = \frac{m\,\Phi_l(x_0)\,\psi_l'(mx_0) - \Phi_l'(x_0)\,\psi_l(mx_0)}{m\,\Psi_l(x_0)\,\psi_l'(mx_0) - \Psi_l'(x_0)\,\psi_l(mx_0)} \tag{4.11}$$

(The dash denotes differentiation with respect to the argument of the function.) For the case of a uniform core surrounded by a uniform outer shell $\tau = 0$ and the equations (4.3) reduce to

$$T_l(s) = \Phi_l(s) = \psi_l(s\delta),\quad U_l(s) = \Psi_l(s) = \chi_l(s\delta) \tag{4.12}$$

where

$$\chi_l(x) = \left(\frac{\pi x}{2}\right)^{1/2} J_{-l-\frac{1}{2}}(x)$$

is the Riccati-Bessel function. It can be easily verified that when $\tau = 0$ and $\delta \to m$ then $c_{l0} \to \infty$, $d_{l0} \to 0$ and the expressions (4.8) and (4.9) simplify to the Mie coefficients. The same limits are obtained by allowing $x_0 \to x$ and suitably rearranging (4.8) and (4.9). Also, on substituting (4.12) into (4.8)-(4.11), we obtain expressions for the coefficients c_l and d_l which are readily seen to be equivalent to the formulae given by Güttler (11).

Wait (32) has suggested an iterative method of determining the scattering from a stratified sphere, consisting of an arbitrary number of homogenous concentric regions. An input impedance and admittance dependent on the mode number l of the T.M. and T.E. waves, are introduced for each shell. By expressing the impedance and admittance of a typical region in terms of the corresponding quantities of the adjacent region, it is possible to obtain the impedance Z_l and the admittance Y_l at the outer surface of the particle and these determine the coefficients c_l and d_l. This technique can be extended to the case where one or more of the shells is inhomogeneous, as in the case considered above, where (4.8) and (4.9) can be written as

$$c_l = \frac{\psi_l'(x) - Z_l\psi_l(x)}{\zeta_l'(x) - Z_l\zeta_l(x)}, \quad d_l = \frac{\psi_l'(x) - Y_l\psi_l(x)}{\zeta_l'(x) - Y_l\zeta_l(x)} \tag{4.13}$$

V. SCATTERING FROM SOFT OBSTACLES

It is usual to refer to particles with refractive index close to 1 and therefore changing only slightly with distance from their centre as soft particles. The Cauchy distribution (2.1) would present such a particle if both $m - 1$ and ϵ are small. In these conditions it is convenient to expand (2.1) in powers of ϵ namely

$$n = m[1 - \epsilon \frac{s^2}{x^2} + \epsilon^2 \frac{s^4}{x^4} - \ldots] \tag{5.1}$$

A parabolic law for the refractive index is obtained if only linear terms in ϵ are retained in (5.1). Substituting (5.1) into (2.6) and neglecting terms of order ϵ^2, we obtain

$$\frac{d^2V_l}{ds^2} + \left(A - C^2 s^2 - \frac{l(l+1)}{s^2}\right) V_l = 0 \qquad (5.2)$$

where

$$A = m^2 - 2\epsilon/x^2 \quad , \quad C^2 = 2\epsilon\, m^2/x^2 \qquad (5.3)$$

A further substitution $\rho = Cs^2$, $V_l(s) = \rho^{-1/4} F_l(\rho)$ leads to an equation for $F_l(\rho)$ similar in form to (3.3) and to the solution of (5.2) which is finite at the origin reads

$$V_l(s) = s^{l+1} \exp\left(-\frac{1}{2} Cs^2\right) {}_1F_1\left(\frac{1}{2} + \frac{3}{4} - \frac{A}{2C} \,;\, 1 + \frac{3}{2} \,;\, Cs^2\right) \qquad (5.4)$$

When the refractive index is given by the first two terms in (5.1), the corresponding solution of the equation (2.5) for $G_l(s)$ is identical with (3.4). We have already observed that with the parabolic form (3.1) for the refractive index, the solution $G_l(s)$ of (2.5) is given exactly by (3.4) in terms of the confluent hypergeometric function. If the parabolic law (3.1) is substituted into (2.6) and terms of order ϵ^3 be neglected, then we obtain the form (5.4) for $V_l(s)$ provided C^2 is replaced by $2\epsilon(m^2 + 8\epsilon/x^2)/x^2$ while A is defined as in (5.3). The two solutions for the Cauchy and parabolic laws are seen to be identical up to terms of order ϵ. A distribution law for the refractive index which is relevant to polymer coils is the Gaussian Law

$$n = m \exp(-\epsilon\, s^2/x^2) \qquad (5.5)$$

Again neglecting terms of order ϵ^2 the solutions of (2.6) and (2.7) have the forms (3.4) and (5.4) respectively.

If in addition to the condition for soft obstacles $|n - 1| \ll 1$ we also assume that $2x|n - 1| \ll 1$ then the classical Rayleigh-Gans theory is obtained. Following van de Hulst (31), the scattering by a spherical particle having a radially symmetric refractive index may be described in terms of the angle functions.

$$\left.\begin{matrix} S_1(\theta) \\ S_2(\theta) \end{matrix}\right. = ix^3 R(\theta) \begin{cases} 1 \\ \cos\theta \end{cases} \tag{5.6}$$

where if $u = 2x \sin(\theta/2)$, $z = r/a$,

$$R(\theta) = \int_0^1 z\,(n^2(xz) - 1)\,\frac{\sin uz}{u}\,dz \tag{5.7}$$

From (5.6) the scattered intensity for parallel and perpendicular polarizations are

$$\left.\begin{matrix} i_1(\theta) \\ i_2(\theta) \end{matrix}\right. = x^6\,|R(\theta)|^2 \begin{cases} 1 \\ \cos^2\theta \end{cases} \tag{5.8}$$

For the parabolic refractive index (2.27)

$$R(\theta) = (m^2 - 1)g(u) - \frac{2m^2\epsilon}{u^2}\left[\frac{3\sin u}{u} - \cos u - 6\,g(u)\right] \tag{5.9}$$

where

$$g(u) = (\sin u - u\cos u)/u^3. \tag{5.10}$$

Also for the Cauchy distribution, $R(\theta)$ is identical with (5.9) when expanded in powers of ϵ, if terms of order ϵ^2 are ignored. The term of order ϵ^2 is

$$\frac{3m^2\epsilon^2}{u^4}\left[5u\sin u - u^5\cos u - 20\left\{\frac{3\sin u}{u} - \cos u - 6g(u)\right\}\right] \tag{5.11}$$

The first term on the right-hand side of (5.9) describes the limiting case of a uniform sphere, when $\epsilon = 0$. From (5.7), we readily derive the form of $R(\theta)$ for two concentric spheres, having different uniform refractive indices in the two regions. We need only introduce the form

$n(s) = m,\ 0 \le s \le x_0$; $n(s) = \delta,\ x_0 \le s \le x$

into (5.7)
and so obtain

$$x^3 R(\theta) = x^3 (\delta^2 - 1) g(u) + x_0^3 (m^2 - \delta^2) g(v) \tag{5.12}$$

where $v = 2ka_0 \sin(\theta/2)$. The result (5.12) was derived by Kerker, Kratohvil and Matijevic (15) who employed the "bisectrix" technique of van de Hulst. However, one can write down (5.12) immediately by the following simple physical argument. Consider two uniform spheres defined by the pair of parameters (a, δ) and (a_0, m) specifying the radius and refractive index, such that $a > a_0$. Let $R_{a,\delta}(\theta)$ and $R_{a_0,m}(\theta)$ denote the Rayleigh-Gans scattering functions for these two spheres. Imagine that a spherical core with parameters (a_0, δ) is removed from the larger sphere and that the second sphere (a_0, m) is inserted into the cavity. The scattering formula (5.12) can be written as

$$x^3 R(\theta) = x^3 R_{a,\delta}(\theta) + x_0^3 R_{a_0,m}(\theta) - x_0^3 R_{a,\delta}(\theta) \tag{5.13}$$

with obvious physical meaning. The corresponding scattering function when the refractive index of the outer shell obeys a power law involves numerical integration.

We mentioned in the introduction that there are certain objections to the method of Albini for treating the scattering from a soft inhomogeneous sphere by the Born approximation. He writes the refractive index of the particle in the form $n^2(r) = 1 - \eta(r)$. The time-independent scattered magnetic field at a far position $\mathbf{r}$ can then be expressed exactly in the integral form

$$\mathbf{H}_s = -\frac{e^{ikr}}{4\pi r'} \int_{V'} e^{-ik(\mathbf{n}\cdot\mathbf{r}')} \left[k^2 \eta(\mathbf{r}')\mathbf{H}' - \frac{iw}{c} (\nabla' \eta \wedge \mathbf{E}') \right] dV' \tag{5.14}$$

where $\mathbf{H}'$, $\mathbf{E}'$ are the total magnetic and electric fields, the dash denotes position inside the volume V' of the particle and $\mathbf{n}$ is unit vector in the direction of the line joining the centre of the particle and the point $\mathbf{r}$. In the Born approximation the total magnetic and electric fields in the integrand on the right of (5.14) are replaced by the incident fields only. Since this implies that the scattered field inside the particle is small compared with the incident field, the particle behaves as a soft obstacle and so $|\eta(r)| \ll 1$. In evaluating (5.14), Albini allows the scattering medium to extend to infinity but we shall restrict this medium to a sphere of radius a; thus $\eta(r) = 0$ for $r > a$. Consider the incident plane wave propagated in the z-direction to have unit intensity, with magnetic field polarized in the y-direction and let $\mathbf{e}_y$ and $\mathbf{e}_z$ be unit vectors in the y and z directions respectively. Then, using the Born approximation and Albini's method of integration, (5.14) yields

$$\underset{\sim}{\mathbf{H}}_s = -\frac{\omega}{c} a^2 \frac{e^{ikr}}{r}\Bigg[kag(\theta)\eta(a)\mathbf{e}_y + \left\{\frac{1}{2} g_1(\theta)\operatorname{cosec}(\theta/2) - ka\, g(\theta)\,\eta(a)\right\}\left\{\cos\theta\, \mathbf{e}_y - \sin\theta\, \sin\phi\, \mathbf{e}_z\right\}\Bigg] \tag{5.15}$$

where r, θ, φ are the polar co-ordinates of position **r** and

$$g_1(\theta) = \int_0^1 \eta(r)\ z \sin uz\ dz \tag{5.16}$$

Albini's expression for $\mathbf{H}_s$ is obtained by putting $\eta(a) = 0$ so that $\mathbf{H}_s$ becomes normal to the direction of propagation. If the particle is assumed homogeneous, then the second term in (5.15) vanishes and (5.15) reduces to

$$\mathbf{H}_s = -\frac{w}{c}\frac{e^{ikr}}{r} ka^3 g(\theta)\eta(a)\,\mathbf{e}_y \tag{5.17}$$

which follows directly from (5.14) if we replace $\mathbf{H}'$ by the incident field and put $\nabla'\eta = 0$. However, (5.17) is parallel to the incident magnetic field, in disagreement with Mie theory. Unless the refractive index at the boundary of the homogeneous particle is continuous ($\eta(a) = 0$), Albini's $\mathbf{H}_s$ will be perpendicular to the direction of propagation at large distances only in the forward and backward directions. Some other initial approximation to the total field is necessary if $\mathbf{H}_s$ is to be transverse in the case where $\eta(a) \neq 0$. An example of such a starting point for a transverse electric scattering field is quoted by Margulies and Scarf (their equation (30)) as appearing in Saxon (26a).

A method of determining the scattering from particles, which is suitable for slowly varying n(r) (soft obstacles) and large x, is based on the Saxon-Schiff theory (Saxon, 26b). The wave equation for the electric scattering field $\mathbf{E}_s$ is rewritten as an integral equation, which differs from the standard form corresponding to (5.14) for $\mathbf{H}_s$ and which yields the W.K.B. result as its zeroth approximation. Uberall (30) obtains an approximate solution to this equation, representing an electromagnetic field which is transverse only in the forward and backward directions. This author comments that the deviations from the transverse character of the field cannot be taken seriously, but just indicate the inadequacies of the theory. However, in applying an approximate method suitable at large angles to a homogeneous sphere for which n = 1.33 and x = 6, he obtains a value for the radar cross-section, which is smaller than the correct Mie value by a factor of about 5. Although his intensity distribution is apparently an improvement on that derived by the Born approximation, the quantitative agreement with the Mie theory is still poor.

VI. NUMERICAL COMPARISONS OF EXACT SCATTERING PATTERNS

A comparison of the scattering intensities by the various types of inhomogeneous spheres considered in sections II-V will be made along the following lines. Since the Cauchy distribution (2.2) readily lends itself to computations of the intensities, we have used this as a standard. Unless stated otherwise we shall assume a common radius a and a common mean refractive index by volume, namely

$$\bar{n} = \frac{1}{V} \int_v n(r)\,dV \qquad (6.1)$$

where V is the volume of the particle. For the Cauchy distribution

$$\bar{n} = \frac{3m}{\epsilon}\left(1 - (\tan^{-1}\sqrt{\epsilon})/\sqrt{\epsilon}\right), \qquad (6.2)$$

for the parabolic law (2.27)

$$\bar{n} = \frac{3m}{16\epsilon}\left[\sin^{-1}(2\epsilon)^{1/2}/(2\epsilon)^{1/2} - (1-4\epsilon)(1-2\epsilon)^{1/2}\right] \qquad (6.3)$$

and for the concentric spheres given by (3.1)

$$\bar{n} = m\left(\frac{a_0}{a}\right)^3 + \frac{3\delta}{(3+\tau)}\left\{\left(\frac{a}{a_0}\right)^\tau - \left(\frac{a_0}{a}\right)^3\right\} \qquad (6.4)$$

When $\tau = 0$, (6.4) reduces to the mean refractive index for a particle consisting of a uniform core, radius a_0 and index m, which is surrounded by a shell of index δ and thickness $a - a_0$*. We have chosen m = 1.20 (the refractive index of bulk polystyrene at $\lambda = 5461$ Å) and the two values $x = 2\pi a/\lambda = 5$ and 10. If the refractive index for the Cauchy distribution is taken as 1 at the particle boundary r = a, then from (2.1), $\epsilon = 0.2$ and from (5.2), $\bar{n} = 1.074$, where both quantities are independent of a. This particular example of the Cauchy distribution for the refractive index is shown by curve D in Fig. 1; also curves B and C represent two cases of uniform concentric spheres, having a mean index 1.074 and indices 1.2 for the core and 1.03 and 1.06 respectively for the outer shell. In Figs. 2 and 4 the intensity $i_1(\theta)$ of the vertically polarized scattered light, which is defined in (2.23), is shown for the above three distributions of refractive index, for x = 5 and 10; the corresponding polarization ratios $\Pi(\theta) = i_2(\theta)/i_1(\theta)$ are drawn in Fig. 3 and 5. (We have plotted $i_1(\theta)$ in preference to $i_2(\theta)$ since the oscillating pattern of $i_1(\theta)$ is much more pronounced.) For comparison, we show by curve A the functions $i_1(\theta)$ and $\Pi(\theta)$ for the uniform sphere of refractive index 1.2, but of smaller radius (x = 3.59) which is so chosen that the total refractive material is the same as in the other three cases. Further details of relevant parameters are given in the legend of Fig. 1. It is observed that the forward intensities $i_1(\theta)$ are approximately the same, the differences between the four distributions only becoming pronounced at angles exceeding 60° and 30°

---

*Equation (6.4) at $\tau = 0$ is misquoted by Kerker, Kratohvil and Matijevic (their formula (32)) (15)

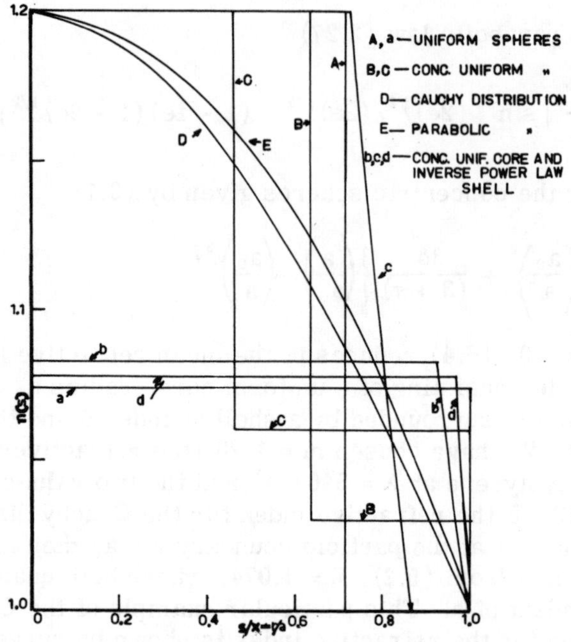

Fig. 1. Distribution profiles, n(s), for refractive index of spheres as a function of r/a = s/x. All distributions except E have the same total refractive material; m = refractive index at centre of sphere.

A, a	**:**	**uniform spheres of indices 1.2 and 1.074 and radii 0.718a and a, respectively**
B, C	**:**	**uniform cores of index 1.2 and radii a_0 = 0.636a and 0.462a, surrounded by uniform shells of indices δ = 1.03 and 1.06 respectively**
D	**:**	**Cauchy distribution, m = 1.2 and ϵ = 0.2**
E	**:**	**Parabolic distribution, m = 1.2 and ϵ = 0.153**
b, c, d	**:**	**uniform cores with refractive indices m = 1.083, 1.20 and 1.078 respectively, surrounded by shells with refractive indices given by the power law a/r, 0.87 a/r and $1.01(a/r)^2$ respectively**

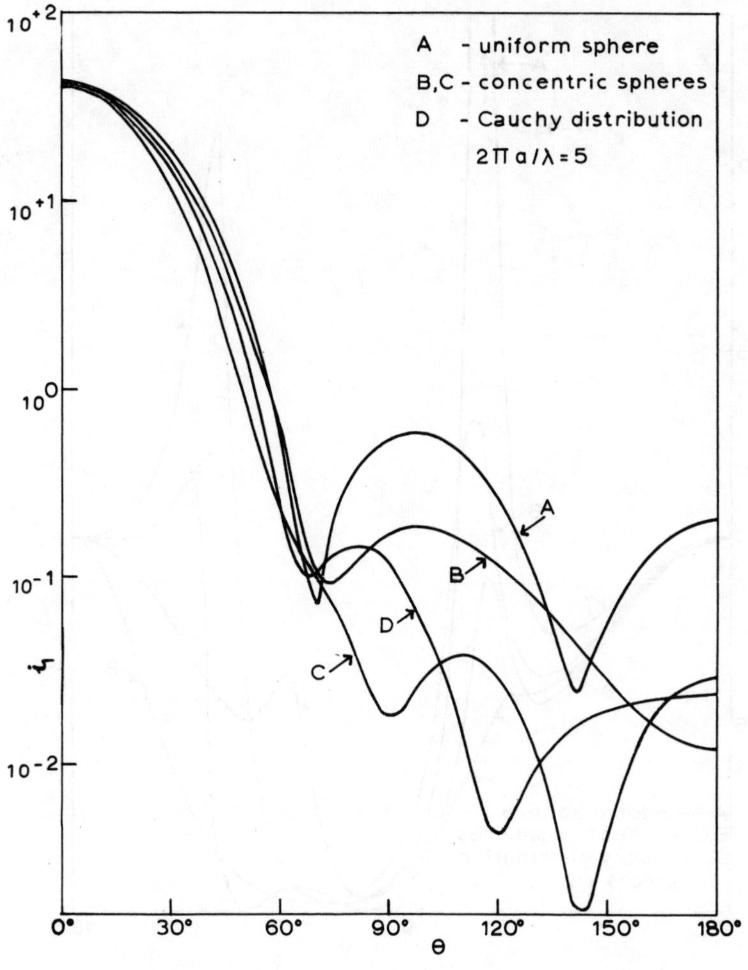

Fig. 2. Vertically polarized intensity i_1 (θ) as a fraction of scattering angle θ for spheres with the same total refractive material. The distribution of the refractive index are given in Fig. 1 by the same letters A, B, C, D; $2\pi a/\lambda = 5$

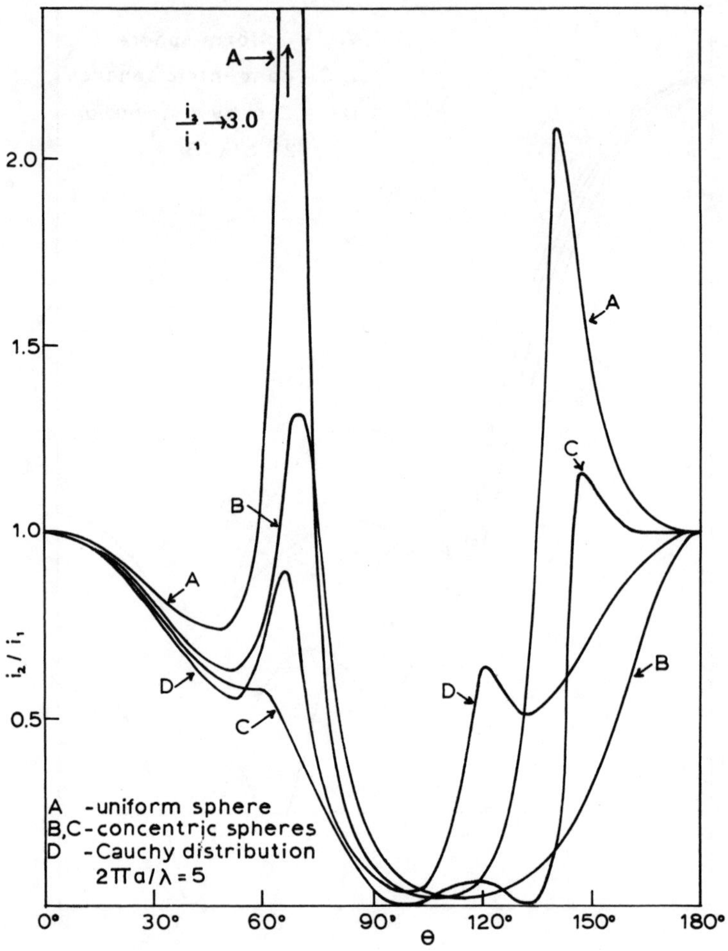

Fig. 3. Polarization ratio $\Pi(\theta) = i_2(\theta)/i_1(\theta)$ as a function of scattering angle θ for the same distributions of refractive index as in Fig. 2; $2\pi a/\lambda = 5$

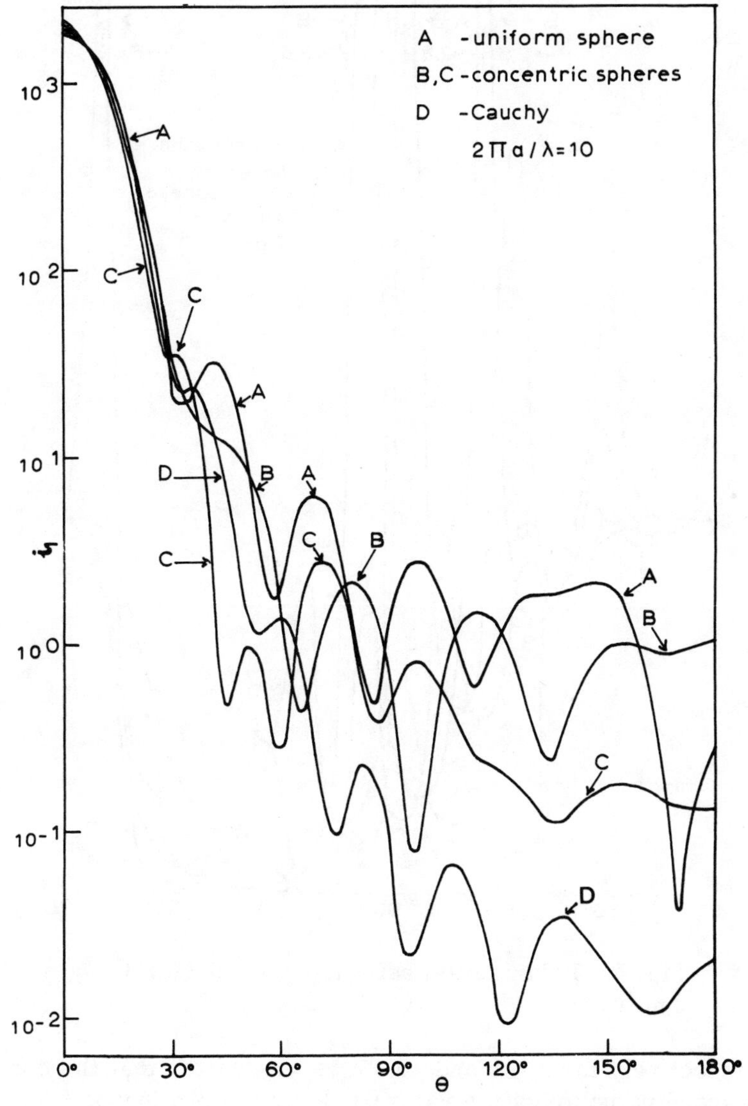

Fig. 4. Vertically polarized intensity $i_1(\theta)$ as in Fig. 2; $2\pi a/\lambda = 10$

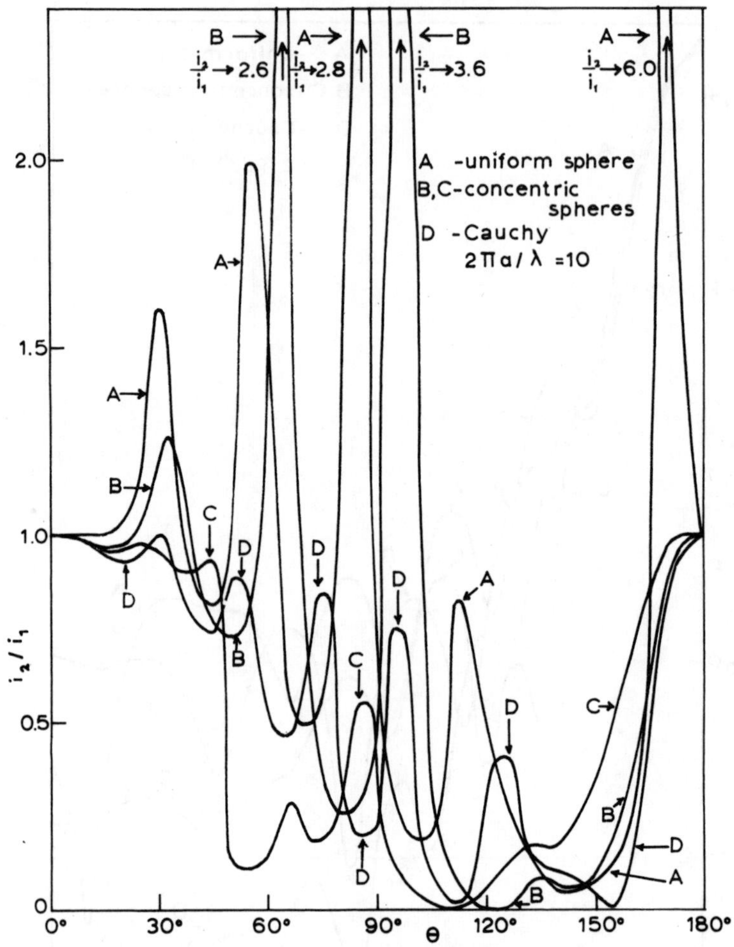

Fig. 5. Polarization ratio $\Pi(\theta)$ as in Fig. 3; $2\pi a/\lambda = 10$

respectively for x = 5 and 10. It is noteworthy that the corresponding polarization ratio $\Pi(\theta)$ for the continuous Cauchy distribution varies much less sharply than that for the discontinuous distributions given by the uniform sphere or the concentric shells. This trend in the polarization ratio with decrease in abruptness of change in refractive index is also manifested by the three curves A, B and C. The variation in polarization ratio becomes stronger, the more pronounced the discontinuities in refractive index.

In Figs. 6-9 curves b, c and d represent concentric spheres, each having a uniform core and a shell with a variable refractive index $n(r)$ which is described by an inverse power law; again $x = 5$ and 10. The refractive index profiles are shown in Fig. 1 and the values of relevant parameters given in the legend. In the cases of b and c, we choose $n(r)$ in the outer shell to be inversely proportional to distance r and, in the case of d, inversely proportional to the square of the distance. For comparison, curve a shows scattering from a uniform sphere of the same radius and total refractive material. In three of the plots of $i_1(\theta)$ (a, b and d) shown in Figs. 6 and 8 there is little difference until angles exceeding 90° and 45° for $x = 5$ and 10 respectively are reached. The reason for this is a combination of (1) refractive indices of the three cores close together (1.074, 1.083 and 1.078) (2) thin shells and (3) refractive indices at the outer boundary somewhat greater than 1. The behavior of $i_1(\theta)$ as described by curve c is quite different. Here the refractive index of the core is 1.20 and consequently, in order to satisfy the condition of the same total refractive material, the refractive index must drop below 1 to a value 0.87 at the boundary. For case c the scattering intensity is generally larger and the back scattering is much greater by two or three orders, than for the other three cases a, b, d. We also observe that, other than at $\theta = 0°$ or 180°, there is only one maximum in curve c at $x = 5$, as compared with two maxima in each of the other cases. When $x = 10$ the sharp drop in $i_1(\theta)$ at angles near 150° is to be noted for curves a, b, d in Fig. 8. The polarization ratios corresponding to the intensities $i_1(\theta)$ in Figs. 6 and 8 are shown in Figs. 7 and 9 respectively. It is observed that in Fig. 7 ($x = 5$) curve c has two very marked peaks and one trough, whereas each of a, b, d has two peaks and two troughs. Generally, for a, b, d, the horizontally polarized intensity $i_2(\theta)$ is smaller than the vertically polarized intensity $i_1(\theta)$, but the reverse in the case for curve c.

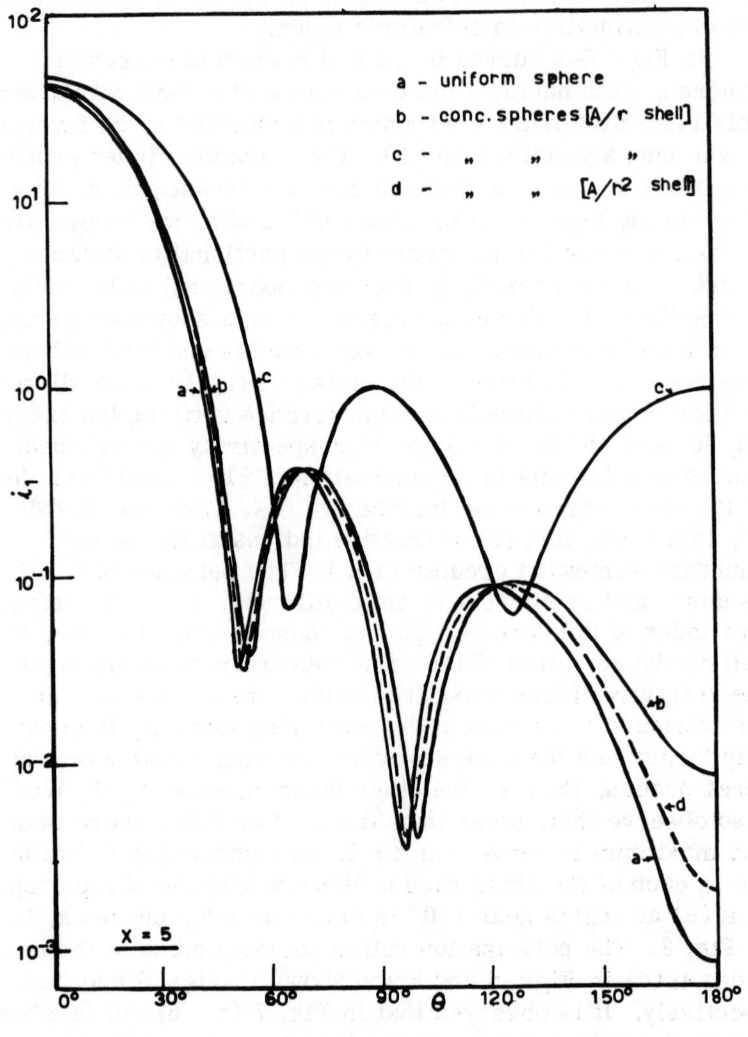

Fig. 6. Vertically polarized intensity $i_1(\theta)$ with same total refractive material and refractive indices given in Fig. 1 by the same letters a, b, c, d; $2\pi a/\lambda = 5$

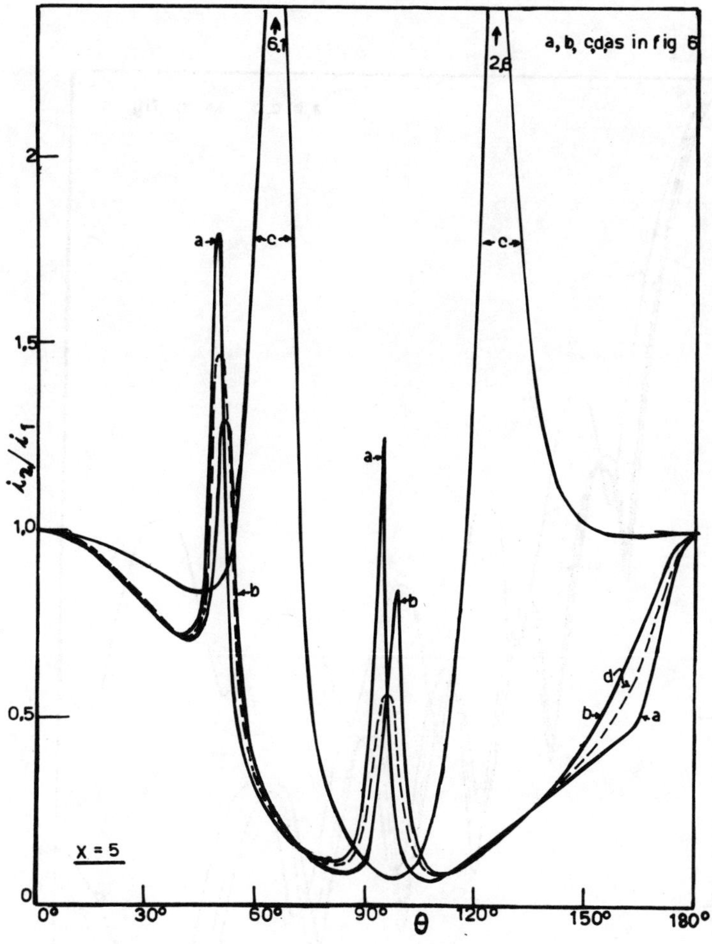

Fig. 7. Polarization ratio $\Pi(\theta)$ with refractive indices as in Fig. 6; $2\pi a/\lambda = 5$

In Figs. 10-13, curve D describes the scattering from the same Cauchy distribution for the refractive index as in Figs. 2-5 and this is compared with scattering patterns by the parabolic distributions, represented by curves E and F. The refractive index profiles shown in Fig. 1 for D and E are so chosen that the indices are equal at the centre of the sphere ($n = 1.2$) and at its boundary ($n = 1$). Consequently the total

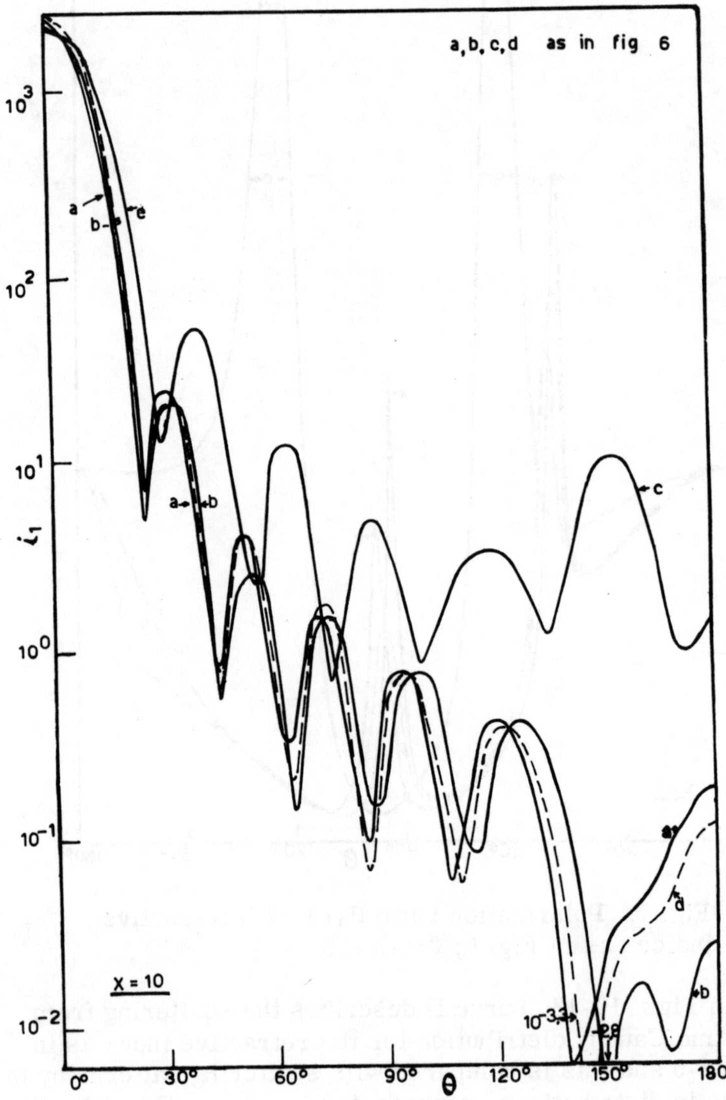

Fig. 8. Vertically polarized intensity $i_1(\theta)$ as in Fig. 6; $2\pi a/\lambda = 10$

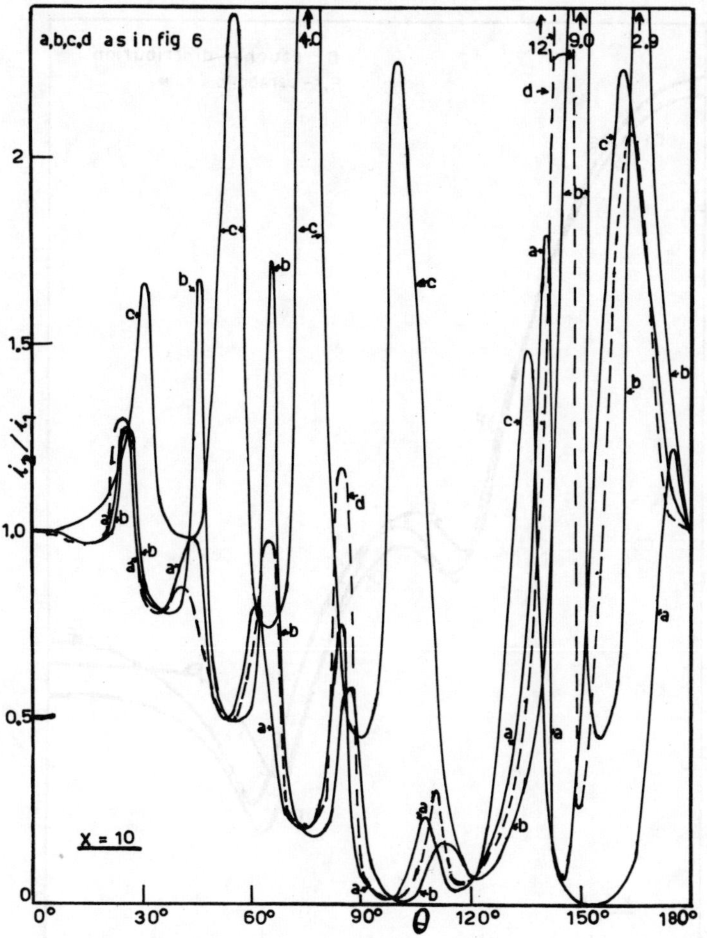

Fig. 9. Polarization ratio $\Pi(\theta)$ as in Fig. 8; $2\pi a/\lambda = 10$

refractive material for the parabolic form E is slightly greater than that for the Cauchy form D, the mean refractive indices $\bar{n}$ being 1.084 and 1.074 respectively. Thus $i_1(\theta)$ for E should exceed that for D over most of the range of angle θ. In order that D and F have equal refractive indices (1.2) at the centre of the sphere and yet represent the same amount of refractive material, the refractive index for

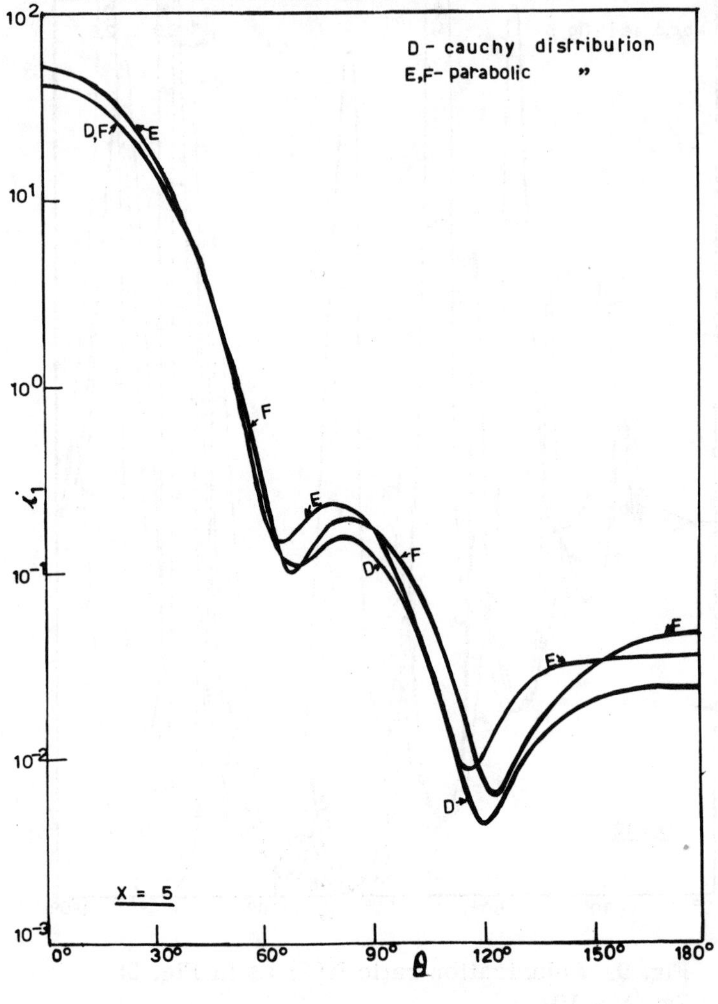

Fig. 10. Vertical polarized intensity $i_1(\theta)$ with refractive indices given by Cauchy or parabolic distribution; $2\pi a/\lambda = 5$

D: Cauchy distribution, $m = 1.2$ and $\epsilon = 0.2$

E, F: parabolic distribution $m = 1.2$ and $\epsilon = 0.153$ and 0.164 respectively.

D, F: have same total refracting material

Refractive indices of D, E shown in Fig. 1; they equal 1 at boundary $r = a$.

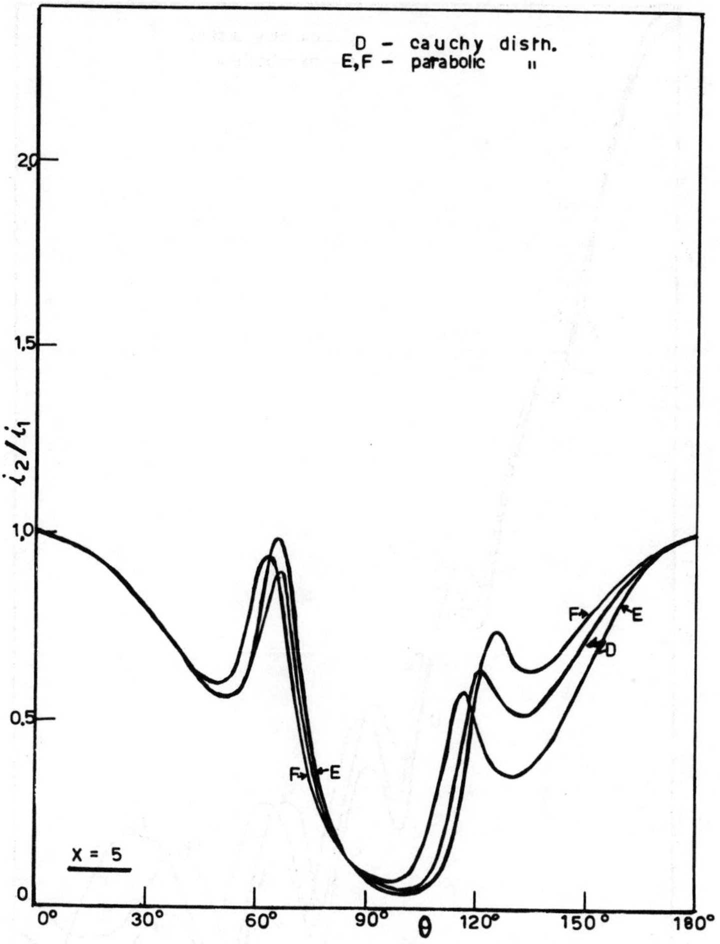

Fig. 11. Polarization ratio $\Pi(\theta)$ for distributions in Fig. 10;

$$2\pi a/\lambda = 5$$

F must diminish to a value somewhat less than 1 (n = 0.97) at the boundary of the particle. This causes F to have higher back scattering than D. The three sets of $i_1(\theta)$ plots for D, E, F are similar in their numbers of maxima and minima and differ by very little for angles below about 60° at both x = 5 and x = 10. However, beyond $\theta = 120°$ the differences

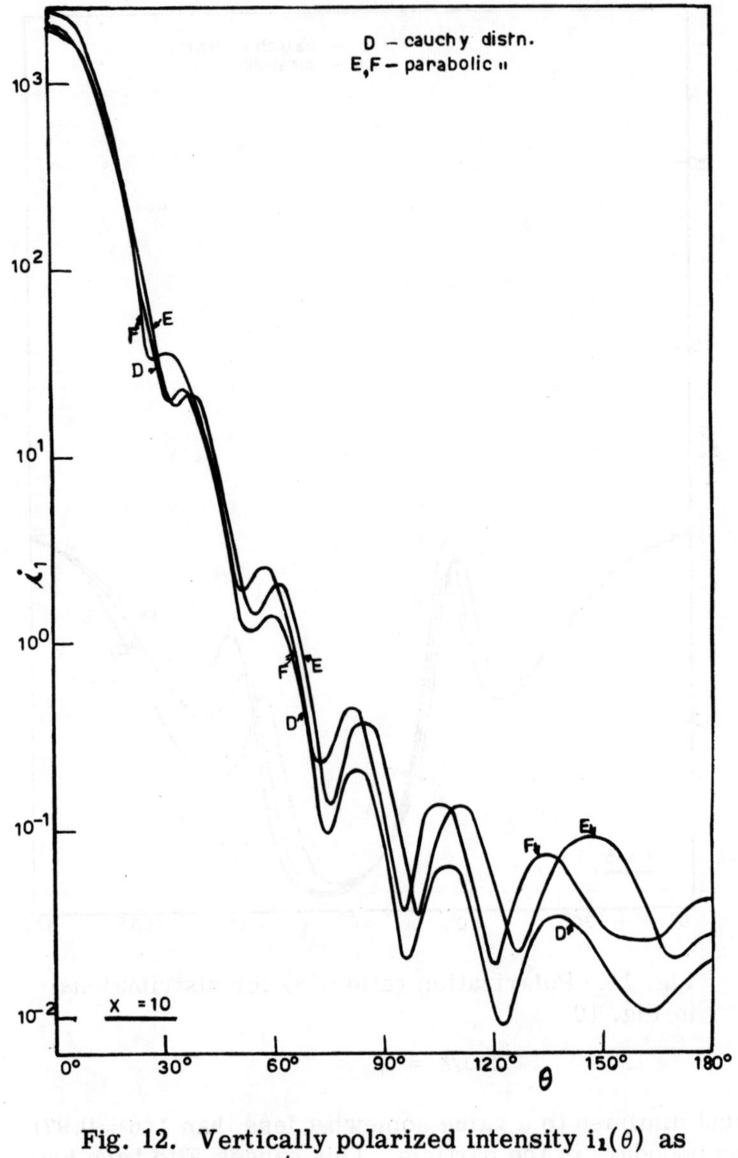

Fig. 12. Vertically polarized intensity $i_1(\theta)$ as in Fig. 10; $2\pi a/\lambda = 10$

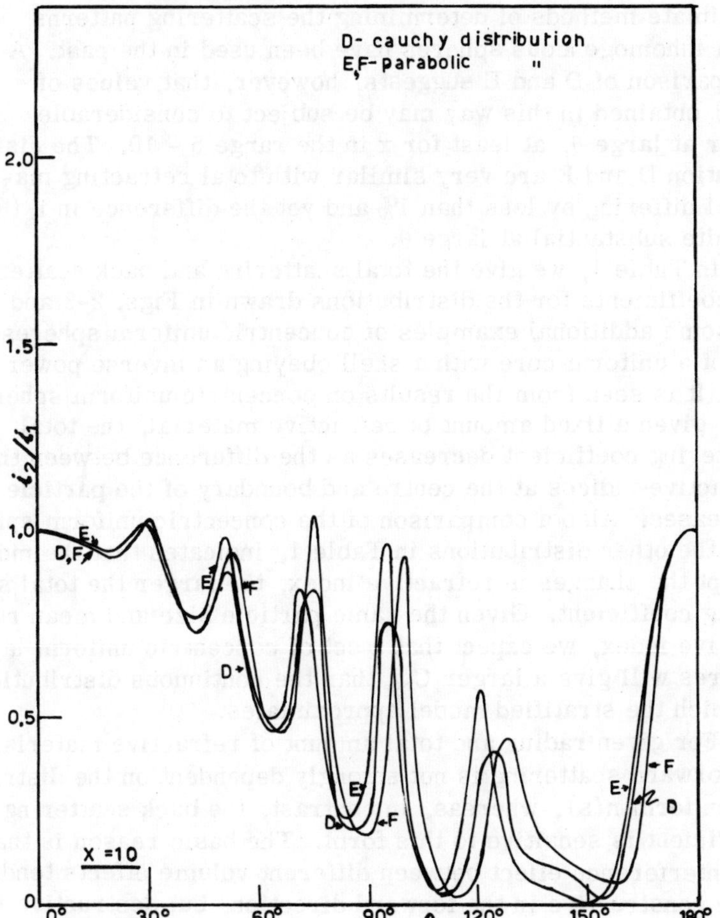

Fig. 13. Polarization ratio $\Pi(\theta)$ as in Fig. 11; $2\pi a/\lambda = 10$

in $i_1(\theta)$ are as much as by factors of 2 and 5 at $x = 5$ and 10 respectively. Since the polarization ratio must equal 1 at the two ends $\theta = 0°$ and $180°$ for a radially symmetrical inhomogeneous particle, the three corresponding curves for $\Pi(\theta)$ coincide at the ends. However, there is still a noticeable difference between the $\Pi(\theta)$ for D, E and F in the region $\theta > 90°$. We mentioned in the introduction that various approximate methods of determining the scattering patterns from inhomogeneous spheres have been used in the past. A comparison of D and E suggests, however, that values of $i_1(\theta)$ obtained in this way may be subject to considerable error at large θ, at least for x in the range 5 - 10. The distribution D and E are very similar with total refracting material differing by less than 1% and yet the difference in $i_1(\theta)$ is quite substantial at large θ.

In Table 1, we give the total scattering and back scattering coefficients for the distributions drawn in Figs. 2-3 and for some additional examples of concentric uniform spheres and of a uniform core with a shell obeying an inverse power law. It is seen from the results on concentric uniform spheres that, given a fixed amount of refractive material, the total scattering coefficient decreases as the difference between the refractive indices at the centre and boundary of the particle decreases. Also a comparison of the concentric uniform spheres with the other distributions in Table 1, indicates that the more abrupt the changes in refractive index, the larger the total scattering coefficient. Given the same particle size and mean refractive index, we expect that a set of concentric uniform layered spheres will give a larger C_{sca} than the continuous distribution to which the stratified model approximates.

For given radius and total amount of refractive material, the forward scattering is not strongly dependent on the distribution form n(s), whereas, in contrast, the back scattering coefficient is sensitive to this form. The basic reason is that the interference effect between different volume effects tends to be constructive in the forward direction, but destructive in the backward direction. However, the back-scattering cross section σ is not easily predicted for specified n(s), since it tends to oscillate with change in the parameters relevant to the scattering. For example, for a uniform dielectric sphere, σ oscillates with increase in ka (see Mikulski and Murphy (22)). From the results on concentric uniform spheres shown in the table, we see that σ also oscillates as the step in the refractive index is varied. The reason for an increase in back scattering when the refractive index drops below 1 at the particle boundary can be illustrated as follows. Consider two volume elements dV_1 and dV_2 of the particle whose refractive indices both

TABLE 1

Total Scattering Coefficient and Back Scattering Coefficient*

Description	Curve	m	δ	$\frac{a_0}{a}$	x = 5 $\frac{C_{sca}}{\pi a^2}$	x = 5 $\frac{\sigma}{\pi a^2} \times 10^3$	x = 10 $\frac{C_{sca}}{\pi a^2}$	x = 10 $\frac{\sigma}{\pi a^2} \times 10^3$
	A	1.2	1	0.717	0.493	32.3	1.524	10.5
	-	1.2	1.01	0.695	0.471	15.3	1.464	0.18
Concentric		1.2						
uniform	–	1.2	1.02	0.669	0.447	4.5	1.400	14.8
spheres	B	1.2	1.03	0.636	0.420	2.0	1.336	39.1
	-	1.2	1.04	0.596	0.391	6.6	1.263	29.1
	-	1.2	1.05	0.542	0.357	10.5	1.189	6.5
	C	1.2	1.06	0.462	0.317	4.6	1.114	5.1
Uniform sphere	a	1.2	-	1	0.260	0.13	1.010	6.9
			n(x)					
Uniform core	c	1.2	0.87	0.722	0.584	15.0	1.781	54.4
Power law shell	b	1.083	1	0.923	0.280	1.3	1.075	1.06
$n = xn(s)/s$	-	1.079	1.02	0.946	0.270	0.49	1.043	3.3
$(x_0 \leq s \leq x)$	-	1.076	1.04	0.967	0.264	0.21	1.032	4.5
Power law shell	d	1.078	1.01	0.968	0.267	0.33	1.033	0.46
$n = x^2 n(s)/s^2$	-	1.074	1.03	0.979	0.263	0.19	1.021	0.59
$(x_0 \leq s \leq x)$								
Cauchy distribution	D	1.2	1	-	0.375	3.8	1.277	0.77
$(\bar{n} = 1.084)$								
Parabolic	E	1.2	1	-	0.457	5.4	1.499	1.7
distribution	F	1.2	0.97	-	0.392	7.2	1.320	1.1

*Same total refractive material in all cases except E; Common mean index $\bar{n} = 1.0738$ and common radius; m = refractive index at center of sphere or of uniform core; n(x) = refractive index at boundary; a_0 = radius of inner core; $x = 2\pi a/\lambda$; $x_0 = 2\pi a_0/\lambda$

exceed 1 and suppose that cancellation occurs between these elements in the backward direction. If now the refractive index of dV_2 is decreased to a value less than 1 while that of dV_1 is unchanged, we will have a tendency toward reinforcement between dV_1 and dV_2. This simple picture of 'backward constructive interference,' which will be discussed for the Rayleigh-Gans region in the following section, is of course only qualitative.

In his treatment of scattering by a plasma coating on a spherical conductor, Murphy (23) chooses for his model a uniform layer of scattering material with refractive index n where $n^2 \leq 1$, including negative values. He calculates that when n^2 is diminished from 1, there is a pronounced drop in the back-scattering cross-section near the value $n^2 = 0$, immediately followed by a strong peak when n^2 becomes negative. This general 'resonance-dip' pattern is also obtained, although less sharply, for a multilayered distribution which approximates to the form $n^2(r) = 1 - \gamma/k^2r^2$, which was mentioned in the introduction. Murphy also discusses briefly the case of two concentric uniform dielectric spheres and shows that if one refractive index is greater than 1 and the other less than 1, then the dip phenomenon (but not the resonance phenomenon) can occur. Since Murphy restricts his treatment of the uniform layer to wave-lengths large compared with the particle size, his results are not strictly comparable with those discussed above. His argument implies that when $x \ll 1$, all the coefficients c_l and d_l defined by (4.8) and (4.9) become simultaneously very small by proper choice of the ratio a_0/a and of $m \gtrless 1$ according as $\delta \lessgtr 1$. It follows that the forward scattering and indeed the total scattering cross-section C_{sca} will also show dips. To verify this conclusion, we compare his condition for the dip (equation (M, 57)) with a formula for the total cross-section C_{sca} from Kerker, Kratohvil and Matijevic (15) (equation (KKM, 3)), which is obtained from an expression by Guttler (11) and is valid at small x. If it is assumed that the dominating term in C_{sca} is due to the 1th mode, then Murphy's dip condition (M, 57) is $C_l = 0$ and this may be written (in our notation) as

$$(\delta^2 - 1)\left[m^2 + \frac{(l+1)}{l}\delta^2\right] + \left(\frac{a_0}{a}\right)^3 (m^2 - \delta^2)\left[\frac{(l+1)}{l}\delta^2 + 1\right] = 0. \quad (6.5)$$

For small particles the main contribution to the total scattering coefficient comes from the first T.M. mode, i.e., from c_1, and hence we should choose $l = 1$ in (6.5). The square of the left-hand side of (6.5) now appears as a factor in the numerator of the expression (KKM, 3) for C_{sca}.

Recently Wait and Jackson (33) and Garbacz (8) have calculated the normalized bistatic cross-sections $\sigma_E(\theta)/\pi a^2$ and

$\sigma_H(\theta)/\pi a^2$ (defined in (2.23) and (2.24) for a sphere having a surface impedance boundary condition. They define the scattering coefficients c_l, d_l by means of (4.13), in which the impedance Z_l and admittance Y_l are assumed independent of the mode number l i.e., they assume $Z_l = 1/Y_l = Z$. Such an approximation is permissible in conditions different from those considered in the present paper, for example, with a highly conducting sphere coated with a thin film of dielectric or a dielectric exhibiting sufficient electric or magnetic loss. Nevertheless, they find certain general properties of the cross-sections $\sigma_E(\theta)$ and $\sigma_H(\theta)$ which are consistent with those of $i_1(\theta)$ and $i_2(\theta)$ illustrated in Figs. 2-13. Forward scattering is found to be insensitive to the impedance of the surface layer, whereas back-scattering is profoundly affected by changes in this impedance. Also the scattering pattern for the E-plane ($i_1(\theta)$) oscillates much more than does that for the H-plane ($i_2(\theta)$).

VII. RESULTS OF RAYLEIGH-GANS AND SOFT OBSTACLE APPROXIMATIONS

A detailed comparison of the Rayleigh-Gans (R. G.) theory with the Mie theory has been made for uniform spheres (see Kerker, Farone and Matijevic (16), Heller (14)) but we know of no corresponding work on inhomogeneous spheres. A brief account of such comparison will be given in the present paper. Fig. 14 shows plots of $i_1(\theta)$ and $i_2(\theta)$ according to the exact 'Mie' theory and the R.G. theory for two typical Cauchy distributions. The conditions for R.G. scattering are satisfied to a first approximation by the parameter values chosen in these examples, namely $m = 1$, $x = 1$ and $\epsilon = 0.05$ and 0.10. The differences in $i_1(\theta)$ are about 10% whilst those in $i_2(\theta)$ are smaller, principally because $i_2(\theta)$ vanishes exactly in the R.G. theory and very nearly in the Mie theory at $\theta = 90°$. We have already seen from the form of curve c in Figs. 6-9 that there is a large back scattering when $n < 1$ at the boundary of the particle (for $x = 5$ and 10). A corresponding behaviour can occur with the Cauchy distribution in the Rayleigh-Gans region provided x and ϵ are in the appropriate range. Fig. 15 depicts Mie plots of $i_1(\theta)$ and $i_2(\theta)$ for the

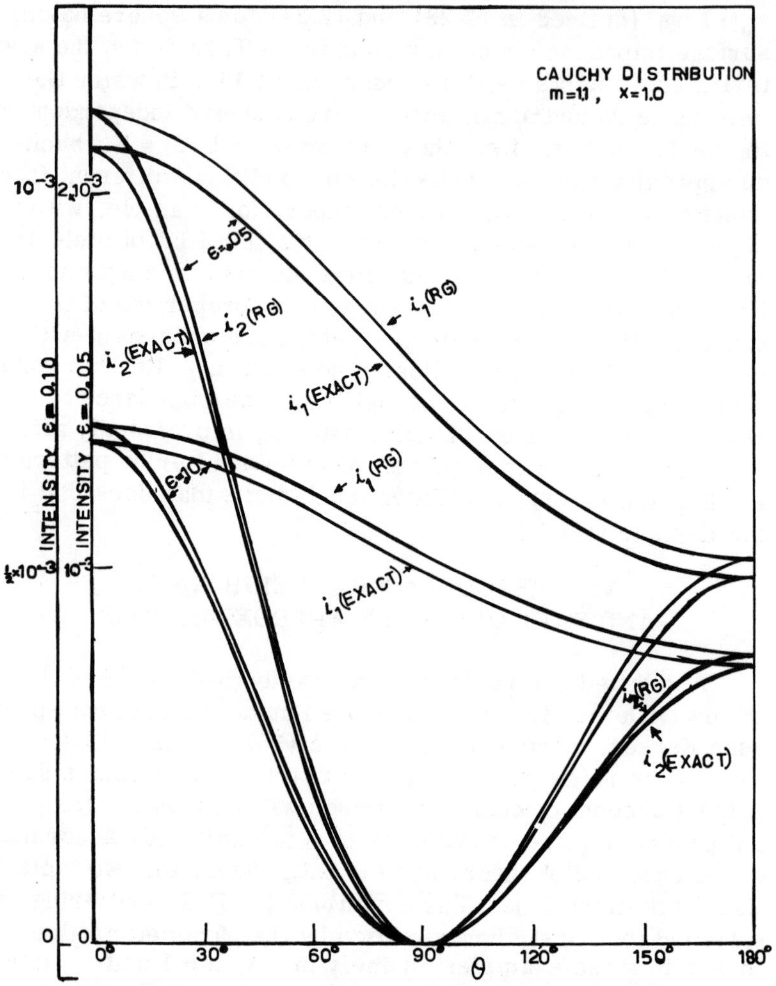

Fig. 14. Vertically and horizontally polarized intensities $i_1(\theta)$, $i_2(\theta)/$. Cauchy distribution for the refractive index with m = 1.1 and ϵ = 0.05 and 0.10;

(R.G.): intensities based on the Rayleigh-Gans approximate theory

(Exact): intensities based on the exact solutions in this paper

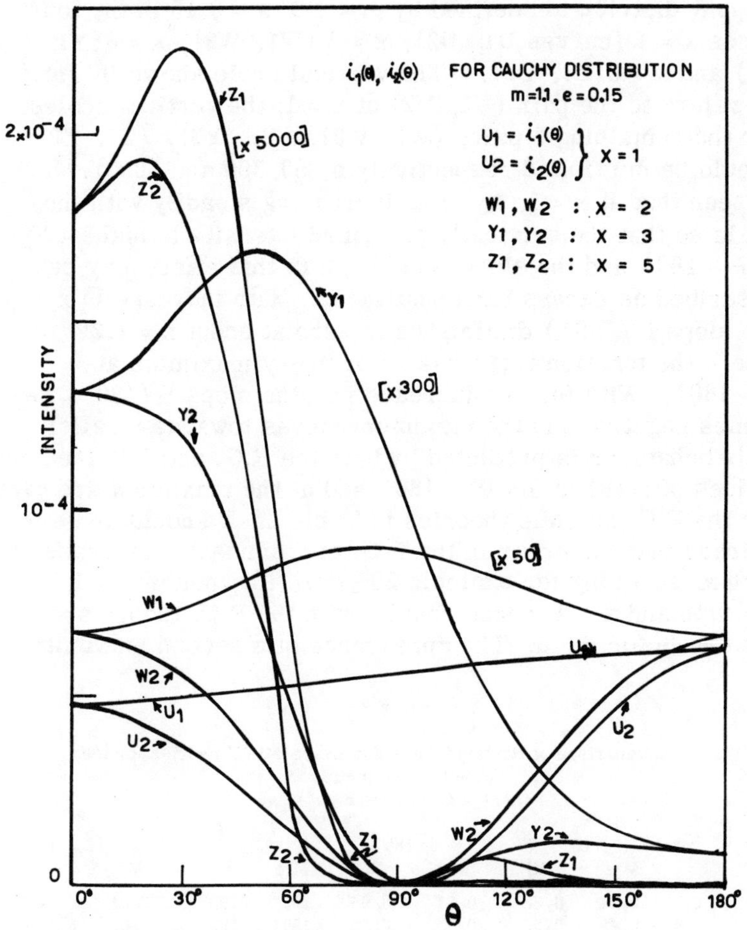

Fig. 15. Intensities $i_1(\theta)$ and $i_2(\theta)$ as in Fig. 14 with m = 1.1 and ϵ = 0.15. Plots for $i_1(\theta)$ and $i_2(\theta)$ labelled respectively Ul, U2, (x = 1) W1, W2 (x = 2), Yl, Y2 (x = 3) and Z1, Z2 (x = 5). Note that vertical scales at x = 2, 3, and 5 are multiplied respectively by 50, 300 and 5000.

Cauchy distribution defined by $m = 1.1$, $\epsilon = 0.15$ in the four cases $x = 1$ (curves U1, U2), $x = 2$ (W1, W2), $x = 3$(Y1, Y2) and $x = 5$(Z1, Z2). (The vertical scale shown in Fig. 15 refers to the pair (U1, U2) at $x = 1$; the vertical scales for the remaining 3 pairs (W1, W2), (Y1, Y2), (Z1, Z2) should be multiplied respectively by 50, 300 and 5000). It is seen that at $x = 1$, $i_1(\theta)$ is increasing steadily with the angle so that the vertically polarized intensity is highest at $\theta = 180°$ and the slope $i_1'(180°) > 0$; this effect may be described as excess back scattering. With increase in x, the slope $i_1'(180°)$ diminishes to zero at about $x = 1.2$ where the function $i_1(\theta)$ has an ordinary maximum at $\theta = 180°$. With further increase in x the slope $i_1'(180°)$ becomes negative and the maximum moves towards smaller θ. This behaviour is predicted by both the R.G. and Mie theories. Values of $i_1(\theta)$ at $\theta = 0°$, $180°$ and at the maximum are given for the R.G. and Mie theories in Table 2. It should be remarked that the error in the R.G. approximation increases with x, attaining for example 20% in $i_1(\theta)$ when $m = 1.1$, $\epsilon = 0.15$ and $x = 2$; hence results with the R.G. theory are not shown for $x = 5$. The appearance of a second maximum

TABLE 2

Comparison of Rayleigh-Gans and Exact 'Mie' Theories for the Cauchy Distribution
$(n(r) = 1.1/(1 + \epsilon r^2/a^2))$

ϵ	x	$i_1(0°)$		$i_1(180°)$		θ_{max}		$i_1(\theta_{max})$	
		Mie	RG	Mie	RG	Mie	RG	Mie	RG
	0.5	$.0_6 74$	$.0_6 88$	$.0_6 81$	$.0_6 95$	180°	180°	$.0_6 81$	$.0_6 95$
	1.0	$.0_4 48$	$.0_4 56$	$.0_4 63$	$.0_4 70$	180°	180°	$.0_4 63$	$.0_4 70$
	1.5	$.0_3 57$	$.0_3 64$	$.0_3 77$	$.0_3 81$	126°	120°	$.0_3 77$	$.0_3 83$
	2.0	.0034	.0036	.0033	.0034	83°	77°	.0033	.0047
0.15	2.5	.0130	-	.0058	. -	64°	-	.0058	-
	3.0	.0392	.0411	.0026	.0035	44°	53°	.0026	.0533
	4.0	.232	.229	.013	.0065	35°	37°	.013	.300
	5.0	.903	.875	.0016	.0015	30°	31°	.0016	1.141
	0.5	$.0_5 18$	$.0_5 15$	$.0_5 11$	$.0_6 86$			$.0_5 11$	
	1.0	$.0_3 114$	$.0_4 93$	$.0_5 81$	$.0_5 38$			$.0_5 81$	
	1.5	.0013	.0011	$.0_3 13$	$.0_3 18$			$.0_3 13$	
0.20	2.0	.0068	.0060	.0033	.0036			.0033	
	3.0	.0756	.0694	.0145	.0140			.0145	
	4.0	.4049	.3887	.0234	.0125			.0234	

$.0_i 1 = 10^{-i+1}$

in the Mie curve for $i_1(\theta)$ at $x = 5$ is to be noted. We have also computed intensities $i_1(\theta)$ and $i_2(\theta)$ for the Cauchy distribution with parameters $m = 1.1$ and $\epsilon = 0.20$ and values of $i_1(\theta)$ at $\theta = 0°$ and $180°$ are shown in Table 2. The difference $i_1(0°) - i_1(180°)$ again becomes positive, and the intensity $i_1(\theta)$ is once more highest at $\theta = 0°$. Since $i_2(\theta)$ behaves much like $i_1(\theta)\cos^2\theta$ it is identical with $i_1(\theta)$ at the two ends and has its minimum value at angles close to 90°. In general the error incurred in the R.G. approximation for $i_2(\theta)$ is smaller than for $i_1(\theta)$.

The occurrence of excess back scattering can be understood by considering the quantity $\overline{n^2} - 1$ where $\overline{n^2}$ is the mean square refractive index of the particle. According to (5.7) and (5.8), the R.G. theory gives identical scattering patterns for any refractive index distribution $n_1(r)$ and the 'complementary' one given by $n_2(r) = (2 - n_1^2(r))^{1/2}$. These two forms have the property that $n_2(r) \gtrless 1$ according as $n_1(r) \lessgtr 1$. In order that the R.G. forward scattering intensities be equal, it is only sufficient that $\overline{n_2^2} = 2 - \overline{n_1^2}$ since $i_1(0°)$ is proportional to $(\bar{n}^2 - 1)^2$ for any distribution $n(r)$. For the three values $\epsilon = 0.10$, 0.15 and 0.20 considered above, the refractive indices at the particle center have a common value 1.1 while those at the boundary equal 1, 0.96 and 0.91 respectively. Making use of (6.2) the corresponding three values of $\bar{n}$ are 1.038, 1.011 and 0.984, and from the formula

$$\overline{n^2} = \frac{3m^2}{2\epsilon^2}\left[\sqrt{\epsilon}\tan^{-1}\sqrt{\epsilon} - \frac{\epsilon}{(1+\epsilon)}\right] \tag{7.1}$$

for the mean square refractive index of the Cauchy distribution, $\overline{n^2} = 1.079$ 1.023 and 0.971 respectively. The forward scattering intensity $i_1(0°)$ vanishes when $\overline{n^2} = 1$ near $\epsilon = 0.17$ and if we move away on either side from this value of ϵ then $i_1(0°)$ increases. If follows that for values of ϵ close to 0.17 the back scattering instensity $i_1(180°)$ will exceed $i_1(0°)$. The general picture is that for small spheres at fixed m and ϵ, the ratio $i_1(180°)/(i_1(0°)$ at first increases with ϵ, until ϵ passes a critical point where the forward scattering is zero and then this ratio starts to decrease. Also, good agreement between the R.G. and exact theories is generally obtained when the mean refractive index satisfies the two basic assumptions of the R.G. theory, and the latter theory is best in the neighbourhood of the angle at which the intensity $i_1(\theta)$ is greatest.

There is no contradiction between the occurrence of excess back scattering and the dip in back scattering discussed by Murphy. In the case of two uniform concentric spheres in the R.G. region, it follows from (5.12) that the forward scattering intensity is zero when

$$(x_0/x)^3 = (1 - \delta^2)/(m^2 - \delta^2) < 1 \tag{7.2}$$

where $m \gtrless 1$ according as $\delta \lessgtr 1$. It is easily seen that if (7.2) holds and $x \neq 0$, then $|R(180°)| \neq 0$, i.e., we have excess back scattering. Similarly the back scattering intensity is zero, but not the forward intensity, when

$$\frac{\sin 2x_0 - 2x_0 \cos 2x_0}{\sin 2x - 2x \cos 2x} = \frac{(1 - \delta^2)}{(m^2 - \delta^2)} < 1 \tag{7.3}$$

and for given m, δ and $x < \pi/2$, (7.3) gives a smaller value of x_0 then (7.2). The relation (6.5) of Murphy holds if $x \ll 1$ but m and δ need not be close to 1 as in the R.G. formula (5.12), where x can be of order 1. If we assume $x \ll 1$ in the expression (5.12) for $R(\theta)$, then $g(u) \approx g(v) = 1/3$ for all angles θ and $R(\theta)$ is very nearly independent of θ. Choosing now $|m - 1| \ll 1$ and $|\delta - 1| \ll 1$ the relation (6.5) becomes practically identical with (7.2) and the scattering intensity may be taken as zero for all θ. The various examples described in this paper indicate that when the difference $n(r) - 1$ changes sign with increase in r from the particle center to its boundary, then we can have a wide range of scattering patterns, including excess back scattering under the appropriate conditions.

Excess back scattering and a maximum in the $i_1(\theta)$ curve have been observed experimentally in the precipitation of alloys (Walker and Guinier (34)) and phase separation in glasses (Maurer (21), Hammel and Ohlberg (12), where references to Russian and other work may be found). The explanation is given in terms of a growing particle of refractive index n_p which differs slightly from the refractive index n_0 of the solvent medium and is surrounded by a region of solvent of refractive index $n_s(r)$ where the precipitating substance is depleted (see Hammel and Ohlberg and Goldstein (1963) for the theory). In the experiments of Hammel and Ohlberg $n_p = 1.49$, $n_0 = 1.52$ so that $n_p < n_0$, whereas $n_s(r) \geq n_0$. It is assumed that any decrease in refractive index of the growing particle is balanced by an increase in refractive index of the region surrounding the particle, and hence the forward scattering intensity is practically zero. Examples of the Cauchy distribution which would correspond to the experimental system of Hammel and Ohlberg are 'complementary' to the one considered in this paper since they would have $m \approx n_p/n_0 = 0.98$ and ϵ negative. Also, in order to satisfy the condition $\overline{n^2} = 1$ for zero forward scattering, the magnitude of ϵ must be considerably smaller that 0.17. However, Hammel and Ohlberg's distribution of the refractive index is quite different from the simple Cauchy form and resembles more the concentric sphere model of section IV, with an inverse power law index for the outer shell. They find that as the particles grow in size (x increases), $i_1(180°)$ is at first the highest value of $i_1(\theta)$ but at some $x \lesssim 1/2$ a maximum occurs in $i_1(\theta)$ at $\theta = 180°$ and then this maximum moves to smaller θ. Our particle size and values of $|\epsilon|$ and $|m|$ are therefore larger than those corresponding to these experiments and in addition, the fact that our curves for $i_1(\theta)$ in Fig. 15 do not show the same tendency to approach zero at $\theta = 0$ is due to our choice $\epsilon = 0.15$, since this does not quite correspond to the condition of zero forward scattering. We conclude that our calculations on the Cauchy distribution are consistent with the experiments of Hammel and Ohlberg.

We briefly discuss some results on the 'soft obstacle' (S.O.) approximation for the Cauchy and parabolic distributions as described in V. It was explained that with the parabolic form, the S.O. approximation gives the exact expression for $G_1(s)$, whereas $W_1(s)$ is correct up to and including order ϵ^2. For small ϵ, therefore, the S. O. method should provide reasonably accurate scattering patterns of this distribution. At the same time, the difference between the scattering functions of the Cauchy and parabolic distributions is of order ϵ^2. Hence the S. O. solution to the parabolic form is also an approximation to the Cauchy one to order ϵ. We have compared the exact scattering results for the Cauchy distribution with the S. O. results for the parabolic case at the common parameters $m = 1.1$ and $\epsilon = 0.05$. The values of $i_1(0°)$ and $i_1(180°)$ are shown for $x = 1$ to 5 in Table 3. The refractive indices are equal at the particle center, their values are 1.048 and 1.044 at $r = a$ and their means are 1.089 and 1.080 for the Cauchy and parabolic particles respectively. Differences in the

TABLE 3

Comparison of S. O. Approximation for the Parabolic Distribution $n(r) = 1.1(1 - 0.1\, r^2/a^2)^{1/2}$ with Rayleigh-Gans and Exact Theories for the Cauchy Distribution $n(r) = 1.1/(1 + 0.05\, r^2/a^2)$

	$i_1(0°)$			$i_1(180°)$		
x	Exact	S. O.	R. G.	Exact	S. O.	R. G.
1	0.00212	0.00 212	0.00224	0.0_3979	0.00100	0.00103
2	0.1405	0.1381	0.1430	0.00189	0.00237	0.00284
3	1.636	1.585	1.654	0.0102	0.0091	0.0061
4	9.205	8.884	9.250	0.00706	0.0052	0.0_552
5	34.86	33.34	35.78	0.00294	00.00342	0.0134

intensity $i_1(0°)$ between the exact Cauchy and the S.O. approximation to the parabolic distribution at specified m and ϵ becomes more pronounced with increase in x. For example, at $m = 1.1$ and $\epsilon = 0.05$, the two values of $i_1(0°)$ differ at the most by about 2% for $x < 3$, by 5% at $x = 5$ an by 10% at $x = 10$. These differences diminish if m is increased at fixed ϵ and x, an example being 1% for $x = 5$ and less than 5% for $x = 10$ if $m = 1.3$. Just as in Figs. 10-13, the scattering intensities for the Cauchy and the parabolic distributions diverge much more at the large angles; from Table 3 we observe that the two values of $i_1(180°)$ can differ by more than 20% for $x \leq 5$ when $m = 1.1$ and $\epsilon = 0.05$. In the case when $\epsilon = 0.05$, $m = 1.3$ and $x \leq 5$, however, the separation in $i_1(\theta)$ is found to be 2% at the most for all values of θ.

Since $\epsilon = (m - 1)/2$ and $(m - 1)/6$ for the two values of m quoted here, it appears that a better criterion than ϵ for the accuracy of the S.O. approximation is the value of $\epsilon/(m - 1)$. The values of $i_1(180°)$ in Table 3 again illustrate how a small change in the form of the refractive index (< 1% in the mean $\bar{n}$), can be responsible for a much greater change in back scattering. In Table 3, the R.G. intensities for the Cauchy distribution with $m = 1.1$ and $\epsilon = 0.05$ are also given. (The S.O. approximation should now be interpreted as applying to the Cauchy form, valid to order ϵ.) We see that the R.G. and S.O. values are comparable in accuracy for the forward angles, but when $x \geq 3$ the R.G. approximation is much poorer at the back angles.

VIII. DISCUSSION

Certain general conclusions can be drawn from the calculations in this paper. For given particle radius and total amount of refractive material, the forward scattering is only slightly affected by changes in the distribution of the refractive index, whereas the back scattering is very sensitive to such changes. Since the scattering generally has its greatest value at $\theta = 0$ we may expect that the total scattering cross-section C_{sca} is governed to a considerable extent by the scattering at low angles. This implies that C_{sca} is less sensitive to the form of the refractive index than the scattering pattern of, say $i_1(\theta)$ at angles sufficiently greater than 0°.

A qualitative argument demonstrating the basic difference in behaviour between forward and backward scattering can be given in terms of the phase angles. Suppose that we use some approximate method of evaluating the scattering pattern from a known distribution $n(r)$ or replace this by a more convenient approximate function. The correct set of phase angles δ_l, η_l will be approximated by a different set $\delta_l + \epsilon_l$, $\eta_l + \mu_l$ where ϵ_l, μ_l are small. To linear terms in ϵ_l and μ_l the backward scattering coefficient (2.27) becomes

$$\frac{\sigma}{\pi a^2} = \frac{1}{x^2} \left| \sum_{l=1}^{\infty} (-1)^l (2l+1)[e \quad - e^{2i\eta} + 2i(\epsilon_l e^{2i\delta_l} - \mu_l e^{2i\eta_l})] \right|^2$$

$$[\exp(2i\delta_l) - \exp(2i\eta_l) + 2i(\epsilon_l \exp(2i\delta_l) - \mu_l \exp(2i\eta_l))] \Big|^2$$

From our computations with the Cauchy and parabolic distributions, it appears that the phases δ_l and η_l are close together for the relevant values of $l(\lesssim x)$ when (1) $n \approx 1$ at the particle boundary, (2) $x \gtrsim 4$, (3) the distribution $n(r)$ is smooth and continuous and (4) the slope $dn(r)/dr$ is moderate. In these circumstances, for each mode $l \lesssim x$ the term in the series (8.1) is approximated by

$$(-1)^l\, 2i(2l+1)(\mu_l - \epsilon_l)\exp(2i\eta_l) \tag{8.2}$$

The corresponding term in the forward scattering series reads

$$2(2l+1)\left[\exp(2i\eta_l) - 1 + i(\mu_l + \epsilon_l)\exp(2i\eta_l)\right] \tag{8.3}$$

Since η_l differs from 0 or π unless $l > x$, we see that the errors ϵ_l and μ_l dominate the lth mode in (8.2) to a much greater extent than in (8.3). The factor $(2l+1)$ makes the error more significant in the higher terms of the series and this is relevant at large x, where the series converges less rapidly. When x is small (< 2), $|c_l| \approx |\delta_l|$ and $|d_l| \approx |\eta_l|$ are both small compared with 1 and it is more difficult to visualize the general effect of the errors ϵ_l and μ_l.

The computations were carried out on the electronic computer Atlas at Manchester University and the authors are indebted to Manchester University Computing Service for the facilities. The series (2.16) for the hypergeometric function was found to converge sufficiently rapidly for the computations on the Cauchy distribution at the values of x and ϵ considered. In the case of the parabolic distribution, convergence of the series (3.8) or (3.11) was found satisfactory at $x = 5$ but not at $x = 10$, where a Kutta-Merson method for numerical integration of (2.6) was used. Here different techniques of summing the series at large x are required but these have not been investigated. For the cases of concentric spheres, standard methods of computing the Bessel functions in different ranges of the argument and order were employed.

ACKNOWLEDGMENTS

This work was initiated and inspired by Professor M. Kerker during the stays of one of us (S.L.) at Clarkson College of Technology, Potsdam, New York, and we are greatly indebted to him for many invaluable suggestions. We also wish to thank Dr. C. Smart of Unilever Research Laboratory, Port Sunlight, England for lengthy discussions on a number of aspects in this paper.

We are indebted to the Nigerian Federal Government for granting a graduate scholarship to G.O.O. during the past three years.

REFERENCES

(1) Aden, A. L. and Kerker, M., J. Appl. Phys., **22**, 1242 (1951).

(2) Albini, F.A., J. Appl. Phys., **33**, 3032 (1962).

(3) Arnush, D., Trans. I.E.E.E. on Antennas and Propagations, **AP-12**, 86 (1964).

(4) Bremmer, H., Terrestrial Waves, 138, Elsevier Publ. Co., Amsterdam (1948).

(5) Espenscheid, W.F., Willis, E., Matijevic, E., and Kerker, M., 39th Nat. Colloid Symposium, Potsdam, New York, June 1965 (to appear in J. Colloid Science).

(6) Friedman, B., Communications on Pure and Applied Mathematics, **4**, 317 (1951).

(7) Electromagnetic Waves (Ed. Langer, R.E.), 301, **1962**, University of Wisconsin Press, Madison, Wisconsin.

(8) Garbacz, R.J., Antenna Lab., Ohio State University, Columbus, Ohio, Rept. No. 1223-3 on AF 33(616) - 8039, 1962; Proc. IRE., **50**, 1837 (1962); Phys. Rev., **133**, A 14 (1964).

(9) Goldstein, M., J. App. Physics, **34**, 1928 (1963).

(10) Gould, R.N. and Burman, R., J. Atmos and Terr. Phys., **26**, 335 (1964).

(11) Güttler, A., Ann. Physik, **11**, 65 (1952).

(12) Hammel, J.J. and Ohlberg, S.M., J. Appl. Phys., **36**, 1442 (1965).
(13) Hart, R.W. and Montroll, E.W., J. Appl. Phys., **22**, 376 (1952).
(14) Heller, W., J. Chem. Phys., **42**, 1609 (1965).
(15) Kerker, M., Kratohvil, J.P. and Matijevic, E., J. Opt. Soc. Amer., **52**, 506 (1962).
(16) Kerker, M., Farone, W.A. and Matijevic, E., J. Opt. Soc. Amer., **53**, 758 (1963).
(17) Levine, S. and Kerker, M., Interdisciplinary Conference on Electromagnetic Scattering, Potsdam, New York (1962), (Ed. Kerker, M.) 37, 1963, Pergamon Press, London.
(18) Lynch, P.J., Phys. Rev., **130**, 1235 (1963).
(19) Marcuvitz, N., Communication on Pure and Mathematics, **4**, 263 (1951).
(20) Margulies, R.S., and Scarf, F.L., Trans. I.E.E.E. on Antennas and Propagation, **AP-12**, 91 (1964).
(21) Maurer, R.D., J. Appl. Phys., **33**, 2132 (1962).
(22) Mikulski, J.J. and Murphy, E.L., Trans. I.E.E.E. on Antennas and Propagation, **AP-11**, 169 (1963).
(23) Murphy, E.L., J. Appl. Phys., **36**, 1918 (1965).
(24) Plonus, M.A., Trans. I.R.E. on Antennas and Propagation, **AP-9**, 573 (1961).
(25) Rheinstein, J., Lincoln Laboratory, Mass. Inst. of Technology, Lexington, Massachusetts, Rept. No. 273 on AF 19(604)-7400, 1962.
(26) Saxon, D.S. (a) "Lectures on the Scattering of Light," Dept. of Meteorology, University of California, Los Angles, Scientific Rept. No. 9, 1955;
(b) Trans. I.R.E. on Antennas and Propagation, **AP-7**, Special Supplement, p. 5320 (1959).
(27) Sayasov, Yu. S., Soviet Phys-Tech. Phys., **6**, 189 (1961).
(28) Scharfman, H., J. Appl. Phys., **25**, 1352 (1954).
(29) Tai, C.T., (a) Nature, **182**, 1600 (1958);
(b) Appl. Sci. Res., **B7**, 113 (1958);
(c) J. Res. Nat. Bur. Std., **67D**, 199 (1963).
(30) Uberall, H., Phys. Rev., **128**, 2429 (1962).
(31) van de Hulst, H.C., Light Scattering by Small Particles, 1957, John Wiley, N. Y.

(32) Wait, J.R., Appl. Sci. Res., **B10**, 441 (1963).
(33) Wait, J.R. and Jackson, C.M., Radio Science, J. Res. Natl. Bur. Std., **69D** 299 (1965).
(34) Walker, C. and Guinier, A., Acta Met., **1**, 568 (1953).
(35) Wyatt, P. J., (a) Phys. Rev., **127**, 1837 (1962);
(b) J. Appl. Phys., **34**, 207S (1963);
(c) Interdisciplinary Conference on Electromagnetic Scattering, Potsdam, N. Y. (1962), (Ed. Kerker, M.) 25, 1963, Pergamon Press, London;
(d) Phys. Rev., **134**, AB1 (1964);
(e) J. Appl. Phys., **35**, 1966 (1964).

Note added in proof

Recently, M. Kerker, L. H. Kauffman and W. A. Farone (J. Opt. Soc. Amer. **56**, 1053 (1966)) have considered scattering from two concentric spheres with power-law dependence for the refractive index in the outer-shell, based on formulae equivalent to our equations (4.8) - (4.11). They choose m = 2.105 (AgCl/core) and (x_o , x) = (0.18, 0.20) and (4.5, 5.0). Their comparison of different profiles is carried out for the same radius, but not for a common mean refractive index by volumes. They make the rather discouraging comment that the sensitivity of electromagnetic scattering to the form of n(r) is slight and that only limited knowledge about the refractive index profile may be possible from a study of scattering signals. Our results are in general consistent with this conclusion in regard to the total and forward angle scattering, but not to large angle scattering. However, much more theoretical and numerical work seems necessary before we can hope to obtain some general trends connecting the profile n(r) with the large angle scattering pattern.

Recently N. C. Wickramasinghe (Mon. Not. Roy. Astro. Soc., **126**, 99 (1963)) and N. C. Wickramasinghe, M. W. C. Dharmawardhana and C. Wyld (Mon. Not. Roy. Astro. Soc. **134**, 25 (1966)) have calculated the efficiency factors for extinction and scattering from interstellar grains, assumed to be spherical graphite cores covered with an ice mantle. They used the formulae of Guttler (11) for scattering from a uniform core surrounded by a uniform outer shell.

DISCUSSION FOLLOWING PAPER BY G. O. OLAOFE AND S. LEVINE

V.A. Erma: Am I correct in assuming that all the calculations you reported are carried out for real values of the parameters?

S. Levine: Yes, we did not consider absorption in the computations but the analysis itself can include this case.

V.A. Erma: I note a striking similarity in your results for the Cauchy and the parabolic distributions. Could it be that the cases you consider involved small values of ϵ? In that case, the two distributions are actually identical, as can be seen by expanding them to first order in ϵ, and accordingly the similarity would be expected.

S. Levine: The scattering patterns for these two distributions are identical to first order ϵ. But an appreciable difference in the intensities begins to appear, when $\epsilon > 0.05$, particularly at large angles and large values of $2\pi a/\lambda$. We would like to stress that our calculations suggest that a small variation in the refractive index profile can lead to quite appreciable differences in the scattering patterns at large angles.

M. Kerker: From your curves it looks as though the total scattering cross-sections might be very similar. Have you had a chance to look at this?

G.O. Olaofe: Since the total scattering cross-section is usually governed in the main by the scattering at small angles, it is only slightly affected by small changes in the form of the index of refraction.

SESSION II:

NON-PARTICULATE SCATTERING

Scattering by an Assembly of Molecules

J. A. Prins
Laboratory of Technical Physics, Technical University
Delft, The Netherlands

The original title of this contribution was: "Principles of Non-particulate Scattering", but on second thought it was changed, as it might suggest that we would only consider scattering by a continuous medium, whereas we shall also need the molecular concept of scattering matter.

In approaching our subject we shall successively make different starts for different purposes; but, whatever our starting point will be, I shall try to comply with a wish of the organizing committee and make some general remarks on the use of correlation functions, leaving it to others to go deeper into this matter.

Regarding the scattering mechanism we shall only need the classical concept of harmonic oscillations, set up by electromagnetic waves and then in their turn emitting them, though most of our conclusions would also apply to other scattering processes.

I. PARTICULATE SCATTERING

The droplets in a cloud or the small NaCl cubes in a salt cellar are good examples of the discrete macroscopic

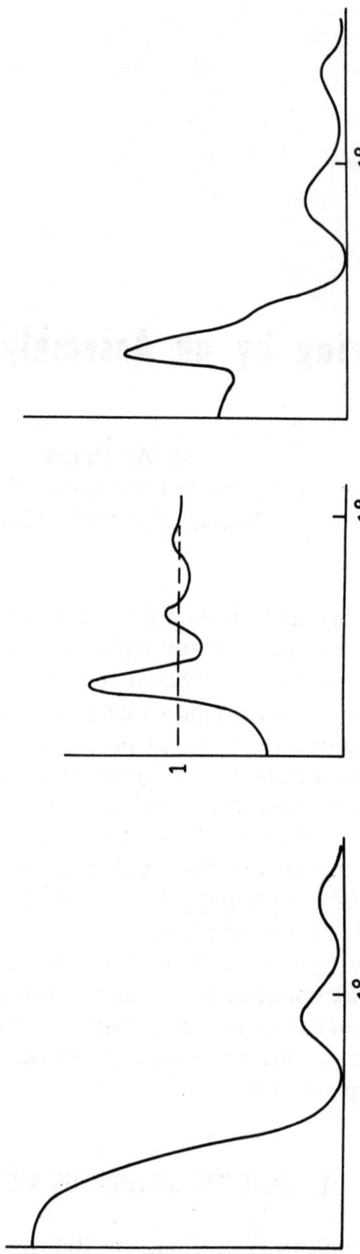

Fig. 1. Intensity of scattering by independent drops (left) of 60μ diameter and ordered drops (right) on a fogged up window pane. Central figure is the radial correlation factor i(s) for mean distance 150 μ.

scatterers which we shall consider first and which may be distributed chaotically or may be correlated to each other in mutual orientation or distance. Orientational correlation is found for instance in a drawn wire, where this "texture" shows up in the x-ray scattering diagram. As an example of correlation in distance we may take the "keeping apart" of circular holes in a metallic disk or of water drops condensed on a cold window pane. These two-dimensional arrangements produce halos round a point source of light viewed through them. In both cases the correlation often proves to be stronger than the minimum required by the geometric limitations (non-overlapping). The degree of radial correlation shows up in the diffraction pattern as a lowering of the scattered intensity at small angles, as compared with that of a chaotic distribution (Fig. 1) (4, 7, 10).

I shall now consider a quite different particulate scatterer: a spherulite between a polariser (V) and a crossed analyser (H), as shown in Fig. 2. We may for

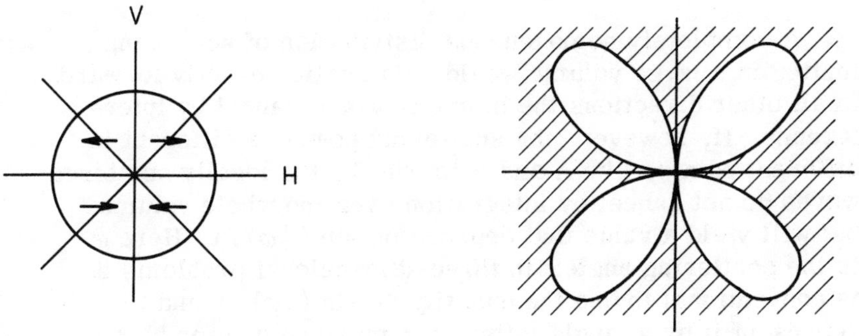

Fig. 2. Phase changes (left) and resulting diffraction pattern (right) of a spherulite between crossed nicols.

instance imagine a polymer film containing a number of such spherulites of equal size (say 10 microns). Geometrically their dimension would give rise to the well-known diffraction pattern of a circular aperture. But the radially symmetric anisotropy of the spherulites will accelerate the wave from for the horizontal component in two diagonally opposed quadrants and retard it in the two other quadrants, as indicated in Fig. 2. The relative retardation of the two diagonal parts is $\frac{1}{2}\lambda$ and this relative shift of the two parts of the wave front will transform its intensity pattern as a function of the scattering direction into a more or less clover leaf like pattern. This "quadripolar" symmetry will also appear in some other cases of scattering by anisotropy between crossed nicols, not however in what follows.

No correlation has as yet entered into the discussion. But if now we suppose the whole film to be submicroscopically anisotropic with a variable direction of anisotropy, resulting in macroscopical isotropy, we may express the distribution of the anisotropy by a correlation function (3). This brings us to the next starting point, the continuous manifold.

II. SCATTERING BY FLUCTUATIONS IN A CONTINUOUS MANIFOLD

A completely homogeneous distribution of scattering matter in a large volume would only scatter exactly forward. In all other directions the intensity would cancel by interference. If, however, the scattering power is different in different points, like A and B in Fig. 3, the locally scattered waves do not cancel by integration over the whole volume, but will yield a value that depends on $\sin(\frac{1}{2}\varphi)/\lambda$. Here φ is the scattering angle; in three-dimensional problems it is conventional to use the quantity $4\pi \sin(\frac{1}{2}\varphi)/\lambda$ and to represent it by a single letter, for instance s, u or h. In one or two dimensions $s = 2\pi \sin(\varphi)/\lambda$.

The scattered intensity as a function of this parameter i(s) is a kind of Fourier transform (invertible) of the distribution of scattering power, expressed as a radial correlation function g(r), the transforming function being cos(rs) in one dimension, sin(rs)/rs in three and J(rs) in two dimensions.

The fluctuation in scattering power may be due to several physical causes, which may be present simultaneously or separately. We consider only three cases:

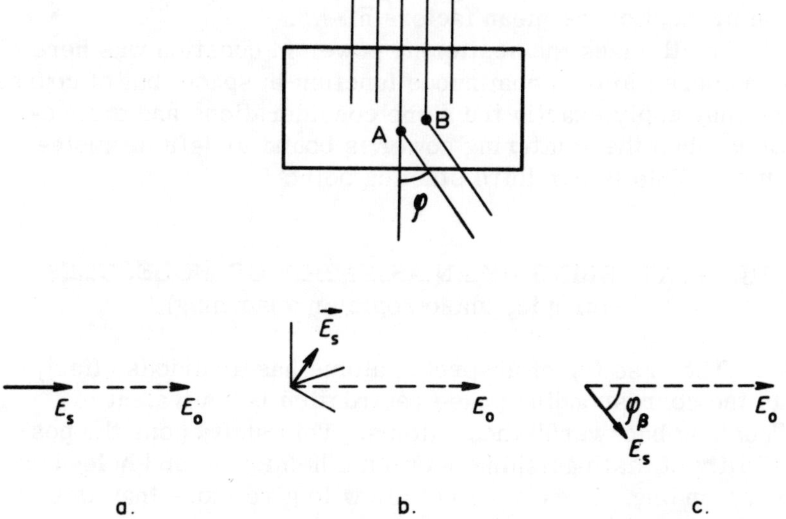

Fig. 3. Light scattering in a large volume (above). Below three scattering mechanisms represented by their phasor diagrams, vectorial in b.

a. fluctuations in optical density = n (the index of refraction),
b. fluctuations in anisotropy = $n_{//} - n_{\perp}$ (the double refraction),
c. fluctuations in absorption = β (from $n = 1 + \alpha - \beta i$).

The last effect (c) means a retardation of 90° of the scattered wave, immediately at the scattering process and leading to a total retardation in forward scattering of 180° (absorption). We shall not discuss this case. Its effect can usually be found by substituting a complex index of refraction in the formulae for the other cases.

The three cases are symbolized in Fig. 3 by their vector diagrams for the incident and scattered electric field strength. In case a. and c. these vectors are simple "phasors." A exp ($i\varphi_\beta$), to be put as a factor before the general time dependence exp ($i\,\omega t$).

The radial correlation function of a fluctuating quantity, say n, is defined as the mean product $\overline{n_A n_B}$ as a function of the distance r_{AB} (Fig. 3); it is mostly divided by the product of the mean factors $\overline{n}_A \cdot \overline{n}_B$.

In all cases the scattering power in question was here considered to be a continuous function in space; but of course, we may apply exactly the same considerations and distinctions when the scattering power is bound to definite molecules. This is our third starting point.

III. SCATTERING BY AN ASSEMBLY OF MOLECULES (isotropic, anisotropic or absorbing)

The case (c) of absorbing atoms has a curious effect, as the corresponding phase retardation is equivalent to "pushing backward" these atoms. This shift opens the possibility of distinguishing between a hemiedric and holoedric surrounding. Time does not allow to give more than this hint.

The scattering by anisotropic molecules has been treated by different authors (6). It has been proposed to use the term paratropy for a tendency of uniaxial molecules to put their axes parallel, and diatropy for putting them at right angles with immediate neighbours. Both cases seem to occur, in nature, as well as in the model liquid filmed by Kast and Stuart (2, 8). Diatropic tendency lowers the local anisotropy and also the scattering it causes, paratropic tendency enhances it.

Similar effects may of course be introduced into the continuum theory of the preceding section. Big paratropic "domains" would here be called liquid crystals.

It is time to leave the orientation problems and to return to the radial correlation function of the number density. In the same way as mentioned in number I for macroscopic particles, it may happen that the radial distances between molecules are even more correlated than the geometric limitations require. This is for instance the case for ions because of their electrostatic forces, which in dilute solutions reduce the small angle scattering to half its value for a gas, and in some strong solutions even more. Thorium ions are a rather trustworthy example (5). As a consequence of their electrostatic repulsion (or hydratation mantle, what amounts to much the same thing) they keep apart at a large distance from each other, forming in this way an array not unlike that of the black dots in frog spawn. Consequently, the diffraction peak due to their mutual distance is relatively sharp and its position shifts in proportion to the cube root of the dilution.

IV. CRITICAL FLUCTUATIONS AND SCATTERING

Whether we have a binary mixture or a simple substance like argon at the critical temperature or just above it, the situation is just the inverse of the preceding one: the fluctuations and thus the critical scattering or opalescence are much larger than they would be in an ideal gas of the same number density. Macroscopically this is due to the (almost) infinite compressibility. The phenomenon then would hold even for a perfect continuum, where the thermal fluctuations may be considered as standing elastic waves, as in Debye's theory of specific heat, the higher frequencies being cut off when their wavelength would approach molecular dimensions. Thus this thermal scattering shows up in the small angle x-ray diffraction pattern with a very high and almost constant intensity, dropping only when approaching the larger angles where the ordinary structural molecular diffraction pattern sets in, at about 10 Å (see Fig. 4). The constant intensity at small angles is determined by the compressibility and kT. It is the value of the compressibility that makes it almost infinite in the critical point, and on the other hand very low in ordinary liquids. The proportionality of the limiting small angle scattering with the compressibility has been verified experimentally for simple substances as well as for liquid mixtures (where of course it is the partial or osmotic compressibility which we have to insert in the formulae), (1, 9).

In the above considerations we have a certain mixture of continuum and molecular theory (which has been worked out in a more exact way by theorists, in the first place

Ornstein and Zernike). It explains why I have changed the original title of this contribution.

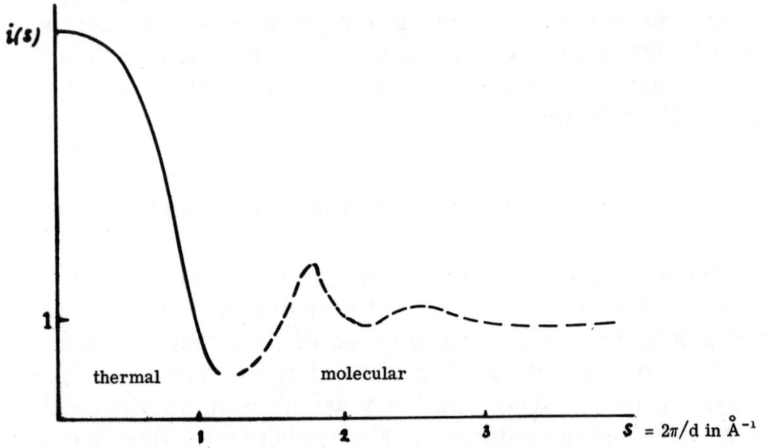

Fig. 4. X-ray small angle scattering (= optical scattering) of thermal origin (left) and large angle scattering of molecular (= structural) origin (right) by a fluid in the critical state, both shown schematically.

REFERENCES

(1) Fixmann, M., "Density Correlations, Critical Opalescence and the Free Energy of Non-uniform Fluids", J. Chem. Phys., **33**, 1357 (1960).

(2) Kast, W. and Stuart, H. A., "Die molekulare Struktur von Flüssigkeiten im Modellversuch", Physik, Zs., **40**, 714 (1939).

(3) Keijzers, A. E. M.; van Aartsen, J. J. and Prins, W., "Light Scattering by Shock Cooled Isotactic Polypropylene Film", J. Appl. Phys. 36,2874 (1965.)

(4) Prins, J. A., "Die Molekülanordnung in Flüssigkeiten und die damit zusammenhängenden Beugungserscheinungen", Naturwissenschaften, **19**, 435 (1931).

(5) Prins, J. A. and Fonteyne, R., "X-ray Evidence on the Ionic Arrangement in Thorium Nitrate Solutions". Physica, **2**, 570 (1935).

(6) Prins, J. A. and Prins, W., "Influence of Molecular Orientation on X-ray and Optical Scattering by Liquids", Physica, 23, 253 (1957).

(7) Reesinck, J. J. M. and de Vries, D. A., "The Diffraction of Light by a Large Number of Circular Objects", Physica, 7, 603 (1940).

(8) Stuart, H. A., "Ueber die molekulare Struktur von Flüssigkeiten", Kolloid-Zeitschr., 96, 149 (1941).

(9) Thomas, J. E. and Schmidt, P. W., "X-ray Study of Critical Opalescence in Argon", J. Chem. Phys., 39, 2506 (1963).

(10) Zernike, F., and Prins, J. A., "Die Beugung von Röntgenstrahlen in Flüssigkeiten als Effekt der Molekülanordnung", Zs. f. Physik, 41, 184 (1927).

DISCUSSION FOLLOWING PAPER BY J. A. PRINS

J. J. Hermans: What assumption was made in the calculation of the distances between thorium ions in the thorium salt solutions?

J. A. Prins: Cubic "close-packing" was taken but if I had used hexagonal close-packing or a more liquid-like arrangement it would have been practically the same. This allows one to obtain the theoretical line without additional assumptions, since the density and the concentration are known. I have repeated the experiments three times with intermissions of about 10 years to make sure of the concordance, the position of the maximum being difficult to measure exactly, of course, at small angles.

T. V. George: The statement that we know the ideal gas exhibits isotropic scattering is disputable. At least there is no experiment to back it up. Moreover, my experiments cast a shadow of doubt on this accepted theory.

J. A. Prins: I quite agree that your experiments did not show a horizontal line. What I gave was the usual picture, and I still have some confidence in it, though I agree it rests mainly on theory.

O. Kratky: At very small angles, indeed, you will find an additional scattering.

J. A. Prins: In what case?

O. Kratky: A gas, owing to the fluctuations.

J. A. Prins: No, that explanation cannot be true. You see, the fluctuations in a gas are adequately described by its compressibility.

O. Kratky: Maybe, but you can't tell.

J. A. Prins: Oh yes, again I feel confident, though it is only a theory. Whether you start with a compressible gas, be it ideal or not, or whether you start from an assembly of molecules moving in different directions, you get exactly the same result. Thermal fluctuations and molecular movement are exactly the same thing.

O. Kratky: But why does the scattering increase when you come near zero?

W. Prins: Professor Kratky is referring to the slight increase when you get very close to the primary beam.

O. Kratky: Yes, yes, I cannot say why, but it does.
J. A. Prins: I am inclined to attribute it to some spurious effect which we have to eliminate. In the case of x-rays it might be due to a contamination of the monochromatic radiation with a harder component in combination with the atomic form factor. It might also be due, especially in the optical case, to the dimensions of the irradiated volume.
O. Kratky: But these dimensions are very, very big. You could not find them.
J. A. Prins: No, perhaps not. But there might be dust particles or microgas bubbles present, of the right dimensions.
O. Kratky: Yes, yes, but indeed under usual conditions you find an increase.
J. A. Prins: Oh, then I would say you have impurities in your gas.
W. Prins: You have observed it, Professor Kratky, but there is no explanation for it?
O. Kratky: Yes, I have observed it but I have not published it. Other people have published it. Note added in proof: Meanwhile I have convinced myself that the arguments raised by Professor Prins are correct. I do agree with him that the increase at small angles must be caused by impurities.

Correlation Function Methods and Double Scattering

H. L. Frisch
Bell Telephone Laboratories, Incorporated
Murray Hill, New Jersey

ABSTRACT

We review briefly the use of correlation functions for electromagnetic scattering. Particular attention is paid to some aspects of the statistical geometry which are revealed in the correlation function. We summarize recent work on the double scattering of electromagnetic radiation and its application to the study of the critical behavior of fluids.

Correlation function methods are employed in many fields of physics, often to measure the temporal regression of fluctuations. Well-known examples are afforded by the theory of turbulence or the Kubo-Green formulation of the transport coefficients of a fluid. Spatial correlation functions, on the other hand, suggest themselves naturally for study whenever we deal with random media found in nature or produced by a human agency. The physical properties of random media depend in an involved way on their geometry which, in turn, is generally largely unknown. The scattering of electromagnetic radiation (E.M.R.) by such media allows one, in principle, to obtain some experimental information about their geometry as revealed through certain integral transforms of the lower order correlation functions. Practical difficulties arise quickly when one attempts to invert (or invert partially) the integral transforms of these correlations functions which curtail sharply the usefulness of the results. We shall first define what we mean by a random medium and its distribution and correlation functions. We shall then give some examples of the variety of geometrical information contained in them. Lastly we will briefly consider what can be learned about these correlation functions from scattering of E.M.R.

A sample of a random medium is thought to consist of a continuous or discrete set of points, V, in space, with a given, fixed frame of reference. Each sample, V, is labeled by a number w and is presumably chosen from a suitable ensemble of samples, the sample space Ω. The sampling procedure is to be prescribed. The medium is described by a suitable "structure" function $\xi(\mathbf{r}, w)$ defined for all points $\mathbf{r}$ in V. This function is to completely determine the geometry of the structure to the extent that it can be resolved by some given experimental procedure. For example, if a sample of a thermostatted fluid is studied by x-rays, the "structure" function is the instananeous total electron density, $\rho_e(\mathbf{r})$, whose fluctuations are responsible for scattering the x-rays, and the ensemble averaging indicated by $\langle \ \rangle$, is to be carried out using the Gibbs canonical ensemble density corresponding to the temperature of the fluid. For a fluid of N spherical molecules, located at $\mathbf{r}_1, \ldots, \mathbf{r}_i, \ldots, \mathbf{r}_N$, each possessing an electron density $f_e(\mathbf{r})$ at distance $|\mathbf{r}|$ from the center of the molecule, $\rho_e(\mathbf{r})$ can be written as

$$\rho_e(\mathbf{r}) = \sum_{i=1}^{N} f_e(\mathbf{r} - \mathbf{r}_i). \tag{1}$$

In the language of probability theory $\xi(\mathbf{r}, w)$ is a <u>random variable.</u> The infinite family of random variables $\{\xi(\mathbf{r}, w), \mathbf{r} \text{ in } V\}$ is a stochastic process and it is this stochastic process which we identify as defining our <u>random medium</u> (see e.g. Frisch, 5). The k-point distribution function (d.f.) of the random medium is

$$F_{1,2,\ldots,k}(x_1, x_2, \ldots, x_k) = \Pr\{\xi(\mathbf{r}_i) \leq x_i,\ i = 1, 2, \ldots, k\} \tag{2}$$

The fundamental theorem of stochastic processes allows us to think of a random medium as a permutationally and marginally consistent infinite family of these d. f. Subject to certain conditions on the random medium (see e.g. Frisch, loc. cit.) an equivalent description of the random medium is provided by the infinite family of correlation functions (c.f.), where the k-point c.f. is

$$\begin{aligned} \langle \xi(\mathbf{r}_1) \ldots \xi(\mathbf{r}_k) \rangle &= \int x_1 \ldots x_k \, dF_{1,\ldots,k}(x_1, \ldots, x_k) \\ &= \gamma_k(\mathbf{r}_1, \ldots \mathbf{r}_k). \end{aligned} \tag{3}$$

In dealing with isotropic porous media it often suffices to consider the special class of "two-phase" random media (see e. g. Prager 11, Frisch, 3). Samples, V, of such media can be divided into volume domains, D_1, of matter of uniform density and D_0, of void, of volume fraction φ and $1 - \varphi$, respectively. The "structure" function $\xi(\mathbf{r}, w)$ is then simply the characteristic function of the matter phase $E(\mathbf{r})$ with

$$E(\mathbf{r}) = \begin{cases} 1 \text{ if } \mathbf{r} \text{ is in } D_1, \\ 0 \text{ otherwise.} \end{cases} \tag{4}$$

Instead of the family of d.f. we consider the family of joint probabilities

$$P_{\epsilon_1\epsilon_2\ldots\epsilon_n}(\mathbf{r}_1, \mathbf{r}_2, \ldots, \mathbf{r}_n) = \Pr\{E(\mathbf{r}_i) = \epsilon_i,\ i = 1, 2, \ldots, n\} \tag{5}$$

with

$$\epsilon_i = \begin{cases} 1 \text{ if } \mathbf{r}_i \text{ is in } D_1 \\ 0 \text{ otherwise.} \end{cases}$$

For this 0, 1 process

$$\gamma_n(\mathbf{r}_1, \ldots, \mathbf{r}_n) = P_{1,\ldots,1}(\mathbf{r}_1, \ldots, \mathbf{r}_n). \tag{6}$$

Furthermore, one can show (Frisch and Stillinger, 6) that the $P_{\epsilon_1 \ldots \epsilon_n}$ $(\mathbf{r}_1, \ldots, \mathbf{r}_n)$ are linear functions of only the $\gamma_1, \ldots, \gamma_n$ of suitable arguments. For $n \leq 2$ this result is well known in the x-ray literature (Porod, 9, 10; Guinier, Fournet, Walker and Yudowitch, 7; Debye, Anderson and Brumberger, 1).

The geometric significance of the correlation functions is very easily seen for these processes. Consider the random throwing of a polyhedron with vertices $\mathbf{r}_1, \ldots, \mathbf{r}_n$ onto these "two-phase" random media; then γ_n is the probability that all vertices fall within D_1. In samples in which there exists a surface separating the void from the material phase which can be developed locally in a canonical power series in the local derivatives of the principal radii of curvature R_1, R_2 of the surface one can (Kirste and Porod, 8; Frisch and Stillinger, 6) show that the Debye correlation function

$$\gamma(r) = [\gamma_2(r) - \gamma_2(\infty)]/\varphi(1-\varphi)$$

$$= 1 - \frac{Sr}{4\varphi(1-\varphi)V}\left[1 - r^2\left\{\frac{1}{12S}\int_S k_1 k_2 da + \frac{1}{32S}\int_S (k_1 - k_2)^2 da\right\} + \ldots\right] \qquad (7)$$

with $S = \langle S(w) \rangle$, the mean surface area for fixed V, etc., $k_i = 1/2R_i$, $i = 1, 2$ and $r < 1/\max(k_1, k_2)$. The first integral in Eq. (7) is related to the topological genus of the surface by the Gauss-Bonnet integral formula.

Equation (7) applies only to surfaces containing no edges, corners, multiple points, or, in general, any singular points at which the radii of convergence of the canonical development of the surface shrink to zero. For example, if the random medium is a random aggregate of rigid spheres of diameter a, with z the average number of contacts a given sphere has with neighbors, one finds (Frisch and Stillinger, 6)

$$\gamma(r) = 1 = \frac{3r}{2(1-\varphi)a} + \frac{zr^2}{4(1-\varphi)a^2} + O(r^3). \qquad (8)$$

The first two terms in Eq. (7) and (8) agree since in this case $S/4\varphi(1 - \varphi)V = 3/2a(1 - \varphi)$. Thus γ_2 or γ contains not only the mean local differential geometry but provides us with basic parameters describing the geometry of packing of the spheres.

Unfortunately, many geometric properties of interest are not contained in γ_2 or any 2 point joint probability. Thus, for a spatially isotropic medium, consider the problem of distinguishing the dispersal of the "matter" phase in convex, disjoint domains in the (multiply connected) "void" phase from the complimentary dispersal of the "void" phase in identical, convex, disjoint domains in the (now multiply connected) "matter" phase. This requires knowledge of the three point joint probabilities (Frisch and Prager, 5). A figure of merit α can be defined which is positive if the "matter" phase is dispersed in the "void" phase and negative if the "void" phase is dispersed in the "matter" phase. If η denotes a unit vector, then

$$\alpha = \lim_{l \to 0}\left\{ \frac{1}{l^3} \int d\eta [P_{010}(\mathbf{r}, \mathbf{r} + l\eta, \mathbf{r} + 2l\eta) - P_{101}(\mathbf{r}, \mathbf{r} + l\eta, \mathbf{r} + 2l\eta)]\right\} \tag{9}$$

In principle, elastic single scattering of all wavelengths λ, $0 < \lambda < \infty$, radiation could determine $\gamma_2(r)$ if the scattering curve, i/s (s), s the scattering vector, were known for all values of the scattering length s and Fourier inversion of the experimental curve could be carried out. Since, experimentally λ is finite, only approximation information about γ_2 can be found if the "band-limited" scattering curve approximates sufficiently well the whole scattering curve. For x-rays with $C(\mathbf{r})$ the electron density correlation function (which for a "two-phase" porous medium is directly proportional to $\gamma_2(r)$)

$$C(\mathbf{r}) = \langle\rho_e(\mathbf{R})\rho_e(\mathbf{R} + \mathbf{r})\rangle = f_\infty^2\, \gamma_2(r); \tag{10}$$

$i(\mathbf{s})$ is (Debye and Bueche, 2)

$$i(\mathbf{s}) = \int d\mathbf{r}_1 \int d\mathbf{r}_2 \exp(i\mathbf{s} \cdot \mathbf{r}_{12})[C(\mathbf{r}_{12}) - C(\infty)], \tag{11}$$

with $\rho_e(\mathbf{R})$ given by (1) and $f_{e o}$ the constant mean number density of electrons. For a simple spherical fluid of number density ρ in the volume V, C(r) is simply related to the molecular pair correlation function of the centers of the molecules $g^{(2)}$ which plays such a central role in the statistical thermodynamics of these fluids,

$$C(\mathbf{r}_{12}) - C(\infty) = \rho \int f_e(\mathbf{r}_{13}) f_e(\mathbf{r}_{32})\, d\mathbf{r}_3 + \rho^2 \int f_e(\mathbf{r}_{13}) f_e(\mathbf{r}_{42}) [g^{(2)}(\mathbf{r}_{34}) - 1]\, d\mathbf{r}_3\, d\mathbf{r}_4. \quad (12)$$

When (12) is substituted into (11) one recovers the usual Zernike-Prins formulation of the scattering curve for spherical fluids. Equation (11) can be inverted, in principle, to give $\gamma(r)$, viz.

$$\varphi(1 - \varphi)\, V f_o^2\, r\gamma(r) = \frac{1}{2\pi^2} \int_0^\infty s i(s) \sin(sr)\, ds. \quad (13)$$

Even if in practice the complete evaluation of Eq. (13) is not feasible, one may be able to study the first few terms of the power series expansion in r of $\gamma(r)$ (cf. Eqs. (7) and (8)) providing i(s) falls off sufficiently rapidly with s, etc. This has been the basis for a novel technique of determining the specific surface of isotropic porous materials (Debye, Anderson and Brumberger, 1) since from Eq. (13) and (7) or (8)

$$i(s) \underset{a}{\sim} 2\pi f_{eo}^2\, S/s^4 \text{ as } s \to \infty \quad (14)$$

Clearly in order that this formula be employed the asymptotic region in the behavior of i(s) must be reached with the value of the x-ray wavelength employed.

The theoretical possibility exists (Frisch and McKenna, 4) that the n point c.f. with $n > 2$ could be studied to some extent by an analysis of multiple scattering of E.M.R. from a random medium, e.g., in the case of visible polarized light by obtaining the coefficients of the scattered intensity as a function of the angle of polarization and the effective local polarizability, $\alpha/4\pi$. For spherical, electromagnetically isotropic molecules $\alpha/4\pi$ is the molecular polarizability. Practical limitations in the availability of sources of polarized E.M.R. of sufficient intensity within the appropriate wavelength regions (or beams of particles) preclude to a large extent the observation of the rather limited information which theory predicts. An analysis of linearly polarized radiation which is scattered once and twice (double scattering) before being observed reveals the following facts (Frisch and McKenna, 4):

(1) The scattered intensity consists of contributions from singly scattered light $\langle J \rangle$; doubly scattered light; $\langle L \rangle$; and interference between singly and multiply scattered light, $\langle K \rangle + \ldots$ The contribution $\langle J \rangle$ involves only the 2 point c.f. $\hat{n}_2(\mathbf{r}_1, \mathbf{r}_2)$, the contribution $\langle L \rangle$ the 4 point c.f. $\hat{n}_4(\mathbf{r}_1, \mathbf{r}_2, \mathbf{r}_3, \mathbf{r}_4)$ and the contribution arising from interference between singly and doubly scattered light, $\langle K \rangle$, the 3 point c.f. $\hat{n}_3(\mathbf{r}_1, \mathbf{r}_2, \mathbf{r}_3)$ of the optically effective density of matter.

(2) In a medium which does not depolarize singly scattered light, e.g. from a fluid of spherically symmetric atoms such as an inert gas, singly and doubly scattered radiation have different polarizations and thus e.g. $\langle L \rangle$ can be wholly distinguished from $\langle J \rangle$ and $\langle K \rangle$ since it is the only contribution seen to terms $O(\alpha^6)$ when the scattered radiation is observed in the direction of the incident electric vector. This scattered intensity is proportional to α^4 and in the limit when the wavelength is much larger than the range of the correlation functions is proportional to k^4, where k is the wave number of the scattered radiation with wave vector $\kappa(|\kappa| = k)$.

(3) The scattered radiation in the direction of the incident electric vector, $E_0 \exp(i\mathbf{k}_0 \cdot \mathbf{r} - i\omega t$, ($\omega$ the frequency, c the velocity of light, ϵ the bulk dielectric constant of the medium) is

$$I_{s,11} = \frac{c\sqrt{\epsilon}}{8\pi} \langle L \rangle_{11} + O(\alpha^6),$$

$$\langle L \rangle_{11} = \frac{\alpha^4 |E_0|^2 |\kappa|^4}{(4\pi\epsilon^2 R^2)} \sum_{j=2}^{3} \langle |\Gamma_{1j}^{(2)}|^2 \rangle,$$

$$<|\Gamma_{1j}^{(2)}|^2> = \int (\eta_1 - \kappa)_1 (\eta_1 - \kappa)_j (\eta_3 + \kappa)_1 (\eta_3 + \kappa)_j$$

$$\times \left[P\left(\frac{1}{(\eta_1 - \kappa)^2 - k^2}\right) - \pi i \delta([(\eta_1 - \kappa)^2 - k^2])\right]$$

$$\times \left[P\left(\frac{1}{(\eta_3 + \kappa)^2 - k^2}\right) - \pi i \delta([(\eta_3 + \kappa)^2 - k^2])\right]$$

$$\hat{N}_4 (\eta_1, \kappa - k_o - \eta_1, \eta_3, k_o - \kappa - \eta_3)\, d\eta_1 d\eta_3,$$

$$\hat{n}_4(\mathbf{r}_1, \mathbf{r}_2, \mathbf{r}_3, \mathbf{r}_4) = <\rho(\mathbf{r}_1)\rho(\mathbf{r}_2)\rho(\mathbf{r}_3)\rho(\mathbf{r}_4)>/\rho^4$$

$$= \frac{1}{(2\pi)^6} \int_V \exp[i(\eta_1 \cdot \mathbf{r}_1 + \eta_2 \cdot \mathbf{r}_2 + \eta_3 \cdot \mathbf{r}_3 + \eta_4 \cdot \mathbf{r}_4)]$$

$$\hat{N}_4 (\eta_1, \eta_2, \eta_3, \eta_4)\, d\eta_1 d\eta_2 d\eta_3 d\eta_4, \qquad (15)$$

with R the large distance from the sample of the random medium at which the scattered radiation is observed. For spherical molecules

$$\rho(\mathbf{r})/\rho = \sum_{i=1}^{N} \Delta(\mathbf{r} - \mathbf{r}_i), \qquad (16)$$

where $\Delta(\mathbf{r} - \mathbf{r}_i)$ has a finite range R and is a measure of the effective density of matter responsible for scattering, so that $\hat{n}_4$ is a linear functional of the molecular correlation functions $g^{(4)}$, $g^{(3)}$ and $g^{(2)}$. Clearly one <u>cannot</u> invert Eq. (15) to obtain $\hat{n}_4$ (γ_4 in a two phase porous medium). Still one can hope to obtain useful information about the range of these functions. Near the critical point of an inert gas the range of spatial correlation in the fluid is of the order of the optical wavelength and doubly scattered light from an intense source (say a laser) should be observable. To apply Eq. (15) to interpret the results care must be taken not to come too close to the critical point since at the critical point itself multiple scattering of all orders becomes overwhelming.

REFERENCES

(1) Debye, P., Anderson, H. R., Jr. and Brumberger, J. Appl. Phys., **28**, 679 (1957).

(2) Debye, P. and Bueche, A. M., J. Appl. Phys., **20**, 518 (1948).

(3) Frisch, H. L., Trans. Soc. of Rheology 9,293 (1965).

(4) Frisch, H. L., and McKenna, J., Phys. Rev., 139, A68 (1965).

(5) Frisch, H. L. and Prager, S., unpublished results (1965).

(6) Frisch, H. L. and Stillinger, F., J. Chem. Phys., **38**, 2200 (1963).

(7) Guinier, Fournet, Walker and Yudowitch, Small Angle Scattering of X-Rays, John Wiley and Sons, New York (1955).

(8) Kirste, R. and Porod, G., Kolloid Z., **184**, 1 (1962).

(9) Porod, G., Kolloid Z., **124**, 83 (1951).

(10) Porod, G., Kolloid Z., **125**, 109 (1952).

(11) Prager, S., J. Chem. Phys., **33**, 122 (1960).

DISCUSSION FOLLOWING PAPER BY H. L. FRISCH

G. Porod: Do you think that a singularity (contact of spheres) though being a mathematical abstraction will be shown in the diffraction pattern of a real system?

H. L. Frisch: I have no reason to believe that indications of singularities in the diffraction pattern will be any less pronounced for this property of a real system than for other properties exhibiting singular behavior. The sharpness of these indications will depend on many factors, e.g. the extent of practical resolution afforded by the experimental arrangement, or the range and degree of cutoff of the effective single particle structure function, etc. In the end, I think, the only meaningful answer to your question will come from experiments conducted on particular, suitably selected systems.

V. Twersky: In your diagram for measuring scattered intensities you have drawn two "beams," one for the wave function and one for its complex conjugate; the single-scattered result for these two beams involves the one particle and two-particle position functions, and the three-particle function enters when one of these beams is doubly scattered. I'd like to point out that if you introduce another "beam" into your picture you can get the three-particle function from the single scattering experiment, and if you introduce four beams you can get the four-particle function. These diagrams that you have drawn correspond essentially to the fact that most measurements are of intensities, i.e., measurements of only the second statistical moments of the instantaneous scattered field. Tomorrow I'll be talking about a system for measuring instantaneous fields and averaging electronically to get n'th moments. In some cases, without the complications of multiple scattering, one may be able to systematically pull out the n-particle statistical position functions.

I am not suggesting that we use more than one incident beam. Even in the picture for the optical case you have only one actual beam in mind: the measurement procedure which gives the <u>intensity</u> is <u>diagrammed</u> as two beams. One of your diagrammed beams is the wave function, the other is its complex conjugate. The determination of the higher moments (also from one actual beam) can be diagrammed as n beams, i.e., as C^n or as $C^{n-m}(C^m)*$ (instead of CC* which is used for the intensity); the measuring and averaging system operates essentially with "n beams" when it provides data for the higher statistical moments.

X-Ray Scattering from Irregular Structures

G. Porod
Physikalisches Institut,
University of Graz, Austria

ABSTRACT

The general features of the scattering from irregular, densely packed systems are briefly discussed. The result is that interparticle interference cannot be neglected even in the case when the scattering pattern is of the gas-type. From this it follows that the concept of "size" becomes unclear with dense packing, and that the usual parameters loose their meaning. The only size-parameter that remains well defined is the so-called mean intersect.

Further it is shown that the criterion for the distinction between globular, fibrillar, and lamellar particles is still valid for densely packed systems, provided that there is no regularity of mutual arrangement.

The study of the asymptotic behaviour of the scattering curve is enhanced by the introduction of the intersect distribution function. In this way a criterion can be given for the presence of singularities—edges and corners—in the internal surfaces. The "degree of angularity" can be determined from the scattering curve.

INTRODUCTION

In the development of the method of X-ray small-angle scattering two different lines of attack were followed. The first, as started by Guinier (5), regarded the effect as caused by individual and independent particles. This aspect, which is particularly suited for dilute solutions, has since been widely elaborated and has lead to many valuable results. Details can be seen in the well-known book by Guinier and Fournet (7).

Kratky, (11) on the other hand, in his study of densely packed systems, particularly cellulose, stressed the necessity of taking into account the effect of interparticular interference. There is general agreement that the X-ray pattern is due to the interference of secondary waves originating from the electrons of the system. In principle it makes no difference in this respect whether two electrons are situated in one and the same particle or in two separate particles near each other. Therefore, we should expect that in a densely packed system interparticle interference cannot be neglected without special reason. But there may be objections to such a simple argument; for, within a particle there is a definite mutual arrangement of the electrons, while between the particles the relation in space is variable, so that one might suspect this interference effect to be largely cancelled. The problem is therefore not yet clear and needs further discussion.

The X-ray pattern, as found by experimentation, resembles much more often the type of particle scattering according to Guinier. The clear visual predominance of interparticle interference is an exception, if we leave aside the cases where the structure itself shows a distinct order. In his study of coals, Riley (20) found both distinct types of scattering with different specimens and he coined the terms of of "gas-type" and "liquid-type" on that occasion. These expressions designate in a clear manner the phenomenon; but it should be borne in mind that by this distinction the question whether interparticle interference plays a role is not yet settled. For instance, Guinier and Belbeoch (6) have shown that a liquid-type can also be caused by a special electron density distribution such that the excess in one region is compensated by an electron defect in the near neighborhood. That case of non-uniform electron density within a colloidal region will not be further considered in this paper. But it shows that the interpretation of the X-ray pattern is not uniquely determined by the visual appearance.

In the following we shall only be concerned with colloidal systems containing two phases of uniform electron density each, which may be designated as "matter" and "voids" respectively. Of course, only the deviations from the average electron density are of consequence for the scattering. Furthermore, we shall assume the system to be isotropic and irregular, that means that no preferred orientation or ordered arrangement exists. In addition, if there is fairly dense packing, particularly if the volume fractions of matter and voids are of the same order of magnitude, the concept of particles may loose its meaning. Our discussion will be general enough as to include the case of typical non-particulate systems, sponge-like structures a.s.o. It is clear that in this generality not all details of the structure can be determined from X-ray scattering. All that can be done, is to find an average size and some broad features of the shape of the colloidal regions. That will be the main topic of the present paper.

First however, it is necessary to make clear the meaning of the concept "size" of a region in a non-particulate system. In this connection it will be convenient to make use of the statistics of "intersects," partly for mathematical reasons, partly for the sake of intuition. Further we shall need a short discussion of the role of interparticular interference and its influence on the X-ray pattern.

INTERPARTICLE INTERFERENCE

In a fundamental paper (1), Debye has shown that an assembly of spheres, even if quite irregularly arranged, must give rise to a liquid-type pattern; the more, the denser the packing. It seems that the impenetrability of the particles alone is already sufficient to produce a small-range order. This point of view was further developed and extended to the liquid structure in the independent work of Debye and Menke (4), and of Prins and Zernicke (22).

In the field of X-ray small-angle scattering the concept of small-range order was particularly stressed by Kratky (11) in his study of the structure of cellulose. The matter seems rather clear with uniform particles of regular shape. But there is some controversy still concerning the question whether or not small-range order is effectuated in a strongly polydisperse system and with irregularly shaped particles. While Hosemann (8) maintains that polydispersity alone is sufficient to destroy completely small-range order and interparticle interference, the calculations by the author (15, 17) lead to the opposite result that even in highly polydisperse systems of spheres there should always remain a clear indication of the liquid-type. The more refined mathematical treatment by Guinier and Fournet (7) also yielded scattering curves of the same type. On the other hand it is a fact that most densely-packed systems produce a gas-type scattering.

So the problem is still open to discussion. In a previous paper by the author (17) the whole question was put from a different point of view. It was asked if the gas-type scattering of a densely packed system is identical with that of the same particles separated at large distance in a dilute system. The answer was in the negative, though of course a stringent solution could not be given. At any rate, the evaluation of the X-ray pattern in terms of "particles" should be made with caution, and the results must not be understood in the naive sense of the particle scattering of a dilute system. We shall follow here this line of thought and make some further developments.

Let us assume a colloidal system consisting of matter and voids with fairly comparable volume fractions w_1 and w_2 respectively. Though the system may well be non-particulate, we shall use the term "particles" in the sense of regions of matter or voids, which can be defined by arbitrary sections, if necessary. The intensity, scattered in a certain direction by that system, is given by the square of the corresponding Fourier-transform of the electron density distribution. As a finite sample of uniform electron density throughout yields no scattering at all only the deviations from the average need be considered. These deviations must be proportional to the volume fractions w_2 and/or w_1 for matter and/or voids. The amplitudes of the particles can so be written as $w_2 f$ (matter) and $-w_1 g$ (voids). Neglecting absolute intensity, we have:

$$i \sim (w_2(f_1 + f_2 + \ldots) - w_1(g_1 + g_2 + \ldots))$$

$$(w_2(\bar{f}_1 + \bar{f}_2 + \ldots) - w_1(\bar{g}_1 + \bar{g}_2 + \ldots)) \qquad (1)$$

where the conjugate complex amplitudes are indicated by overlining. Carrying out the product in (1), we find the intensity as a sum of contributions of the form (for the jth particle):

$$i_j \sim w_2^2 f_j \bar{f}_j + (w_2 f_j \overline{F}_j + w_2 \bar{f}_j F_j)/2 \qquad (2)$$

with: $F_j = w_2(f_1 + f_2 + \ldots) - w_1(g_1 + g_2 + \ldots)$ with f_j omitted; (3)

the first term in (2) obviously means pure particle scattering, while the other terms represent the interference with the surrounding. The factor 1/2 must be applied, because otherwise each mixed product would appear twice in the final result. Now we can arrive at a final result only, if we assume (as is necessary in any other problem of statistics or probability calculus, too) that all possible situations occur in our system. The jth particle will, therefore, be repeated many times with different surroundings. If we take together the contributions of all particles of the jth type, the first term in (2) will remain unchanged, while the amplitude of the surrounding has to be replaced by the average $\langle F_j \rangle$. This average amplitude is identical with the amplitude of the averaged surrounding, as follows directly from the principles of Fourier transform. A schematic example is shown in Fig. 1. Whatever that average surrounding may be in a special case, we can always expect to find two characteristic features. First, it must start with the value of $-w_1$ from a real particle, as by definition there is void around it; and secondly, at some distance the average electron density must be reached, as in an irregular system long-range order is excluded.

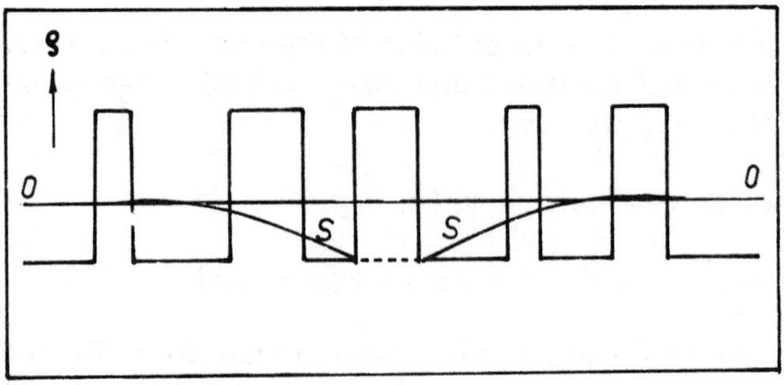

Fig. 1. Schematic representation of intersecting line with regions of high and of low electronic density. 0 - Average electronic density. S - Average surrounding function.

Now let us supplement the average surrounding by the region occupied by the particle itself (broken line in Fig. 1). In this way we get the "hole" in which the particle is situated. As the depth of the hole is $-w_1$, its amplitude may be put $-w_1 F'$:

$$\langle F_j \rangle = -w_1 (F'_j - f_j) \tag{4}$$

Taking the average of (2) with respect to all possible surroundings and substituting (4) we obtain:

$$\langle i_j \rangle \sim w_2 f_j \bar{f}_j - w_1 w_2 (f_j \bar{F}'_j + \bar{f}_j F'_j)/2 \tag{5}$$

Similar contributions are given also by the voids with the corresponding amplitudes g, G, G'. Putting it all together, the total scattered intensity will be (indices omitted):

$$i \sim w_2 \langle f\bar{f} \rangle + w_1 \langle g\bar{g} \rangle - w_1 w_2 (\langle f\bar{F}' \rangle + \langle \bar{f}F' \rangle + \langle g\bar{G}' \rangle + \langle \bar{g}G' \rangle /2 \tag{6}$$

From (6) we can draw the following general conclusions: first, with real particles the "hole" must necessarily be larger than the particle itself. The consequence is that the form factor F' (= amplitude) drops to zero more rapidly with increasing scattering angle than does the form factor f; therefore, we should expect a liquid-type pattern around the primary beam, which goes over to pure particle scattering at larger angles. That interference effect is not cancelled by taking the average of all particles, as it always operates in the same sense. If on the other hand gas-type scattering is found by experiment, this seems only possible if the hole is identical with the particle, so that by the interference only the intensity is altered, but not its relative course with the scattering angle. The strict condition for such a case is that the surface of the particles contacts matter and voids in the ration $w_1 : w_2$. The "particles" as determined from gas-type scattering are therefore not real, separate particles, but some sections out of larger coherent regions.

Secondly, formula (6) shows a clear symmetry with respect to matter and voids. That is in agreement with Babinet's principle, which must hold for X-ray scattering, too. This point is important. It was particularly stressed by Kratky (11), who made wide use of it. We have now another support for our above conclusion that gas-type scattering must not be confused with the pure particle scattering of dilute systems. In an irregular densely packed system there is no reason why the X-ray pattern should be more indicative of matter rather than of voids.

This situation can be illustrated by a simple model, treated in a previous paper (16). Let us assume lamellae of uniform thickness of matter as well as of voids packed close together at random. The result will be a system consisting of lamellae of different thickness (1, 2, 3 - ... times the original one), varying according to the laws of probability like the series of throws of a die. The calculation of the scattering function is simple and need not be repeated here. The result is a pure gas-type, identical with that of a dilute system of the original lamellae, only, which is the same for both matter and voids. By this model, though oversimplified of course, both aspects of our above discussion are clearly shown.

SIZE

The most general method for the calculation of scattering functions makes use of the well-known correlation function G(r) introduced by Debye and Bueche (3). It is related to the scattered intensity by:

$$j(h) = 4\pi \int_0^\infty dr \cdot rG(r)(\sin rh)/h; \text{ with } h = (4\pi \sin\theta)/\lambda; \tag{7}$$

where 2 θ is the scattering angle and j(h) means the standard form of the intensity as used by the author (16).

The correlation function defines in a strict, though not very intuitive manner the range within the system, which gives rise to coherent scattering. The size of that range can be defined by means of the correlation function and deduced from the scattering curve in different ways. The most common of these size parameters is the well-known radius of gyration of Guinier. But we may use other quantities, too, which are obtained by integrating over the correlation functions. In a dilute particulate system these "integral" parameters (19) refer to the size of the real particles and are well suited for their definition. With a densely packed system this is no longer the case. As we have seen above, the integral parameters cannot be attributed to the real particles of matter only. This fact is also in agreement with the definition of the correlation function. It satisfies Babinet's principle in so far as it remains unchanged when we interchange the role of matter and voids. Furthermore, in the correlation function no distinction is made between distances r that connect points within one and the same particle, and distances connecting points that belong to separate particles. Therefore, if we wish to have a measure for the true sizes of the regions of matter and voids, we must look for some other parameter.

Such a parameter is found by the introduction of the concept of "intersects." Let us imagine the colloidal system intersected by arrows or straight lines at random, everywhere and in all directions. The chords which are cut out in this way, may be called "intersects." It seems plausible that the average intersects $\bar{l}_1$ and $\bar{l}_2$ of matter and voids respectively are a rather intuitive measure of size. It is only the question how to determine them from the scattering curve.

From pure geometrical reasoning it could be shown that the mean intersect is related in a simple way to the specific surface:

$$\bar{l}_1 = 4V_1/S \quad \text{and} \quad \bar{l}_2 = 4V_2/S \qquad (8)$$

where S is the surface (common to both phases) and V_1, V_2 are the volumes of matter and/or voids.

It was shown independently by Debye et al. (2) and the author (16), and found experimentally by VanNordstrand and Hach (21) that the internal surface can be determined from the asymptotic course of the scattering curve. The evaluation can be made just as well with the slit-distorted curve ($\tilde{j}$). Expressed in terms of the mean intersect $\bar{l}$ of the system the relations are:

$$j(h) \rightarrow 8\pi/\bar{l}h^4; \quad \tilde{j}(h) \rightarrow 4\pi^2/\bar{l}h^3; \quad \text{for large h.} \qquad (9)$$

In agreement with Babinet's principle the parameter $\bar{l}$ is connected symmetrically with the mean intersects of matter and voids:

$$1/\bar{l} = 1/\bar{l}_1 + 1/\bar{l}_2; \ \bar{l} = 4w_1w_2V/S = \bar{l}_1w_2 = \bar{l}_2w_1; \qquad (10)$$

therefore, a measure of size can be obtained for the two phases building up the colloidal system, which is impossible with integral parameters. Furthermore, there is still a difference in the manner of how size is averaged (9, 18, 13). This is best seen from a numerical example. For a sphere $\bar{l}$ is 2/3 of the diameter; for an infinitely long cylinder it becomes equal to the diameter; and for an infinitely large plate, two times the thickness. The radius of gyration, for instance, overvalues the large distances and becomes infinite in the last two cases. It could not express, therefore, the fine colloidal dispersion of the system.

SHAPE

It seems clear that for a non-particulate system the concept of shape cannot be defined in a rigorous way. Nevertheless, there must be a certain distinction if we look at structures like precipitates, porous materials, fibers a.s.o. Obviously it is here only the question of a general characterization, whether the colloidal regions be, roughly speaking, isometric or anisometric in one or two dimensions. We may, therefore, distinguish broadly between three limiting cases, which can be designated as globular, fibrillar and lamellar systems. The question is how to recognize these types from the scattering curve. The theory of particulate systems suggests two possible criteria; but their application to our problem requires some more consideration.

The first method is the use of characteristic numbers, expressed by the ratio of two size parameters, for instance $R/\bar{l}$. According to the above said, the ratio should increase with rising anisometry. It is, therefore, a well suited measure of anisometry, so to say, in the case of individual particles. But we cannot be sure that this will also be true for densely packed systems for the following reasons: all integral parameters, as we have seen, lose more or less their direct connection with the real structural units of matter, when the packing becomes too dense; secondly, they involve the whole correlation function and the whole scattering curve, particularly at very small angles, where the influence of the large distances predominates. But it is just this part of the X-ray pattern that is chiefly influenced and distorted by interparticular interference. In consequence of this, the method of characteristic numbers is exposed to serious error in the case of densely packed systems.

The other method makes use of the direct course of the scattering curve. It is well known by the fundamental work of Guinier that this should be represented to a first approximation by a bell-shaped curve of the Gauss-type. It is true that this statement holds for particles of any shape, but the angular region, where the approximation is fairly good, becomes the smaller, the more anisometric the particles. For very long rods and very large platelets that region becomes restricted to such small angles that they are hardly more accessible by experiment. In that case other approximations have to be used, as was shown long ago (12, 14):

$$\text{rods: } j(h) = 2\pi h^{-1} \cdot j'(h); \quad \text{plates: } j(h) = 4\pi h^{-2} \cdot j''(h) \quad (11)$$

Here the scattering function is split into a Lorentz-factor h^{-1} or h^{-2} and a cross-section factor j' or j''. The latter is again of the Gauss-type and refers to the cross-section or thickness in a way similar to the scattering function of a globular particle to the whole particle.

It is true that formula (11) must become invalid for very small angles. But apart from this it is a very good approximation even for particles with moderate anisometry. This has often been verified by experiment and also by the direct calculation of the scattering functions of special types of bodies. The shortcoming is that (11) is only derived for dilute systems of separate particles. We need a new argument, therefore, which can also be applied to non-particulate systems.

To that purpose, let us imagine an arbitrary structure formed of rodlets or fibrils, which may also be bent and connected with each other. It is only essential to exclude a regular arrangement in space, for instance the fibrils lying parallel. The scattering of a pinhole beam under an angle 2θ can formally be regarded as a reflection by fictive reflection planes. The scattered amplitude is then the Fourier-transform of the electron distribution projected onto the normal of the plane, as is well-known already from crystal structure analysis. Therefore, when we consider a special situation as shown in Fig. 2, the scattering remains uneffected by a rotation around the normal.

The amplitude always tends toward zero with an increasing scattering angle, and it does so the more rapidly the larger the extension of a region in the direction of the reflection normal. Consequently, a finite value of the amplitude is only obtained with a fibril lying nearly parallel to the reflection plane, within an angular range of δ, say. The neighboring fibrils, being not parallel to the one in question, will make hardly any contribution. If we now imagine the

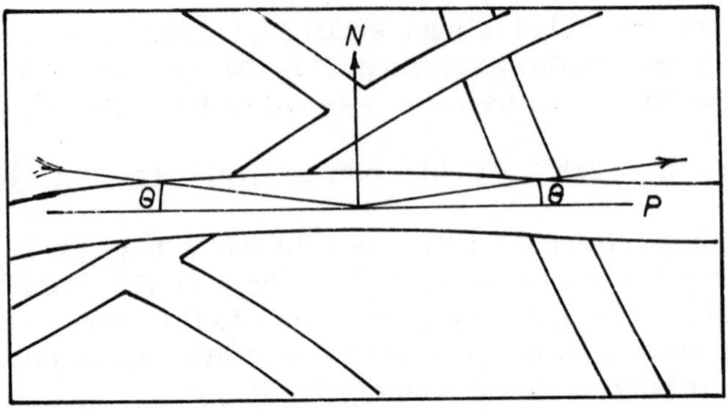

Fig. 2. Scattering from a fibrillar system with one fibril lying in favorable position. θ - Half scattering angle. P- Plane of reflection. N - Normal of reflection.

scattering angle for instance, doubled, the angular range of the fibril axis, up to which the amplitude drops to zero; will obviously be halved. In general: the effective range of orientation goes inversely with θ and h. The scattered intensity will clearly be proportional to the number of fibrils lying in a favorable position, which implies the factor h^{-1} in formula (11). The amplitude, as far as it refers to the cross section, will be nearly unchanged by the slight tilting of the axis; its square is the cross-section factor.

The same argument can be used for the case of lamella-shaped structural units. The only difference is that now the amplitude is sensitive to any tilting of the lamella plane rather than of an axis. Consequently, the effective range has to be considered for the normal of the lamella, which implies the square of δ and the Lorentz-factor of h^{-2}, in agreement with (11) again.

Of course, the above considerations can be put in a more refined mathematical form. But there would be little use in doing so, as we are dealing here with irregular structures, which from their very definition show no definite geometry in a strict mathematical sense. A general and plausible argument is of more use than a detailed calculation. So we might feel sure enough to rely on the application of (11) to densely packed systems. The rule of evaluation is simple enough:

a bell-shaped scattering curve implies a globular system. If that type is only obtained after multiplication by h, the system is fibrillar. Finally, if multiplication by h^2 is necessary in order to get the Gauss-type, this means a lamellar structure.

SURFACE STRUCTURE

The methods developed so far furnish little or no information regarding the fine structure of the internal surface. In fact, if we put the question whether the colloidal regions have a smooth boundary, or if there are edges and corners, neither the appearance of the scattering curve nor the comparison of general parameters will supply a satisfactory answer. On the other hand, it seems rather plausible that such a clear-cut distinction must be hidden somehow in the X-ray pattern and, therefore, also in the correlation function. If this suggestion is true, we may argue that the requested criterion will probably be implied in the initial part of G(r), as the neighborhood of the surface involves only small distances. It is therefore reasonable to use the expansion into a power series:

$$G(r) = 1 - ar + br^2 + cr^3 + \dots ; \quad \text{with: } a = 1/\bar{l}; \qquad (12)$$

where the coefficients may be called "differential" parameters. The first of these is already known to be the reciprocal of the mean intersect. It has therefore a clear connection with the internal surface. It is perhaps not too far-fetched to assume that the other parameters will depend on more detailed features of the surface. The study of this question was begun in a recent paper by Kirste and the author (10). It can be shown that with smooth particles, that means without edges and corners, the parameter b must vanish, while c is positive and related to the average curvature of the surface. That result is verified for instance by the well-known correlation function of the sphere:

$$\text{sphere: } G(r) = 1 - 3r/2D + r^3/2D^3; \quad D = \text{diameter}; \qquad (13)$$

which is, by the way, already the complete series without neglecting higher terms. Further, the verification holds simultaneously for all ellipsoids. For it is known that an ellipsoid is equivalent to a certain superposition of spheres.

A strict formula could not be given for the parameter b in general. But the treatment of the corresponding two-dimensional case clearly suggested that it should be related to the presence of edges and corners.

In a paper presented at the preceding Conference on X-ray Small-Angle Scattering in Syracuse, New York, (19), a new approach to this problem was made by the use of the intersect distribution function. Under the assumption of a particulate system a general proof was given that the parameter b has a non-vanishing value for angular bodies. Further it could be shown that the following relation holds: if we multiply the scattering function by h^4 (or the slit-distorted function by h^3) and draw a horizontal line in the height of the asymptotic constant value, the difference of the areas below and above that line should be proportional to b. The full formula is:

$$\int_0^\infty dh\,(\lim jh^4 - jh^4) = 6\pi^2 A_0/\bar{l} = 12\pi^2 b; \text{ with: } A_0 = 2\bar{l}b \tag{14}$$

A similar relation applies to the slit-distorted curve:

$$\int_0^\infty dh\,(\lim \tilde{j}h^3 - \tilde{j}h^3) = 8\pi^2 A_0/\bar{l} = 16\pi^2 b; \tag{15}$$

where A_0 means the initial value of the intersect distribution function: $A_0 = A(0)$. As shown in (14), it is connected in a simple way with the parameter b, which in turn is a measure of the "angularity" of the particles. The problem is now to show that formula (14) and (15) can be used not only for separate particles, but also for a densely packed non-particulate system. That means, it must be proved that there exists a similar relation between the intersect distribution function and the parameter b. This is not self-evident as the intersects of matter and voids must be considered simultaneously.

Let us imagine our system to be intersected by one straight line which cuts out a linear sequence of intersects

l_1 and l_2 of matter and voids alternatingly. The corresponding distribution functions may be designated as $A(l_1)$ and $B(l_2)$ respectively. These functions may be thought as represented by a power series expansion with the intitial values of A_0 and B_0. The first task is then to establish a connection between the correlation function $G(r)$ and $A(l_1)$, $B(l_2)$. Here we meet a serious difficulty. Though it is rather obvious and can be proved rigorously that the sequence of the l_1 and l_2 determines unambiguously the scattering of the system and consequently also $G(r)$, the knowledge of $A(l_1)$ and $B(l_2)$ is not sufficient. In general we must expect an additional statistical correlation between the intersects of matter and of voids such that the probability of finding a certain value of l_2 depends on the value of the preceding l_1. This should be not a special exception, but the rule. In fact, it is hard to imagine a system without a correlation of that kind.

On account of this we shall restrict our study to the first terms of the power series expansion. That means that we discuss only the behavior for small distances near the internal surface. Now let us place two points at a fixed distance r on the intersection line and ask for the probability that the left point will be found in matter and the right one in void. In a previous paper (16) it was shown that all probabilities of that and a similar kind can be expressed in terms of the correlation function. For our special case we have:

$$P(r) = w_1 w_2 (1 - G(r)) = w_1 w_2 (r/\bar{l} - br^2 - cr^3 \ldots) \quad (16)$$

In order to find the requested relation we must deduce a second expression for the probability $P(r)$ in terms of A and B. Of course, the situation underlying $P(r)$ can only be effectuated, if a border-point between matter (left) and void (right) is situated within the distance r. On the intersecting line there is on the average one such border-point on a length $(\bar{l}_1 + \bar{l}_2)$. The probability that it lies within r is therefore given by $r/(\bar{l}_1 + \bar{l}_2)$. But this is not yet equal to $P(r)$, for we must take into account the cases, where more than one border-point lie within r. Thereby a certain fraction of the original probability is cancelled again. For our purpose we need only consider the two cases that either

l_1 or l_2 is small enough to be situated within the endpoints of the distance r. The probability that more than one small intersect occur together, is negligibly small of the second or higher order and can make a contribution only to terms higher than r^2.

Let us now consider in detail the case that l_2 is less than r. Then all situations will be unfavorable, where the border-point lies less than $(r - l_2)$ from the left endpoint. We must cancel, therefore, the fraction $(r - l_2)/r$ of the original probability. For a special value between l_2 and $l_2 + dl_2$, which occurs with a probability $B(l_2)\,dl_2$, we have to subtract $(r - l_2)\,B(l_2)\,dl_2/(\bar{l}_1 + \bar{l}_2)$ and the analogous expression for l_1. Taking the integral we have:

$$P(r) = (r - \int_0^r (r - l_1)\ A(l_1)\,dl_1 - \int_0^r (r - l_2)\,B(l_2)\,dl_2)/(\bar{l}_1 + \bar{l}_2)\,; \tag{17}$$

from the above assumptions it is clear that the power series in r, as given by (17), can only be correct for the first terms r and r^2. On account of this it will be sufficient and means no loss of accuracy to replace the functions $A(l_1)$ and $B(l_2)$ by the initial values A_0 and B_0, which are constants. This simplification enables us to carry out the integration in (17). With the use of (10) we finally have:

$$P(r) = w_1 w_2 (r - r^2 (A_0 + B_0)/2 + \ldots)/\bar{l}; \tag{18}$$

This should be the same as (16). By comparison we find:

$$b = (A_0 + B_0)/2\bar{l} \tag{19}$$

The only difference against the case of single particles is that A_0 is replaced by the sum $(A_0 + B_0)$. That means that with this slight modification the criterion for angularity, as expressed by (14) and (15), is valid for non-particulate systems, too.

SUMMARY

The influence of dense packing and of interparticle interference is discussed in general. It is shown that even with gas-type scattering the usual determination of particle size becomes invalid. The only parameter that refers to the true size of the colloidal regions, is the mean intersect.

Regarding shape the distinction is made between globular, fibrillar and lamellar systems. They correspond to three different types of scattering curves. A general relation is established between the intersect distribution functions and the correlation function. Thereby the proof is given that the criterion for the distinction between smooth and angular surface is valid also for non-particulate systems.

REFERENCES

(1) Debye, P., Physik. Z., **28**, 135 (1927).

(2) Debye, P., Anderson, H. R. and Brumberger, H., J. Appl. Phys. **28**, 679 (1957).

(3) Debye, P. and Bueche, A.M., J. Appl. Phys., **20**, 518 (1949).

(4) Debye, P. and Menke, H., Physik. Z., **31**, 797 (1930).

(5) Guinier, A., Ann. Phys., **12**, 161 (1939).

(6) Guinier, A. and Belbeoch, B., Makromolek. Chemie, **31**, 1 (1959).

(7) Guinier, A. and Fournet, G., Small-Angle Scattering of X-Rays, John Wiley & Sons, New York (1955).

(8) Hosemann, R., Z. Physik, **113**, 751 (1939); Kolloid-Z., **117**, 13 (1950).

(9) Kahovec, L. Porod, G. and Ruck H., Kolloid-Z., **113**, 16 (1953).

(10) Kirste, R. and Porod, G., Kolloid-Z., **184**, 1 (1962).

(11) Kratky, O., Naturwiss., **30**, 542 (1942).

(12) Kratky, O. and Porod, G., Acta Phys. Austriaca **2**, 255 (1948).

(13) Mittelbach, P. and Porod, G., Kolloid-Z., **202**, 40 (1965).

(14) Porod, G., Acta Phys. Austriaca, **2**, 255 (1948).

(15) Porod, G., Z. Naturforsch., **A-4**, 401 (1949).

(16) Porod, G., Kolloid-Z., **124**, 83 (1951).

(17) Porod, G., Kolloid-Z., **125**, 51 (1952).

(18) Porod, G., Makromolek. Chemie, **35**, 1 (1960).

DISCUSSION FOLLOWING PAPER BY G. POROD

H. L. Frisch: In principle, one should be able to obtain more information about the geometry of a random porous medium by simultaneously analyzing x-ray scattering data as well as data obtained from fluid flow porosities, tracer diffusion, dielectric constant measurements, etc. Have you considered the practical possibilities which might arise from such joint studies?

G. Porod: Small-angle scattering in itself is certainly not unambiguous. The combination with data obtained from other methods is, therefore, of great value. But I have not considered so far in this connection the phenomena mentioned by Dr. Frisch. It seems to me very difficult to establish a direct relation between them and small-angle scattering.

J. A. Prins: I think it would be useful to consider extreme cases of smooth surfaces and just the opposite: extremely spiked surfaces (like tetrahedrical ZnO particles) which have many singularities instead of none.

G. Porod: I fully agree with this suggestion. In general there will be a mixture of different types in a real system. For testing the theory it is necessary to have clear-cut extreme cases like the pointed out by Prof. Prins.

H. L. Frisch: Another possibility for studying effects due to correlation in orientation (as well as position), at least in molecular systems, may come about by analysis of incoherent scattering using laser sources. Y. H. Pao, R. Bersohn and I have calculated depolarization ratios for two photon scattering for various point group symmetries for linearly polarized light and circularly polarized light. E.g. for the symmetry $\bar{4}3n$, if only scattering by individual molecules (coherent scattering) is assumed then the depolarization ratio for linearly polarized light is 3/2 which does not seem to agree with the experimental value. Correlation in position alone does not yield an additional contribution but correlations in orientation definitely do contribute.

The Scattering of Light by Solid Polymer Films Having Partially Ordered Structure*

R. S. Stein, P. Erhardt,** S. Clough, † J. J. van Aartsen‡

and

M. B. Rhodes

Polymer Research Institute,
University of Massachusetts,
Amherst, Mass.

ABSTRACT

Recent developments in the techniques of studying the light scattering from films of crystalline high polymers are reviewed. A comparison is made between theories for calculating scattering on the basis of discrete models and on the basis of statistical correlation function type theories. The limitations of previous "random orientation

*Partly supported by a contract with the Office of Naval Research and by grants from the Army Research Office (Durham), and the Petroleum Research Fund.

**Work done while on leave from General Electric Research Laboratory, Present Address: Chemical Development Operations, General Electric Company, Pittsfield, Mass.

†Partly supported by an N.S.F. Cooperative Fellowship, Present Address: U.S. Army Natick Lab. Natick, Mass.

‡Present Address: Delft Technical University, Delft, Netherlands. The assistance of the Netherlands Organization for the Advancement of Pure Research (Z.W.O.) is appreciated in awarding of an OECD Postgraduate Travel Grant.

fluctuation" type theories are discussed and two procedures for generalizing the theory (in two-dimensions) are proposed. The first of these is based upon the assumption that an arbitrary structure may be described by means of interpolation between the limits of a rod and disc-like type of structure in terms of a single interpolation parameter. The simpler random fluctuation type theory is a special intermediate case of the more general theory. The second more general approach is based upon the expansion of an arbitrary distribution of orientation correlation of scattering elements in terms of Fourier series in the angles between their optic axes and in the angle between the optic axis and the polarization direction. The system is described in terms of the coefficients in this Fourier expansion. It is shown that the degree of non-randomness of the orientation fluctuations may be determined from a study of the dependence of the scattered intensity upon the angle ψ between the polarization direction and the plane of measurement of scattered intensity.

INTRODUCTION

In the previous I.C.E.S. conference two approaches to the use of the scattering method in studying heterogenieties in crystalline polymeric solids were discussed (15). The first of these involved calculating the scattering from model structures such as anisotropic spheres representing idealized spherulites consisting of spherically symmetrical aggregates of crystals found in crystalline polymers. While such spherulites are usually imperfect and volume filling, the low-angle light scattering may be well approximated by the idealized model of isolated perfect spheres. The scattering patterns were found to be in good agreement with those found in experiments where the scattering sample is placed between parallel (V_v) or perpendicular (H_v) polarizers. It is possible to determine the spherulite size from such experiments in good agreement with that found by microscopic observation. It was shown from the observed dependence of scattering upon the azimuthal scattering angle and upon the relative intensities of the H_V and V_V scattering patterns that most of the scattering arises from the difference between the principal polarizabilities of the spherulite rather than from the refractive index differences between the spherulite and the surroundings. Changes in scattering during the growth of spherulites were accounted for.

RECENT PROGRESS IN THEORY OF SPHERULITE SCATTERING

Previous theories for the scattering by spherulites have been generalized (3, 17). It has been shown that if the crystal optic axes are oriented at an angle, β, to the spherulite radius, the scattering patterns are similar to the previous treated cases of $\beta = 0°$ or $90°$ except that the scattering patterns are rotated through the angle β. These results were in agreement with the observations of Rhodes and Stein (15, 11) that the patterns obtained from a form of polytetrafluoroethylene spherulites are rotated through 45° as compared with those obtained from polyethylene films.

Also, the effect of helicoidal orientation of the optic axis of the spherulite through the angle ω (Fig. 1) (where ω varies linearly with r at constant β), results in higher angle scattering maxima with a spacing related to the helicoidal period and with an orientation dependent upon β. Figure 2 shows such a predicted scattering pattern (for a two-dimensional spherulite) which is in good agreement with experiment (1). The low-angle scattering, characteristic of the size and anisotropy of the spherulite is toward the center of the pattern whereas the maxima related to the helix period are seen at higher angles.

A third area of progress is in the description of deformation of the spherulite accompanying the stretching of samples (3). The scattering patterns have been shown to undergo a characteristic transformation which may be used as a

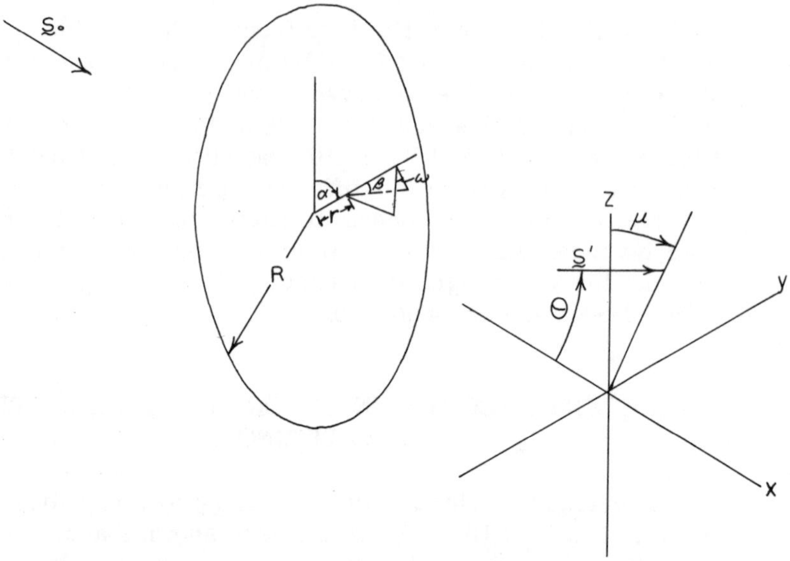

Fig. 1. The angles β and ω for orientation of crystals within spherulites (reprinted from Ref. B).

measure of the amount of spherulite deformation. A typical result is shown in Fig. 3 for the change in the H_V scattering pattern accompanying the 50% elongation of an anisotropic three-dimensional spherulite. The detailed change in the pattern is dependent upon the shape change occurring upon stretching and the way in which the crystals change their orientation within the deformed spherulite. The results presented here were obtained on the basis of assuming a constant volume affine deformation in which the density of scattering material remains constant and the angles between the crystal optic axes and the radii of the deformed spherulite do not change. Other models for the transformation have been considered (3, 17, 14) and good agreement with experiments have been found (14, 8).

The scattering from other model systems has also been considered such as for randomly oriented anisotropic rods (17). These are useful in interpreting scattering data from systems having less order than spherulites, such as linear

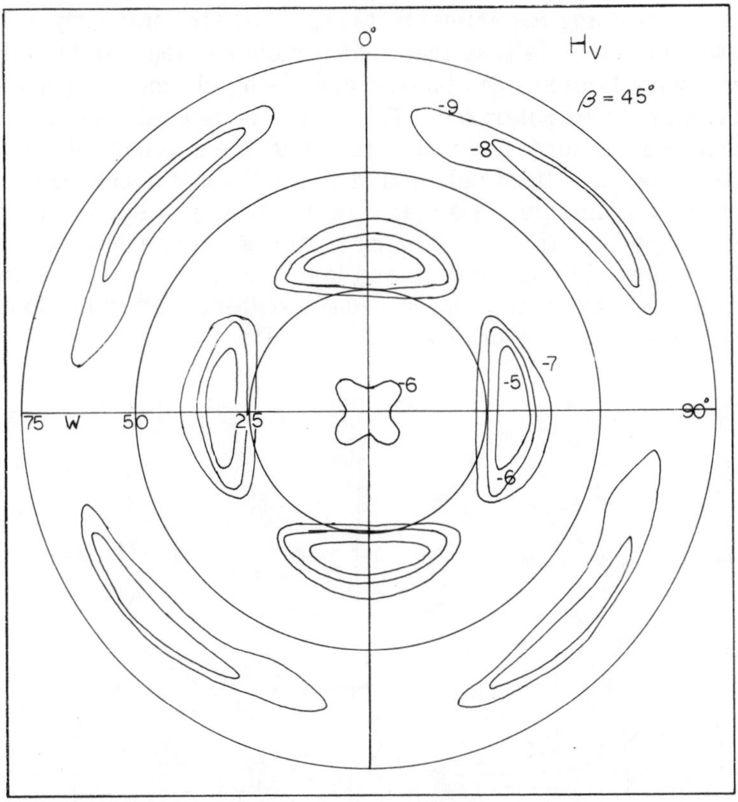

Fig. 2. The predicted H_V scattering pattern showing the maxima resulting from helicoidal crystal orientation for spherulite containing five helix periods in its radius where $\beta = 45°$.

aggregates of crystals as appear to occur during the initial stages of crystallization of polytetrafluoroethylene (13) and stretched rubber (26).

RECENT EXPERIMENTAL PROGRESS

The most significant development since the last Conference has been the application of lasers as light sources for light scattering experiments (12). While the intensity of low-powered lasers is less than that for conventional light sources (mercury lamps), the laser output is highly monochromatic, collimated and polarized. The resultant intensity is consequently considerably greater than that from conventional sources after they have been collimated to the degree necessary for low-angle experiments. A schematic diagram of a set-up for obtaining photographic scattering patterns using a low-power (0.1 joule) ruby crystal pulsed laser is shown in Fig. 4 and a typical comparison between results obtained using the laser and conventional source is shown in Fig. 5.

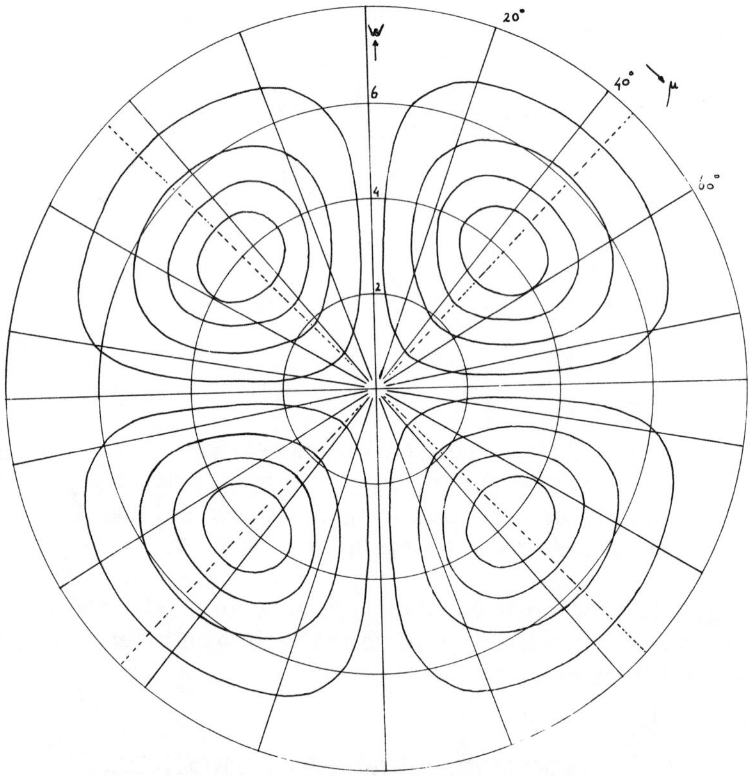

Fig. 3a. The H_V scattering pattern for an anisotropic three-dimensional spherulite for $\beta = 0°$ without deformation.

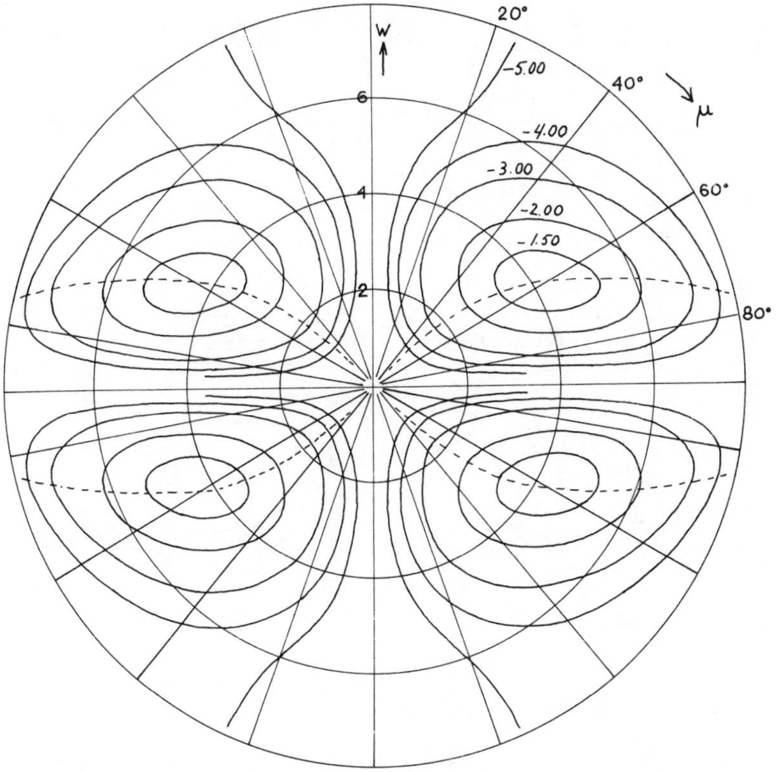

Fig. 3b. The H_V scattering pattern for an anisotropic three-dimensional spherulite for $\beta = 0°$ at 50% extension.

One advantage of using the laser is the extremely short exposure time required. A single flash of the laser is usually sufficient to obtain a picture. This may take about 500 μ sec without special instrumentation, or may be considerably less using special techniques such as Q-spoiling. The very high energies now available permit studies of very low scattering systems. These short-time experiments permit studies of systems changing rapidly with time and enable one to follow light scattering changes accompanying rapid sample deformation and relaxation (8, 4) and crystallization (26).

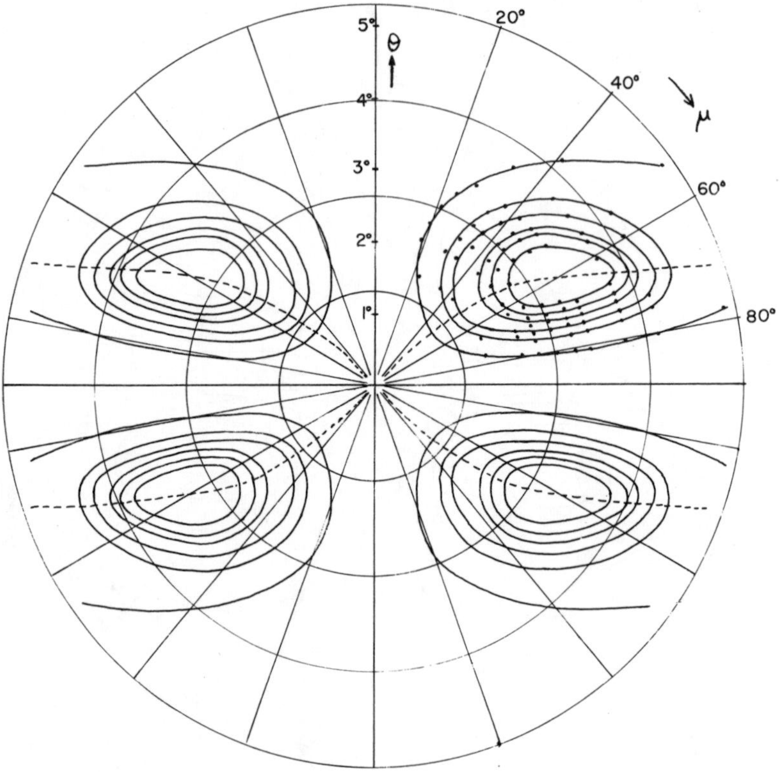

Fig. 3c. The H_V scattering pattern for an anisotropic three dimensional spherulite for $\beta = 0°$ experimentally measured for a medium density polyethylene film stretched 50%.

For many purposes, continuous gas lasers are more convenient than pulsed lasers even though available energies are less, in that they permit easier allignment of the apparatus rather than the "hit-or-miss" procedure necessary with pulsed lasers. For highly scattering systems, one can often visually monitor the scattering pattern, and intensity is often sufficient for taking pictures with short exposure time or for following changes with motion pictures at speed up to 1000 frames-per-second or more (5). Figure 6 shows a portion of a motion picture film taken at 560 frames-per-

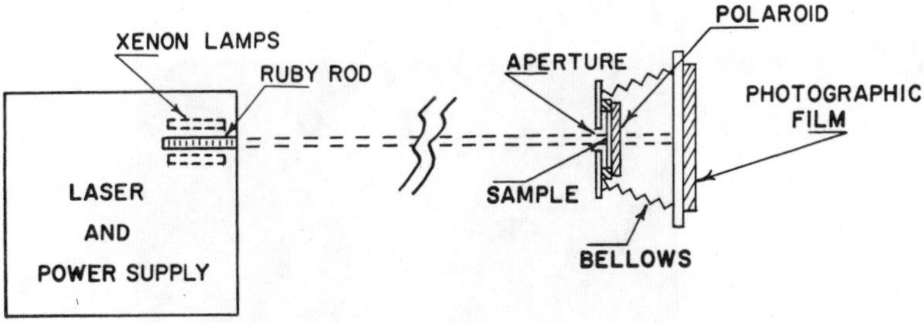

Fig. 4. A schematic diagram of an experimental set-up for laser photographic scattering experiments (reprinted from J. Polymer Sci., **62**, S74 (1962)).

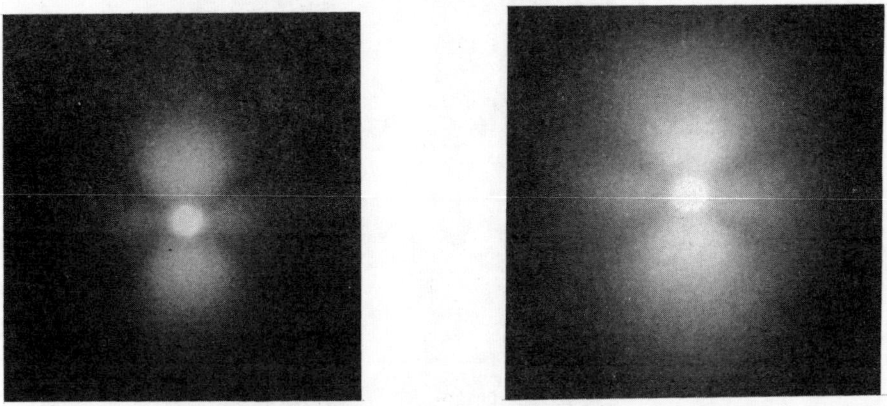

Fig. 5. A V_V photographic scattering pattern obtained with a single laser flash (500 μ sec) for a medium density polyethylene film, λ = 6943 Å (A), compared with (B), a pattern obtained using a conventional source with 4.5 hr. exposure time, λ = 5461 Å. (Reprinted from J. Polymer Sci., **62**, S74 (1962)).

second during the elongation of a polyethylene film at a rate of 625% per second. The rapid deformation of the pattern occurring within a few frames of picture is evidence of the rapid deformation of the spherulite that is possible.

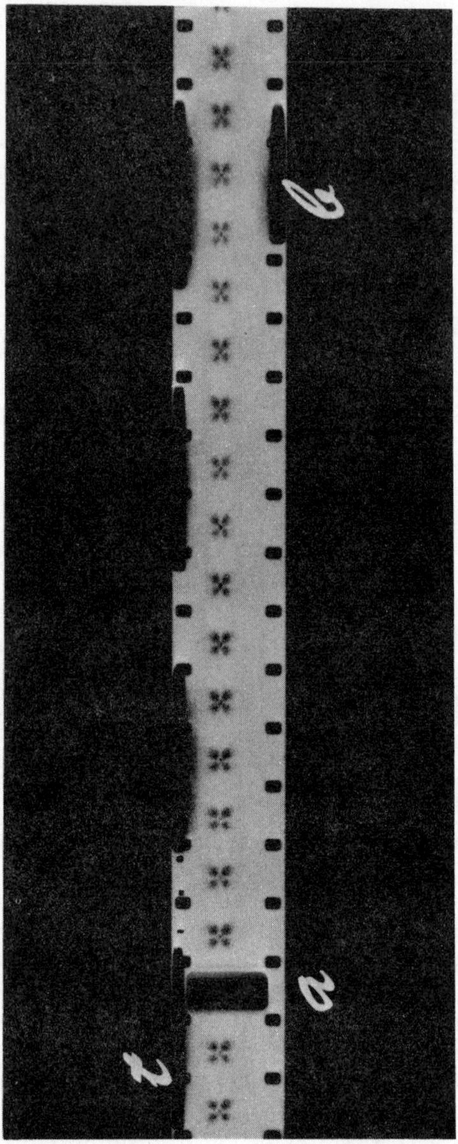

Fig. 6. A light scattering motion picture taken at 560 frames/sec during the 12% deformation of a polyethylene film at a rate of 625%/sec (reprinted from Polymer Letters, 3, 553 (1965)).

Subsequent changes in scattering intensity provide evidence for slower changes in crystal orientation within deformed spherulites.

Besides permitting shorter exposure times, the high degree of parallelness and monochromaticity permits extending the scattering technique to lower angles and resolving details not previously seen. For example, Moore has seen higher order scattering maxima from ringed spherulites (7) and Samules has obtained good low-angle patterns from low scattering small polypropylene spherulites (14).

Light scattering experiments with pulsed (10) and continuous (14, 24, 6) lasers with photometric apparatus have also been carried out. By using red-sensitive photomultiplier detectors comparable sensitivity and much better resolution than could be obtained previously may be achieved. For systems having low scattering power such as gases, the scattering cell can be put directly in the laser cavity where up to 100 × increase in intensity may be obtained as a result of multiple passage of the incident beam through the sample (2).

Present laser light scattering techniques do not make use of the coherence properties of laser light. Additional information about the scattering system could be obtained through the resulting possibility of determining phase relationships by interference between the scattered and incident beams.

Another experimental advance is the use of the microscope for obtaining light scattering patterns. By lowering the condenser lens and stopping down the condenser diaphragm as for "axial illumination," a parallel beam of light may be passed through a sample on the microscope stage, Fig. 7. The use of a rotating stage and mechanical stage is convenient for shifting the illuminated area of the sample. Additional apertures or pinholes (25μ - 100μ dia.) may be mounted under the sample for further localizing the illuminated area. In Fig. 8 the area defined by such a pinhole is shown superposed on a photomicrograph of the structure of a spherulitic polyethylene sample in (a) and the corresponding H_V light scattering pattern is shown in (b). By this technique,

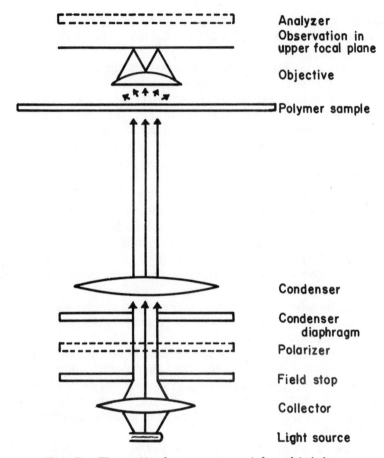

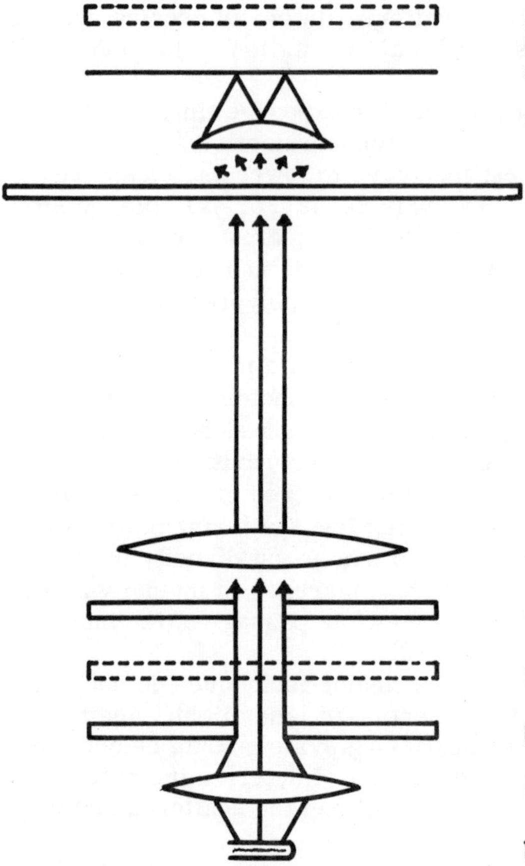

Fig. 7. The optical arrangement for obtaining light scattering patterns with the microscope.

the variation in structure from point-to-point on a sample may be studied. For example, in Fig. 9, a series of H_V photomicrographic scattering patterns obtained for an annealed dispersion cast polytetrafluoroethylene film is shown obtained by using a 25μ aperture and shifting the sample in 50μ steps using a mechanical stage. One sees patterns characteristic of both spherulitic and non-spherulitic regions. The spherulitic patterns are of two-types interrelated by 45° rotation, characteristic of spherulities with their optic axes at either 45° or 90° to the spherulite radius (11).

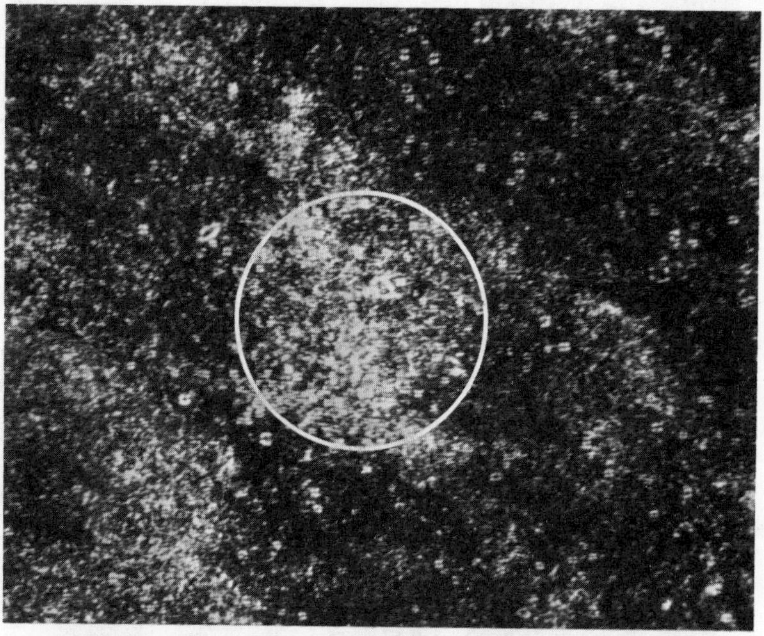

(a)

(b)

Fig. 8. The relationship between the sample field and the scattering pattern using the microscope technique. The circle in (a) designates the field of the sample producing the H_V scattering pattern in (b).

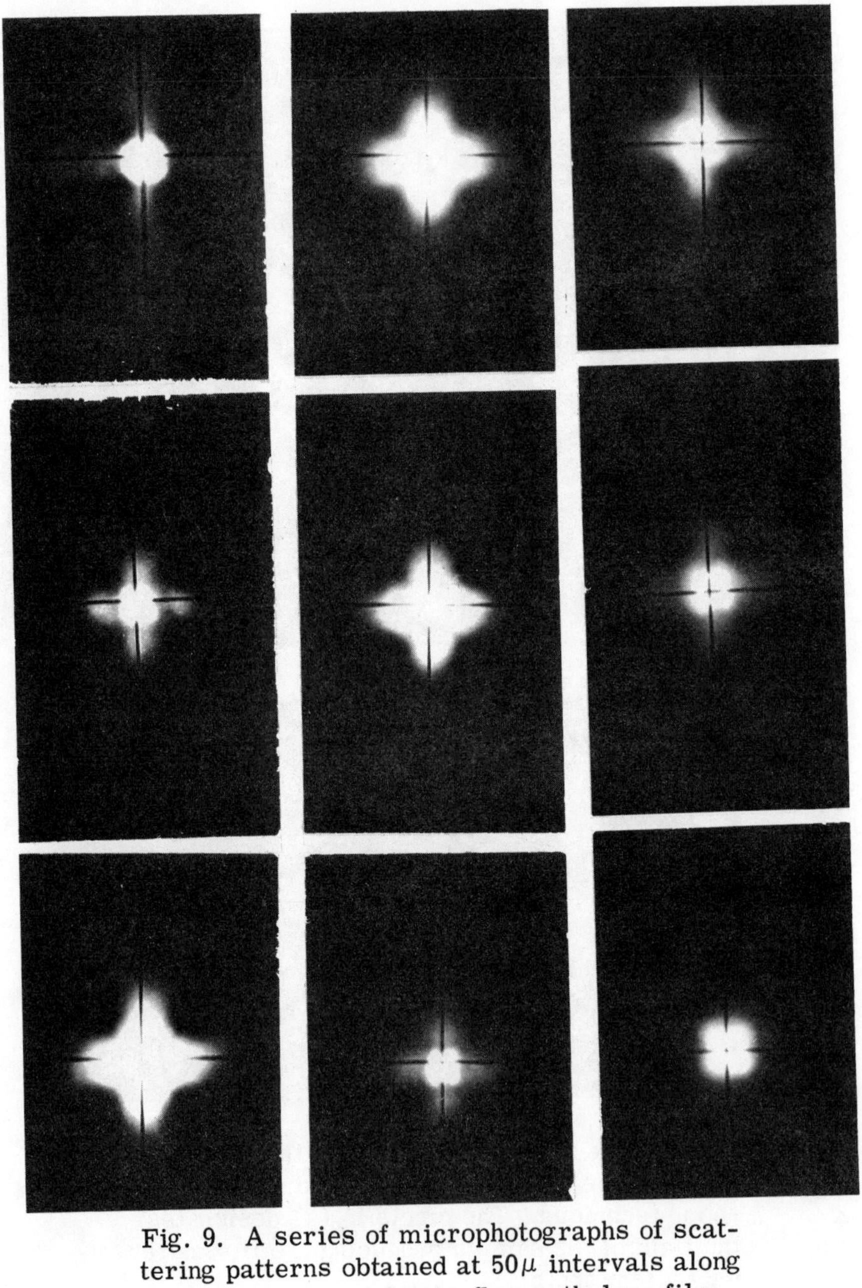

Fig. 9. A series of microphotographs of scattering patterns obtained at 50μ intervals along a heterogeneous polytetrafluoroethylene film.

The calibration of the microscopic or other photographic low-angle scattering techniques for determination of spherulite size may be readily accomplished by replacing the sample with a diffraction grating* of known spacing. For normal incidence, diffraction occurs at an angle θ_d given by

$$\sin \theta_d = \frac{n\lambda_0}{a} \quad (1)$$

where λ_0 is the wavelength in air, a is the distance between lines of the grating, and n is the order of diffraction. Now

$$\tan \theta_d = \frac{L_d}{D} \quad (2)$$

where L_d is the distance from the center of the diffraction pattern to the diffraction spot on the photographic film, and D is the grating-to-photographic film distance. Similarly, for a scattering experiment

$$\tan \theta_s = \frac{L_s}{D} \quad (3)$$

where L_s is the distance from the center of the scattering pattern to the scattering maximum on the photographic film and θ_s is the scattering angle between the incident and scattered ray (to the maximum) measured in air. Since D is the same in both the diffraction and scattering experiment and any modification of θ_s or θ_d by the microscope (or other) optics will be the same provided the L's are taken close together,

$$\theta_s = \tan^{-1}\left\{ \frac{L_s}{L_d} \tan\left[\sin^{-1}\left(\frac{n\lambda_0}{a}\right) \right] \right\} \quad (4)$$

Figure 10 shows a photomicrograph of a spherulitic field (of polyethylene), a scattering pattern and a diffraction pattern (taken with the same microscope optics using a 2000 line per inch grating). The spherulite radius, R, is calculated from (15, 20)

$$w = 4\pi(R/\lambda) \sin(\theta'_s/2) = 4.1 \quad (5)$$

*A replica grating mounted on a microscope slide is adequate for this purpose.

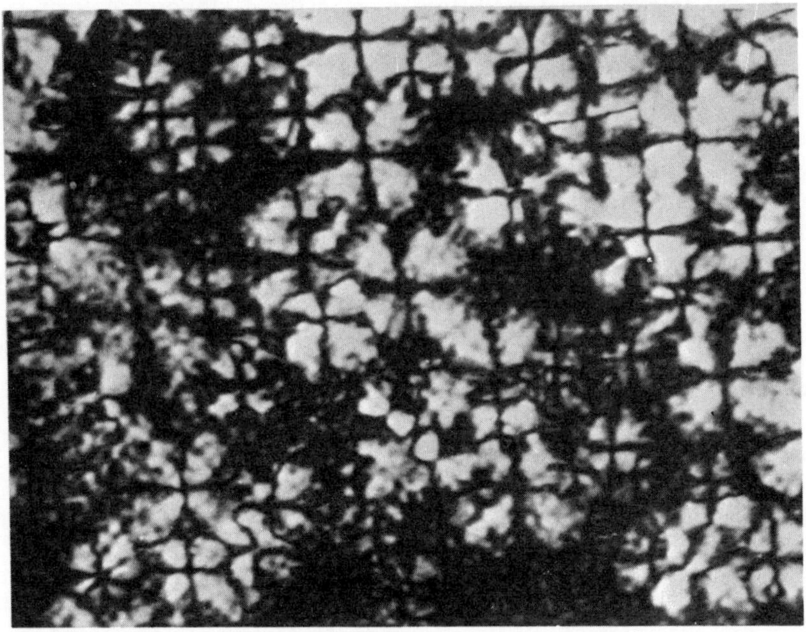

(a)

Fig. 10. The determination of the spherulite size for a polyethylene film from the microscope light scattering pattern using a diffraction grating for calibration. (a) the microscope field

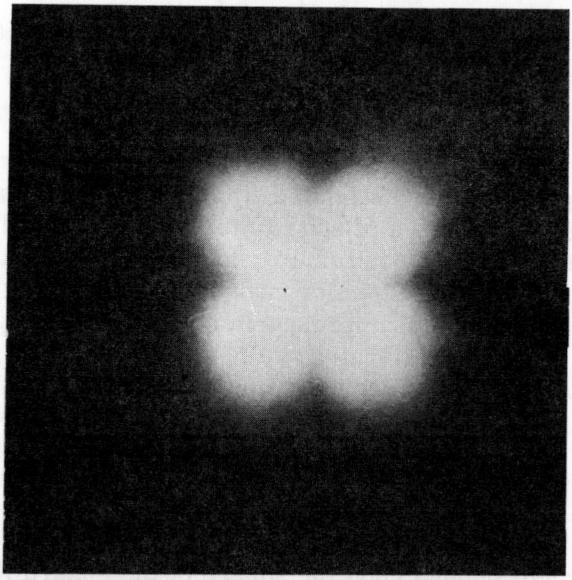

(b)

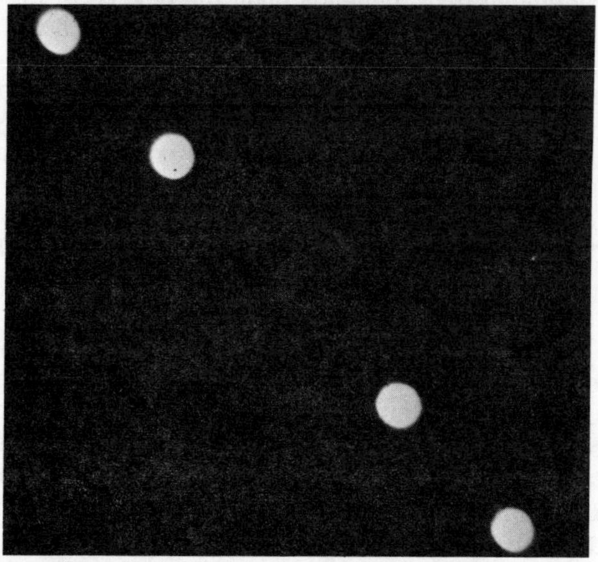

(c)

Fig. 10 (Cont'd.) (b) the scattering pattern obtained by the microscope technique, and (c) a diffraction pattern (obtained with the same microscope optics using a 2000 line per inch grating).

where λ and θ_s' are the wavelength and scattering angle in the medium of refractive index n_m, and (19)

$$n_m = (\sin \theta_s / \sin \theta_s'). \qquad (6)$$

This gives R = 14.5μ which is in reasonable agreement with the average radius estimated from the photomicrograph. A comparison of sizes of spherulites for several samples as measured by light scattering using a gas laser and zirconium arc source, using the microscope light scattering technique and estimated from microscopic observation using a micrometer eyepiece calibrated against a calibrated slide is shown in Table 1. The agreement among the scattering methods is excellent and these are in reasonable agreement with the range of sizes observed, especially on considering that there is a distribution of sizes and that the scattering average is highly weighted in favor of the larger sizes (21). Also, if there is heterogeniety in spherulite type, the scattering will depend upon the square of the spherulite anisotropy which, in turn, depends upon the degree of crystallinity (amount of secondary crystallization) and the degree and kind of orientation of crystallities (and amorphous regions) within the spherulite. Moore and Matsuoka have shown (9) that the intensity of the H_V pattern is very dependent upon the degree of secondary crystallization.

STATISTICAL DESCRIPTION OF SCATTERING SYSTEMS

For systems where it is not possible to characterize the scattering in terms of a discrete model, one employs the correlation function technique in terms of which the probability of correlation of the average refractive index, anisotropy, and optic axis orientation between two scattering elements separated by a given distance is described. In the previous report (15, 22) the results of such a description were presented for the limiting case of the so called "random orientation approximation" where it is assumed that the above probabilities depend only upon the separation of the volume elements.

This method permits the separation of contributions to

TABLE 1

Sperulite Radius in Microns as Determined by

	Gas Laser Scattering		Zr Arc Scattering		Microscope Scattering	Microscope
	Direct Calculation	Grating Calculation	Direct Calculation	Grating Calculation	Grating Calculation	Polarization or Phase
Standard Polyethylene Preparation	4.57	5.09	3.50	3.65	3.50	2.5-7.5 Range
Cross-Linked Medium Density Annealed Polyethylene	1.38	1.60	1.20	1.45	1.80	1.0-1.5 Range
Marlex (Preparation 5-25)	10.3	11.4	10.0	10.7	10.5-12.0	14.4 (Average of the Scattering Field)
Marlex (Preparation 4)	35.1	30.2	33.5	39.0	No Observable H_V Scattering Pattern	Two Distinct Size Ranges (a) 9-13 (b) 30-50

scattering arising from average refractive index, anisotropy and orientation fluctuations in that the latter two types contribute to H_V scattering whereas all three contribute to V_V scattering. It was shown that most of the wide angle scattering from polyethylene films at larger angles arises from fluctuations in the orientation of anisotropic crystals occurring over distances of many crystal sizes but smaller than the spherulite size. Thus, the arrangement of crystals within spherulites is ordered and gives rise to internal heterogeniety producing scattering at larger angles. Such shorter range order even occurs in samples where the higher order orientation of spherulites has not developed.

The scattering from spherulites could be treated in terms of such probability functions. For example, the scattering from isotropic spheres could be described in terms of the correlation function (23)

$$\gamma(r) = 1 - \frac{3}{4}\left(\frac{r}{R}\right) + \frac{1}{16}\left(\frac{r}{R}\right)^3 \qquad (7)$$

giving the probability that two volume elements separated by distance r lie within a sphere of radius R. As seen from the plot in Fig. 11a, this varies from one at $r = 0$ to zero at $r = 2R$. This is compared in Fig. 11b with an orientation correlation function h(r) for an anisotropic disc (17) of radius R (with radial optic axis orientation) which describes the degree of parallelness of orientation of two optic axes separated by distance r. It is of interest to note that this function is negative at some distances indicating a tendency toward perpendicular orientation of optic axes at these distances.

The scattering properties of such systems may be described in terms of these functions. However, it is a cumbersome way to deal with the scattering from highly ordered systems and a direct calculation of the scattered amplitude is easier. It is however, the best approach to use for more disordered systems which may not be adequately described in terms of a discrete model.

Because of the dependence of the orientation functions employed in the "random-approximation" upon only the scaler separation of scattering elements, the predicted scattering patterns are cylindrically symmetrical about the incident beam, and the scattering photographs should be independent of the azimuthal scattering angle, μ. The great dependence that we have seen of the spherulite scattering photographs upon azimuthal angle clearly indicates that this approximation is extremely poor for structures as ordered as spherulites. This observation casts some doubt upon the application of the random approximation to wider angle scattering. A test is to determine the degree of cylindrical symmetry of the wide-angle scattering about the incident beam by determining the variation of scattered intensity in a photometric experiment as the polarizer and analyzer are rotated through the angle ψ, keeping them parallel $[I_{\parallel}(\psi)]$ or perpendicular $[I_{+}(\psi)]$ (Fig. 12). The random orientation approximation predicts independence of ψ at small θ's (17, 16) characteristic of spherically symmetrical regions of correlated orientation. The results of a typical experiment of this type is shown in Fig. 13, in which appreciable ψ dependence is seen.

These results indicate that the correlated regions are extended in shape and that the probability of correlated orientation does not only depend upon the separation of the volume elements but also upon the direction that the separation vector makes with the optic axis. A two-dimensional theory incorporating these ideas has been developed and will be discussed in the next section (17, 16).

NON-RANDOM ORIENTATION FLUCTUATIONS IN TWO-DIMENSIONS

The intensity of scattering is calculated from the relationship (15)

$$I = K \sum_i \sum_j (\mathbf{M}_i \cdot \mathbf{O})\,(\mathbf{M}_j \cdot \mathbf{O}) \cos k(\mathbf{r}_{ij} \cdot \mathbf{s}) \tag{8}$$

where $\mathbf{M}_i$ and $\mathbf{M}_j$ are the induced dipoles in the ith and kth volume elements given by

$$\mathbf{M}_i = \delta(\mathbf{a}_i \cdot \mathbf{E})\,\mathbf{a}_i + \alpha_2\,\mathbf{E} \tag{9}$$

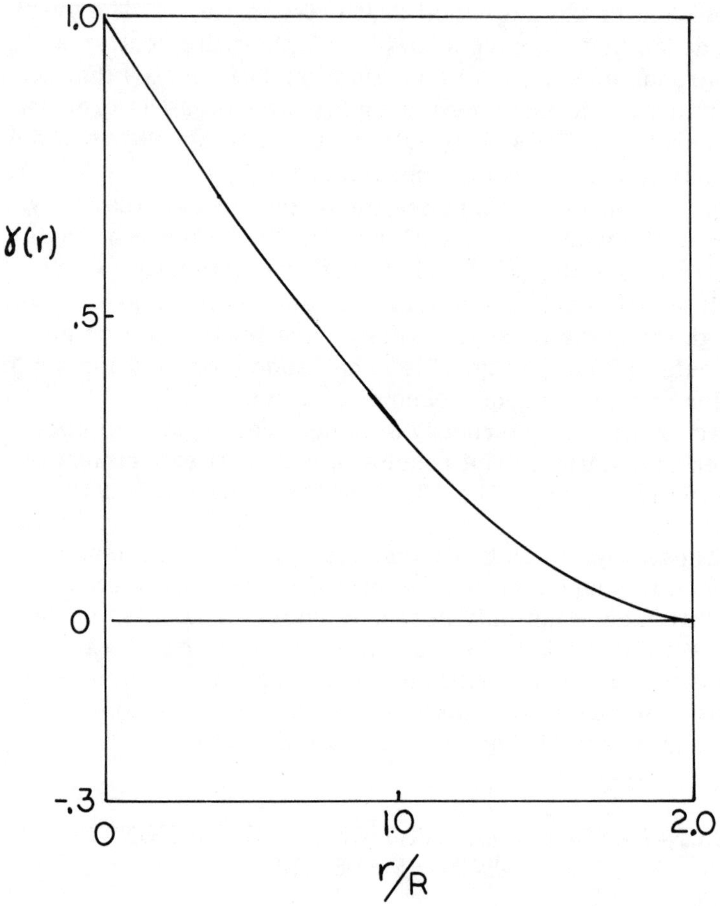

(a)

Fig. 11. The variation of (a) the density correlation function $\gamma(r)$, for an isotropic sphere of radius R (reprinted from J. Appl. Phys., **34**, 46 (1963)).

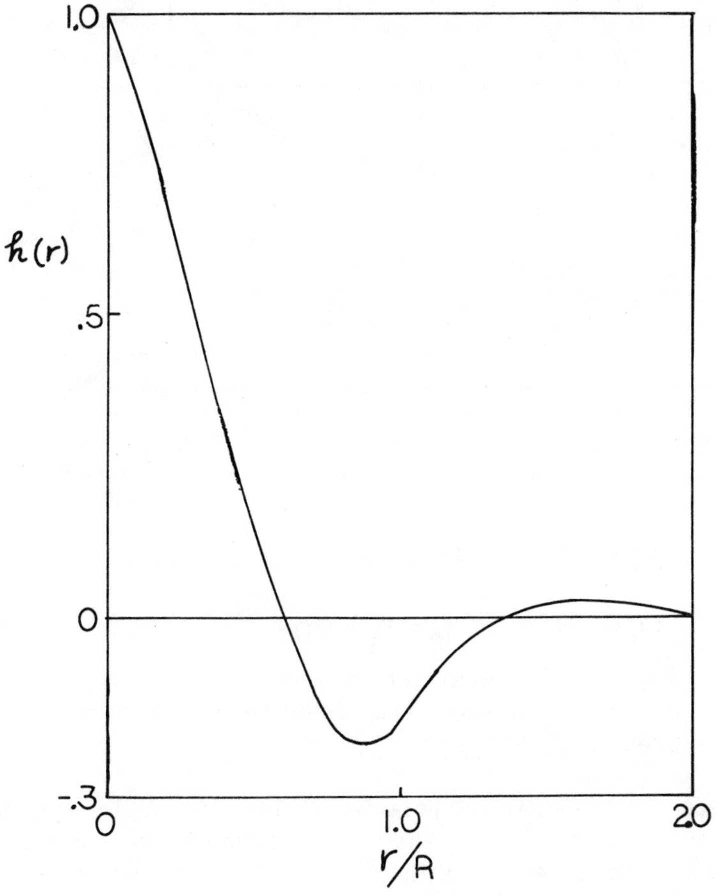

(b)

Fig. 11 (Cont'd). The orientation correlation function h(r) for an anisotropic disc of radius R with the separation distance, r, of the scattering elements (reprinted from a paper in press in J. Polymer Sci.).

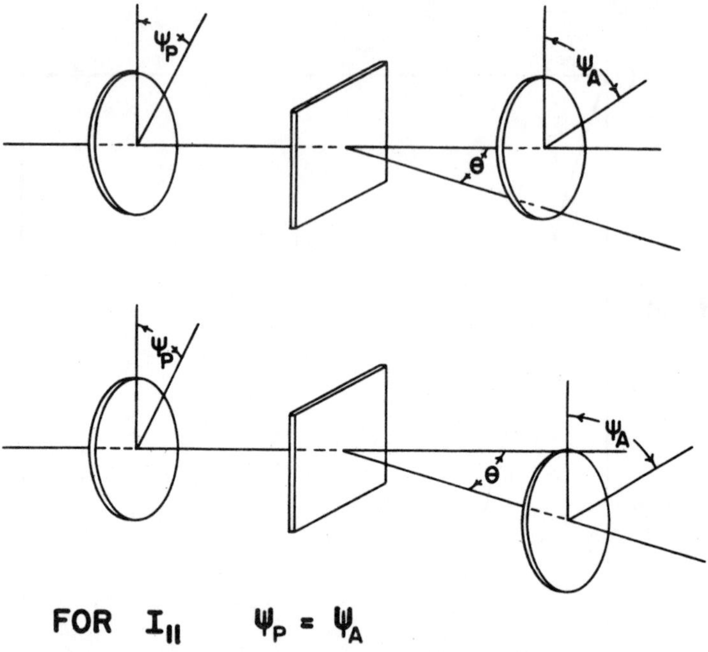

Fig. 12. The polarizer and analyzer rotation angles, ψ_1 and ψ_2. (reprinted from a paper in press in J. Polymer Sci.)

where α_1 and α_2 are the polarizabilities along and perpendicular to the optic axis of the volume element. $\mathbf{a}_i$ is a unit vector in the direction of the optic axis of the volume element. δ is the anisotropy (assumed constant throughout the medium) defined by

$$\delta = \alpha_1 - \alpha_2 \tag{10}$$

E is the field strength of the incident beam at the volume element

$$\mathbf{E} = E_0[(\cos\psi)\ \mathbf{k} + (\sin\psi)\ \mathbf{j}]. \tag{11}$$

O is a unit vector perpendicular to the scattered beam and in the direction of the scattered field passed by the

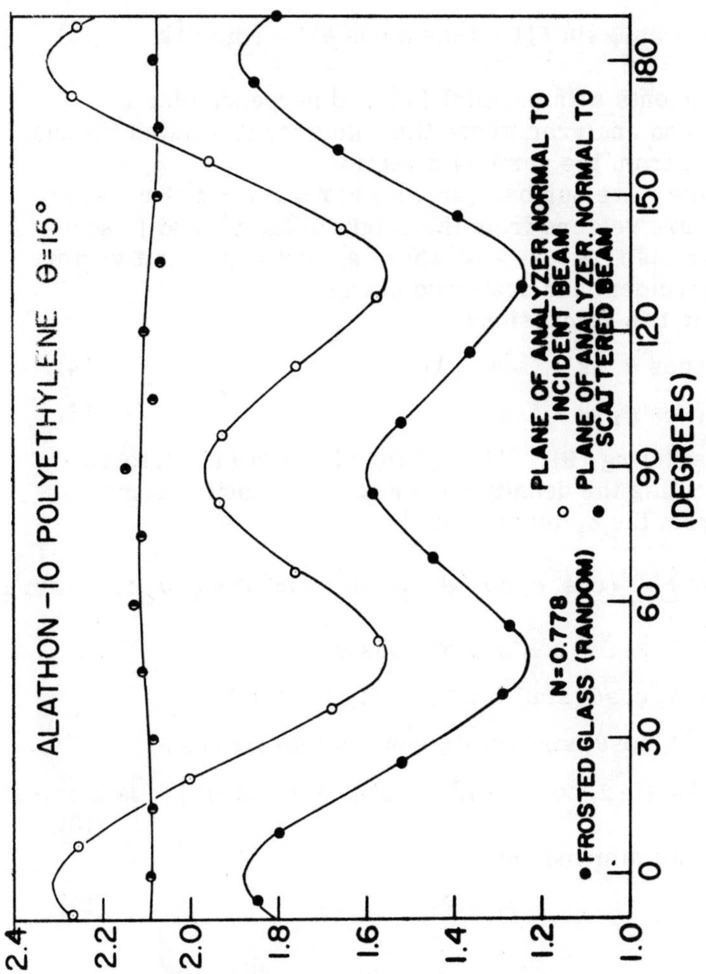

Fig. 13. The variation of $I_{\parallel}(\psi)$ with ψ for a film of low density polyethylene at $\theta = 15°$. The variation for frosted glass is shown for comparison (reprinted from a paper in press in J. Polymer Sci.)

analyzer in the scattered beam given by

$$\mathbf{O}_{\parallel} = (\sin\psi \sin\theta)\mathbf{i} + (\sin\psi\cos\theta)\mathbf{j} + (\cos\psi)\mathbf{k} \qquad (12)$$

$$\mathbf{O}_{+} = (\cos\psi \sin\theta)\mathbf{i} + (\cos\psi\cos\theta)\mathbf{j} - (\sin\psi)\mathbf{k} \qquad (13)$$

for experiments with parallel ($\parallel$) and perpendicular (+) polarizer and analyzer where the polarizer is rotated through the angle ψ from the vertical direction.

k is the wave number $(2\pi/\lambda)$ and $\mathbf{r} = \mathbf{r}_{ij} = \mathbf{r}_i - \mathbf{r}_j$ where $\mathbf{r}_i$ and $\mathbf{r}_j$ are vectors from the origin to the ith and j^{th} scattering elements. $\mathbf{s} = \mathbf{s}_0 - \mathbf{s}'$ where $\mathbf{s}_0$ and $\mathbf{s}'$ are unit vectors along the incident and scattered beams.

Now in two-dimensions

$$\mathbf{a}_i = (\cos\theta_i)\mathbf{k} + (\sin\theta_i)\mathbf{j} \qquad (14)$$

$$\mathbf{a}_j = (\cos\theta_j)\mathbf{k} + (\sin\theta_j)\mathbf{j}\,. \qquad (15)$$

Upon substituting (9), (11), (12), (14) and (15) into Eq. (8) [neglecting the density and cross-correlation terms arising from the α_2 term in (9)]

$$\begin{aligned} I_{\parallel} = K E_0^2 \delta^2 \sum_i \sum_j \{ & \cos^2\theta_i \cos^2\theta_j \cos^4\psi + \sin^2\theta_i \sin^2\theta_j \cos^2\theta \sin^4\psi \\ & + 2\cos^2\theta_i \sin^2\theta_j \cos^2\psi \sin^2\psi \cos\theta \\ & + 2\cos^2\theta_i \cos\theta_j \sin\theta_j \cos^3\psi \sin\psi (1+\cos\theta) \\ & + 2\sin^2\theta_i \cos\theta_j \sin\theta_j \sin^3\psi \cos\psi \cos\theta\,(1+\cos\theta) \\ & + \cos\theta_i \sin\theta_i \cos\theta_j \sin^2\psi \cos^2\psi (1+\cos\theta)^2 \} \cos k(\mathbf{r}_{ij}\cdot\mathbf{s}). \end{aligned} \qquad (16)$$

Now if in two dimensions,*

$$\theta_{ij} = \theta_j - \theta_i \qquad (17)$$

the term

$$(\cos^2\theta_i \cos^2\theta_j) = \cos^4\theta_i \cos^2\theta_{ij} + \sin^2\theta_i \cos^2\theta_i \sin^2\theta_{ij} - 2\cos^3\theta_i \sin\theta_i \sin\theta_{ij} \cos\theta_{ij}\,. \qquad (18)$$

*The three dimensional case is more complex as is seen, for example, in Equation A1 of Reference 22

In the random orientation fluctuation approximation the values of θ_{ij} are not correlated with θ_i so, for example

$$<\cos^4\theta_i \cos^2\theta_{ij}>_{av} = <\cos^4\theta_i>_{av} \cos^2\theta_{ij}. \quad (19)$$

If there is no macroscopic orientation all values of θ_i are equally probable, and

$$<\cos^4\theta_i>_{av} = 3/8. \quad (20)$$

The consequence of macroscopic orientation utilizing the random orientation fluctuation approximation has been discussed (18). Proceeding in this way for all of the terms in Eq. (18) the unoriented random orientation approximation gives

$$\begin{aligned} <\cos^2\theta_i \cos^2\theta_j>_{av} &= 3/8 \cos^2\theta_{ij} + 1/8 \sin^2\theta_{ij} \\ &= 1/4 \cos^2\theta_{ij} + 1/8. \end{aligned} \quad (21)$$

Similarly

$$<\sin^2\theta_i \sin^2\theta_j>_{av} = 1/4 \cos^2\theta_{ij} + 1/8. \quad (22)$$

$$<\cos^2\theta_i \sin^2\theta_j>_{av} = - 1/4 \cos^2\theta_{ij} + 3/8. \quad (23)$$

$$<\cos^2\theta_i \cos\theta_j \sin\theta_j>_{av} = 0 \quad (24)$$

and

$$<\sin^2\theta_i \cos\theta_j \sin\theta_j>_{av} = 0$$

if positive and negative values of θ_{ij} are equally probable (as is almost always the case).

$$<\cos\theta_i \sin\theta_i \cos\theta_j \sin\theta_j>_{av} = 1/4 \cos^2\theta_{ij} - 1/8. \quad (26)$$

Upon substituting into (16), this gives

$$\begin{aligned} I_{\parallel} = K E_0^2 \delta^2 \sum_i \sum_j \Big\{ & \left[\frac{1}{4}\cos^2\theta_{ij} + \frac{1}{8}\right] \cos^4\psi \\ & + \left[\frac{1}{4}\cos^2\theta_{ij} + \frac{1}{8}\right. \cos^2\theta \sin^4\psi \\ & - 2\left[\frac{1}{4}\cos^2\theta_{ij} - \frac{3}{8}\right] \sin^2\psi \cos^2\psi \cos\theta \\ & + \left[\frac{1}{4}\cos^2\theta_{ij} - \frac{1}{8}\right] (1 + \cos\theta)^2 \sin^2\psi \cos^2\psi \Big\} \cos k(\mathbf{r}_{ij} \cdot \mathbf{s}) \end{aligned} \quad (27)$$

The constant terms do not contribute since

$$\sum_j \sum_i \cos k(\mathbf{r}_{ij} \cdot \mathbf{s}) = 0 \tag{28}$$

because all values of the argument of the cosine are equally probable.
Thus

$$I_{\parallel} = \frac{1}{4} K E_0^2 \delta^2 \sum_i \sum_j \{\cos^2 \theta_{ij} [\cos^4 \psi + \cos^2 \theta \sin^4 \psi - 2 \sin^2 \psi \cos^2 \psi \cos\theta + (1 + \cos\theta)^2 \sin^2 \psi \cos^2 \psi] \cos k(\mathbf{r}_{ij} \cdot \mathbf{s})\}. \tag{29}$$

At small values of θ, this reduces to

$$I_{\parallel} = \frac{1}{4} K E_0^2 \delta^2 \sum_i \sum_j \{[\cos^4 \psi + 2 \sin^2 \psi \cos^2 \psi + \sin^4 \psi] \cos^2 \theta_{ij} \cos k(\mathbf{r}_{ij} \cdot \mathbf{s})\}$$

$$= \frac{1}{4} K E_0^2 \delta^2 \sum_i \sum_j [\cos^2 \theta_{ij} \cos k(\mathbf{r}_{ij} \cdot \mathbf{s})] \tag{30}$$

which is independent of ψ. The ψ dependence predicted by Eq. (29) at values of θ at which measurements are usually made (less than 30°) is rather small.

In general, the probability of finding a particular θ_{ij} will depend upon the angle β_i (as well as upon the vector $\mathbf{r}_{ij}$) defined by

$$\beta_i = \theta_i - \alpha_{ij} \tag{31}$$

where α_{ij} is the angle between $\mathbf{r}_{ij}$ and the vertical direction (Fig. 14). In the random orientation function approximation, the dependence upon the angular coordinates, α_{ij} of $\mathbf{r}_{ij}$ is neglected and only the dependence upon the scalar distance r_{ij} is described by the equations

$$f(r_{ij}) = 2 \langle \cos^2 \theta_{ij} \rangle_{r_{ij}} - 1 \tag{32}$$

in two-dimensions or

$$f(r_{ij}) = [3 \langle \cos^2 \theta_{ij} \rangle_{r_{ij}} - 1]/2 \tag{33}$$

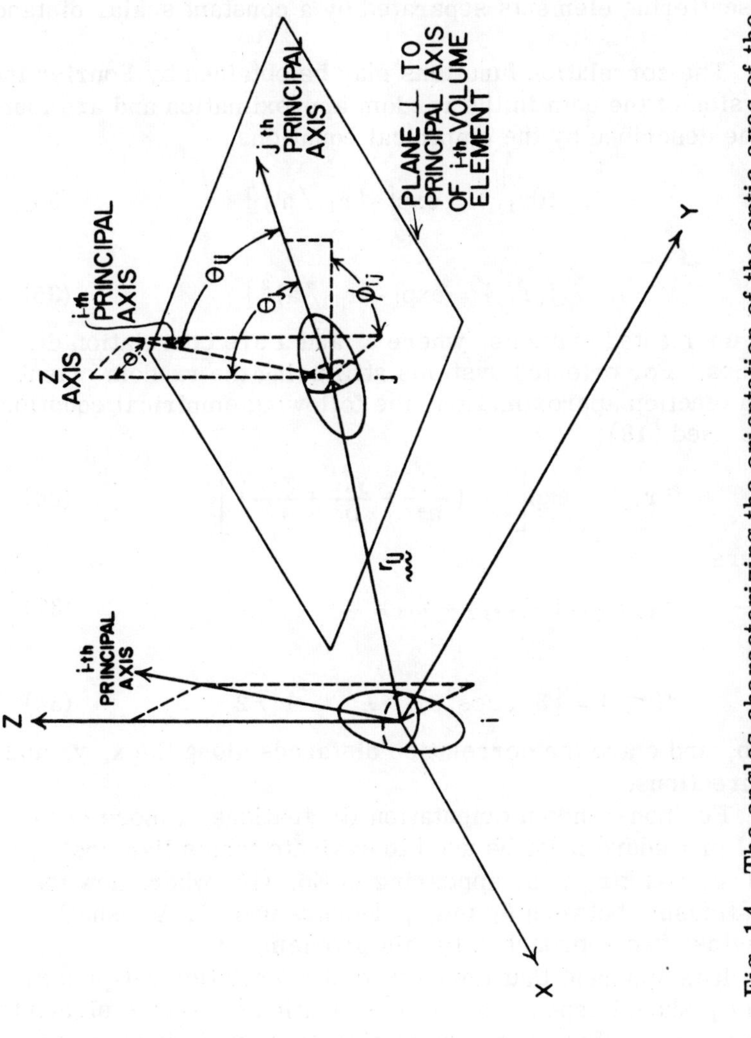

Fig. 14. The angles characterizing the orientation of the optic axes of the scattering elements and of their separation vector, $\mathbf{r}_{ij}$.

in three-dimensions where $f(r_{ij})$ is the orientation correlation function and $< > r_{ij}$ designates an average over-all pairs of scattering elements separated by a constant scalar distance r_{ij}

The correlation functions may be obtained by Fourier inversion of the data in the random approximation and are found to be described by the empirical equations

$$f(r_{ij}) = \exp[-(r_{ij}/a')] \tag{34}$$

or

$$f(r_{ij}) = \exp[-(r_{ij}/a)^2] \tag{35}$$

for unoriented systems, where a' and a are correlation distances. For oriented systems still using the random orientation function approximation, the following empirical equation was used (18);

$$f(\mathbf{r}_{ij}) = \exp\left[-\left(\frac{x_{ij}^2}{a^2} + \frac{y_{ij}^2}{b^2} + \frac{z_{ij}^2}{c^2}\right)\right] \tag{36}$$

where

$$\mathbf{r}_{ij} = x_{ij}\,\mathbf{i} + y_{ij}\,\mathbf{j} + z_{ij}\,\mathbf{k} \tag{37}$$

and

$$f(\mathbf{r}_{ij}) = [3 < \cos^2\theta_{ij} >_{\mathbf{r}_{ij}} - 1]/2 \tag{38}$$

a, b, and c are the correlation distances along the x, y, and z directions.

For non-random orientation fluctuations, a more general procedure must be used to evaluate terms like $\cos^2\theta_i \cos^2\theta_j \cos k(\mathbf{r}_{ij} \cdot \mathbf{s})$ appearing in Eq. (16) where now the relationship between θ_i and θ_j depends upon β. We shall consider two approaches to this problem.

It is apparent that the degree of correlation between θ_i and θ_j should depend upon the separation of volume elements i and j, $\mathbf{r}_{ij}$. When the volume elements are infinitely separated there will be no correlation and, in two-dimensions

$$\begin{aligned} < \cos^2\theta_i \cos^2\theta_j >_{\mathbf{r}_{ij}} &= < \cos^2\theta_i >_{av} < \cos^2\theta_j >_{av} \\ &= (1/2)(1/2) = 1/4 \end{aligned} \tag{39}$$

if there is no macroscopic orientation. On the other hand, when $r_{ij} = 0$, $\theta_i = \theta_j$ and

$$<\cos^2\theta_i \cos^2\theta_j>_{r_{ij}=0} = <\cos^4\theta_i>_{av} = 3/8. \tag{40}$$

Thus, it is reasonable to assume

$$<\cos^2\theta_i \cos^2\theta_j>_{r_{ij}} = \frac{1}{8} F(r_{ij}) + \frac{1}{4} \tag{41}$$

where $F(r_{ij})$ is a function of r_{ij} which varies between 1 and 0 as r_{ij} goes from 0 to ∞. For the random orientation case, $F(r_{ij}) = f(r_{ij}) = 2 <\cos^2\theta_{ij}>_{r_{ij}} - 1$ in two-dimensions, and

$$<\cos^2\theta_i \cos^2\theta_j>_{r_{ij}} = \frac{1}{4} <\cos^2\theta_{ij}>_{av} + \frac{1}{8} \tag{42}$$

in agreement with Eq. (21). For non-random orientation correlations,

$$F(r_{ij}) = F(r_{ij}, \alpha_{ij}, \beta_i) = F(r_{ij}, \alpha_{ij}, \theta_i). \tag{43}$$

The dependence of $F(r_{ij})$ upon angular coordinates characterizes the shape of the correlated region. The random case where there is no angular dependence corresponds to the region of correlated orientation being circularly (or spherically) symmetrical. A possible assumption is to have the shape factor and the size factor independent:

$$F(r_{ij}) = G(\alpha_{ij}, \beta_i)\, f(r_{ij}). \tag{44}$$

For a system with no macroscopic orientation $F(r_{ij})$ will not explicitly depend upon α_{ij} but only upon β_i. This corresponds to the correlated regions being extended in shape in a particular direction, but where these directions are oriented with angular randomness with respect to each other for different regions.

THE ROD-DISC INTERPOLATION DESCRIPTION OF NON-RANDOM ORIENTATION FLUCTUATIONS

The first approach we have adopted is to characterize the shape of the correlated region by a single parameter,

ϵ which varies from +1 to -1 for the extremes of shape and is zero for the random (angularly independent) case.

One limit of angular dependence of $F(r_{ij})$ would be for G to be non-zero only when $\beta_i = 0$ (or $\theta_i = \alpha_{ij}$). That is, two scattering elements have their optic axes directions correlated in orientation only when these directions lie parallel to the vector r_{ij}. Since this corresponds to the situation in an infinitesmally thin isolated rod (or fiber) where the optic axes are parallel to the rod axes. we refer to this as "rod-like" correlation. For such a case $\theta_i = \theta_j = \alpha_{ij}$, so

$$<\cos^2\theta_i \cos^2\theta_j>_{r_{ij}} = (\cos^4\alpha_{ij} - \frac{1}{4}) f(r_{ij}) + \frac{1}{4} \quad (45)$$

or

$$G(\alpha_{ij}, \beta_i) = 8 \cos^4\alpha_{ij} - 2. \quad (46)$$

Similarly, when $\epsilon = -1$ for "disc-like" correlations, orientation is correlated only when $\beta_i = 90°$ and

$$<\cos^2\theta_i \cos^2\theta_j>_{r_{ij}} = (\sin^4\alpha_{ij} - \frac{1}{4}) f(r_{ij}) + \frac{1}{4}. \quad (47)$$

Our proposed approach is to choose a function for $<\cos^2\theta_i \cos^2\theta_j>_{r_{ij}}$ which may as a limit go from (45) to (47) as ϵ goes from +1 to -1 and reduce to the random case when $\epsilon = 0$. A function having these properties is

$$<\cos^2\theta_i \cos^2\theta_j>_{r_{ij}} = P(\alpha_{ij}) f(r_{ij}) + \frac{1}{4} \quad (48)$$

where

$$P(\alpha_{ij}) = \frac{1}{8} G(\beta_i, \alpha_{ij}) = \epsilon^2 \cos^4\alpha_{ij} + \epsilon(1-\epsilon)\cos^2\alpha_{ij} + \frac{1}{8}(1 - 4\epsilon + \epsilon^2) \quad (49)$$

Proceeding similarly for the other terms in Eq. (16), one obtains

$$<\sin^2\theta_i \sin^2\theta_j>_{r_{ij}} = Q(\alpha_{ij}) f(r_{ij}) + \frac{1}{4} \quad (50)$$

where

$$Q(\alpha_{ij}) = \epsilon^2 \cos^4\alpha_{ij} - \epsilon(\epsilon+1)\cos^2\alpha_{ij} + \frac{1}{8}(1 + 4\epsilon + \epsilon^2) \quad (51)$$

$$< \cos^2\theta_i \sin^2\theta_j >_{r_{ij}} = H(\alpha_{ij})\, f(r_{ij}) + \frac{1}{4} \tag{52}$$

where

$$H(\alpha_{ij}) = \epsilon^2 \sin^2\alpha_{ij} \cos^2\alpha_{ij} - \frac{1}{8}(1+\epsilon)(1-\epsilon) \tag{53}$$

and

$$< \sin\theta_i \cos\theta_i \sin\theta_j \cos\theta_j >_{r_{ij}} = K(\alpha_{ij})\, f(r_{ij}) \tag{54}$$

where

$$K(\alpha_{ij}) = \epsilon^2 \sin^2\alpha_{ij} \cos^2\alpha_{ij} + \frac{1}{8}(1+\epsilon)(1-\epsilon). \tag{55}$$

The terms of the sort $(\cos^2\theta_i \cos\theta_j \sin\theta_j)$ are odd functions of the θ's which give zero after integrating over any sort of symmetrical distribution. Upon substituting back into (16) and converting the sum to integrals, one obtains*

$$I_{\parallel} = K E_0^2 \delta^2 A \int_{r=0}^{\infty} \Big\{ \int_{\alpha=0}^{\pi} [\cos^4\psi\, P(\alpha) + \cos^2\theta \sin^4\psi\, Q(\alpha)$$
$$+ 2 \sin^2\psi \cos^2\psi \cos\theta\, H(\alpha) + \sin^2\psi \cos^2\psi (1+\cos\theta)^2 K(\alpha)]$$
$$\cos(w \sin\alpha)\, d\alpha \Big\} f(r)\, r d(r) \tag{56}$$

where

$$w \sin\alpha = -k(\mathbf{r}_{ij} \cdot \mathbf{s}) \tag{57}$$

and

$$w = k r_{ij} \sin\theta. \tag{57a}$$

Upon integrating over α, this yields

*In converting the sums to integrals the subscripts on α_{ij} and r_{ij} are dropped in these equations and elsewhere in the manuscript.

$$I_{\parallel} = 2\pi K E_0^2 \delta^2 A \Big\{ \frac{1}{8} [\cos^4\psi + (1+\cos^2\theta)\sin^2 \cos^2\psi + \cos^2\theta \sin^4\psi]$$

$$\int_0^\infty J_0(w)\, f(r)\, r\, dr + 3\epsilon[\epsilon \cos^4\psi + \epsilon \sin^4\psi \cos^2\theta$$

$$- \epsilon(1 + 4\cos\theta + \cos^2\theta)\sin^2\psi\cos^2\psi] \int_0^\infty \frac{J_2(w)}{w^2} f(r)\, r\, dr$$

$$+ \epsilon[(1-\epsilon)\cos^4\psi - (1+\epsilon)\sin^4\psi\cos^2\theta + \epsilon(1+4\cos\theta+\cos^2\theta)]$$

$$\int_0^\infty \frac{J_1(w)}{w} f(r)\, r\, dr + \frac{\epsilon}{8}[(\epsilon-4)\cos^4\psi + (\epsilon+4)\sin^4\psi\cos^2\theta$$

$$- 2\epsilon \sin^2\psi\cos^2\psi] \int_0^\infty J_0(w)\, f(r)\, r\, dr \Big\} \tag{58}$$

where $J_0(w)$, $J_1(w)$ and $J_2(w)$ are Bessel Functions of order zero, one, and two, respectively.

For random correlations where $\epsilon = 0$, only the first term remains which is almost independent of ψ at small values of θ. The remaining terms are strongly ψ dependent and result in a ψ dependence of $I_{\parallel}$ when $\epsilon \neq 0$.

If Eq. (35) is used for f(r) one obtains after integrating over r

$$I_{\parallel} = 2\pi K E_0^2 \delta^2 A a^2 \Big\{ \frac{1}{16} [\cos^4\psi + (1+\cos^2\theta)\sin^2\psi\cos^2\psi + \cos^2\theta\sin^4\psi]\, e^{-w^2/4}$$

$$+ 6\epsilon^2[\cos^4\psi + \sin^4\psi\cos^2\theta - (1 + 4\cos\theta + \cos^2\theta)\sin^2\psi\cos^2\psi]$$

$$[(e^{-w^2/4} - 1 + [w^2/4])/w^4] + \epsilon[(1-\epsilon)\cos^4\psi - (1+\epsilon)\sin^4\psi\cos^2\theta$$

$$+ \epsilon(1+4\cos\theta+\cos^2\theta)\sin^2\psi\cos^2\psi][(1-e^{-w^2/4})/w^2]$$

$$+ (1/16)\,\epsilon[(\epsilon-4)\cos^4\psi + (\epsilon+4)\sin^4\psi\cos^2\theta$$

$$- 2\epsilon\sin^2\psi\cos^2\psi]\, e^{-w^2/4} \Big\} \tag{59}$$

where

$$w = 2\pi(a/\lambda)\sin\theta. \tag{60}$$

While the above treatment predicts a reasonable sort of

variation of $I_{\parallel}$ with ψ, the θ dependence of this variation is not right, there being too great a variation of $I_{\parallel}$ with ψ at small θ's (where there is appreciable contribution from pairs of volume elements separated by large distances). This indicates that the separation-of-variables assumption introduced in going from Eq. (43) to Eq. (44) is not good and that the angular dependence of $F(r_{ij})$ varies with r_{ij}, the correlations becoming more spherically symmetrical with increasing r_{ij}. One empirical way of introducing this is to let ϵ be a function of r_{ij} as for example

$$\epsilon(r_{ij}) = \epsilon_0 \exp\left[-(r_{ij}^2/b^2)\right] \tag{61}$$

where now ϵ_0 is the shape factor for the correlations of closely spaced scattering elements and b is a correlation distance for persistence of angular dependence of correlation (which may or may not be the same as a, the correlation distance itself).

If Eq. (61) is used, this may be substituted into Eq. (58) after modification such that the $\epsilon(r)$ is included in the integrations over r. The results of this as well as for the parallel calculation of I_+ are given in Fig. 15 and calculated for the case where a = b and $w^2 = 4.00$. It is seen that both $I_{\parallel}$ and I_+ are fairly independent of ψ for the random orientation correlation case when $\epsilon_0 = 0$ but vary appreciably at other values of ϵ_0. Since I_+ depends only upon ϵ_0^2, its variation is the same for positive and negative values of ϵ_0 and it is not possible to distinguish between rod-like and disc-like fluctuations from its observation. However, $I_{\parallel}$ differs for positive and negative values of ϵ_0, the theory predicting intensity maxima at $\psi = 0°$ and 180° for positive values and at $\psi = 90°$ and 270° for negative values of ϵ_0.

A comparison with the experimental measurements on polyethylene shown in Fig. 13 shows the largest maxima at $\psi = 0°$ and 180°, but a lower maximum is seen at $\psi = 90°$. The experimental measurements of I_+ show maxima at odd multiples of $\psi = 45°$ whereas the theory predicts I_+ maxima at 0°, 90°, and 180° (of equal height).

The differences between experiment and theory are results of the overly simple possibilities for the type and shape of the correlated region permitted by the theoretical model. The

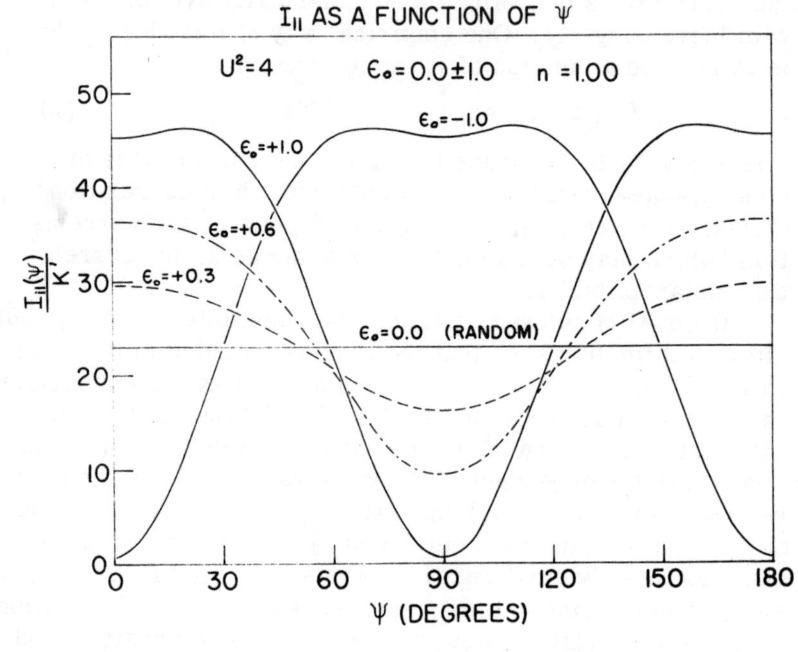

Fig. 15. The calculated variation of scattered intensity with ψ calculated for various values of ϵ_0(using Eq. (61) for the variation of ϵ (r_{ij}) with r_{ij}) for a = b at U^2 = 4.00.
(a) parallel polaroids [$I_{\parallel}$]

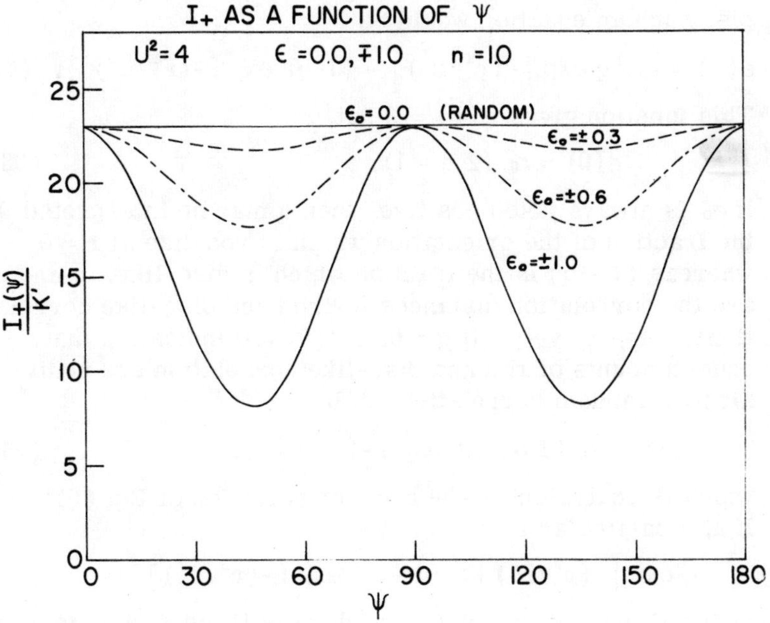

Fig. 15 (Cont'd) (b) crossed polaroids [I_+].
Reprinted from J. Polymer Sci. C No. 13 (1966))

larger maximum of $I_{\parallel}$ at 0° might indicate a greater tendency toward positive values of ϵ_0 corresponding to rod-like correlations for the scattering element separation, r_{ij}, contributing most to the scattering at $\theta = 15^{\circ}$ where the measurements were taken. However, the secondary maximum at $\psi = 90^{\circ}$ might indicate that at some other r_{ij} there may be a tendency for disc-like corrrlations. This would indicate the desirability of using a more general equation than Eq. (61) for $\epsilon(r)$ which would permit ϵ to assume positive values at some r's and negative at others. For example, such an equation would be

$$\epsilon(r) = \epsilon_0 \left\{ q \exp\left[-(r^2/b^2)\right] - (1-q) \exp\left[-(r^2/c^2)\right] \right\}. \quad (62)$$

This function gives $\epsilon(\infty) = 0$ but

$$\epsilon(0) = \epsilon_0 (2q - 1). \quad (63)$$

If ϵ_0 is always taken positive, then q may be interpreted as the fraction of the orientation which is rod-like at $r = 0$ whereas $(1 - q)$ is the fraction which is disc-like. b and c are the correlation distances for rod and disc-like correlations, respectively. If $q = 0.5$, $\epsilon(0) = 0$ indicating that equal amounts of rod and disc-like correlation are equivalent to random correlation. If $b = c$

$$\epsilon(r) = \epsilon_0 (2q - 1) \exp\left[-(r^2/b^2)\right] \quad (64)$$

which is equivalent to the simpler variation of Eq. (61). If at a particular r

$$q \exp\left[-(r^2/b^2)\right] > (1 - q) \exp\left[-(r^2/c^2)\right] \quad (65)$$

$\epsilon(r)$ will be positive at that r whereas if the second term is larger, $\epsilon(r)$ will be negative.

The result of using such an $\epsilon(r)$ in the calculation of $I_{\parallel}$ is shown in Fig. 16 for $\epsilon_o = 1$, $q = 0.5$, $(b^2/a^2) = 10^3$, $(c^2/a^2) = 10^{-3}$. It is seen that this function does give a secondary maximum in $I_{\parallel}$ at $\psi = 90^{\circ}$ as found experimentally.

A complete study of the nature of the orientation correlations requires a measure of the dependence of both $I_{\parallel}$ and I_{+} upon ψ at all θ's. It would be hoped that a technique for inversion of the data could be worked out to permit the calculation of the form of $\epsilon(r)$ and $f(r)$. So far this has not been possible and the approach has been to determine the

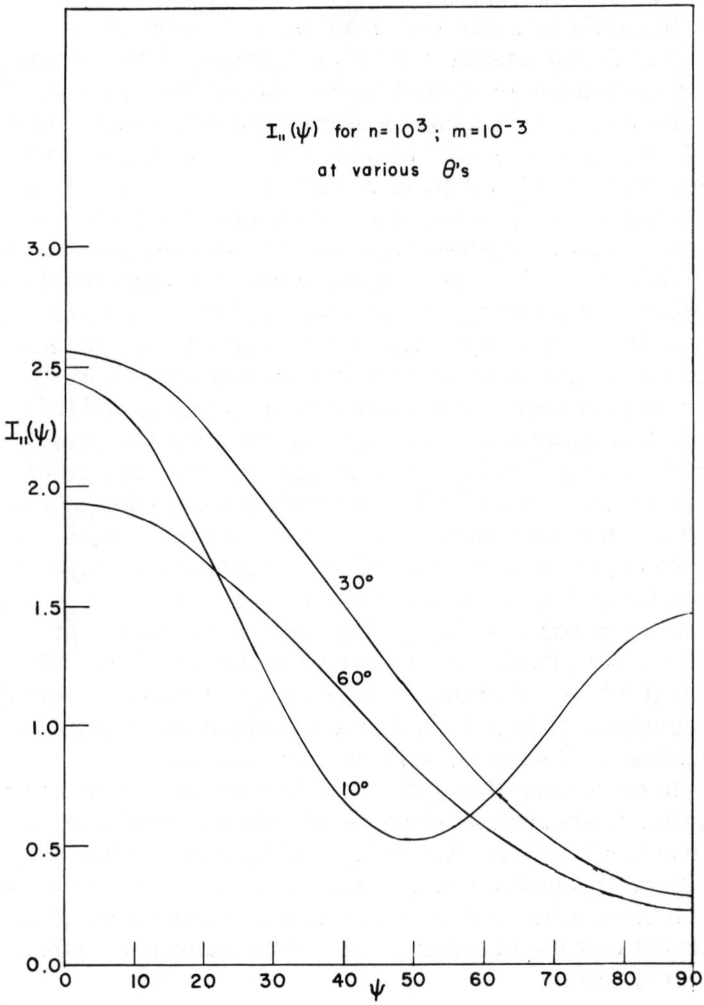

Fig. 16. The calculated variation of $I_{\parallel}$ with ψ for several values of θ using Eq. (62) for $\epsilon(r)$ where $\epsilon_0 = 1$, $q = 1/2$, $(b^2/a^2) = 10^3$ $(c^2/a^2) = 10^{-3}$ and $a = \lambda$. (Part reprinted from a paper in press in J. Polymer Sci.)

parameters for empirically assumed functions for $\epsilon(r)$ and $f(r)$ by trial and error.

It should be noted that even the more complex $\epsilon(r)$ of Eq. (62) is not adequate for all situations. For example, while the parameters used in the calculations for Fig. 16 predict an $I_{\parallel}$ in reasonable agreement with experiments, the I_{+} prediction is still at fault (16). The reason is that this development is dependent upon the type of correlations describable by equations like the empirical Eq. (49) in which ϵ is an interpolation parameter between the extremes of rod-like and disc-like correlations. This function is not capable of duplicating correlations having other types of symmetry such as spherical (or circular in two-dimensions). This latter type of symmetry is very likely since highly ordered polymers form spherulitic aggregates and it is likely that spherulitic symmetry is preserved in less ordered systems. Also, this formalism is not capable of describing correlated regions which are extended in a direction other than along or perpendicular to the optic axis. For example, in non-spherulitic polytetrafluoroethylene, the optic axis appears to lie at 45° to the direction of maximum correlation (13), giving rise to $I_{\parallel}$ maxima at $\psi = 45°$, not predictable by the preceding equations. Consequently it is desirable to develop non-random orientation fluctuation theory in terms of a somewhat more general formalism. This is done in the next section.

In comparing theoretical predictions with experimental results, it should be remembered that the results of two-dimensional theories are being compared with measurements on three-dimensional systems. While the difference in dimensionality undoubtedly leads to differences, it is believed that the preceding arguments based upon symmetry are still valid.

DESCRIPTION OF NON-RANDOM ORIENTATION FLUCTUATIONS IN TERMS OF A HARMONIC EXPANSION

As discussed in previous sections, the random orientation fluctuation approximation implies that the probability, $P(\theta_{ij})$, of a given angle, θ_{ij}, between the ith and jth scattering elements depends only upon their separation, $\mathbf{r}_{ij}$ and is independent of the angle β_i between the ith optic axis and $\mathbf{r}_{ij}$. In two-dimensions, $P(\theta_{ij})$ may be expanded in a Fourier series in θ_{ij}

$$P(\theta\ \ ) = L_0 + L_1 \sin \theta \ \ + L_2 \sin 2\theta_{ij} + \cdots$$
$$+ M_1 \cos \theta \ \ + M_2 \cos 2\theta_{ij} + \cdots \qquad (66)$$

The L's and M's are, in general, functions of r_{ij} and β_i. The averages of the distribution in θ_{ij} may then be related to the coefficients of this series. For example

$$F_1 = 2 \langle \cos^2 \theta_{ij} \rangle_{r_{ij}, \beta_i} - 1 = \langle \cos 2\theta_{ij} \rangle_{r_{ij}, \beta_i}$$
$$= \int_0^{2\pi} \cos 2\theta_{ij}\ P(\theta_{ij})\ d\theta_{ij} = M_2 \int_0^{2\pi} \cos^2 2\theta_{ij}\ d\theta_{ij}$$
$$= \pi M_2 \qquad (67)$$

and

$$F_2 = \langle 2 \sin\theta_{ij} \cos\theta_{ij} \rangle_{r_{ij},\beta_i} = \langle \sin 2\theta_{ij} \rangle_{r_{ij}, \beta_i}$$

$$= \int \sin 2\theta_{ij}\ P(\theta_{ij})\ d\theta_{ij} = \pi L_2 . \qquad (68)$$

By normalization

$$\int_0^{2\pi} P(\theta_{ij})\ d\theta_{ij} = 1 = 2\pi L_0 \qquad (69)$$

so

$$L_0 = 1/2\pi . \qquad (70)$$

It is noted that in two dimensions, these F's are functions of r_{ij} and β_i. This formalism may be extended to three-dimensions in which case $P(\theta_{ij}, \phi_{ij})$ is dependent upon the spherical coordinates θ_{ij} and ϕ (Fig. 17) defining the

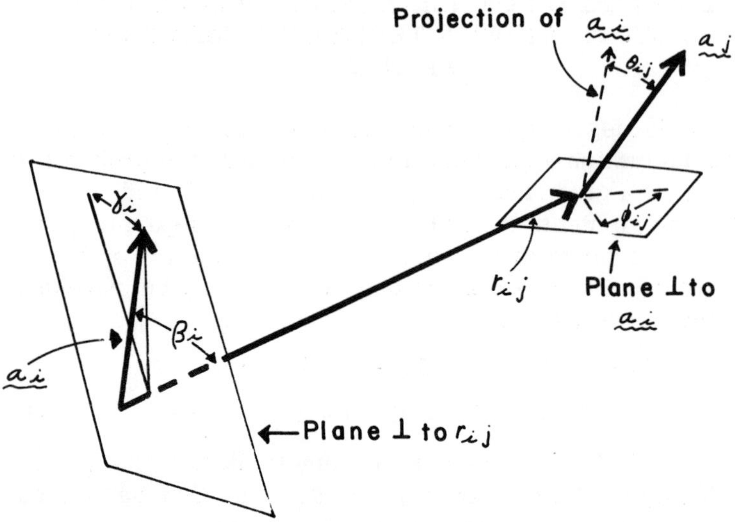

Fig. 17. The angles θ_{ij}, ϕ_{ij}, β_i and γ_i describing the optic axis orientation in three-dimensions.

orientation of a relative to that of a_i. In this case $P(\theta_{ij}, \phi_{ij})$ may be expanded in spherical harmonics as

$$P(\theta_{ij}, \phi_{ij}) = \sum_{l=1}^{\infty} \sum_{m=-1}^{+1} C_{l,m} Y_{l,m}(\theta_{ij}, \phi_{ij}) \tag{71}$$

where

$$Y_{l,m}(\theta_{ij}, \phi_{ij}) = \frac{1}{\sqrt{2\pi}} P_l^{|m|}(\theta_{ij}) e^{im\phi_{ij}} \tag{72}$$

where the $P_l^{|m|}(\theta_{ij})$'s are the associated Legendre polynomials. This gives

$$P(\theta_{ij}, \phi_{ij}) = \frac{1}{\sqrt{2\pi}} \Bigg\{ C_{0,0}\frac{1}{\sqrt{2}} + C_{1,0}\sqrt{\frac{3}{2}} \cos\theta_{ij}$$

$$+ \left[C_{1,1} e^{-i\phi_{ij}} + C_{1,1} e^{i\phi_{ij}} \right] \sqrt{\frac{3}{4}} \sin\theta_{ij}$$

$$+ C_{2,0}\sqrt{\frac{5}{8}}\,[3\cos^2\theta_{ij} - 1]$$

$$+\left[C_{2,-1}\,e^{-i\phi_{ij}} + C_{2,1}\,e^{i\phi_{ij}}\right]$$

$$\sqrt{\frac{15}{4}}\,\sin\theta_{ij}\,\cos\theta_{ij} + \left[C_{2,-2}\,e^{-2i\phi_{ij}} + C_{2,2}\,e^{2i\phi_{ij}}\right.$$

$$\left.\sqrt{\frac{15}{16}}\,\sin^2\theta_{ij} + \cdots\right\} \qquad (73)$$

where the $C_{l,m}$'s are functions of $\mathbf{r}_{ij}$, β_i, and γ_i, the azimuthal angle defining the orientation of $\mathbf{a}_i$ with respect to $\mathbf{r}_{ij}$.

In a manner similar to the two-dimensional case, in three-dimensions

$$F_1(r_{ij}, \beta_i, \gamma_i) = \langle(3\cos^2\theta_{ij} - 1)/2\rangle_{r_{ij},\beta_i,\gamma_i}$$

$$= \int_{\phi_{ij}=0}^{2\pi}\int_{\theta_{ij}=0}^{\pi}[3\cos^2\theta_{ij} - 1]/2$$

$$\cdot P(\theta_{ij}, \phi_{ij})\sin\theta_{ij}\,d\theta_{ij}\,d\phi_{ij} = \sqrt{\frac{4\pi}{5}}\,C_{2,0} \qquad (74)$$

where γ_i is the cylindrical angle of rotation of $\mathbf{a}_i$ about $\mathbf{r}_{ij}$ measured in a plane perpendicular to $\mathbf{r}_{ij}$.

To calculate I_+ in two-dimensions using this approach, one substitutes Eq. (9), (11), (13), (14) and (15) into Eq. (8) to obtain (neglecting density and cross correlations)

$$I_+ = K E_0^2\,\delta^2\Big\{[K_1 + K_2\cos^2\theta - 2K_3\cos\theta]\sin^2\psi\cos^2\psi$$

$$+ K_4[\cos^2\psi\cos\theta - \sin^2\psi]^2\Big\} \qquad (75)$$

where

$$K_1 = \sum_i\sum_j \cos^2\theta_i\cdot\cos^2\theta_j\,\cos k(\mathbf{r}_{ij}\cdot\mathbf{s}) \qquad (76)$$

$$K_2 = \sum_i\sum_j \sin^2\theta_i\,\sin^2\theta_j\,\cos k(\mathbf{r}\quad\cdot\mathbf{s}) \qquad (77)$$

$$K_3 = \sum_i\sum_j \cos^2\theta_i\,\sin^2\theta_j\,\cos k(\mathbf{r}_{ij}\cdot\mathbf{s}) \qquad (78)$$

and

$$K_4 = \sum_i \sum_j \sin\theta_i \cos\theta_i \sin\theta_j \cos\theta_j \cos k\,(\mathbf{r}_{ij} \cdot \mathbf{s}) \,. \tag{79}$$

To evaluate K_1 one uses

$$\cos^2\theta_i = \frac{1}{2}\,(1 + \cos 2\theta_i) \tag{80}$$

So

$$K_1 = \frac{1}{4} \sum_i \sum_j (1 + \cos 2\theta_i)(1 + \cos 2\theta_j) \cos k\,(\mathbf{r}_{ij} \cdot \mathbf{s})$$

$$= \frac{1}{4} \sum_i \sum_j [1 + \cos 2\theta_i + \cos 2\theta_j + \cos 2\theta_i \cos 2\theta_j] \cos k\,(\mathbf{r}_{ij} \cdot \mathbf{s})$$

$$= \frac{1}{4} \sum_i \sum_j \cos 2\theta_i \cos 2\theta_j \cos k\,(\mathbf{r}_{ij} \cdot \mathbf{s})$$

$$= \frac{A}{4} \int_{r_{ij}} \langle \cos 2\theta_j \cos 2\theta_j \rangle_{r_{ij}} \cos k\,(\mathbf{r}_{ij} \cdot \mathbf{s})\, d\mathbf{r}_{ij} \,; \tag{81}$$

where A is the area of the sample (obtained by integrating over $d\,\mathbf{r}_{ij}$).

The simplifying assumption has been made in this development that terms of the sort $\sum_i \sum_j \cos 2\,\theta_j \cos k\,(\mathbf{r}_{ij} \cdot \mathbf{s})$ are zero. This is not generally the case as is shown in a separate publication (16a). This leads to an additional term in the expressions for the K_j's, and results in an extra term dependent upon ψ in the final expressions for intensity of scattering.

Now

$$\langle \cos 2\theta_i \cos 2\theta_j \rangle_{r_{ij}}$$

$$= \langle \cos 2\theta_i\, [\cos 2\theta_i \cos 2\theta_{ij} - \sin 2\theta_i \sin 2\theta_{ij}] \rangle_{r_{ij}}$$

$$= \langle \cos^2 2\theta_i \cos 2\theta_{ij} - \sin 2\theta_i \cos 2\theta_i \sin 2\theta \rangle_{r_{ij}} \,. \tag{82}$$

But

$$\cos^2 2\theta_i = \frac{1}{2}\,(1 + \cos 4\theta_i) \tag{83}$$

and

$$\sin 2\theta_i \cos 2\theta_i = \frac{1}{2} \sin 4\theta_i \;. \qquad (84)$$

Thus

$$< \cos 2\theta_i \cos 2\theta_j >_{r_{ij}}$$

$$= \frac{1}{2} < \cos 2\theta_{ij} + \cos 4\theta_i \cos 2\theta_{ij} - \sin 4\theta_i \sin 2\theta_{ij} >_{r_{ij}}$$

$$= \frac{1}{4\pi} \int_{\beta_i=0}^{2\pi} [F_1 + \cos 4(\alpha + \beta_i) F_1 - \sin 4(\alpha + \beta_i) F_2] \, d\beta_i \;. \qquad (85)$$

The evaluation of this integral depends upon the functional dependence of F_1 and F_2 upon β_i. These may be expanded in Fourier series in β_i in two-dimensions (or in spherical harmonics in three-dimensions) so

$$F_1 = T_0 + \sum_{n=1}^{\infty} [T_n \cos(n\beta_i) + Z_n \sin(n\beta_i)] \;. \qquad (86)$$

If F_1 has two-fold symmetry about r_{ij} so that

$$F_1(\beta_i) = F_1(-\beta_i) \qquad (87)$$

the coefficients of the sine terms are zero so $Z_n = 0$. If F_1 has two-fold symmetry about a perpendicular to r_{ij} so that

$$F_1(\beta_i) = F_1(180^\circ - \beta_i) \;. \qquad (88)$$

This leads to a vanishing of T_n for odd values of n so that

$$F_1 = \sum_{n=0}^{\infty} T_{2n} \cos(2n\beta_i) \;. \qquad (89)$$

The above symmetry requirements are reasonable for structures without asymmetry or "handedness" but would be limiting for example, in the case of some spherulites such as polytetrafluoroethylene where, within a given spherulite, the optic axis lies either at a positive or a negative angle to the radius.

Similarly,

$$F_2 = S_0 + \sum_{n=1} [R_n \cos(n\beta_i) + S_n \sin(n\beta_i)]$$

$$= \sum_{n=0}^{\infty} S_{2n} \sin(2n\,\beta_i) \tag{90}$$

where the cosine terms and the odd sine terms have been eliminated from considerations of the antisymmetry of F_2 where

$$F_2(\beta_i) = -F_2(-\beta_i) \tag{91}$$

and

$$F_2(\beta_i) = -F_2(180^\circ - \beta_i)\,. \tag{92}$$

The T_{2n} and S_{2n} coefficients are functions of $\mathbf{r}_{ij}$.

In three-dimensions, spherical harmonic expansions are used where, for example

$$F_1(\beta_i,\ \gamma_i) = \sum_{l=1}^{\infty} \sum_{m=1}^{-l} D_{l,m} Y_{l,m}(\beta_i,\ \gamma_i) \tag{93}$$

where

$$Y_{l,m}(\beta_i\,,\ \gamma_i) = \frac{1}{\sqrt{2\pi}}\ P_l^{|m|}(\beta_i)\ e^{im\gamma_i} \tag{94}$$

where γ_i is the cylindrical angle describing the orientation of $\mathbf{a}_i$ with respect to $\mathbf{r}_{ij}$ (Fig. 17).

Using Eqs. (89) and (90) for two-dimensions, the integrals in Eq. (85) become

$$\frac{1}{2\pi}\int_0^{2\pi} F_1\, d\beta_i = \frac{1}{2\pi}\sum_{n=0}^{\infty}\left[\int_0^{2\pi} T_{2n}\cos(2n\beta_i)\, d\beta_i\right] = T_0 \tag{95}$$

$$\frac{1}{2\pi}\int_0^{2\pi} \cos 4(\alpha+\beta_i)\cdot F_1\, d\beta_i = \frac{1}{2\pi}\sum_{n=0}^{\infty}\left\{\int_0^{2\pi}\left[\cos 4\alpha\cos 4\beta_i - \sin 4\alpha \sin 4\beta_i\right] T_{2n}\cos(2n\,\beta_i)\, d\beta_i\right\} = \frac{1}{2}\ T_4\cos 4\alpha \tag{96}$$

$$\frac{1}{2\pi}\int_0^{2\pi} \sin 4(\alpha+\beta_i)\cdot F_2\, d\beta_i = \frac{1}{2\pi}\sum_{n=0}^{\infty}\left\{\int_0^{2\pi}\left[\sin 4\alpha\cos 4\beta_i + \cos 4\alpha \sin 4\beta_i\right] S_{2n}\sin(2n\,\beta_i)\, d\beta_i\right\} = \frac{1}{2}\ S_4\cos 4\alpha\,. \tag{97}$$

Therefore, from Eqs. (81) and (85)

$$K_1 = \frac{A}{8} \int_{r_{ij}} \left[T_0 + \frac{1}{2} (T_4 - S_4) \cos 4\alpha \right] \cos k (\mathbf{r}_{ij} \cdot \mathbf{s}) \, d\mathbf{r}_{ij} \tag{98}$$

Now

$$\begin{aligned} K_2 &= \sum_i \sum_j \sin^2\theta_i \sin^2\theta_j \cos k (\mathbf{r}_{ij} \cdot \mathbf{s}) \\ &= \sum_i \sum_j (1 - \cos^2\theta_i)(1 - \cos^2\theta_j) \cos k (\mathbf{r}_{ij} \cdot \mathbf{s}) \\ &= \sum_i \sum_j \left[1 - \cos^2\theta_i - \cos^2\theta_j + \cos^2\theta_i \cos^2\theta_j \right] \cos k (\mathbf{r}_{ij} \cdot \mathbf{s}) \\ &= \sum_i \sum_j \cos^2\theta_i \cos^2\theta_j \cos k (\mathbf{r}_{ij} \cdot \mathbf{s}) = K_1 . \end{aligned} \tag{99}$$

Similarly

$$\begin{aligned} K_3 &= \sum_i \sum_j \cos^2\theta_i \sin^2\theta_j \cos k (\mathbf{r}_{ij} \cdot \mathbf{s}) \\ &= \sum_i \sum_j \left[\cos^2\theta_i - \cos^2\theta_i \cos^2\theta_j \right] \cos k (\mathbf{r}_{ij} \cdot \mathbf{s}) \\ &= - \sum_i \sum_j \cos^2\theta_i \cos^2\theta_j \cos k (\mathbf{r}_{ij} \cdot \mathbf{s}) = -K_1 . \end{aligned} \tag{100}$$

Finally

$$\begin{aligned} K_4 &= \sum_i \sum_j \sin\theta_i \cos\theta_i \sin\theta_j \cos\theta_j \cos k (\mathbf{r}_{ij} \cdot \mathbf{s}) \\ &= \frac{1}{4} \sum_i \sum_j \left[\sin 2\theta_i \sin 2\theta_j \right] \cos k (\mathbf{r}_{ij} \cdot \mathbf{s}) \\ &= \frac{A}{4} \int_{r_{ij}} \langle \sin 2\theta_i \sin 2\theta_j \rangle_{r_{ij}} \cos k (\mathbf{r}_{ij} \cdot \mathbf{s}) \, dr_{ij} . \end{aligned} \tag{101}$$

Now

$$\langle \sin 2\theta_i \sin 2\theta_j \rangle$$

$$= \langle \sin^2 2\theta_i \cos 2\theta_{ij} + \sin 2\theta_i \cos 2\theta_i \sin 2\theta_{ij} \rangle_{r_{ij}}$$

$$= \frac{1}{2} < \cos 2\theta_{ij} \; - \cos 4\theta_i \; \cos 2\theta_{ij} \; + \sin 4\theta_i \; \sin 2\theta_{ij} >_{r_{ij}}$$

$$= \frac{1}{2} \left[T_0 - \frac{1}{2} (T_4 - S_4) \cos 4\alpha \right] . \qquad (102)$$

Thus

$$K_4 = \frac{A}{8} \int_{r_{ij}} \left[T_0 - \frac{1}{2} (T_4 - S_4) \cos 4\alpha \right] \cos k\,(r_{ij} \cdot s)\, dr_{ij} . \qquad (103)$$

On substituting back into Eq. (75) this gives

$$I_+ = \frac{1}{8} K\, A\, E_0^2\, \delta^2 \int_{r=0}^{\infty} \int_{\alpha=0}^{2\pi} \Big\{ T_0\, \Phi_1\, (\theta, \psi)$$

$$\frac{1}{2} (T_4 - S_4)\, \Phi_2\, (\theta, \psi) \cos 4\alpha \Big\} \cos(w \sin \alpha)\, d\alpha \cdot r\, dr \qquad (104)$$

where

$$\Phi_1 = (1 + \cos \theta)^2 \sin^2\psi \cos^2\psi + (\cos^2\psi \cos \theta - \sin^2\psi)^2 \qquad (105)$$

and

$$\Phi_2 = (1 + \cos \theta)^2 \sin^2\psi \cos^2\psi - (\cos^2\psi \cos \theta - \sin^2\psi)^2 . \qquad (106)$$

It is noted that as θ approaches $0°$,

$$\Phi_1 = \cos^4\psi + 2 \sin^2\psi \cos^2\psi + \sin^4\psi = 1 \qquad (107)$$

and

$$\Phi_2 = - \left[8 \cos^4\psi - 8 \cos^2\psi + 1 \right] = - \cos 4\psi . \qquad (108)$$

Thus the first term in Eq. (104) represents the contribution from random orientation fluctuations and becomes independent of ψ at small θ, whereas the second term represents the contribution from non-randomness [of amount characterized by the relative values of $(T_4 - S_4)$ to T_0] and varies with ψ as $\cos 4\psi$.

It is of interest to note that only the Fourier coefficients

T_0, T_4 and S_4 appear in the final equation. The scattering is not sensitive to other moments of the dependence of the F's upon β_i.

The integration of Eq. (104) over α may be accomplished using

$$\int_{\alpha=0}^{2\pi} \cos 4\alpha \cos(w \sin \alpha)\, d\alpha = \int_{\alpha=0}^{2\pi} [8 \cos^4 \alpha - 8 \cos^2 \alpha + 1] \cos(w \sin \alpha)\, d\alpha$$

$$= 2\pi \left[24 \frac{J_2(w)}{w^2} - 8 \frac{J_1(w)}{w} + J_0(w) \right] \tag{109}$$

so that

$$I_+ = \frac{\pi}{4} K A E_0^2 \delta^2 \int_{r=0}^{\infty} \left\{ T_0 \Phi_1(\theta, \psi) J_0(w) + \frac{1}{2} (T_4 - S_4) \Phi_2(\theta, \psi) \left[24 \frac{J_2(w)}{w^2} - 8 \frac{J_1(w)}{w} + J_0(w) \right] \right\} r\, dr . \tag{110}$$

The integration over r is dependent upon the dependence of T_0, T_4 and S_4 upon r. In the previous work, the r dependence of T_0 was assumed gaussian as represented by Eq. (35), in an analogous manner to the gaussian approximation for f(r) in the random theory.

$$T_0 = \rho_0 \exp[-r^2/a_0^2] \tag{111}$$

A constant ρ_0 implies that the amount of orientation correlation monotonically decreases with increasing r and does not permit a more complex type of variation as might result from more highly organized structure. A somewhat more general approach would be to use a gaussian function to describe the asymptotic behavior but allow ρ_0 to be represented by a power series in r

$$\rho_0(r) = \sum^{\infty} \rho_{0i}\, r^i \tag{112}$$

as is done for the radial part of atomic wave functions in quantum mechanics. This could represent the oscillating behavior of the correlation function calculated for spherulites (Fig. 11).

It is reasonable to represent T_4 and S_4 similarly as for example

$$T_4 = \rho_4 \exp[-r^2/a_4^2] \tag{113}$$

and

$$S_4 = \sigma_4 \exp[-r^2/b_4^2] \tag{114}$$

where, generally, for example

$$\rho_4 = \sum_{i=0}^{\infty} \rho_{4i}\, r^i \,. \tag{115}$$

In the approximation where ρ_4 and σ_4 are independent of r

$$(T_4 - S_4) = \rho_4 \exp[-r^2/a_4^2] - \sigma_4 \exp[-r^2/b_4^4] \tag{116}$$

This equation is in the same form as the empirical Eq. (62) for $\epsilon(r)$ assumed in the preceding section. If $a_0 = a_4 = b_4$, this would be an equivalent situation to that described in Eq. (44) where the correlation function is factorable into a shape and a distance term.

Using Eqs. (111), (113) and (114) with constant ρ's and σ's in Eq. (110) one obtains

$$I_+ = \frac{\pi}{4} K A E_0^2 \delta^2 \left\{ \rho_0 \Phi_1(\theta,\psi) \int_{r=0}^{\infty} J_0(w) \exp[-r^2/a_0^2]\, r\,dr \right.$$

$$+ \frac{1}{2} \Phi_2(\theta,\psi) \int_{r=0}^{\infty} \left[24 \frac{J_2(w)}{w^2} - 8 \frac{J_1(w)}{w} + J_0(w) \right]$$

$$\left. \left[\rho_4 \exp[-r^2/a_4^2] - \sigma_4 \exp[-r^2/b_4^2] \right] r\,dr \right\} . \tag{117}$$

The integrations over r may be accomplished using the general equation (25)

$$\int_0^{\infty} J_\nu(at) \exp[-p^2 t^2]\, t^{\mu-1} dt$$

$$= \frac{\Gamma\left(\frac{1}{2}\mu + \frac{1}{2}\nu\right)\left(\frac{1}{2} a/p\right)^{\nu}}{2 p^{\mu} \Gamma(\nu+1)} {}_1F_1\left(\frac{1}{2}\nu + \frac{1}{2}\mu;\ \nu+1;\ -a^2/4p^2\right) \tag{118}$$

where ${}_1F_1(\ )$ represents a generalized hypergeometric function defined by

$$ {}_1F_1(\alpha;\rho;z) = 1 + \frac{(\alpha)_1}{1!\,(\rho)_1} z + \frac{(\alpha)_2}{2!\,(\rho)_2} z^2 + \cdots $$

$$ = \sum_{n=0}^{\infty} \frac{(\alpha)_n}{n!\,(\rho)_n} z^n \tag{119} $$

where

$$ (\alpha)_n = \alpha(\alpha+1)(\alpha+2)\cdots(\alpha+n-1);\ (\alpha)_0 = 1 . \tag{120} $$

Thus

$$ \int_0^{\infty} J_0(w)\exp[-r^2/a^2]\, r\, dr = \frac{a^2}{2}\exp[-w^2/4] \tag{121} $$

where

$$ w = 2\pi\,(a/\lambda)\sin\theta\ . \tag{122} $$

Similarly

$$ \int_0^{\infty} \frac{J_1(w)}{w}\exp[-r^2/a^2]\, r\, dr $$

$$ = (a^2/w^2)\left[1 - \exp[-w^2/4]\right] \tag{123} $$

and

$$ \int_0^{\infty} \frac{J_2(w)}{w^2}\exp[-r^2/a^2]\, r\, dr $$

$$ = (2a^2/w^4)\left[\exp[-w^2/4] - 1 + (w^2/4)\right] \tag{124} $$

Thus

$$ I_+ = \frac{\pi}{4} K A E_0^2 \delta^2 \left\{ \frac{1}{2}\rho_0\,\Phi_1(\theta,\psi)\, a_0^2 \exp[-w_0^2/4] \right. $$

$$ + \frac{1}{2}\Phi_2(\theta,\psi)\left[\rho_4 a_4^2 \left(\frac{48}{w_4^4}\left[\exp[-w_4^2/4] - 1 + (w_4^2/4)\right]\right.\right. $$

$$ \left. - \frac{8}{w_4^2}\left[1 - \exp[-w_4^2/4]\right] + \frac{1}{2}\exp[-w_4^2/4]\right) $$

$$- \sigma_4^2 b_4^2 \left(\frac{48}{V_4^4} \left[\exp[-V_4^2/4] - 1 + (V_4^2/4) \right] \right.$$

$$\left. \left. - \frac{8}{V_4^2} \left[1 - \exp[-V_4^2/4] \right] + \frac{1}{2} \exp[-V_4^2/4] \right) \right] \Bigg\} \qquad (125)$$

where

$$w_0 = 2\pi \, (a_0/\lambda) \sin\theta \qquad (126)$$

$$w_4 = 2\pi \, (a_4/\lambda) \sin\theta \qquad (127)$$

and

$$V_4 = 2\pi \, (b_4/\lambda) \sin\theta \, . \qquad (128)$$

In the more general case where ρ_0, ρ_4, and σ_4 are permitted to vary with r in the manner of Eqs. (112) and (115), the integration over r may still be carried out using Eq. (118) giving

$$I_+ = \frac{\pi}{4} K A E_0^2 \delta^2 \sum_{n=0}^{\infty} \Gamma\left(\frac{n+2}{2}\right) \Bigg\{ \Phi_1(\theta, \psi) \frac{\rho_{0n} a_0^{n+2}}{2}$$

$$_1F_1 \left[\frac{n+2}{2}; 1; (-w_0^2/4) \right] + \frac{1}{2} \Phi_2(\theta, \psi) \Bigg[\rho_{4n} a_4^{n+2}$$

$$\left(\frac{3}{2} \, {}_1F_1 \left[\frac{n+2}{2}; 3; (-w_4^2/4) \right] - 2 \, {}_1F_1 \left[\frac{n+2}{2}; 2; (-w_4^2/4) \right] \right.$$

$$\left. + \frac{1}{2} \, {}_1F_1 \left[\frac{n+2}{2}; 1; (-w_4^2/4) \right] \right) - \sigma_{4n} b_4^{n+2} \left(\frac{3}{2} \, {}_1F_1 \left[\frac{n+2}{2}; 3; (-V_4^2/4) \right] \right.$$

$$\left. \left. - 2 \, {}_1F_1 \left[\frac{n+2}{2}; 2; (-V_4^2/4) \right] + \frac{1}{2} \, {}_1F_1 \left[\frac{n+2}{2}; 1; (-V_4^2/4) \right] \right) \right] \Bigg\} \qquad (129)$$

Thus, the angular dependence of the intensity of the scattering is generally described in terms of the correlation distances a_0, a_4 and b_4 and the power series coefficients describing the radial dependence of correlation, ρ_{0n}, ρ_{4n}, and σ_{4n}.

The calculation of $I_{\parallel}$ proceeds in a similar manner. Starting with Eq. (16), one may write in terms of the K_i's

$$I_{\parallel} = K E_0^2 \delta^2 \Big\{ \cos^4\psi K_1 + \cos^2\theta \sin^4\psi K_2 + 2\cos\theta \sin^2\psi \cos^2\psi K_3 + 2(1+\cos\theta)\cos^3\psi \sin\psi K_5 + 2(1+\cos\theta)\cos\theta \sin^3\psi \cos\psi K_6 + (1+\cos\theta)^2 \sin^2\psi \cos^2\psi K_4 \Big\} \quad (130)$$

where

$$K_5 = \sum_i \sum_j \cos^2\theta_i \sin\theta_j \cos\theta_j \cos k(\mathbf{r}_{ij}\cdot\mathbf{s}) \quad (131)$$

and

$$K_6 = \sum_i \sum_j \sin^2\theta_i \sin\theta_j \cos\theta_j \cos k(\mathbf{r}_{ij}\cdot\mathbf{s}) . \quad (132)$$

The evaluation of K_5 proceeds as before

$$K_5 = A \int_{r_{ij}} \langle \cos^2\theta_i \sin\theta_j \cos\theta_j \rangle_{r_{ij}} \cos k(\mathbf{r}_{ij}\cdot\mathbf{s})\, dr_{ij}. \quad (133)$$

Now

$$\langle \cos^2\theta_i \sin\theta_j \cos\theta_j \rangle_{r_{ij}} = \frac{1}{4} \langle (1+\cos 2\theta_i)(\sin 2\theta_j) \rangle_{r_{ij}}$$

$$= \frac{1}{4} \langle \sin 2\theta_j + \cos 2\theta_i \sin 2\theta_j \rangle_{r_{ij}} . \quad (134)$$

The first term does not contribute when summed over r_{ij}. The second becomes

$$\langle \cos 2\theta_i \sin 2\theta_j \rangle_{r_{ij}}$$

$$= \langle \sin 2\theta_i \cos 2\theta_i \cos 2\theta_{ij} \rangle_{r_{ij}} + \langle \cos^2 2\theta_i \sin 2\theta_{ij} \rangle_{r_{ij}}$$

$$= \frac{1}{2} \langle \sin 4\theta_i F_1 \rangle_{r_{ij}} + \frac{1}{2} \langle (1+\cos 4\theta_i) F_2 \rangle_{r_{ij}}$$

$$= \frac{1}{4\pi} \int_0^{2\pi} \Big\{ [\sin 4\alpha \cos 4\beta_i + \cos 4\alpha \sin 4\beta_i] \sum_{n=0}^{\infty} T_{2n} \cos(2n\beta_i)$$

$$+ [1 + \cos 4\alpha \cos 4\beta_i - \sin 4\alpha \sin 4\beta_i] \sum_{n=0}^{\infty} S_{2n} \sin(2n\beta_i) \Big\} d\beta_i$$

$$= \frac{1}{4} [T_4 - S_4] \sin 4\alpha + S_0 \quad . \tag{135}$$

Now S_0 is zero because of the symmetry requirements of F_2 in Eq. (91). On substituting Eq. (135) into Eqs. (133) and (134)

$$K_5 = \frac{A}{16} \int_{r=0}^{\infty} \int_{\alpha=0}^{2\pi} [T_4 - S_4] \sin 4\alpha \cos(w \sin \alpha) \, d\alpha \, r \, dr. \tag{136}$$

The integral over α gives zero since $\sin 4\alpha$ is an odd function of α and $\cos(w \sin \alpha)$ is an even function. Thus *

$$K_5 = 0 \quad . \tag{137}$$

---

*If the symmetry restrictions were not imposed on F_1 and F_2 so that both $\sin(n\beta_i)$ and $\cos(n\beta_i)$ terms were retained in both Fourier expansions, the substitution of the more complete series into Eq. (135) would lead to

$$< \cos 2\theta_i \cos 2\theta_j >_{r_{ij}} = S_0 + \frac{1}{4} [T_4 - S_4] \sin 4\alpha + \frac{1}{4} [Z_4 + R_4] \cos 4$$

which would lead to

$$K_5 = \frac{A}{16} \int_{r_{ij}} (Z_4 + R_4) \cos 4\alpha \cos k (\mathbf{r}_{ij} \cdot s) \, dr_{ij}$$

The inclusion of the $(Z_4 + R_4)$ term from K_5 and K_6 would result in the additional term in Eq. (140) in the brackets $\{ \}$

$$\Big\{ + \Phi_5 (Z_4 + R_4) \cos 4\alpha \Big\}$$

where

$$\Phi_5 = (\cos^2 \psi - \sin^2 \psi \cos \theta) \sin \psi (1 + \cos \theta)$$

Similarly

$$K_6 = \sum_i \sum_j \sin^2\theta_i \sin\theta_j \cos\theta_j \cos k(\mathbf{r}_{ij} \cdot \mathbf{s})$$

$$= \sum_i \sum_j [\sin\theta_j \cos\theta_j - \cos^2\theta_i \sin\theta_j \cos\theta_j] \cos k(\mathbf{r}_{ij} \cdot \mathbf{s}) . \qquad (138)$$

The first term is zero and the second is K_5. Thus*

$$K_6 = -K_5 = 0 . \qquad (139)$$

Eq. (130) then becomes

$$I_{\parallel} = \frac{1}{8} K A E_0{}^2 \delta^2 \int_{r=0}^{\infty} \int_{\alpha=0}^{2\pi} [T_0 \Phi_3(\theta, \psi) + \frac{1}{2}(T_4 - S_4)\Phi_4(\theta, \psi)] \cos 4\alpha \cos(w \sin\alpha)\, d\alpha \cdot r\, dr \qquad (140)$$

where

$$\Phi_3 = (\cos^2\psi - \cos\theta \sin^2\psi)^2 + (1 + \cos\theta)^2 \sin^2\psi \cos^2\psi . \qquad (141)$$

and

$$\Phi_4 = (\cos^2\psi - \cos\theta \sin^2\psi)^2 - (1 + \cos\theta)^2 \sin^2\psi \cos^2\psi \qquad (142)$$

As θ approaches zero, Φ_3 approaches unity and Φ_4 approaches $\cos 4\psi$.

The integrations proceed as before giving for $I_{\parallel}$, equations identical with Eqs. (125) and (129) except that $\Phi_1(\theta,\psi)$ and $\Phi_2(\theta,\psi)$ are replaced by $\Phi_3(\theta,\psi)$ and $\Phi_4(\theta,\psi)$. Eq. (125) and its $I_{\parallel}$ counterpart were programmed for the CDC 3600 computer and results are plotted in Figs. 18 through 22.

The calculations are confined to the case where ρ_0, ρ_4 and σ_4 are independent of r. For the random orientation fluctuation case where $\rho_4 = \sigma_4 = 0$, the ψ dependence arises from the ψ variation of Φ_1 which is

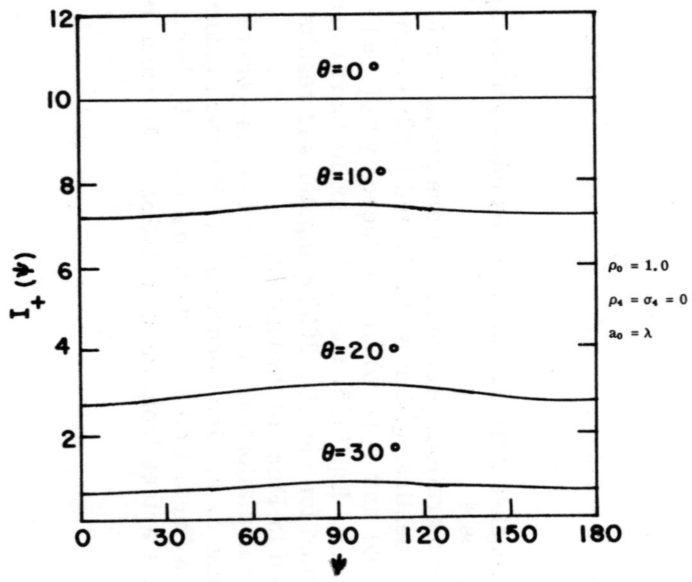

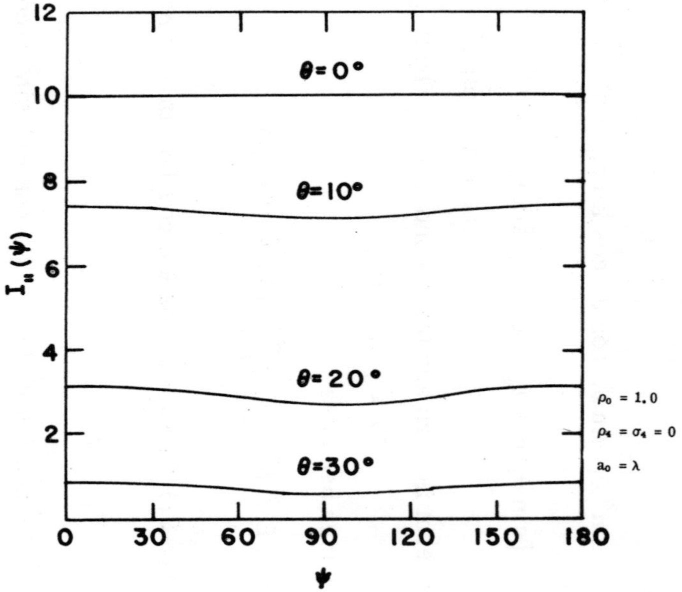

Fig. 18. The variation of (a) I_+ and (b) $I_\parallel$ with ψ at several values of θ for the limit of random orientation fluctuations where $\rho_0 = 1.0$, $\rho_4 = \sigma_4 = 0$ and $a_0 = \lambda$.

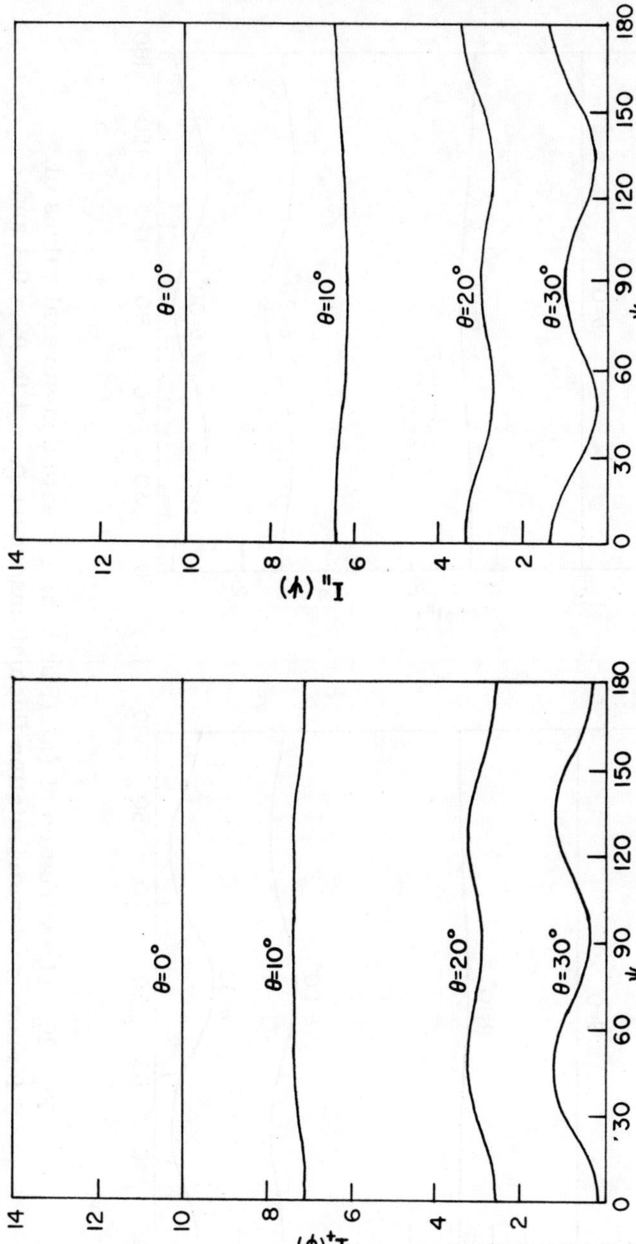

Fig. 19. The variation of (a) I_{+} and (b) $I_{\parallel}$ with ψ at several values of θ for non-random orientation fluctuations where $\rho_0 = 1.0$, $\rho_4 = 0.9$ and $\sigma_4 = 0.1$ and where $a_0 = a_4 = b_4 = \lambda$.

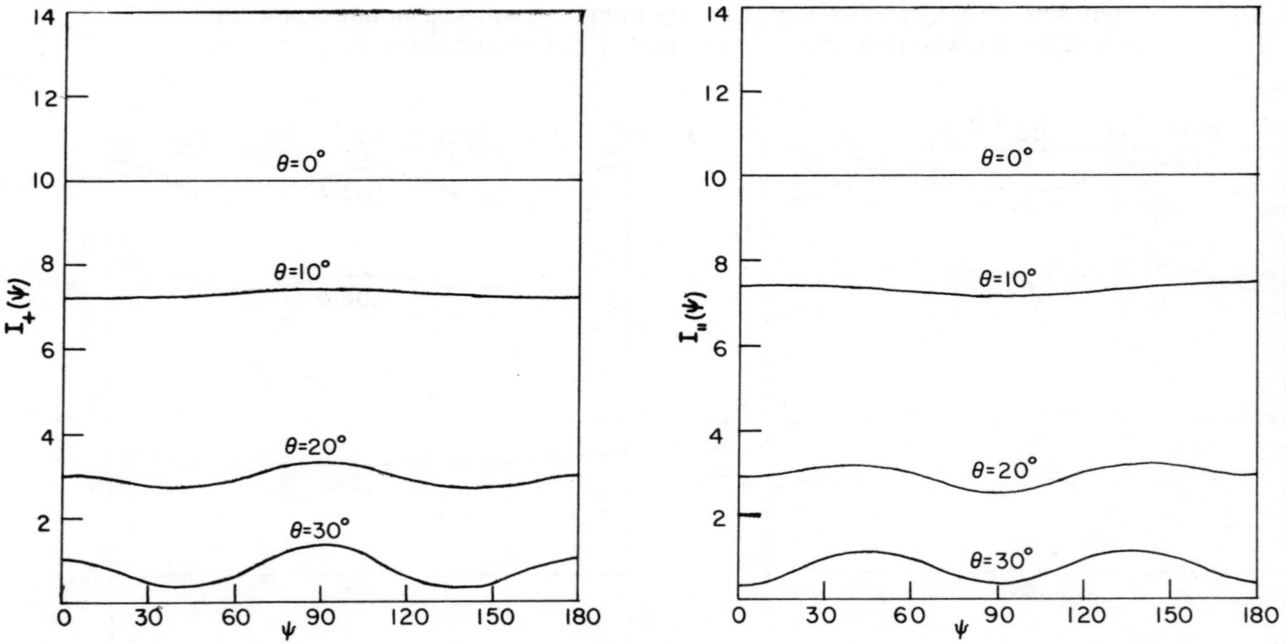

Fig. 20. The variation of (a) I_+ and (b) $I_{\parallel}$ with ψ at several values of θ for non-random orientation fluctuations where $\rho_0 = 1.0$, $\rho_4 = 0.1$ and $\sigma_4 = 0.9$ and where $a_0 = a_4 = b_4 = \lambda$.

small at small θ. This is plotted at several θ's for I_+ and I for the case where $a_0 = \lambda$ and $\rho_0 = 1.0$ in Figs. 18a and 18b. This may be contrasted with the non-random case in Figs. 19a and 19b where $\rho_0 = 1.0$, $\rho_4 = 0.9$ and $\sigma_4 = 0.1$ and $a_0 = a_4 = b_4 = \lambda$. In this case, little ψ dependence is seen at $\theta = 0°$ but there is an increase with increasing θ by a small amount dependent upon the size of ρ_4 and σ_4. The I_+ maxima are found at $\psi = 45°$ and $135°$ while the $I_{\parallel}$ maxima occur at $\psi = 0°$ and $90°$ and are of comparable height. This corresponds to the experimental situation found for polyethylene in Fig. 13 and in references (17) and (16). On the other hand, Fig. 20 shows the corresponding plots where the values of ρ_4 and σ_4 are reversed in which case the I_+ maxima are at $\psi = 0°$ and $90°$, whereas the $I_{\parallel}$ maxima are at 45° and 135° corresponding to experimental observations with polytetrafluorethylene films.

The physical significance of these situations is that the size and sign of ρ_4 is related to the size of F_1 which depends upon the tendency of optic axes to lie parallel to each other, and a large positive ρ_4 coefficient indicates a tendency for them to be parallel when $\beta_i = 0°$ or $90°$ whereas a negative ρ_4 indicates a greater tendency toward parallelness when $\beta_i = 45°$. The size and sign of σ_4 is related to the size of F_2 which is a measure of the tendency of optic axes to lie at 45° to each other and a positive σ_4 is related to the tendency for θ_{ij} to be close to 45° when β_i is 22.5°.

The effect of different correlation distances for T_0, T_4 and S_4 are seen in Fig. 21 in which I_+ is plotted as a function of ψ for several values of the ratio n:m at a given θ (where $n = a_4^2/a_0^2$ and $m = b_4^2/a_0^2$). It is seen that at a particular scattering angle, one may either get intensity maxima occurring at $\psi = 45°$, $135°$ or $0°$, $90°$ for a given set of values of ρ_0, ρ_4, and σ_4 depending upon the relative values of a_0, a_4 and b_4.

Depending upon the relative values of the correlation distances, one may obtain intensity maxima at $\psi = 0°$, $90°$ at some values of θ and at $\psi = 45°$, $135°$ at other values as can be seen in Fig. 22. This arises because of the different dependence of T_4 and S_4 upon r

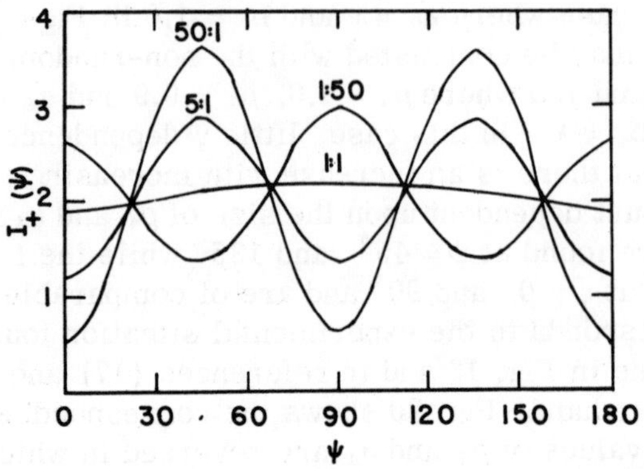

Fig. 21. The variation of $I_+(\psi)$ with ψ at $\theta = 20°$ as a function of the correlation distance ratio (n:m) [where $n = a_4^2/a_0^2$ and $m = b_4^2/a_0^2$] where $\rho_0 = 0.7$, $\rho_4 = 0.2$, $\sigma_4 = 0.1$ and $a_0\ \lambda$.

where T_4 may be bigger than S_4 for some values of r but smaller for others. This is an example of a case where correlations are not factorable into a shape and a separation factor, so that the ψ dependence of intensity may be of different form at different θ.

It is to be noted that all of the intensity equations obtained in this section have four-fold symmetry because of the presence of only cos 4ψ terms. They are not capable of accounting for the difference between the intensity of $I_{\parallel}(\psi)$ for polyethylene at $\psi = 0°$ and $\psi = 90°$ seen in Fig. 13. This difference is explainable, however, by the inclusion of the additional terms arising from

$$\sum_i \sum_j$$

$\cos 2\theta_i \cos k(\mathbf{r}_{ij} \cdot \mathbf{s})$ terms as discussed in Reference (16a) which give rise to a cos 2ψ dependence which contributes negligibly to I_+ but appreciably to $I_{\parallel}$. These terms are characterized by additional correlation functions, $[T_2 - S_2]$ having a magnitude and a variation with r which depend upon the sample morphology.

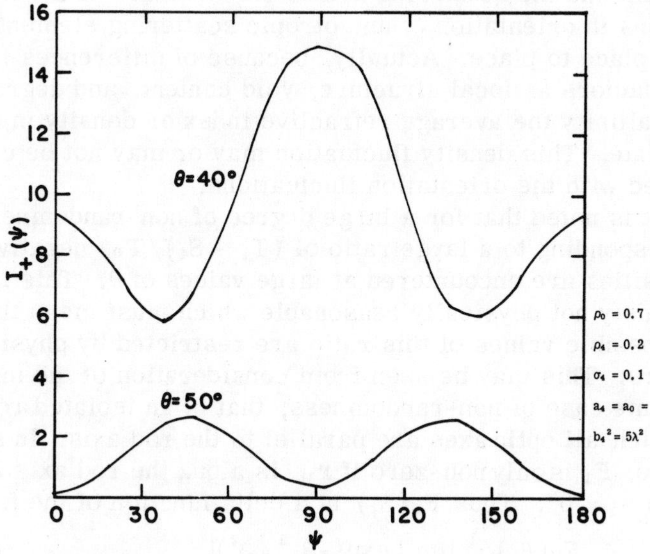

Fig. 22. The variation of $I_+(\psi)$ with ψ for $\theta = 40°$ and $\theta = 50°$ where $\rho_0 = 0.7$, $\rho_4 = 0.2$, $\sigma_4 = 0.1$ $a_4 = a_0 = \lambda$ and $b_4 = \sqrt{5}\,\lambda$. The form of the ψ variation is strongly dependent upon θ.

This prediction is consistant with the experimental observation that I_+ patterns always have four-fold symmetry with maxima either at $\psi = 0°$ and $90°$ or $45°$ and $135°$, but $I_{\parallel}$ patterns often have two-fold symmetry as can be seen from the photometric scans (3, 16, 16a, 17), from V_V low-angle light scattering photographs (15, 20), and is predicted by calculations of the scattering from discrete anisotropic aggregates such as spherulites (3, 15, 17, 20) and rods (17). In addition to the difference between $I_{\parallel}$ and I_+ resulting from this additional term, differences will arise from the differing contributions from density fluctuation and cross-correlation terms as discussed later.

The above development of anisotropic orientation correlations applies to the case where the density (or average polarizability, $\bar{\alpha}$,) is uniform throughout the scattering medium and the scattering arises only because of the fluctuations in orientation of anisotropic scattering elements from place to place. Actually, because of differences in such factors as local structure, void content, and degree of crystallinity the average refractive index or density may fluctuate. This density fluctuation may or may not be correlated with the orientation fluctuations.

It is noted that for a large degree of non-randomness corresponding to a large ratio of $(T_4 - S_4)/T_0$, negative intensities are encountered at large values of θ. This is obviously not physically reasonable which must mean that the possible values of this ratio are restricted by physical factors. This may be seen from consideration of the most extreme case of non-randomness, that of an isolated rod in which all optic axes are parallel to the rod axis. In such a case, F_1 is only non-zero if r_{ij} is along the rod axis for which $\beta_i = 0°$. Thus $F_1(\beta_i)$ is a delta function of the form

$$F_1(\beta_i) = \lim_{\Delta \to 0} [\exp(-\beta_i^2/\Delta^2)] \tag{143}$$

Now, the gaussian function may be fitted to a Fourier expansion

$$\exp(-\beta_i^2/\Delta^2) = T_0 + T_2 \cos(2\beta_i) + T_4 \cos(4\beta_i) + \cdots \tag{144}$$

where

$$T_0 = 2 \int_{-\pi/2}^{\pi/2} \exp(-\beta_i^2/\Delta^2)\, d\beta_i \tag{145}$$

$$\cong 2 \int_{-\infty}^{\infty} \exp(-\beta_i^2/\Delta^2)\, d\beta_i = 2\Delta\sqrt{\pi} \tag{146}$$

The limits of integration may be approximated as $\pm\ \infty$ rather than $\pm\ \pi/2$ if Δ is sufficiently small so that the value of the integral is negligible beyond $\pm\ \pi/2$. Similarly

$$T_4 \cong 2 \int_{-\infty}^{\infty} \cos(4\beta_i) \exp(-\beta_i^2/\Delta^2)\, d\beta_i = 2\Delta\sqrt{\pi}\exp(-4\Delta^2). \tag{147}$$

For this perfect rod-like orientation,

$$F_2 = \langle \sin 2\,\theta_{ij} \rangle_{r_{ij}} = 0 \tag{148}$$

since $\theta_{ij} = 0^\circ$ for all volume elements on the rod.

Thus, in the limit of perfect rod-like orientation

$$\frac{T_4 - S_4}{S_0} = \lim_{\Delta \to 0} \left[\frac{2\,\Delta\sqrt{\pi}\,\exp(-4\Delta^2)}{2\,\Delta\sqrt{\pi}} \right] = \lim_{\Delta \to 0} \left[\exp(-4\Delta^2) \right] = 1\,. \tag{149}$$

For a less sharp dependence of the F's upon β_i, Δ will be greater than zero and S_4 will become finite so that

$$\frac{T_4 - S_4}{S_0} < 1\,. \tag{150}$$

Actual systems are condensed phases consisting of an assembly of rod-like entities. In such cases all correlation will not be longitudinal as in an isolated rod but transverse correlation will occur in a manner dependent upon the manner in which the rods may pack to fill space. This will result in a ratio of $(T_4 - S_4)/S_0$ considerably less than one preventing intensities from assuming negative values.

Another physical factor working toward preventing this paradox is that $(T_4 - S_4)$ and T_0 will actually have different dependences upon r. The scattering at large values of θ arise from pairs of scattering elements separated by small values of r. For rods of finite width, the correlations become more random and less dependent upon β_i when r becomes comparable with the width of the rod, in which case $(T_4 - S_4)/T_0$ presumably decreases with decreasing r sufficiently to prevent the intensity from becoming negative with increasing θ.

THE CONTRIBUTION OF DENSITY FLUCTUATIONS

In going from Eq. (8) to Eq (16) and (75) the terms corresponding to density fluctuations and cross-correlations between density and orientation fluctuations have been neglected. The equations should actually be written

$$I_{\parallel} = I_{\parallel,d} + I_{\parallel,o} + I_{\parallel,x} \tag{151}$$

and

$$I_{+} = I_{+,d} + I_{+,o} + I_{+,x} \tag{152}$$

where the results previously given in Eqs. (125) or (129) and their equivalents for $I_{\parallel}$ represent the orientation fluctuations terms, $I_{+,o}$ and $I_{\parallel,o}$ of the above equations. The I_d and I_x terms are the additional terms arising from density and cross-correlations. The I_d terms arise from the second term of Eq. (9) whereas the I_x terms arise from the cross-products of the first and second term. The I_d terms have been described [Eqs. (20) and (204) of Ref. (16)] and are

$$I_{\parallel,d} = C^2 E_0^2 \Phi_6 (\theta,\psi) \sum_i \sum_j (\Delta\bar{\alpha})_i (\Delta\bar{\alpha})_j \cos k (\mathbf{r}_{ij} \cdot \mathbf{s}) \tag{153}$$

and

$$I_{+,d} = C^2 E_0^2 \Phi_7 (\theta,\psi) \sum_i \sum_j (\Delta\bar{\alpha})_i (\Delta\bar{\alpha})_j \cos k (\mathbf{r}_{ij} \cdot \mathbf{s}) \tag{154}$$

where

$$\Phi_6 (\theta,\psi) = [\cos^2 \psi + \cos\theta \sin^2 \psi]^2 \tag{155}$$

and

$$\Phi_7 (\theta,\psi) = \sin^2 \psi \cos^2 \psi (1 - \cos\theta)^2 \tag{156}$$

It is noted that for small θ, Φ_6 approaches unity, whereas, Φ_7 approaches zero. Such behavior forms the basis for the separation of the contribution to scattering arising from density and orientation fluctuations.

To the approximation that cross-correlation can be neglected, the evaluation of the parameters from the scattering experiments can now be described for the simpler cases,

$$I_{+} (\psi,\theta) = K E_0^2 \left\{ \Omega_3 \Phi_7 (\psi,\theta) + \Omega_1 \Phi_1 (\psi,\theta) + \Omega_2 \Phi_2 (\psi,\theta) \right\} \tag{157}$$

$$I_{\parallel} (\psi,\theta) = K E_0^2 \left\{ \Omega_3 \Phi_6 (\psi,\theta) + \Omega_1 \Phi_3 (\psi,\theta) + \Omega_2 \Phi_4 (\psi,\theta) \right\} \tag{158}$$

where

$$\Omega_3 = \sum_i \sum_j (\Delta\bar{\alpha})_i (\Delta\bar{\alpha})_j \cos k (\mathbf{r}_{ij} \cdot \mathbf{s})$$

$$= A \int_{r_{ij}} (\Delta \bar{\alpha})_i \; (\Delta \bar{\alpha})_j \; \cos k \, (\mathbf{r}_{ij} \cdot \mathbf{s}) \, d\,\mathbf{r}_{ij}$$

$$= A \langle (\Delta \bar{\alpha})^2 \rangle_{av} \int_{r_{ij}} \gamma \, (\mathbf{r}_{ij}) \cos k \, (\mathbf{r}_{ij} \cdot \mathbf{s}) \, d\,\mathbf{r}_{ij}$$

$$= A \langle (\Delta \bar{\alpha})^2 \rangle_{av} \int_{r=0}^{\infty} \gamma(r) \int_{\alpha=0}^{2\pi} \cos (w \sin \alpha) \, d\alpha \, r \, dr$$

$$= 2\pi A \langle (\Delta \bar{\alpha})^2 \rangle_{av} \int_{r=0}^{\infty} \gamma(r) \, J_0(w) \, r \, dr \qquad (159)$$

in which $\gamma(\mathbf{r}_{ij})$ is the correlation function for density fluctuations, defined for a macroscopically unoriented medium as

$$\gamma(\mathbf{r}_{ij}) = \gamma(r) = \frac{\langle (\Delta \bar{\alpha})_i \; (\Delta \bar{\alpha})_j \rangle_{r_{ij}}}{\langle (\Delta \alpha)^2 \rangle_{av}} \; . \qquad (160)$$

Ω_1 is obtained from Eq. (110) and is

$$\Omega_1 = \frac{\pi}{4} A \, \delta^2 \int_{r=0}^{\infty} T_0(r) \, J_0(w) \, r \, dr \qquad (161)$$

and

$$\Omega_2 = \frac{\pi}{8} A \, \delta^2 \int_{r=0}^{\infty} [T_4(r) - S_4(r)] \left[24 \frac{J_2(w)}{w^2} - 8 \frac{J_1(w)}{w} + J_0(w) \right] r \, dr \, . \qquad (162)$$

From the definitions of the Φ_i's, it follows that

$$I_+(0^\circ, \theta) = \cos^2\theta \, [\Omega_1 - \Omega_2] \qquad (163)$$

$$I_+(90^\circ, \theta) = \Omega_1 - \Omega_2 \qquad (164)$$

$$I \quad (0^\circ, \theta) = \Omega_1 + \Omega_2 + \Omega_3 \qquad (165)$$

$$I_+(45^\circ, \theta) = \frac{1}{2}(1 + \cos^2\theta)\,\Omega_1 + \cos\theta\,\Omega_2 + \frac{1}{4}(1 - \cos\theta)^2\,\Omega_3 \qquad (166)$$

Therefore, by solving these simultaneously, one obtains

$$\Omega_1 = [4I_+(45^\circ, \theta) - (1 - 6\cos\theta + \cos^2\theta)\, I_+(90^\circ, \theta) - (1 - \cos\theta)^2\, I_{\parallel}(0^\circ, \theta)] / 8\cos\theta \qquad (167)$$

$$\Omega_2 = [4I_+(45^\circ, \theta) - (1 + \cos\theta)^2\, I_+(90^\circ, \theta)$$

$$- (1 - \cos\theta)^2 I_{\parallel} (0^{\circ}, \theta)]/8\cos\theta \tag{168}$$

$$\Omega_3 = [4I_{+} (45^{\circ}, \theta) + (1 - \cos\theta)^2 I_{+} (90^{\circ}, \theta) + (1 + \cos\theta)^2 I_{\parallel} (0^{\circ}, \theta)]/4\cos\theta \tag{169}$$

In this manner, Ω_1, Ω_2 and Ω_3 may be calculated from experimental data as a function of θ.

If $\gamma(r)$ is given by a gaussian function,

$$\gamma(r) = \exp[-r^2/a_d^2], \tag{170}$$

then

$$\Omega_3(\theta) = \pi A \langle(\Delta\alpha)^2\rangle_{av} a_d^2 \exp[-w_d^2/4] \tag{171}$$

where

$$w_d = 2\pi\langle(a_d/\lambda)\rangle \sin\theta \tag{172}$$

(The subscript, d, refers to density fluctuations). Thus

$$\ln[\Omega_3(\theta)] = \ln[\pi A \langle(\Delta\bar{\alpha})^2\rangle_{av} a_d^2] - \pi^2 (a_d/\lambda)^2 \sin^2\theta \tag{173}$$

so the slope of a plot of $\ln[\Omega_3(\theta)]$ against $\sin^2\theta$ gives a_d while the intercept gives $\langle(\Delta\bar{\alpha})^2\rangle_{av}$.

If $T_0(r)$ may be approximated by Eq. (111), then

$$\Omega_1(\theta) = \frac{\pi}{8} A \rho_0 \delta^2 a_0^2 \exp[-w_0^2/4] \tag{174}$$

so that a_0 and δ^2 may be obtained from the slope and intercept of a plot of $\ln[\Omega_1(\theta)]$ against $\sin^2\theta$. If the more complex Eq. (112) must be used for $T_0(r)$, the plot of $\ln[\Omega_1(\theta)]$ against $\sin^2\theta$ will not be a straight line, and the parameters δ^2, a_0 and ρ_{0i} must be obtained by fitting $\Omega_1(\theta)$ to the more complex expression [obtained from Eq. (129)]

$$\Omega_1(\theta) = \frac{\pi}{8} A \delta^2 \sum_{n=0}^{\infty} \left\{ \Gamma\left(\frac{n+2}{2}\right) \rho_{0n} a_0^{n+2} \cdot F_1\left[\frac{n+2}{2}; 1, (-w_0^2/4)\right] \right\} \tag{175}$$

Similarly, if T_4 and S_4 may be approximated by Eqs. (113) and (114), with constant ρ_4 and σ_4, then

$$\Omega_2(\theta) = \frac{\pi}{8} A\, \delta^2 \left\{ \rho_4\, a_4^2 \left(\frac{48}{w_4^4} \left[\exp(-w_4^2/4) - 1 + (w_4^2/4) \right] \right.\right.$$

$$\left. - \frac{8}{w_4^2} \left[1 - \exp(-w_4^2/4) \right] + \frac{1}{2} \exp(-w_4^2/4) \right)$$

$$- \sigma_4\, b_4^2 \left(\frac{48}{V_4^4} \left[\exp(-V_4^2/4 - 1 + (V_4^2/4) \right] \right.$$

$$\left.\left. - \frac{8}{V_4^2} \left[1 - \exp(-V_4^2/4) + \frac{1}{2} \exp(-V_4^2/4) \right) \right\} \qquad (176)$$

The parameters $\delta^2 \rho_4$, $\delta^2 \sigma_4$, a_4, and b_4 must then be obtained by fitting the variation of $\Omega_2(\theta)$ with θ to Eq. (176). It is unlikely that scattering data would be sufficiently precise to warrant trying to obtain the additional parameters imposed by using the more complex equation of the sort of Eq. (115) for ρ_4 and σ_4.

CROSS-CORRELATION BETWEEN DENSITY AND ORIENTATION FLUCTUATIONS

The neglect of cross-correlation between density and orientation fluctuations implies that the probability that the optic axis at a particular volume element lies at a given angle, θ_{ij}, to that at a second volume element does not depend upon the relative densities (or average refractive indices) at these two volume elements. In actual systems this is not the case, particularly where the system may be considered as an assembly of discrete scattering particles.

Consider, for example, the limiting situation discussed in the last section of a thin anisotropic rod imbedded in an isotropic matrix of different density, where all of the optic axes of the volume elements of the rod lie parallel to the rod axis. For two volume elements to have the same density, they must both lie on the rod. If they do, their optic axes will be parallel. In this case, there is perfect cross-correlation between density and orientation fluctuations and the two are described by identical correlation functions.

If we have an assembly of such rods in the matrix, a

given pair of volume elements (both on rods) may either be on the same rod or on different rods. In the former case, there will be perfect correlation in orientation while in the latter, the degree of orientation correlation is dependent upon the packing of the rods. Thus, cross-correlation is less perfect than for the preceding case of the isolated rod. Such cross-correlation also leads to a two-fold symmetry in the ψ dependence for $I_{\parallel}$ with different intensities occurring at $\psi = 0°$ and $90°$, as has been shown by rod scattering calculations using the amplitude summation approach (17). Similar considerations apply to other forms of anisotropic objects such as spherulites.

For a polycrystalline polymer one expects some degree of cross-correlation since if both volume elements lie in crystalline regions, one might expect a different degree of correlation of optic axis orientation than if one is in a crystalline region and one in an amorphous region, or if both are in amorphous regions. The degree of such cross-correlation depends upon the texture of the polymer and the relative disposition, size and shape of crystalline and amorphous regions.

The approach to a quantitative treatment of these cross-correlations is to consider the result of substituting Eq. (9) into Eq. (8) giving (using

$$\alpha_2 = \bar{\alpha} - \frac{1}{3}\delta)$$

$$I = K \sum_i \sum_j \Big\{ (\bar{\alpha}_i - \frac{1}{3}\delta)(\bar{\alpha}_j - \frac{1}{3}\delta)(\mathbf{E}\cdot 0)^2 + \delta^2 (\mathbf{a}_i\cdot\mathbf{E})(\mathbf{a}_i\cdot 0)(\mathbf{a}_j\cdot\mathbf{E})(\mathbf{a}_j\cdot 0) + 2\delta(\mathbf{E}\cdot 0)(\bar{\alpha}_i - \frac{2}{3}\delta)(\mathbf{a}_i\cdot\mathbf{E})(\mathbf{a}_j\cdot 0) \Big\} \cos k(\mathbf{r}_{ij}\cdot\mathbf{s}) \tag{177}$$

in which the three terms correspond to I_d, I_0 and I_x. The cross-correlation term is then

$$I_x = 2\delta(\mathbf{E}\cdot 0) \sum_i \sum_j \Big[\bar{\alpha}_i (\mathbf{a}_j\cdot\mathbf{E})(\mathbf{a}\ \cdot 0)\Big] \cos k(\mathbf{r}_{ij}\cdot\mathbf{s})$$

$$= 2\delta(\mathbf{E}\cdot 0)\, A \int_{r_{ij}} \Big[(\Delta\bar{\alpha}_i)(\mathbf{a}_j\cdot\mathbf{E})(\mathbf{a}_j\cdot 0) \cos k(\mathbf{r}_{ij}\cdot\mathbf{s})\, d\,\mathbf{r}_{ij} \tag{178}$$

where

$$\Delta \overline{\alpha}_i = \overline{\alpha}_i - \langle \overline{\alpha}_i \rangle_{av} \tag{179}$$

where the double average in the last term represents an average over volume elements with respect to direction and position.

This gives, for example, for $I_{+,x}$

$$I_{+,x} = 2 \delta A (\cos \theta - 1) \sin \psi \cos \psi \int_{r_{ij}} (\Delta \overline{\alpha}_i) [\sin \psi \cos \psi \cos \theta (a_j \cdot j)^2 - \sin \psi \cos \psi (a_j \cdot k)^2 + (\cos^2 \psi \cos \theta - \sin^2 \psi) (a_j \cdot j)(a_j \cdot k)] \cos k (r_{ij} \cdot s) \, d r_{ij} \tag{180}$$

The evaluation of this integral requires the calculation of terms of the sort

$$K_7 = \delta \int_{r_{ij}} \langle (\Delta \overline{\alpha}_i) \cos^2 \theta_j \rangle_{r_{ij}} \cos k (r_{ij} \cdot s) \, d r_{ij} \tag{181}$$

the value of which depends upon how θ_j depends upon $\Delta \overline{\alpha}_i$. Their evaluation requires specification of cross-correlation functions and will not be attempted in this paper.

FLUCTUATIONS IN ANISOTROPY AND ITS CROSS-CORRELATION

For simplicity, the anisotropy of a volume element, δ, was assumed constant throughout the medium. Generally this will fluctuate and a subscript i should be included in δ_i. As has been pointed out by Stein and Wilson (22), this gives rise to still additional terms in Eq. (177) involving $\delta_i \delta_j$, $\delta_i \overline{\alpha}_j$ and products like $\delta_i \cos^2 \theta_j$. The first of these depends upon correlations in anisotropy and the second and third represent cross-correlations between anisotropy and density and optic axis orientation, respectively.

The approach to treating anisotropy correlations has been described (22)
where

$$\delta_i = \delta_0 + \Delta \delta_i \tag{182}$$

where δ_0 is the average anisotropy

$$\delta_0 = \langle \delta_i \rangle_{av} \tag{183}$$

The correlation function $\psi(r_{ij})$ was introduced

$$\psi(r_{ij}) = \frac{\langle(\Delta\delta_i)(\Delta\delta_j)\rangle_{r_{ij}}}{\langle(\Delta\delta_i)^2\rangle_{av}} \tag{184}$$

This correlation function could be introduced into the equations for non-random orientation fluctuations in the same manner as it was included in the random theory. In practice it was assumed that the contribution to scattering arising from such fluctuations was small and no specific evaluation of $\psi(r_{ij})$ or $\langle(\Delta\delta_i)^2\rangle_{av}$ was made. At the present stage of refinement of the theory, it does not appear profitable to include this additional complication.

CONCLUSIONS

A theory has been developed which may describe correlations in orientation so that a continuous degree of order ranging from a random collection of crystals to a highly symmetrical arrangement such as is found in spherulitic polymers may be treated. While the probability of correlation of orientation is expanded in an infinite series of orthonormal functions, the light scattering properties of the system are dependent on only a few coefficients of this series. While this has the advantage of limiting the number of parameters required to generally describe a scattering system, it means that the scattering experiment does not uniquely define the orientation correlation, being dependent upon only certain moments of the correlation angle distribution. This also leads to a limitation of the variety of types of scattering patterns obtainable from unoriented systems.

It is believed that the techniques used here are extendable to the description of systems possessing macroscopic orientation. In this case, the probability of correlation, P (θ_{ij}) does not only depend upon the magnitude of the separation of the scattering elements, r_{ij} and upon the angle

β_i which $\mathbf{r}_{ij}$ makes to $\mathbf{a}_i$ but also upon α_{ij}, the angular coordinate of $\mathbf{r}_{ij}$ with respect to an external reference axes. This requires the introduction of vector correlation functions and the specification of additional parameters describing this anisotropy. This is compensated, however, by the possibility of making additional measurements of the dependence of scattering intensity upon angles relative to this reference axis.

REFERENCES

(1) Birnboim, M. H., Magill, J. H. and Berry, G. C., this volume.

(2) Bridge, N. J. and Buckingham, A. D., J. Chem. Phys., 40, 2733 (1964).

(3) Clough, S., van Aartsen, J. J. and Stein, R. S., J. Appl. Phys. 36, 3072 (1965).

(4) Erhardt, P., Sasaguri, K. and Stein, R. S., J. Polymer Sci., C5, 179 (1964).

(5) Erhardt, P. and Stein, R. S., Polymer Letters, 3, 553 (1965).

(6) Leite, R. C. C., Moore, R. S. and Porto, S. P. S., J. Chem. Phys., 40, 3741 (1964).

(7) Moore, R. S., Polymer Preprints, 6, 113 (1965).

(8) Moore, R. S. and Matsuoka, S., paper presented before the 4th International Congress on Rheology, Brown University, Providence, Rhode Island, August (1963).

(9) Moore, R. S. and Matsuoka, S., J. Polymer Sci., C5, 163 (1964).

(10) Pecora, R., J. Chem. Phys., 40, 1604 (1964).

(11) Rhodes, M. B. and Stein, R. S., Polymer Letters, 1, 663 (1963).

(12) Rhodes, M. B., Keedy, D. A. and Stein, R. S., J. Polymer Sci., 62, S73 (1962).

(13) Rhodes, M. B. and Stein, R. S., J. Polymer Sci., 62, S84 (1962).

(14) Samuels, R., J. Polymer Sci., No. 13, 37 (1966).

(15) Stein, R. S., in Proceedings of the Interdisciplinary Conference on Electromagnetic Scattering, edited by M. Kerker, Pergamon Press, New York, 1963, pp. 430-458.

(16) Stein, R. S., Erhardt, P., and Adams, G., ONR Technical Report No. 74, Contract No. 3357(01), Project NR: 356-378, Polymer Research Institute, University of Massachusetts, Amherst, Massachusetts, July, 1965.

(16a) Stein, R. S., Erhardt, P., Clough, S., and Adams, G., J. Appl. Phys., in press.

(17) Stein, R. S., Erhardt, P., van Aartsen, J. J., Clough, S. and Rhodes, M. B., J. Polymer Sci., C, No. 13, 1 (1966).

(18) Stein, R. S. and Hotta, T., J. Appl. Phys., 35, 2237 (1964).

(19) Stein, R. S. and Keane, J. J., J. Polymer Sci., 17, 21 (1955).

(20) Stein, R. S. and Rhodes, M. B., J. Appl. Phys., 31, 1873 (1960).

(21) Stein, R. S., Stidham, S. N. and Wilson, P., ONR Technical Report No. 36, Contract No. 3357(00), Project NR: 356-378, Polymer Research Institute, University of Massachusetts, Amherst, Massachusetts, August, 1961.

(22) Stein, R. S. and Wilson, P., J. Appl. Phys., 33, 1914 (1962).

(23) Stein, R. S., Wilson, P. R. and Stidham, S. N., J. Appl. Phys., 34, 46 (1963).

(24) van Aartsen, J. J., private communication.

(25) Watson, G. N., A Treatise on the Theory of Bessel Functions, Cambridge University Press, Cambridge, 1952, p. 393.

(26) Yau, W. and Stein, R. S., Polymer Letters, 2, 231 (1964).

DISCUSSION FOLLOWING PAPER BY R. STEIN

J. A. Prins: You have treated the spherulites as a whole and on the other hand the correlation inside a spherulite. I thought both essentially right. Have you the same conviction? I should want to have the transitional cases, too, as the two cases are rather different and need to be linked up.

R. Stein: The cases of non-random orientation fluctuations which we have considered do not pass continuously to the quadrapole-like symmetry of spherulite scattering. It is possible to describe spherulite scattering in terms of angular dependent correlation functions which oscillate between positive and negative values. This gives the same result as the amplitude summation over the spherulite which we have used. It would be desirable to formulate correlation functions which would pass continuously from those spherulite-type functions to random functions as a randomness parameter was changed. Such functions would have a degree of angular dependence that would vary with the separation of the scattering elements and could be characterized by a measurment of the variation of the dependence of intensity upon polarizer rotation angle ψ with the scattering angle θ. Note Added in Proof: Mr. Erhardt and I have recently formulated the scattering theory for non-random orientation fluctuations in terms of a spherical harmonic expansion of the correlation function where the coefficients are functions of r. This recent development which was not presented in my talk will be discussed in the written version of the manuscript.

R. H. Munis: How did you obtain the angular calibration of your photographic plate?

R. S. Stein: One way to do this is to insert a diffraction grating in place of the sample and observe the pattern. But one can do it fairly well by simply measuring the distances involved in the geometry of the system.

G. C. Berry: We have occasionally observed a "clover leaf" pattern which is confined to very small angles superimposed in the pattern expected in H_V light for the size of the spherulite observed microscopically, and I would like to know if you have seen them in your experiments, and if so, can explain their origin.

R. Stein: We have observed superimposed patterns in cases where two sizes or types of spherulites are microscopically observed. I have not seen the very small angle pattern that you refer to. It would appear that such a pattern would arise from more long range correlations of orientations over distances larger than those of the individual spherulites. Perhaps there is anisotropy resulting from strain in the film.

A Microbeam Light Scattering Technique for Studying Spherulite Morphology*

M. H. Birnboim, J. H. Magill, G. C. Berry
Mellon Institute, Pittsburgh

A light scattering apparatus has been constructed using a plane polarized laser light source for scattering studies on spherulitic polymer films. The apparatus, shown schematically in Fig. 1, includes as special features, a removable lens to reduce the beam diameter to its diffraction limit (here ca. 50 micron), a cell stage with an x-y movement mounted on a holder which may be rotated through 360°, a removable microscope for examination of the area from which light is being scattered, and a polaroid disc that may be rotated through a known angle relative to the laser. The scattering from a diffraction grating provides a convenient size calibration.

This apparatus has been useful in light scattering studies on relatively large spherulites having a complicated morphology. The scattering behavior can be determined at different known positions on the spherulite and analyzed after the methods advanced by Stein and collaborators. Thus, Fig. 2(b) shows a wide beam H_v scattering pattern from the nylon 9.6 spherulites in Fig. 2(a). Figures 2(c) and (d) are examples of scattering patterns obtained at different positions on a spherulite. An analysis of these, and other patterns (not

*Invited paper, not presented at the conference.

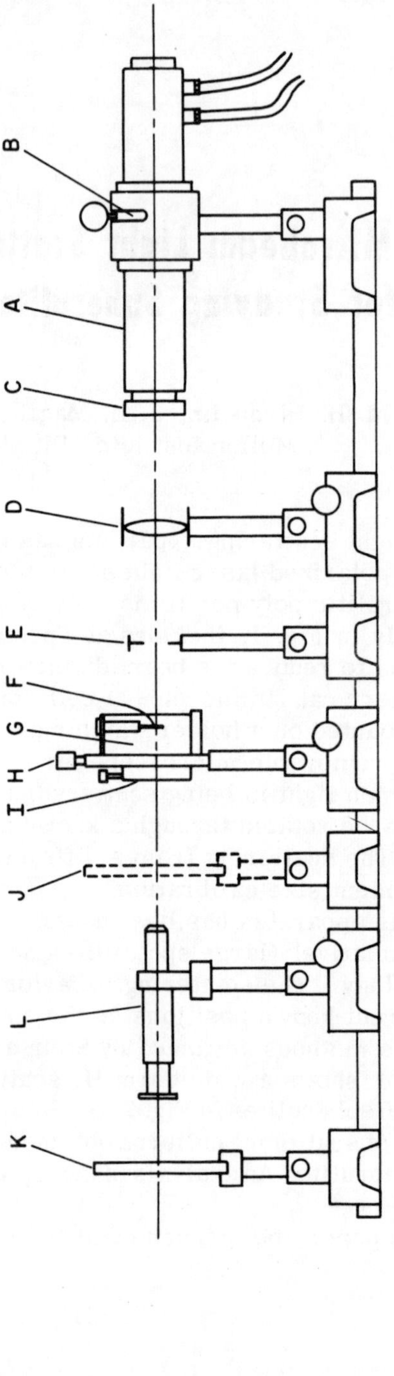

Fig. 1. Light scattering apparatus showing laser A with red filter C, lens D, sample F in cell G, cell stage H, analyzer I, microscope L and plate holder K or J.

shown) from selected positions on the spherulite illustrate the general utility of the microbeam light scattering technique in the determination of spherulite morphology. Examination of the patterns of nylon 9.6 suggest that two mutually perpendicular polarization directions in the crystallites (comprising the spherulite) are responsible for the complex scattering pattern. One, corresponding to the chain axis, is inclined to, and twists about the spherulite radius in the growth direction. The other, corresponding to the H-bond direction, is nearly co-linear with the radius, but fluctuates about it with a characteristic period differing from the twist period. Thus, a study of the polarization behavior at different positions on a spherulite provides a method for investigating spherulite morphology.

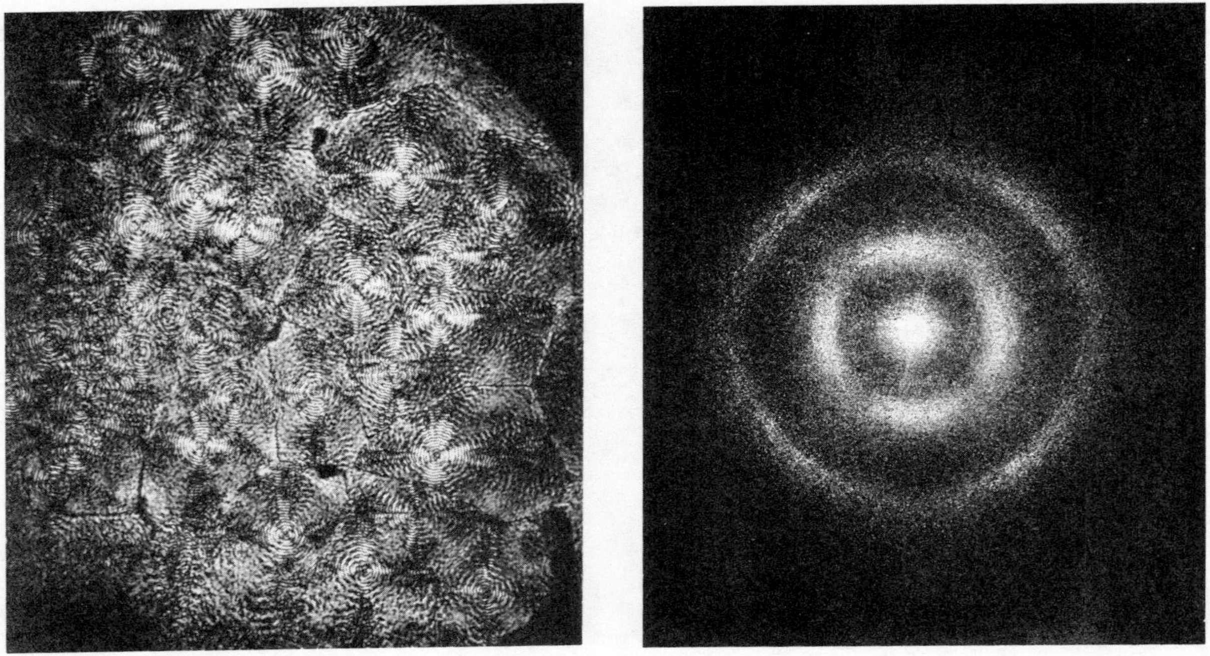

(a) (b)

Fig. 2. (a) Nylon 9.6 specimen (crystallized at 218°C) viewed between crossed polars at ×75. (b) Wide beam H_v scattering pattern from (a).

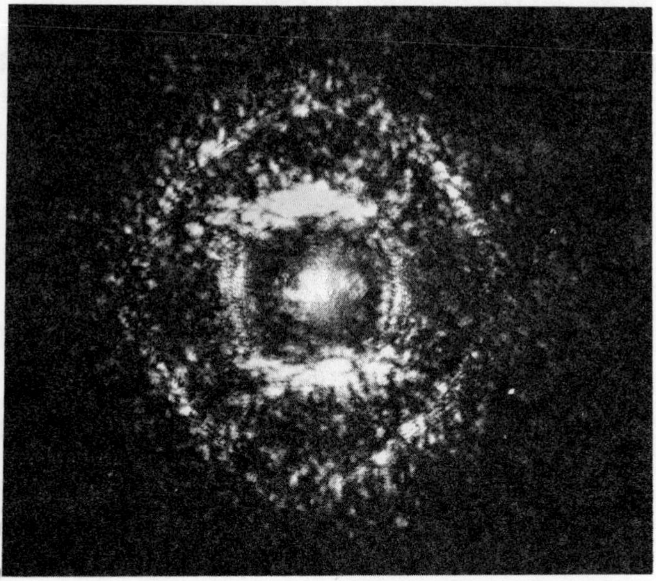

(c)

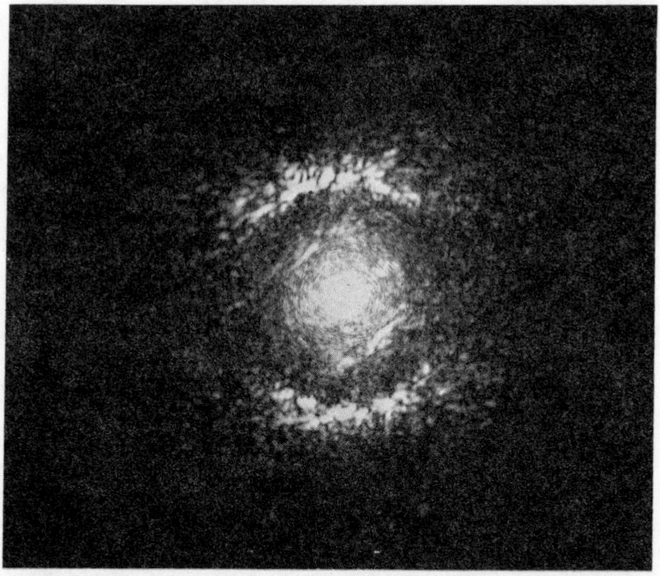

(d)

Fig. 2. (cont'd) (c) Microbeam H_v scattering along horizontal radius of a spherulite. (d) Microbeam V_v scattering from the same position as (c).

Light Scattering of Polymer Solids and Gels

W. Prins
Laboratory of Physical Chemistry,
Technische Hogeschool,
Delft, The Netherlands.

ABSTRACT

Some preliminary observations are reported concerning the light scattering of isotactic polypropylene and of polyvinylalcohol gels.

It appears that, at least qualitatively, the H_v scattering of shock cooled polypropylene does not show the cloverleaf symmetry found in the case of polyethylene.

The chemical crosslinking of a 5% aqueous polyvinylalcohol solution leads unexpectedly to a large rise in V_v as well as H_v scattering. Similar light scattering behavior is also found in the case of gels, which are formed when 5% polyvinyl alcohol is dissolved in warm water/glycol mixtures and subsequently cooled without chemical crosslinking. In both cases, the development of strong H_v scattering with a maximum at a certain scattering angle, is attributed to a microphase separation, with anisotropic regions of the order of 1000 Å.

I. SOLID STATE SCATTERING OF POLYPROPYLENE

As pointed out by Stein and Wilson (2), the light scattering of solid polymer films can be analysed in terms of a density correlation function $\gamma(r)$ and an orientation correlation function f(r), if it is assumed that these functions are both spherically symmetric. This assumption does not seem to be particularly attractive for crystalline polymer films, since it is known that spherulitic crystallization can occur in such films, which would certainly lead to a non-spherically symmetric f (r). If anywhere, the spherical symmetry might be approached best in shock cooled films with very poorly developed spherulites. Recently Keyzers, van Aartsen and Prins (1) have measured the light scattering of such shock cooled isotactic polypropylene film quantitatively on the basis of the spherical symmetry assumption.

One test for the validity of this analysis can be obtained by measuring the scattering under an angle θ as a function of the elevation ω above the horizontal plane which holds the measuring arm of the photometer. If $\gamma(r)$ and f(r) are both spherically symmetric, an extension of the Stein and Wilson derivation then shows that the following relations should hold:

$$I_{\parallel}(\omega) = V_v - (V_v - H_v)\frac{\sin^2\omega \sin^2\theta}{\cos^2\omega\cos^2\theta + \sin^2\omega} \quad (1)$$

$$I_{\perp}(\omega) = H_v \quad (2)$$

In these equations V_v and H_v have their usual meaning, $I_{\parallel}(\omega)$ is the intensity measured at an elevation ω between parallel polarizer and analyser, $I_{\perp}(\omega)$ the same in the crossed position.

Since in practice the photometer arm is restricted to the horizontal plane, the scattering at an elevation ω is measured as shown in Fig. 1. A sample, without any macroscopic orientation, is held vertically between a polarizer and analyser which can be rotated together through an angle ω in such a fashion that their relative polarization directions, crossed or parallel, are not changed. It is evident that the

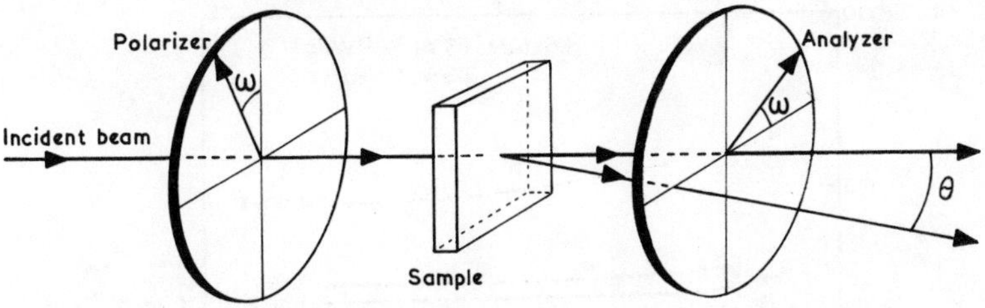

Fig. 1. Arrangement for measuring $I_{\parallel}(\omega)$ and $I_{\perp}(\omega)$ with the measuring arm in the horizontal plane by rotating polarizer and analyzer in crossed or parallel position.

scattered intensities $I_{\perp}(\omega)$ and $I_{\parallel}(\omega)$ can now be measured in the horizontal plane at any angle θ.

Because of irregularities in the polaroid polarizers, no quantitative data have yet been obtained. Preliminary measurements show that $I_{\perp}(\omega) \approx H_v$, which is consistent with equation 2. Thus, we can provisionally conclude that the assumption of spherical symmetry for $\gamma(r)$ and $f(r)$ is not contradicted by experiment for shock cooled isotactic polypropylene.

Since it has not yet been possible to calculate what Eqs. 1 and 2 will be if the spherical symmetry is dropped, this experiment cannot, therefore, provide us with the final answer as regards the absence or presence of spherical symmetry.

II. SCATTERING BY POLYVINYLALCOHOL GELS

In the course of studies on polymer networks obtained by crosslinking in solution, it was observed that visually clear 5% PVA solutions in water become turbid upon crosslinking with 0.1 to 0.6% thiodiacetaldehyde. Furthermore, it was observed that addition of glycol led to optical clarification in the case of crosslinked PVA, whereas the non-crosslinked solution now in turn became turbid.

Measurements of the V_v and H_v component of the scattered light as a function of θ can provide some further understanding of these observations in terms of the structure of

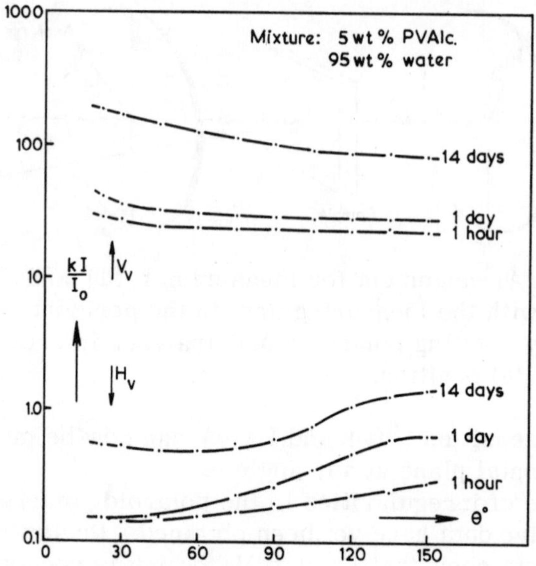

Fig. 2. V_v and H_v light scattering of a 5% PVA solution in water as a function of angle θ and time. Vertical scale is logarithmic.

the gels. 5% PVA (Elvanol, fully hydrolyzed, DP_η = 1830) and 0.1 to 0.6% bis (2, 2- diethoxyethyl) sulfide solutions in water are filtered at 85°C through a fine pore glass filter. After cooling one portion is acidified with 4N H_2SO_4 until 0.5N acid, to liberate the aldehyde end groups and effect the acetalization with the hydroxyl groups of the PVA. The gelation occurs in several hours, the light scattering becomes constant after 14 days. All measurements are done at room temperature.

In Figs. 2 and 3 the scattering intensities of a PVA solution and a crosslinked gel are compared on a logarithmic scale. It is seen that the crosslinked gel develops, in addition to a much stronger V_v component, a pronounced H_v scattering, which exhibits a maximum shifting to smaller angles the longer the time after gelation. The H_v component is negligible in the non-crosslinked solution. Since it is known that acetalization of polyvinylalchol— which occurs during crosslinking—decreases the solubility of PVA, the light scattering

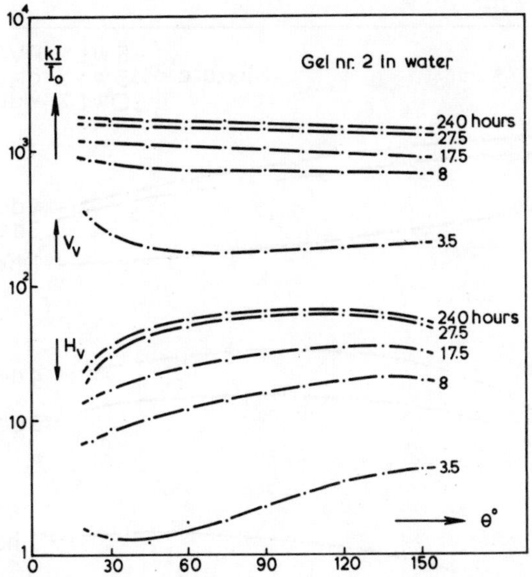

Fig. 3. V_v and H_v scattering of a 5% crosslinked PVA gel in water.

data might be interpreted as being caused largely by anisotropic regions (or orientation correlated regions) of crosslinks which develop in the course of about 24 hours after the crosslinking has been started. The gradually shifting maximum in the H_v scattering should then be related to the growth of these regions. Multiple scattering may occur to a minor extent (ratio of transmitted to incident beam is about 90%) but should not affect the shift in the maximum.*

Upon addition of ethylene glycol to a non-crosslinked and crosslinked sample, the type of scattering recorded in Figs. 4 and 5 is obtained. In the PVA solution (Fig. 4) one observes a rapid rise in V_v scattering followed by a somewhat

*Newer measurements on thin gel strips have revealed an appreciable low angle H_v scattering, followed by a minimum at larger angles. The maxima in Figs. 3-5 were shown to be caused by multiple scattering. (see M.C.A. Donkersloot, J. Gouda, J. J. van Aartsen and W. Prins. Reprints IUPAC SYMPOSIUM ON MACRO MOLECULAR CHEMISTRY, Tokyo-Kyoto, 1966)

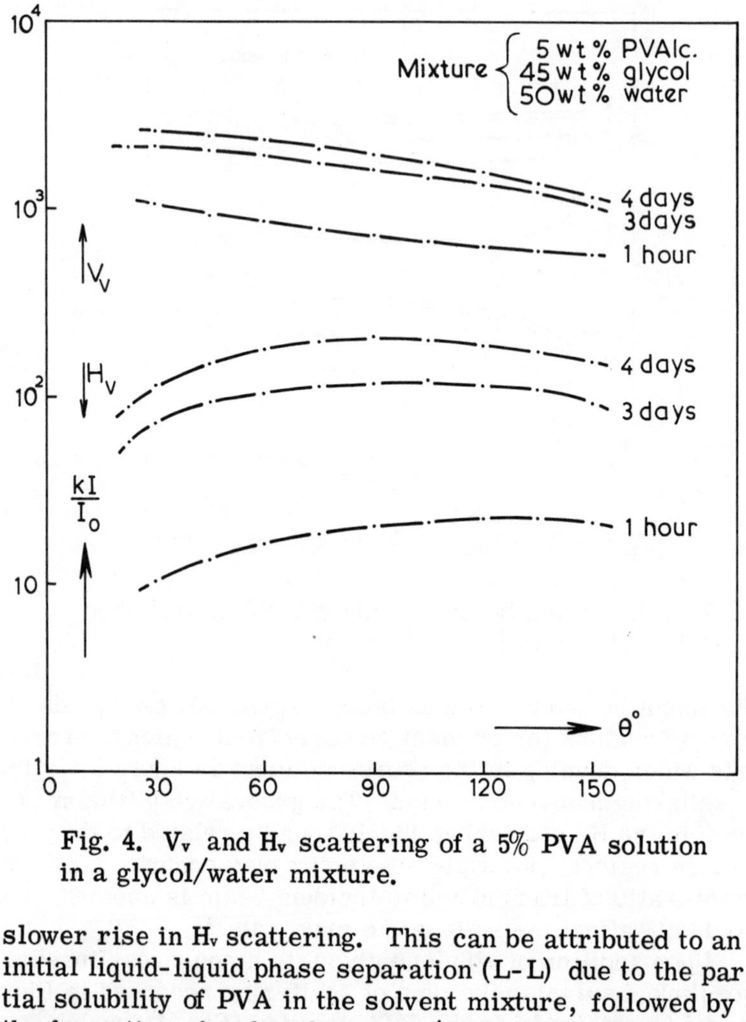

Fig. 4. V_v and H_v scattering of a 5% PVA solution in a glycol/water mixture.

slower rise in H_v scattering. This can be attributed to an initial liquid-liquid phase separation (L-L) due to the partial solubility of PVA in the solvent mixture, followed by the formation of ordered regions (solid-liquid phase separation, S-L). The size of the ordered regions again seems to increase with time because the maximum in H_v shifts to smaller angles.

In the crosslinked PVA gel (Fig. 5) one observes a decrease of V_v and H_v until in a 40 : 60 water/glycol mixture (around the gel) the scattering is at a minimum, comparable in magnitude to the scattering of the PVA solution in

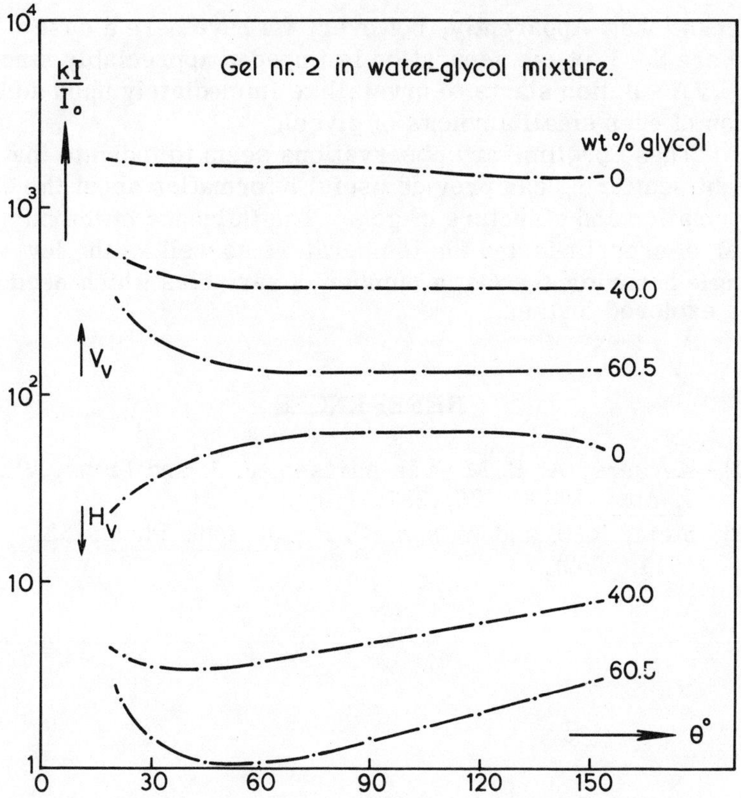

Fig. 5. V_v and H_v scattering of a 5% crosslinked PVA gel in water/glycol mixtures. Solvent composition refers to the surrounding liquid.

water. Since it was found from formaldehyde treatment of PVA in solution that acetalization leads to increased solubility in glycol, it seems logical to conclude that the crosslink regions disentangle into isotropic low-scattering regions. At the same time the PVA chains between crosslinks are prevented from ordering because of the presence of crosslinks.

At still higher glycol contents (not shown in Fig. 5) the scattering increases again. It seems plausible to suggest that now the PVA chains do become insoluble in spite of the crosslinks. Apparently, however, we have here a case where S - L phase separation is impeded appreciably since a PVA solution starts to crystallize immediately upon addition of even small amounts of glycol.

These preliminary observations seem to indicate that light scattering can provide useful information about the formation and structure of gels. The influence of the number of crosslinks and the temperature as well as the low angle behavior are just a number of variables which need to be explored further.

REFERENCES

(1) Keyzers, A. E. M.; van Aartsen, J. J. and Prins, W., J. Appl. Phys., **36**, 2874 (1965).

(2) Stein, R. S. and Wilson, P. R., J. Appl. Phys., **33**, 1914 (1962).

DISCUSSION FOLLOWING PAPER BY W. PRINS

J. M. Greenberg: (a) I do not understand your terminology such as cross-linking. (b) [after a series of questions] Do you mean that your particles (polyvinylalcohol) simply grow as for example - the scattering by water vapor in this room would increase as the vapor condenses.

W. Prins: The acetalization of PVA chains as a result of cross-linking leads to insoluble chain portions. These seem to form clusters, which are either optically anisotropic or correlated in orientation, because of the appearance of a strong H_v component in the scattering. The size of these clusters is roughly indicated by the maximum in the H_v versus θ data. Low angle measurements still have to be done. These might lead to a somewhat different interpretation.

R. H. Marchessault: What are the relative contributions of density fluctuations and orientation fluctuations to the total scattering observed for PVA gels.

W. Prins: On the basis of the data obtained so far, I cannot answer your question. I can only say the the cross-linked gel in water exhibits about a 100-fold increase in V_v as well as H_v over the scattering exhibited by the PVA solutions in water.

M. Goldstein: In plots of the V_v and H_v components versus scattering angle θ, do you get maxima in the intensity or are the intensities monotonically decreasing functions of θ?

W. Prins: The angular dependency so far has only been measured between 30° and 150° and is not very pronounced. In the H_v scattering there is an angular dependence with a maximum that shifts toward smaller angles the longer one waits. The maximum is thought to be related to the average size of the correlated region.

Light Scattering in Simple Liquids

D. J. Coumou, J. Hijmans and E. L. Mackor
Koninklijke/Shell Laboratorium, Amsterdam
(Shell Research N.V.)

ABSTRACT

New light-scattering and refractive index data for some simple liquid systems are used to test the validity of some current theories of optical scattering in liquids. In particular, the following topics are discussed: contribution of temperature or pressure fluctuations to the isotropic scattering; validity of the Cabannes-expression for the ratio of total to isotropic scattering in liquids; concentration dependence of the isotropic - and anisotropic scattering-contributions in binary liquid mixtures; comparison of anisotropic scattering factors in vapors and in dilute solutions.

INTRODUCTION

A direct calculation of macroscopic optical properties such as the light-scattering intensity, from a molecular model is in practice only feasible for dilute systems, where the molecules can be treated to a good approximation as independent particles. For dense systems one is, as a rule, forced to use a continuum-theory, using macroscopic concepts such as the dielectric constant from the start. Thus, for instance, the theory by Einstein-Smoluchowski (6, 15) expresses the isotropic part of the Rayleigh-factor (the scattering intensity per unit solid angle and per unit volume relative to the intensity of the incident beam) in terms of the mean square fluctuation in the dielectric constant, ϵ, as:

$$R_{is}(90°) = \frac{\pi^2}{2\lambda^4} V <(\Delta\epsilon)^2>. \qquad (1)$$

Such a continuum theory is, however, not adequate for calculating a quantity like the anisotropic scattering intensity, since it is intimately related to a property (the anisotropy) of the individual molecules. In order to be able to make predictions about such a quantity one therefore usually extrapolates the results of the molecular theory for dilute systems into the liquid region. Thus, for instance, one frequently assumes the validity in the liquid region of the expression for the ratio of the anisotropic to the isotropic part of the Rayleigh factor in terms of the depolarisation ratio Δ_u,

$$\frac{R_{an}}{R_{is}} = \frac{13\Delta_u}{6-7\Delta_u} \qquad (2)$$

This relation has been derived by Cabannes (1) for independently scattering particles. Although arguments in favour of the validity of this expression for liquids have been presented (12), we feel that it still needs experimental verification. A way of doing this is to measure the total Rayleigh factor and the depolarisation-ratio Δ_u directly and to deduce the isotropic part of the Rayleigh factor from independent measurements of the temperature - or pressure-derivatives of the refractive index. The latter is related to the dielectric constant by

$$n^2 = \epsilon \quad . \qquad (3)$$

The expression for the isotropic scattering factor in terms of $(\partial n/\partial p)_T$ or $(\partial n/\partial T)_P$ is commonly derived under the assumption (2) that the mean square fluctuation in the dielectric constant is proportional to the mean square density fluctuation in the medium. Since, however, the thermodynamic state of the medium depends on two variables, viz. density and temperature (or density and pressure) independent fluctuations in the second variable (T or p) should in principle also contribute to $<(\Delta\epsilon)^2>$, and thus to the isotropic Rayleigh factor. The actual magnitude of these (admittedly small) contributions can be estimated when both $(\partial n/\partial T)_P$ and $(\partial n/\partial p)_T$ as well as the compressibility and the expansion coefficient of the liquid are known. We shall first examine these two questions, viz. the magnitudes of the contributions to R_{is} from temperature or pressure fluctuations, and the validity of the Cabannes relation (1) for liquids, and then turn our attention to mixtures.

For liquid mixtures the situation is similar as for pure liquids. Here also, a satisfactory theory (developed by Kirkwood and Goldberg (9) and by Stockmayer, (16) exists for the isotropic part of the Rayleigh factor. After subtraction of the contribution from density fluctuations this quantity is found to be proportional to the mean square concentration fluctuation. However, in order to be able to separate the anisotropic from the isotropic part of the scattering factor one is again forced to apply Cabannes relation (1) in a density-region where its validity has not been proved. As an indirect way of verifying whether this procedure is justified, one can check whether the isotropic scattering factors obtained by means of the Cabannes relation from light-scattering data, are consistent with existing thermodynamic data. Thus, using the Kirkwood-Goldberg (5, 9) expression for the mean square concentration fluctuation in terms of the concentration-derivative of the chemical potential, one can evaluate from the isotropic Rayleigh-factors, the activity coefficients (or the Gibbs free energies) for various mixtures, and compare these to the results obtained from vapour-pressure measurements.

In the absence of a satisfactory molecular theory of anisotropic light-scattering in liquids, it seems worthwhile to characterize at least qualitatively the typical behaviour of the anisotropic Rayleigh-factor as a function of concentration, and to compare it to the behaviour of the isotropic scattering-factor. In particular it is of interest to compare the molar anisotropic scattering factor of a highly anisotropic compound dissolved in a nearly isotropic liquid, with the anisotropic Rayleigh-factor of this compound in the vapour-phase. Such a characterization of anisotropic scattering in liquids may be helpful in a discussion from the molecular point of view.

I. ISOTROPIC SCATTERING FROM TEMPERATURE OR PRESSURE FLUCTUATIONS.

When the thermodynamic state of the medium is characterized by its density, $\rho = N/V$, and its temperature T the mean square fluctuation in the dielectric constant can be expressed as:

$$\langle(\Delta\epsilon)^2\rangle = \left(\frac{\partial\epsilon}{\partial V}\right)_T^2 \langle(\Delta V)^2\rangle + 2\left(\frac{\partial\epsilon}{\partial V}\right)_T \left(\frac{\partial\epsilon}{\partial T}\right)_V \langle\Delta V\Delta T\rangle + \left(\frac{\partial\epsilon}{\partial T}\right)_V^2 \langle(\Delta T)^2\rangle \quad (4)$$

where ΔT and ΔV represent fluctuations in the temperature and the volume occupied by a given number of particles in the medium. According to the statistical-mechanical theory of fluctuations (10), we have:

$$\langle(\Delta V)^2\rangle = VkT\kappa_T; \quad \langle\Delta V\Delta T\rangle = 0; \quad \langle(\Delta T)^2\rangle = \frac{kT^2}{c_V}, \quad (5)$$

where κ_T is the isothermal compressibility and c_v the specific heat at constant volume. The second of these equations expresses the fact that V and T are statistically independent variables. This is generally the case for the extensive variable of one thermodynamic couple (P and V) and the intensive variable of a different couple (T and S) . Writing

$$V\left(\frac{\partial \epsilon}{\partial V}\right)_T = -\frac{1}{\kappa_T}\left(\frac{\partial \epsilon}{\partial P}\right)_T ; \quad \left(\frac{\partial \epsilon}{\partial T}\right)_V = \left(\frac{\partial \epsilon}{\partial T}\right)_P + \frac{\alpha_P}{\kappa_T}\left(\frac{\partial \epsilon}{\partial P}\right)_T \tag{6}$$

where α_p is the thermal expansion coefficient, and substituting (4) , (5) and (6) into (1) , one finds after some elementary thermodynamic transformations:

$$R_{is}(90°) = \frac{\pi^2}{2\lambda^4} \frac{kT}{\kappa_T} \left(\frac{\partial \epsilon}{\partial p}\right)_T^2 \left\{ 1 + \left(\frac{\kappa_T}{\kappa_S} - 1\right) x^2 \right\}. \tag{7}$$

Here κ_s is the adiabatic compressibility and x is an abbreviation of the quantity,

$$x = 1 + \frac{\kappa_T}{\alpha_P} \frac{(\partial \epsilon/\partial T)_P}{(\partial \epsilon/\partial p)_T} . \tag{8}$$

In the usual treatments only the first term, due to density fluctuations, is taken into account, and the second term, which is proportional to the small quantity x^2 is neglected. Let us now consider ϵ as a function of density and pressure. Then one obtains instead of (4)

$$\langle(\Delta\epsilon)^2\rangle = \left(\frac{\partial \epsilon}{\partial V}\right)_P^2 \langle(\Delta V)^2\rangle + 2\left(\frac{\partial \epsilon}{\partial V}\right)_P \left(\frac{\partial \epsilon}{\partial p}\right)_V \langle\Delta V \Delta p\rangle + \left(\frac{\partial \epsilon}{\partial p}\right)_V^2 \langle(\Delta p)^2\rangle \tag{9}$$

where

$$\langle(\Delta V)^2\rangle = VkT\kappa_T; \quad \langle\Delta V \Delta p\rangle = -kT; \quad \langle(\Delta p)^2\rangle = \frac{kT}{\kappa_s V} \tag{10}$$

As p and V are not statistically independent the correlation term no longer vanishes. Using the transformation

$$V\left(\frac{\partial\epsilon}{\partial V}\right)_p = \frac{1}{\alpha_p}\left(\frac{\partial\epsilon}{\partial T}\right)_p \;;\; \left(\frac{\partial\epsilon}{\partial p}\right)_v = \left(\frac{\partial\epsilon}{\partial p}\right)_T + \frac{\kappa_T}{\alpha_p}\left(\frac{\partial\epsilon}{\partial T}\right)_p \qquad (11)$$

one now obtains

$$R_{is}(90°) = \frac{\pi^2}{2\lambda^4}\,\frac{kT\kappa_T}{\alpha_p^2}\left(\frac{\partial\epsilon}{\partial T}\right)_p^2 \left\{1 + \frac{2x}{1-x} + \frac{\kappa_T}{\kappa_s}\,\frac{x^2}{(1-x)^2}\right\} \qquad (12)$$

where x is still given by (8). Although this expression is, of course, equivalent to (7), the presence of the linear term in (12) shows that making the approximation, that only density fluctuations contribute, becomes more serious when the latter are assumed to take place at constant pressure than when the temperature is used as the second state variable. The actual values of the quantity x, as determined from the pressure and temperature dependence of the refractive index (5) and literature data for κ_T and α_p, are given in Table 1 for a number of liquids. From these values which run from 0.01 up to 0.05, and the magnitudes of the ratios $\kappa_T/\kappa_s \sim 1.3$ for most liquids, it is seen that the correction term in Eq. (7) is only of order 10^{-3} to 10^{-4}, whereas the second term in Eq. (12) can contribute up to 10% of the Rayleigh factor.

In Table 2 we have compared the measured values of the quantity $\rho(\partial\epsilon/\partial\rho)_T = -V(\partial\epsilon/\partial V)_T$, which mainly determines $R_{is}(90°)$, with the values of $\rho(d\epsilon/d\rho)$ as obtained by means of the Clausius-Mosotti relation

$$\frac{\epsilon-1}{\epsilon+2} = \frac{4\pi}{3}\rho\alpha \qquad (13)$$

where α is the polarisability of a molecule. From this relation one would obtain:

$$\rho\frac{d\epsilon}{d\rho} = \frac{(\epsilon-1)(\epsilon+2)}{3}\,. \qquad (13')$$

As is seen the values derived from (13') are systematically too high by about 5-10%.

TABLE 1

Values of x from Refractive Index Data

	$-(\partial n/\partial T)_p \times 10^5$ $(°C)^{-1}$	$(\partial n/\partial p)_T \times 10^{12}$ cm^2/dyn	$\alpha_p \times 10^3$ $(°C)^{-1}$	$\kappa_T \times 10^{12}$ cm^2/dyn	x
benzene	63.8	52.3	1.21^5	95	0.046
toluene	56.2	48.6	1.08	92	0.015
cyclohexane	53.8	50.8	1.21	112	0.018
iso-octane	48.7	62.9	1.19	152	0.011
n-hexane	52.8	66.5	1.38	170	0.022
n-octane	47.6	52.8	1.15	125	0.020
n-decane	44.8	46.9	1.04	105	0.036
n-hexadecane	40.6	39.1	0.90	83	0.042
carbon tetrachloride	58.6	52.8	1.21	106	0.028
carbon disulphide	81.6	68.2	1.19	94	0.055
methyl ethyl ketone	51.0	44.2	1.30	108	0.041

TABLE 2

Values of $\rho(\partial\epsilon/\partial\rho)_T$ from Refractive Index-data and from Clausius-Mosotti Equation

	n	$\rho(\partial\epsilon/\partial\rho)_T$ (expt.)	$\rho(d\epsilon/d\rho)$ Cl.-Mos.
benzene	1.503	1.65^{5}	1.79
toluene	1.499	1.58	1.76^{5}
cyclohexane	1.426	1.29	1.39
iso-octane	1.391	1.15	1.22^{5}
n-hexane	1.374	1.07^{5}	1.15
n-octane	1.398	1.18	1.26
n-decane	1.413	1.26	1.33
n-hexadecane	1.435	1.35	1.43
carbon tetrachloride	1.460	1.45^{5}	1.57
carbon disulphide	1.634	2.37	2.60
methyl ethyl ketone	1.379	1.13	1.17

II. VALIDITY OF THE CABANNES RELATION FOR PURE LIQUIDS

As we have seen, the evaluation of $\langle(\Delta\epsilon)^2\rangle$ from density fluctuations alone is justified, provided we consider the latter as taking place at constant temperature. Accordingly we can approximate Eq. (7) by

$$\cdot R_{i}(90^\circ) = \frac{2\pi^2 n^2}{\lambda^4}\,\frac{kT}{\kappa_T}\left(\frac{\partial n\lambda^4}{\partial p_T}\right)^2 . \qquad (14)$$

For a number of liquids we have calculated by means of this equation $R_{is}(90^\circ)$ from our measurements (5) of n, $(\partial n/\partial p)_T$ and from existing compressibility data. For the same liquids we have also measured (5) the total scattering factors $R_{tot} = R_{is} + R_{an}$, and the depolarisation ratios $\Delta_u = I_h/I_v$, i.e. the ratios of the intensities of scattered light polarised parallel and perpendicular to the plane of observation, the subscript u indicating that unpolarised incident light is used. In Table 3 the experimentally determined ratios R_{tot}/R_{is} are compared with the values obtained from the depolarisation ratio by means of Cabannes relation,

$$\frac{R_{tot}\ (90^{\bullet})}{R_{tot}\ (90^{\circ})} = \frac{6 + 6\Delta_u}{6 - 7\Delta_u} \ . \tag{15}$$

The agreement is seen to be very satisfactory, which seems to confirm the applicability of (15) to dense media.

III. CONCENTRATION DEPENDENCE OF THE ISOTROPIC SCATTERING IN MIXTURES

An expression for the isotropic Rayleigh factor of a mixture can be derived in a similar way as the one for pure liquids, Eq. (7). Expressing the dielectric constant as a function of the temperature, T and the particle numbers for both components, N_1 and N_2, in a given volume element of the scatterer, we have

$$\begin{aligned} <(\Delta\epsilon)^2> &= \left(\frac{\partial\epsilon}{\partial T}\right)^2_{N_1 N_2} <(\Delta T)^2> + \left(\frac{\partial\epsilon}{\partial N_1}\right)^2_{N_2 T} <(\Delta N_1)^2> \\ &+ 2\left(\frac{\partial\epsilon}{\partial N_1}\right)_{N_2 T} \left(\frac{\partial\epsilon}{\partial N_2}\right)_{N_1 T} <\Delta N_1 \Delta N_2> \\ &+ \left(\frac{\partial\epsilon}{\partial N_2}\right)^2_{N_1 T} <(\Delta N_2)^2> \end{aligned} \tag{16}$$

The terms involving $<\Delta T \Delta N_1>$ and $<\Delta T \Delta N_2>$ vanish, since T and N_1 or N_2 are statistically independent variables. Instead of ΔN_1 and ΔN_2 we introduce as new variables the relative concentration fluctuation

$$\frac{\Delta c}{c} = \frac{\Delta N_2}{N_2} - \frac{\Delta N_1}{N_1} \tag{17}$$

and the volume change which would be caused by the fluctuations ΔN_1 and ΔN_2 if the volume would be allowed to expand freely,

$$\Delta V = \left(\frac{\partial V}{\partial N_1}\right)_{N_2 T} \Delta N_1 + \left(\frac{\partial V}{\partial N_2}\right)_{N_1 T} \Delta N_2 \ . \tag{18}$$

Transforming the derivatives of ϵ accordingly by,

$$\left(\frac{\partial \epsilon}{\partial N_1}\right)_{N_2 T} = \left(\frac{\partial V}{\partial N_1}\right)_{N_2 T} \left(\frac{\partial \epsilon}{\partial V}\right)_{T, c} - \frac{c}{N_1} \left(\frac{\partial \epsilon}{\partial c}\right)_{T, v} \tag{19a}$$

$$\left(\frac{\partial \epsilon}{\partial N_2}\right)_{N_1 T} = \left(\frac{\partial V}{\partial N_2}\right)_{N_1 T} \left(\frac{\partial \epsilon}{\partial V}\right)_{T, c} + \frac{c}{N_2} \left(\frac{\partial \epsilon}{\partial c}\right)_{T, v} \tag{19b}$$

one obtains

$$<(\Delta\epsilon)^2> = \left(\frac{\partial \epsilon}{\partial T}\right)_{v, c} <(\Delta T)^2> + \left(\frac{\partial \epsilon}{\partial V}\right)^2_{T, c} <(\Delta V)^2>$$

$$+ \left(\frac{\partial \epsilon}{\partial c}\right)^2_{T, v} <(\Delta c)^2> \ . \tag{20}$$

The term involving $<\Delta V \Delta c>$ vanishes, since as can easily be shown (8) , V and c are statistically independent variables. Substituting $<(\Delta T)^2>$ and $<(\Delta V)^2>$ from (5) and the corresponding expression for the mean square concentration fluctuation,

$$<(\Delta c)^2> = \frac{kT}{N_1} \Big/ \left(\frac{\partial \mu_2}{\partial c}\right)_{p, T} \tag{21}$$

one obtains for the isotropic scattering factor

$$R_{is}(90°) = R_d + R_c \ . \tag{22}$$

Here R_d is the contribution from density fluctuations which is identical to (7) (or 14), and

$$R_c = \frac{\pi^2}{2\lambda^4} kT \frac{V}{N_1} \frac{(\partial\epsilon/\partial c)^2_{T, V}}{(\partial\mu_2/\partial c)_{T, p}} \tag{23}$$

TABLE 3

Cabannes Factors

	Δ_u	$R(90) \times 10^6$ cm^{-1}	$R_{is} \times 10^6$ (eqn. (14))	Cab. (exp.) $= R_{tot} / R_{is}$	Cab. (Δ_u) (eqn. (15))	$\frac{\text{Cab. } (\Delta_u)}{\text{(Cab. (expt.)}}$
benzene	0.42	15.8	5.90	2.68	2.78	1.03^5
toluene	0.48	18.4	5.23	3.52	3.36^5	0.95^5
cyclohexane	0.049	4.56	4.25	1.07	1.11	1.04
iso-octane	0.047	5.15	4.57	1.12^5	1.11	0.98^5
n-hexane	0.073	5.32	4.46	1.19	1.17^5	0.98^5
n-octane	0.12	4.85	3.96	1.22^5	1.30	1.06
n-decane	0.15	4.95	3.79	1.30^5	1.39	1.06^5
n-hexadecane	0.26	5.75	3.44	1.67	1.81	1.08
carbon tetrachloride	0.042	5.38	5.09	1.05^5	1.09^5	1.04
carbon disulphide	0.65	83.9	12.0	6.99	6.83	0.98
methyl ethyl ketone	0.16	4.18	3.12	1.34	1.42^5	1.06

is the contribution from concentration fluctuations. Introducing mole fractions x_1 and x_2, which are related to c by

$$c = \frac{x_2}{x_1} = \frac{x_2}{1-x_2} \tag{24}$$

and the excess chemical potential μ_2^e, defined by

$$\frac{\partial \mu_2}{\partial x_2} = \frac{kT}{x_2} + \frac{\partial \mu_2^e}{\partial x_2} , \tag{25}$$

we can write (23) in the form

$$R_c = R_{id} \Big/ \left\{ 1 + \frac{x_2}{kT} \frac{\partial \mu_2^e}{\partial x_2} \right\} \tag{26}$$

with

$$R_{id} = \frac{\pi^2}{2\lambda^4} \frac{x_1 x_2}{\rho} \left(\frac{\partial \epsilon}{\partial x_2}\right)^2 \tag{27}$$

representing the isotropic concentration scattering factor for an ideal solution. The function

$$1 - \frac{R_{id}}{R_c} = \frac{x_2}{kT} \frac{\partial \mu_2^e}{\partial x_2} = \frac{x_1 x_2}{kT} \frac{\partial^2 g^e}{\partial x_1 \partial x_2} \tag{28}$$

is a measure for its deviation from ideality and is directly related to the excess free energy of the mixture, g^e.

Assuming tentatively that the Cabannes relation (15) is applicable not only to pure liquids but also to liquid mixtures, one can thus evaluate the excess Gibbs free energy from light-scattering data (4). First one determines the isotropic scattering factor from the total Rayleigh factor and the depolarisation, then the density scattering as given by Eq. (7) is subtracted, the ideal concentration scattering is calculated from the density and the concentration dependence of the refractive index, and finally the function (28) is evaluated and integrated numerically with respect to x_2. The results are shown in Figs. 1-6. In Figs. 1-3 the

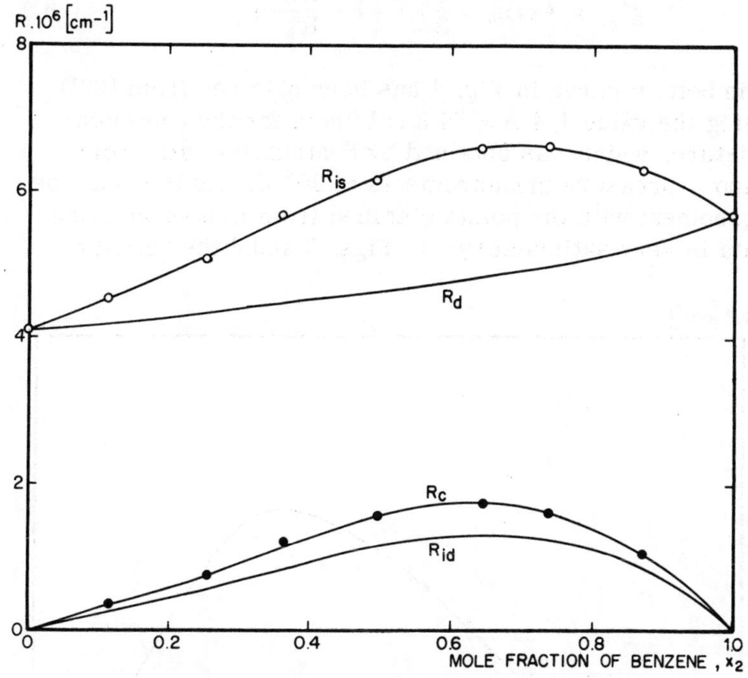

Fig. 1. The isotropic scattering factor, R_{is}, its contributions from density and concentration fluctuations, R_d and R_c, and the "ideal" scattering, R_{id} as a function of concentration for the system benzene-cyclohexane.

relative magnitudes and the concentration dependences of R_{is}, R_d, R_c, and R_{id} are given for mixtures of benzene with cyclohexane, neopentane, and methanol. Fig. 4 shows the function (28) for these mixtures. For the mixture cyclohexane-benzene this function is relatively small and has a practically symmetric concentration dependence, in agreement with the conclusion by Scatchard, Wood, and Mochel (14) that this system behaves as a regular mixture. In this case the function (28) directly gives the excess Gibbs free energy

$$g^{e}_{reg} = Ax_1x_2 = \frac{1}{2}kT\left(1 - \frac{R_{id}}{R_c}\right) \quad . \tag{28'}$$

The bottom curve in Fig. 4 has been obtained from (28') using the value 1/4 A = 75.8 cal/mole for the equimolar mixture, which was obtained by Scatchard et alii from vapour pressure measurements at 30° C. As is seen, the agreement with the points obtained from light-scattering data is very satisfactory. In Figs. 5 and 6 the activity

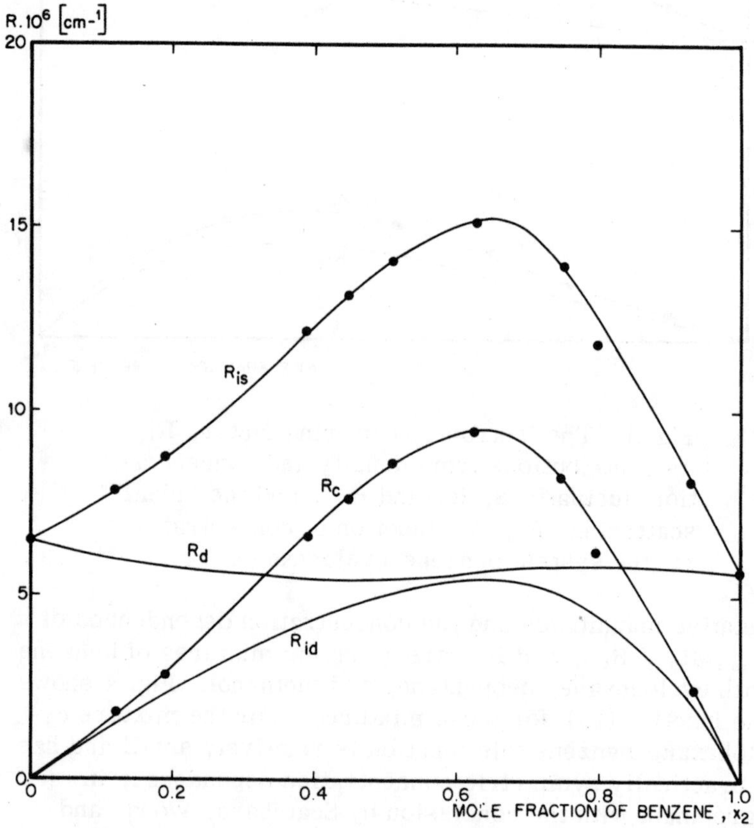

Fig. 2. Isotropic scattering, density-scattering, concentration-scattering and ideal scattering for neopentane-benzene.

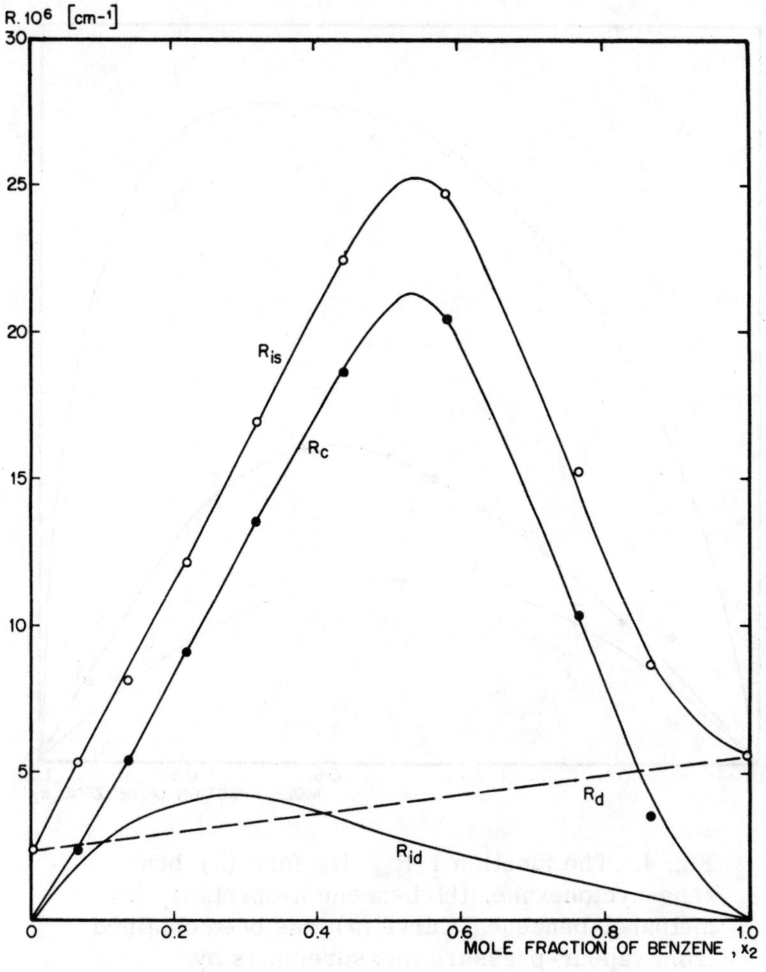

Fig. 3. Isotropic-, density-, concentration-, and ideal-scattering for methanol-benzene.

coefficients and the Gibbs free energies for the two other mixtures as obtained by numerical integration of the function (28), are compared to the results from vapour pressure measurements (11).

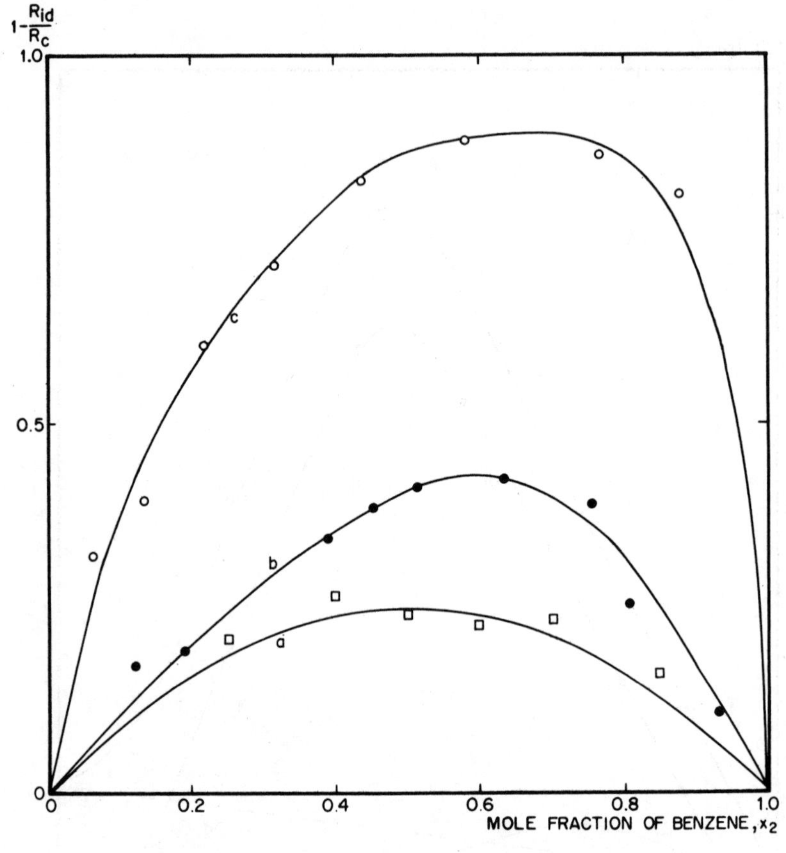

Fig. 4. The function $1\text{-}R_{id}/R_c$ for: (a) benzene-cyclohexane, (b) benzene neopentane, (c) methanol-benzene. Curve (a) has been obtained from vapour-pressure measurements by Scatchard, Wood and Mochel (14).

Here also the agreement is satisfactory, which indirectly supports the applicability of the Cabannes relation to liquid mixtures.

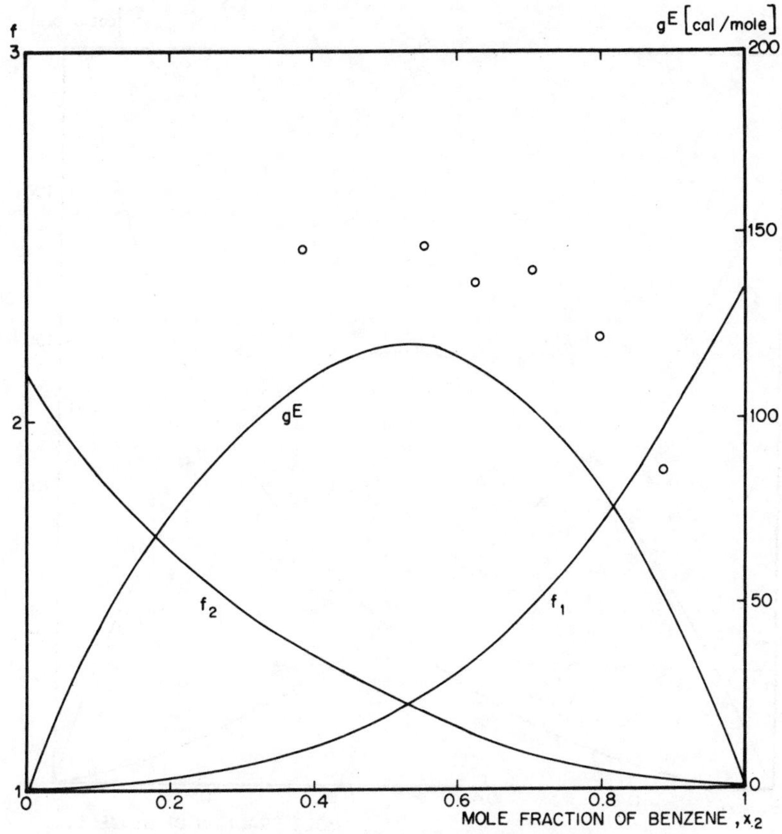

Fig. 5. Activity coefficients and excess Gibbs free energies for neopentane-benzene. The circles have been obtained from vapour-pressure data by Mathot and Desmyter (11) at 0°C, the curves from our light-scattering data at 25°C.

IV. COMPARISON OF THE ANISOTROPIC SCATTERING FACTORS FOR LIQUIDS, VAPOURS AND LIQUID MIXTURES.

As a result of the much larger position correlations between the molecules, the isotropic scattering from a liquid is in general appreciable smaller than from the cor-

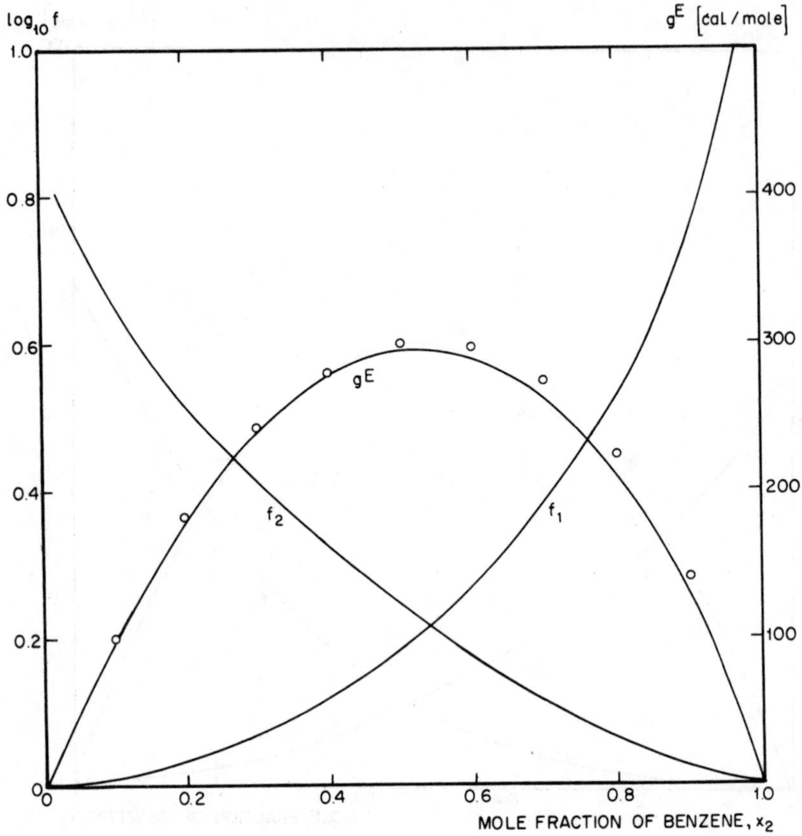

Fig. 6. Activity-coefficients and excess Gibbs-functions for methanol-benzene. Curves: light-scattering data; circles: vapour pressure data by Scatchard and Ticknor (13) (both at 23 °C).

responding vapours. This is illustrated in Table 4, where the values of the molar isotropic Rayleigh factor (3) (i.e. the Rayleigh factor multiplied by the molar volume) for a number of liquids are compared to the values of the same quantity in the vapour phase. The latter were calculated from the expression

$$R_{is}^{v}\ (90°) = \frac{8\pi^4}{\lambda^4}\ \rho<\alpha>^2 , \qquad (29)$$

TABLE 4

Molar Isotropic Scattering Factors in Liquid and Vapour Phase

	$R^{l}_{is,m} \times 10^4$ $\frac{cm^2}{mole}$	$R^{v}_{is,m} \times 10^4$ $\frac{cm^2}{mole}$	$\frac{R^{l}_{is,m}}{R^{v}_{is,m}}$
benzene	5.28	56.24	0.094
toluene	5.58	79.37	0.070
nitrobenzene	5.22	88.14	0.059
carbon disulphide	7.23	40.35	0.18
carbon tetrachloride	4.93	58.25	0.084[5]
cyclohexane	4.61	62.42	0.074
iso-octane	7.62	125.9	0.060[5]
n-hexane	5.85	73.30	0.080
n-octane	6.46	125.9	0.051
n-decane	7.41	192.7	0.038[5]
methyl ethyl ketone	2.81	34.91	0.080[5]

TABLE 5

Molar Anisotropic Scattering Factors in Liquid and Vapour Phase

	$R^{l}_{an,m} \times 10^4$ $\frac{cm^2}{mole}$	$R^{v}_{an,m} \times 10^4$ $\frac{cm^2}{mole}$	$\frac{R^{l}_{an,m}}{R^{v}_{an,m}}$
benzene	8.85	5.42	1.63
toluene	14.0	8.32	1.68
nitrobenzene	62.1	11.5	5.40
carbon disulphide	43.3	14.1	3.07
carbon tetrachloride	0.28	-	-
cyclohexane	0.34	0.90	0.37
iso-octane	0.96	2.46	0.39
n-octane	1.45	4.09	0.35[5]
n-decane	2.27	5.51	0.41
methyl ethyl ketone	0.95	1.72	0.55

derived by Gans (7), in which

$$\langle\alpha\rangle = \frac{1}{3}\,(\alpha_1 + \alpha_2 + \alpha_3) \tag{30}$$

is the mean polarisability of an independently scattering molecule. Data for this quantity have been taken from tables by Stuart (17).

The molar anisotropic scattering factors on the other

hand are of the same order of magnitude for liquids (3) and for vapours. This can be seen from Table 5, where the values of $R^{l}_{an,m}$ and $R^{v}_{an,m}$ are compared for the same liquids. The scattering factors of the vapours were obtained from Gans' expression (7)

$$R^{v}_{an} \quad (90°) = \frac{13}{90} \frac{8\pi^4 \rho \gamma^2}{\lambda^4} \tag{31}$$

using data by Stuart (7) for the molar anisotropy factor, γ.

$$\gamma^2 = (\alpha_1 - \alpha_2)^2 + (\alpha_2 - \alpha_3)^2 + (\alpha_3 - \alpha_1)^2 \tag{32}$$

A similarly striking difference is found in the behavior of the isotropic and the anisotropic part of the Rayleigh factor in liquid mixtures. In Fig. 7 we have plotted both contributions as a function of concentration for the systems methanol-benzene as obtained from our measurements (3) by means of Cabannes relation. Whereas the isotropic contribution shows a maximum, the anisotropic Rayleigh factor is a smoothly varying function of composition. In Fig. 8 we have compared the values of R^{l}_{an} from two different mixtures each consisting of a highly anisotropic compound (nitrobenzene) and a nearly isotropic compound (carbon tetrachloride and cyclohexane). Although the isotropic contributions in the two cases differ almost by an order of magnitude, the anisotropic contributions are practically identical smooth functions of concentration. As illustrated in Fig. 9 a similar behaviour is found comparing $R^{l}_{an,m}$ for mixtures of carbon-di-sulfide with carbon tetrachloride and cyclohexane. These results suggest that anisotropic molecules dissolved in an isotropic liquid behave as far as their anisotropic scattering is concerned in a similar way as anisotropic molecules in the vapour phase. Therefore, it is interesting to compare the values of $R^{l}_{an,m}$ at infinite dilution, viz.

$$R^{(0)}_{an,m} = \left(\frac{\partial R^{l}_{an,m}}{\partial x_2} \right)_{x_2 = 0} \tag{33}$$

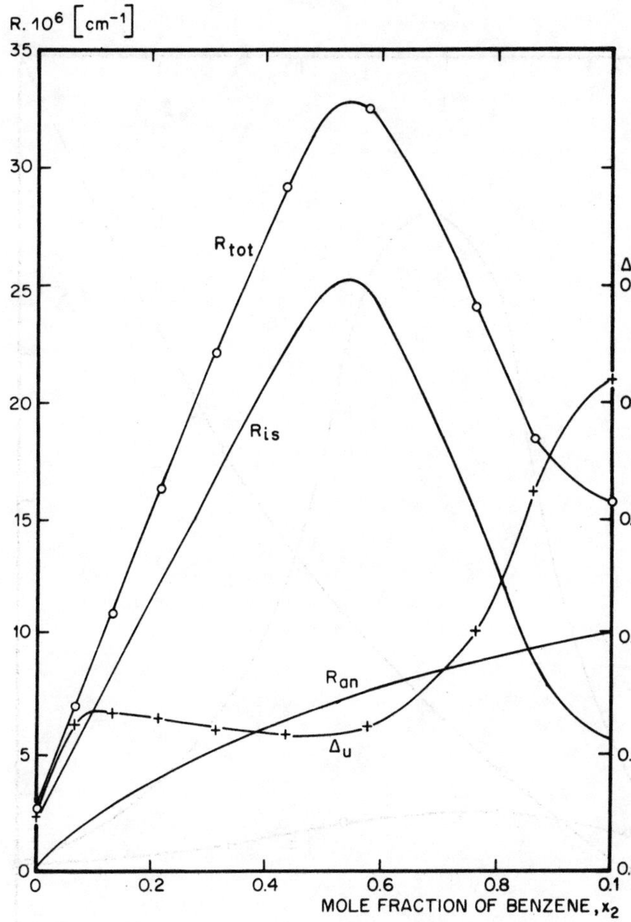

Fig. 7. The total scattering factor R_{tot} , and its isotropic and anisotropic parts, R_{is} and R_{an} for methanol-benzene, as a function of concentration.

with the values, $R^{v}_{an,m}$, in the vapour phase.

In Table 6 we have compared the values of R_{an} for various anisotropic pure liquids, for the corresponding vapours, and for the anisotropic liquids dissolved in near-isotropic solvents at infinite dilution. The ratios of the

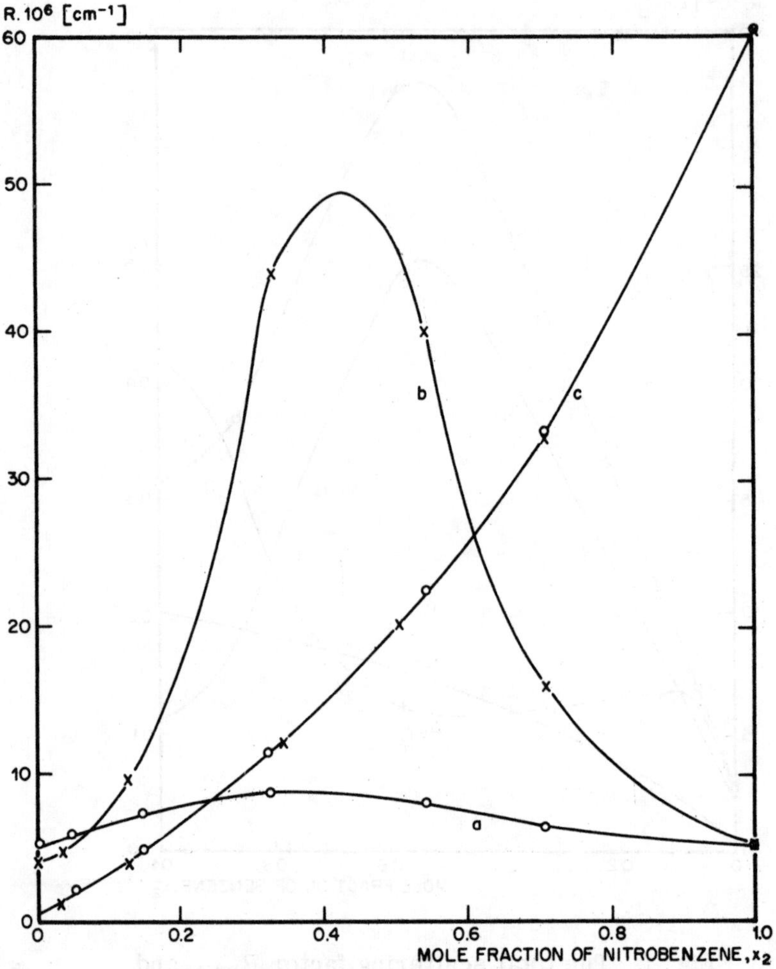

Fig. 8. The isotropic scattering factor for CCl_4-nitrobenzene (a), and for cyclohexane-nitrobenzene (b), and the anisotropic scattering factor for both systems (c), as a function of concentration.

latter two quantities are reasonably well-represented by the equation,

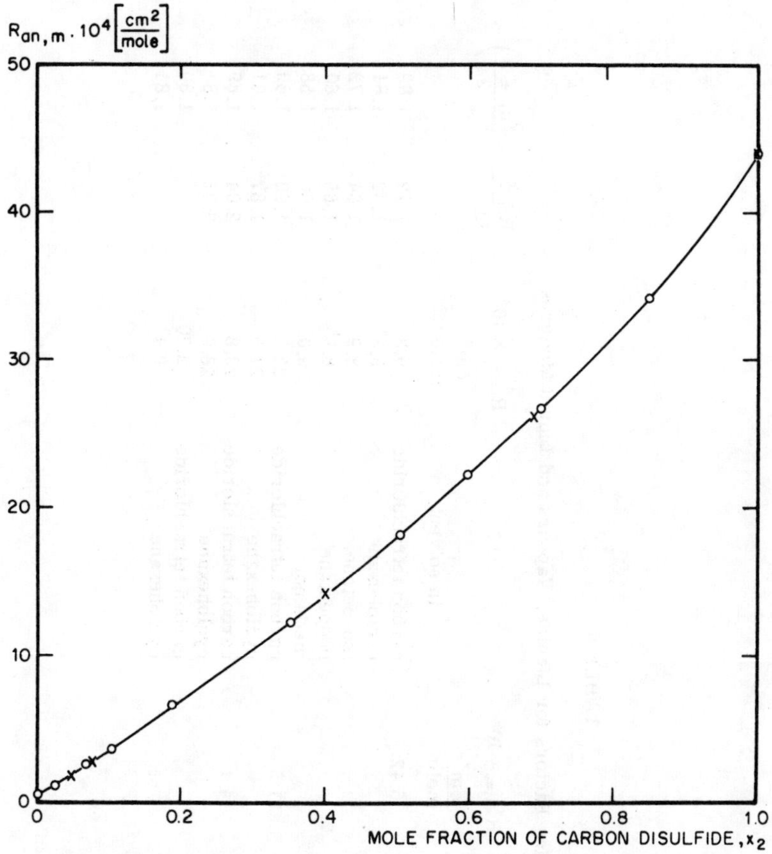

Fig. 9. The molar anisotropic scattering factor for carbon tetrachloride-carbon disulfide (x) and cyclohexane-carbon disulfide (0) as a function of concentration.

$$\frac{R^{(0)}_{an,m}}{R^{v}_{an,m}} = \left(\frac{n_1^2 + 2}{3}\right)^2 \qquad (34)$$

which would be obtained when the liquid mixture is represented as a system of independently scattering anisotropic molecules subjected to an electric field

$$E_i = \frac{1}{3}(n_1^2 + 2) E \qquad (35)$$

TABLE 6

Molar Anisotropic Scattering Factors for Liquids, Vapours and Liquid Mixtures

anisotropic compound	$R^{l}_{an,m} \times 10^4$ $\frac{cm^2}{mole}$	$R^{v}_{an,m} \times 10^4$ $\frac{cm^2}{mole}$	in solvent	$R^{o}_{an,m} \times 10^4$ $\frac{cm^2}{mole}$	$\frac{R^{o}_{an,m}}{R^{v}_{an,m}}$	$\left(\frac{n_1^2+2}{3}\right)^2$
benzene	8.85	5.42	carbon tetrachloride	9.3	1.72	1.89
			cyclohexane	9.8^5	1.82	1.81
			iso-octane	8.9	1.64	1.72
			neopentane	8.9^5	1.65	1.60
			methanol	9.0	1.66	1.58
nitrobenzene	62.1	11.5	carbon tetrachloride	22.9	1.99	1.89
			cyclohexane	21.5	1.87	1.81
carbon disulphide	43.3	14.1	carbon tetrachloride	28.8	2.04	1.89
			cyclohexane	28.9	2.05	1.81
3-methyl-1-butyne	3.11		carbon tetrachloride	2.60		1.89
1, 5-hexadiyne	9.7		cyclohexane	9.4^5		1.81

with E representing the electric field of the incident wave, and n_1 the dielectric constant of the solvent.

REFERENCES

(1) Cabannes, La Diffusion Moleculaire de la Lumiere, Les Presses Universitaire de France 1929, p. 44.

(2) Cabannes, La Diffusion Moleculaire de la Lumiere, Les Presses Universitaire de France 1929, p. 221.

(3) Coumou, D. J., Hijmans, J. and Mackor, E. L., Trans. Faraday Soc. **60**, 2244 (1964).

(4) Coumou, D. J. and Mackor, E. L., Trans. Faraday Soc. **60**, 1726 (1964).

(5) Coumou, D. J., Mackor, E. L. and Hijmans, J., Trans. Faraday Soc. **60**, 1539 (1964).

(6) Einstein, A., Ann. Physik, **33**, 1275 (1910).

(7) Gans, P. J., Ann. Physik, **37**, 881 (1912) and 65, 97 (1921).

(8) Hill, T. L., Statistical Mechanics, McGraw-Hill, 1956, p. 21.

(9) Kirkwood, J. G. and Goldberg, R. J., J. Chem. Phys. **18**, 54 (1950).

(10) Landau, L. D. and Lifschitz, E. M., Statistical Physics, Pergamon, (1958) Ch. XII.

(11) Mathot, V. and Desmyter, J. Chem. Phys. **21**, 782 (1953).

(12) Prins, J. A. and Prins, W., Physica, **22**, 576 (1956), and **23**, (1957).

(13) Scatchard and Ticknor, J. Am Chem. Soc., **74**, 3724 (1952).

(14) Scatchard, Wood, and Mochel, J. Phys. Chem. **43**, 119 (1939), and J. Am. Chem. Soc. **62**, 712 (1940).

(15) Smoluchowski, R., Ann. Physik., **25**, 205 (1908).

(16) Stockmayer, W. H., J. Chem. Phys. **18**, 58 (1950).

(17) Stuart, H. A., Die Struktur des freien Moleküls, Springer Verlag, Berlin (1952), tables 98 and 99.

DISCUSSION FOLLOWING PAPER BY J. HIJMANS

H. L. Frisch: Am I correct in thinking that the usual experimental arrangements are such as to correspond to the case where Eq. (7) is valid rather than (12) ? If so, can you give an example of a practical realization of an experiment in which we must allow for pressure fluctuations? As the critical point of a simple liquid is approached the extra contribution proportional to $\langle (T)^2 \rangle$ should vanish since C_V appears to possess an (infinite) singularity at the critical point.

J. Hijmans: Equations (7) and (12) are equivalent as long as they are not approximated by their first term. But sometimes, i.e. in cases when only the temperature derivative of the refractive index is known, (e.g. Carr and Zimm, J. Chem. Phys. **18**, 1616 (1950)) Eq. (12) is used in the truncated form. This may be dangereous.

J. J. Hermans: Do I understand correctly that the compressibility of all the mixtures investigated was measured as a function of their composition?

J. Hijmans: Yes, in most cases it has been measured. In one or two cases, simple linear extrapolations have been done.

M. Kerker: I should like to corroborate your statement that light scattering can be used to measure vapor pressure lowering. We have carried out light scattering and vapor pressure lowering measurements in aqueous solutions of heteropolyacids, obtaining excellent correlation between the two. (Kerker, Kratohvil, Ottewill and Matijevic, J. Phys. Chem. **67** 1097 (1963)).

R. Stein: Would you interpret the larger values of the anisotropic component in a liquid to that in a gas for carbon disulfide and nitrobenzene as meaning that there is a greater correlation of orientation of neighboring molecules in these liquids?

J. Hijmans: Yes, it looks that way.

R. Gammon: As I understand it, you define the anisotropic part of the scattered light in terms of the depolarization through the Cabannes factor. I would like to comment that one can also describe this part of the scattered light as being inelastic. In recent work done with H. Z. Cummins, reported in Applied Physics Letters, **6**, 171 (1965), on the spectral analysis of the light scattered from pure liquids, we found that essentially all of the depolarized scattered light is inelastically scattered, forming a broad background under the completely polarized Rayleigh (elastic scattering) and Brillouin (Doppler shifted) components. Previous workers in India (1942), the United States (1948) and Russia (1955) had evidence for this but their results were less conclusive.

J. Hijmans: As our experimental arrangement does not allow an analysis of the detailed spectral intensity distribution of the scattered light we have simply "defined" the anisotropically scattered light as the depolarized part of the scattering. I agree that a spectral analysis of the polarized and the depolarized components of the scattering would be very interesting.

M. Goldstein: Mr. Gammon's comment raises a question as to the interpretation usually given to the depolarization of liquids. It is not clear that the interpretation in terms of local order of molecules possessing the same anisotropy they have in the gas phase is consistent with the high degree of spectral broadening. Does this imply a much higher amount of rotational motion than of translational? Perhaps Dr. Pecora can answer this.

J. Hijmans: It is not self-evident that a separation of the scattering from liquids into a part due to density fluctuations and a part due to anisotropy fluctuations can be made under all circumstances. This depends mainly on whether or not the relaxation time for the establishment of orientational equilibrium is short compared to the duration of the orientation fluctuations. This point has been discussed in detail by Landau and Lifshiftz (Electrodynamics of Continuous Media, Sec. 94).

R. Pecora: I see no reason to question the interpretation usually given to the depolarization of light scattered by liquids. A formal theory including an analysis of the frequency shifts has been given by Pecora and Steele (J. Chem. Phys. **42**, 1872 (1965)). This theory shows that the integrated (over all frequency shifts) intensity of the depolarized part of the scattered light is given in terms of the molecular anisotropy (in the liquid) and local orientational correlation factors by the usual formulae.

W. Prins: It seems to me that it would be very interesting to do similar observations on solutions in order to see if the depolarization of the solute scattering also occurs only in the frequency shifted scattering. In this case it probably would be necessary to have the intensity of the solute scattering (due to concentration fluctuations) appreciably higher than the scattering due to density fluctuations. This can be achieved with (polymer) solutions. e.g., by working near the critical consolute temperature T_c . Since the gradient of the osmotic pressure goes to zero at this critical temperature, the Rayleigh line should be sharpened the closer one is to T_c , while at the same time the intensity goes up tremendously. Also, spectral resolution of the scattering in very viscous solutions, gels or glasses should be of interest.

Light Scattering Phenomena Near the Critical Point*

D. McIntyre and A. M. Wims
National Bureau of Standards,
Washington, D.C. 20234

In recent years intensive study of all types of physical phenomena (including electromagnetic scattering) near the critical point of fluid and of non-fluid systems has led to a new understanding of the molecular correlations in this region. A cross-section of the current theoretical concepts of critical phenomena interrelating such diverse phenomena as magnetic susceptibilities near the Curie point and phase separations of fluid systems near their critical points is summarized in the proceedings of a recent conference on critical phenomena (36). Scattering measurements offer the most direct experimental way of determining the correlation function in a fluid system near the critical point, and many experimental scattering studies have been reported.

Measurements of light and x-ray scattering near the critical point have had two main pursuits. For reasons of personal interest and existing experimental convenience these pursuits often do not overlap in the same study. One aim has been to determine the range of molecular interaction in a variety of molecular systems where the long range forces are still relatively weak. This goal was discussed at the last ICES meeting by Debye (16). Since that time many additional systems have been investigated and shown to have ranges of interaction which are in reasonable accord with the expected effective molecular diameters (8, 17, 37, 38, 9, 35).

The other aim has been to theoretically and experimentally determine what correlations exist very near the critical point. The detailed comparison of the various theories and their limitations are reviewed in several theoretical papers of ref. 36. Fortunately the various theoretical developments have been able to yield a functional form for the correlation function so that the theoretical and experimental comparison of the angularly dependent critical opalescence can be made in some semi-quantitative manner. It is customary to present and evaluate the experimental scattering data in the form required by the theory of correlated density fluctuations given by Ornstein and Zernike (O-Z) (34). Green (24) first suggested an alternative correlation function having a long range correlation, and Fisher (23) presented an attractive explicit formulation based on lattice gas models. The effects predicted by the newer theories indicate that a shorter ranged correlation exists very near the critical point. Thus the correlation function for the Ornstein-Zernike theory decays as $(e^{-kr})/(r)$; whereas Fisher's correlation function decays as $e^{-kr}(1/r)^{1+\eta}$, where η is a small constant, ≤ 0.1.

SCATTERING EQUATIONS

The scattering equations are most simply formulated using a one component system. However, the bulk of the experimental measurements of critical opalescence have been made on binary mixtures of simple liquids. To interpret these measurements of scattering near the critical point it is necessary to eliminate the contribution of the density fluctuations from the total scattering. In principle the scattering due to density fluctuations can be evaluated either by independent compressibility measurements (or its optical equivalent), or by calculations based on an additivity relation using the compressibilities of the pure components, or by considering only strong opalescence near the critical temperature (T_c) so that the scattering at higher temperatures is negligible.

Münster and Schneeweiss (27) have presented a rather complete development of the scattering equations both for x-rays and light in two-component systems. They have also related their expressions for the angular dependence of critical opalescence to those of Orstein-Zernike and Debye (15). Considering scattering to occur due to average fluctuations of refractive index (Δn) at different regions $\vec{q}$ and $\vec{q}'$, the scattering intensity (I) can be expressed as a ratio of the incident intensity (I_o),

$$\frac{I(\theta)}{I_o} = \frac{2\pi^2 n^2 (1+\cos^2\theta)}{R^2\lambda^4} \iint \overline{\Delta n\, \Delta n'}\; e^{-i\vec{h}.(q-q')}\, d\vec{q}\, d\vec{q}', \qquad (1)$$

where λ is the wavelength of the incident radiation, R is the distance between the scattering source and obserber, θ is the scattering angle, and $\vec{h}$ is the vector defined as $4\pi/\lambda \sin(\theta/2)(\vec{s}-\vec{s}_o)$. $\vec{s}_o$ and $\vec{s}$ are unit vectors in the directions of the incident and scattered radiation, respectively. By substituting the correlation function, G(r), for the average refractive index changes in a two component system, the expression for the scattering reduces to Eq. 3, where C_2^* is the concentration of component 2 expressed as a ratio of masses, V is the scattering volume and i(h) is a reduced intensity defined in Eq. 2.

$$i(h) = \frac{I(\theta)}{I_o}\, \frac{R^2\lambda^4}{(2\pi n^2)(1+\cos^2\theta)}\, \frac{1}{V(dn/dc)^2} \qquad (2)$$

$$i(h) = C_2^{*2} \int G(r)\, e^{-i\vec{h}\cdot\vec{r}}\, d\vec{r} \qquad (3)$$

For the Ornstein-Zernike correlation function,

$$G(r) = \frac{A\Gamma^{kr}}{r}$$

the Fourier integral can be solved to give Eq. 4.

$$i(h) = \frac{4\pi A}{(k^2+h^2)}\, C_2^{*2} \qquad (4)$$

Thus the reciprocal scattering, $[i(h)]^{-1}$, will, when plotted against h^2, be a set of parallel straight lines. The slope will be characteristic of the local range of forces and the intercept will be characteristic of the thermodynamic state. $1/\kappa$ is proportional to the correlation length. When evaluated explicitly in terms of volume fractions (φ_i) the expression for i(h) becomes Eq. 5, where l is the characteristic length of Debye.

$$i(h) = \frac{C_2^{\,2}}{\varphi_2 \frac{\partial}{\partial \varphi_2}\left(\frac{\pi}{kT}\right) + \varphi_2^{\,2}\left(\frac{l^2}{6}\right) h^2} \qquad (5)$$

Equation 5 gives an explicit thermodynamic equation relating the scattering at zero angle to $(\partial \pi / \partial \varphi_2)$, where π is the osmotic pressure of the solution. Since $(\partial \pi / \partial \varphi_2)$ must become zero at the critical temperature, it is essential to plot the zero angle scattering data as a function of temperature to determine if the curves appear to intersect the temperature axis at the critical temperature. For temperatures not too far away from the critical temperature, an analytic theory will give $[i(0)]^{-1}$ as a linear function of temperature, although Fisher (23) has shown that lattice theories would predict a dependence of $\Delta T^{5/4}$.

Thus, the shape of the scattering curve and the behavior of the activity curves derived from the scattering at zero angle are the important experimental quantities to be derived from scattering measurements only. Since it is known that the major difference between the theories lies in the region of long range correlations, it is of course necessary to get scattering measurements as close as possible to the incident beam. Without these measurements not only will the shape of the scattering curves be falsely interpreted, but also the thermodynamic functions will not be properly extrapolated to the critical temperature which is determined independently by phase separation measurements. There are very few other ways to obtain sufficiently precise data to describe accurately the correlation function and the thermodynamic state near the critical point except by scattering measurements. Unfortunately no system has yet been studied over a sufficiently wide angular range, particularly very small h values, and sufficiently close to the critical temperature to answer unequivocally what exact correlation function is adequate.

CRITICAL OPALESCENCE OF FLUID SYSTEMS

Although solid systems have been studied in recent years, their opalescence has been studied only by x-rays at a considerable temperature (a few degrees) away from the critical temperature. Single component (liquid-gas) condensation experiments have been measured in the past by light scattering and x-ray scattering. Extremely near the critical point ($< 0.01\,°K$) the measurements are difficult to interpret because of the unavoidable existence of a density gradient due to the high compressibility of the gas. Schmidt's data on argon and nitrogen (37, 38) are representative of the recent low angle x-ray scattering work on gases. The ΔT values, $(T - T_c)$, are approximately $0.05°K$ at temperatures of $\sim 150\,°K$. The values of h are still rather high ($\sim 400 \times 10^{-6}\,\text{Å}^{-2}$), and in view of the work reported on binary solutions, the experiments may not be meaningful in observing deviations due to the difference in the predicted long range correlations near the critical point. However, they do clearly show that over the experimental range of h^2 that has been studied the angular dependence of the O-Z theory is followed.

BINARY MIXTURES

The detailed study of the opalescence of a homogeneous liquid mixture just before demixing or separation into two phases is reported, historically, only a few years later than the observations made on gases near their critical points. Early measurements of critical opalescence, extending from the publication of the O-Z theory to the post war years, were very difficult to make. Thus the dependence of the opalescence on

$$h^2 \sim \left(\frac{\sin^2 (\theta)/2)}{\lambda^2} \right)$$

was most easily demonstrated by the change in color in the forward and backward scattering when incident white light was used.

The transverse scattering changes from a dependence on λ^{-4} to a dependence on λ^{-2}. The range of molecular interaction was first estimated by noting the discrepancy between the observed critical temperature (the temperature of phase separation) and the extrapolation of the scattering at a fixed transverse angle. In this respect it is interesting to realize that much of the thinking today about the inadequacy of the O- Z theory is itself based upon considerations of the extrapolation of the zero angle scattering as a function of temperature. Other experimenters measure the depolarization of the scattered light near the critical point. Although this measurement is relatively accurate and simple to make at a fixed scattering angle, the interpretation of the results is very difficult. The onset of multiple scattering occurs at some moderate ΔT away from the critical point in most of the systems chosen, and multiple scattering drastically changes the polarization of the scattered light.

Table 1 characterizes most of the experimental work on binary mixtures that has been published in the last fifteen years. Certainly the experimental results clearly demonstrate the complexity of the experimental problem. In retrospect it appears that most of the work is much more coherent than previously thought. That is, if one favors an interpretation of the results that allows a change in the very strong long range correlation to occur near the critical point ($\Delta T < 0.1$) and to become less dominant away from the critical point, then almost all of the seemingly discordant results from the experiments listed in Table 1 can be explained. The classification of binary mixtures may appear arbitrary, but it has the virtue of keeping the work separated by easily remembered markers. Also it keeps chemical types separated for those chemists, who like the authors, believe that the chemical differences will certainly be exhibited by the detailed temperature and angular dependence of the opalescence.

The Class I mixtures are those of almost non-polar hydrocarbons and halocarbons. They have large positive excess mixing functions: free energies, heats, entropies, and volumes. Probably the next least polar compound would be perfluorotributylamine and isopentane (Class II.A.1). The remaining components in Class II A, B, C are more polar and the alcohols in II D already show the characteristic thermodynamic functions of associated liquids. The aqueous systems in III are sufficiently associated to allow the formation of lower critical solutions at atmospheric pressures. The polymer systems in Class IV are extremely interesting because the study of the coexistence curves and the critical opalescence can lead to molecular information about the polymer that is difficult to determine by any other means. Also, the polymer systems are interesting because they can be studied farther away from the critical point where their large interaction distances are already beginning to show up as large correlations in the angularly dependent critical opalescence. The polydispersity which must exist in any synthetic polymer sample prepared by present polymerization techniques would probably *a priori* exclude these studies from any conclusive test of the basic theory based upon a rigorous analysis valid only for two component systems. However, it is not obvious, until one encounters a "simple" binary mixture in the laboratory, that these "simple" binary mixtures are very difficult to certify as being "pure". There are no "simple" systems listed in Table I which have been studied by two or more independent groups in a systematic manner, starting from the purification and analysis of each component, and leading to the construction of the coexistence curve and scattering functions. In view of the chemical purification procedures described in the literature, it is probably safe to predict that most of the reported binary systems did not have better than 99.5 mole percent purity, and the very best are not better than 99.9 mole percent pure. No doubt the extra investment of labor to purify carefully will show very little new information, but it is not known for certain. The study of MacQueen, Meeks, and Rice (28) has shown what extremely different coexistence curves can be obtained by the introduction of small amounts of water. In view of this work,

Table 1

Angular Measurements of Critical Opalescene in Binary Mixtures

Mixture	Investigation[1]	Δn^2	ΔT m deg[3]	$\Delta h_o^2 \times 10^6$ Å^{-2} [4]	T_c	(Comp.) Critical[5]	Reference
I. Fluorocarbon (1) - Hydrocarbon (2)							
1) perfluoromethylcyclohexane-carbon tetrachloride	L	0.173	20	0.04-4.8	28.31	V_2 56.0	39
2) n-perfluoroheptane-iso-octane	X	0.131	100	100-5000	23.78	X_1 38.5	1, 4, 3, 2
	L) X)	-	8	(0.1-11) (40-10^5)	23.84 23.67	V_2 55.	14
	X	-	7	6-100	23.90	X_2 58.4	5
	L	-	<100	<0.01	23.78	X_2 58.4	26
3) n-perfluoroheptane-n-heptane	L	0.127	80	0.35-10.8	50.04	V_2 54	8
II. Polar-non-polar Systems							
A) Amine (1) - Hydrocarbon (2)							
1) (perfluoro) tributylamine-isopentane	L) X)	0.060	80	(.35-4.8) (20-1000)	22.01	W_2 32.3	17
2) aniline-cyclohexane	L	0.160	40	0.04-11	29.8	W_2 54	7
	L	-	50	0.56-7.6	30.08	W_2 52.72	18
	L	-	2	0.04-4.9	29.60	X_2 55.5	33
	L	-		0.4-4	29.89	V_2 59.4	12
B) Nitrohydroncarbon (1) - hydrocarbon (2)							
1) nitrobenzene-isopentane	L	0.198	-	0.04-5	30.50	W_2 50.0	7
2) nitrobenzene-n-heptane	L	0.167	-	0.35-4.8	19.53	W_2 51.55	6
	X	-	30	(17-6000)	19.53	W_2 51.55	6
3) nitroethane-3-methylpentane	L	0.015	7	0.04-10.8	26.54	W_2 53.4	30

C) Ether (1)-hydrocarbon (2)							
1) β, β' dichlorodiethyl ether-n-decane	L	0.050	40	3.5-10.8	26.04	W_2 39.4	9
	X	-	-	24 - 50			11
2) β, β' dichlorodiethyl ether-n-dodecane	L	0.035	2	0.09-11	33.50	W_2 40.6	12
D) Alcohol (1)-hydrocarbon (2)							
1) methanol-cyclohexane	L	0.097	-	0.04-5	49.2	W_2 69.6	7
	L	-	80	0.56-7.6	45.15	W_2 70	18
2) methanol—n-hexane	L	0.044	100	0.04-5	28.1	W_2 67.4	7
3) phenol—n-heptane	L	0.155	100	0.04-5	35.7	W_2 51.0	7
III. Aqueous Systems							
Water (2) - Other (1)							
1) phenol-water	L	0.209	-	0.04-5	65.0	W_2 66.0	7
2) triethylamine-water	L	0.067	20	0.04-5	12.4	W_2 60.3	7
	L	-	90	0.3-10	18.39	W_2 75.6	13
3) isobutyric acid-water	L	0.060	20	0.04-5	26.5	W_2 62.6	7
4) 2, 6 dimethylpyridine-water	L	0.16	20	0.35-4.7	33.93	W_2 29.94	35
IV. Polymers (1)							
1) polystyrene-cyclohexane	L	0.17	100	0.6-5	(19.2-29.2)	V_1 (6.8-1.25)	19, 20, 21, 22
	L	-	20	0.09-5	22.31	V_1 8.6	32
	X	-	60	5-1000	23.78	V_1 5.0	10
2) polystyrene-ethylcyclohexane	L	-	-	-	52.8	V_1 (6.6-3.6)	28

[1] L = Light Scattering: X = X-ray Scattering.

[2] Δn is the difference in refractive index of the pure components.

[3] ΔT is the difference between the separation temperature of the mixture and the closest temperature at which scattering was measured.

[4] (Δh_o) is the range of angle covered in the experiment $(h = \frac{4\pi}{\lambda_o} \sin\theta/2)$.

[5] X is mole fraction, W is weight fraction, and V is volume fraction at the critical composition.

all work in new binary systems must be based upon a careful evaluation of the effect of probable impurities.

It is encouraging to note in Fig. 1 that the derivative of the activity curve which is proportional to I_0^{-1}, has the same shape for three chemically different binary systems at approximately one-half degree above the critical temperature. All of the systems were normalized to the same value of I_0^{-1} at the critical concentration. The reported critical concentrations were shifted to superimpose the perfluoromethylcyclohexane-carbon tetrachloride mixtures (39), and the β, β' dichlorodiethyl ether-n-decane (35) systems on the same volume fraction (0.403) as that of aniline in the cyclohexane-aniline. The points on either side of the critical concentration were expanded or contracted by

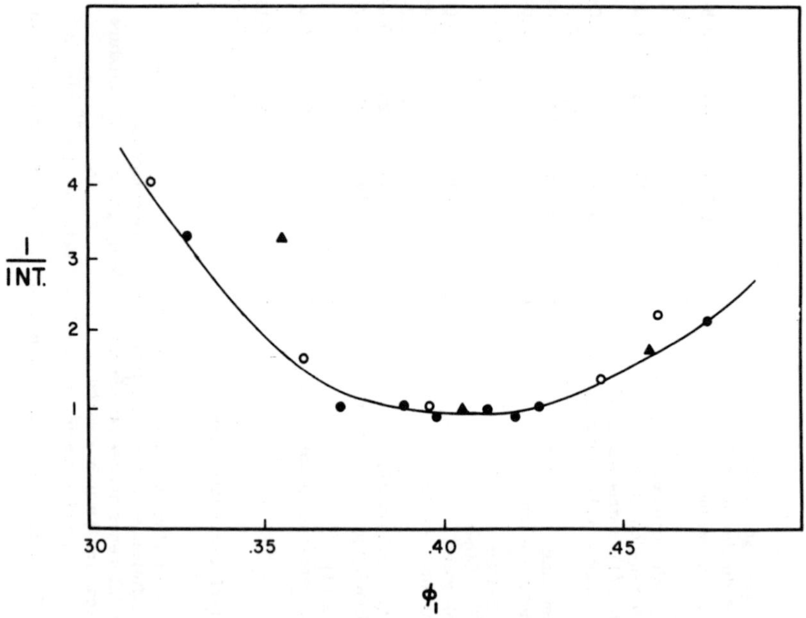

Fig. 1. Reciprocal of scattered light at zero angle (I_0^{-1}) as a function of volume fraction of the first component in the binary systems:

● aniline-cyclohexane

Δ perfluoromethylcyclohexane-carbon tetrachloride, (ref. 39).

O n-decane— β, β' dichlorodiethyl ether, (ref. 35).

the multiplicative factor used in shifting the reported values for the respective volume fractions of perfluoromethyl cyclohexane (0.44) and n-decane (0.28) to that of cyclohexane-aniline (0.403). The volume fraction of perfluoromethyl-cyclohexane, aniline, and n-decane were used because they were all less than 0.5. The volume fraction of aniline was used for normalization since it is the intermediate value. The molar volumes of the components in the cyclohexane-aniline system are also more nearly equal than the components in the other binary systems. It is unfortunate that there are not more concentrations near the critical concentration for the perfluorocarbon system to determine if the curve is more asymmetric than the others. Also it would be interesting to compare not I_o^{-1} but $(\partial \ln a_1)/(\partial \ln \varphi_1)$ for the three systems, particularly at the critical temperature. This necessitates a determination of (dn/dc) and a good knowledge of the absolute scattering at zero angle. Away from the critical point this is an easy task, but near the critical point an accurate measurement becomes extremely difficult due to the intense scattering.

SCATTERING FROM BINARY MIXTURES NOT TOO NEAR THE CRITICAL TEMPERATURE

Figure 2 and Fig. 3 are typical of the scattering data from all binary systems studied to date when the temperature of the measurement is not too near the critical temperature ($\Delta T > 0.1$). Every binary system listed in Table I has been found to obey an O-Z plot of parallel lines in this temperature range. Those cases which have been reported to differ can always be explained either as due to the artifacts of multiple scattering or as due to a solution composition far from the critical concentration. The same types of plots have been found in x-ray scattering for binary systems and even inert gases. Thus it is for a ΔT of less than 0.1°C that the experimental data begin to differ. Unfortunately the experimental difficulties begin to increase below this temperature. There are unsettled questions as to the exact nature of the correlation function over a wide range of h. It appears that for polymers I_o^{-1} may be linear over the whole range of light and x-ray measurements (10), that perfluoro compounds may show either an increase or decrease in slope (17, 5), and that for ether compounds the slope may decrease. However, these details, in addition to the fact that over any small angular range all data follow an O-Z plot, should make it obvious that a gentle curvature may exist in all systems and be the reason for apparent discrepancies between light and x-ray results.

It is gratifying to observe how well the O-Z theory describes all of the data in this temperature range. The

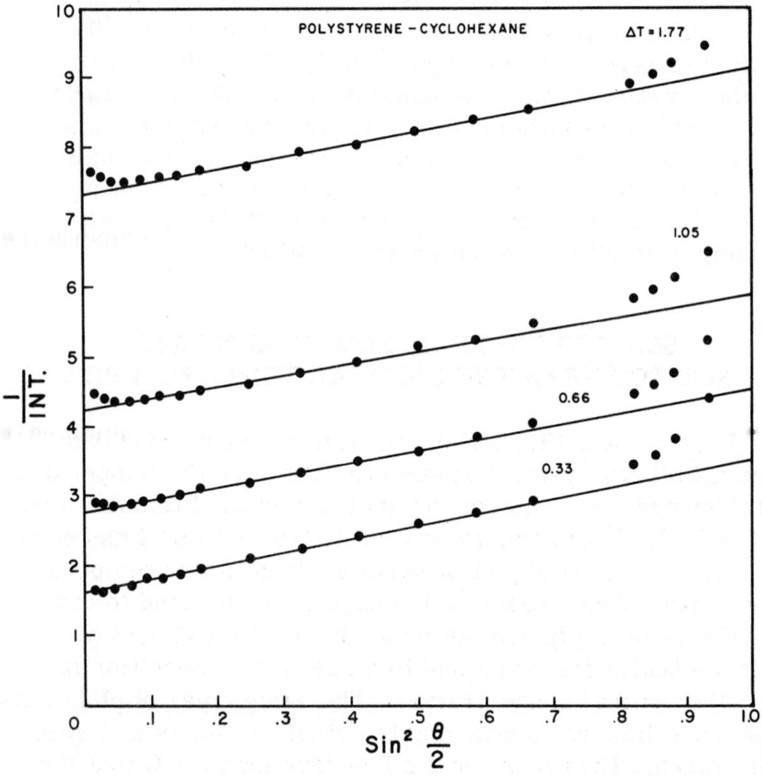

Fig. 2. Reciprocal of scattered intensity in arbitrary units as a function of $\sin^2(\theta/2)$ for a polymer solution $T_c = 22.31\,°C$; at the critical concentration, and $\lambda = 546$ nm; (ref. 32).

fact that for different mixtures the plots of $1/I_o$ (Fig. 4) in this range can be made to intersect close to the phase separation temperature also makes it probable that there is no significant long range correlation which is being completely overlooked by the lack of measurements at h_o values below 0.04.

Only Brady's results (1, 4, 3, 2) far away from the critical temperature add any addtitional molecular information. No other analogous x-ray experiments using other systems have been performed with concentrations differing greatly from the critical concentration. However, his discovery of clusters existing in critical mixtures away from the critical concentration and several degrees above the critical temperature is sufficiently important to warrant further studies with other systems.

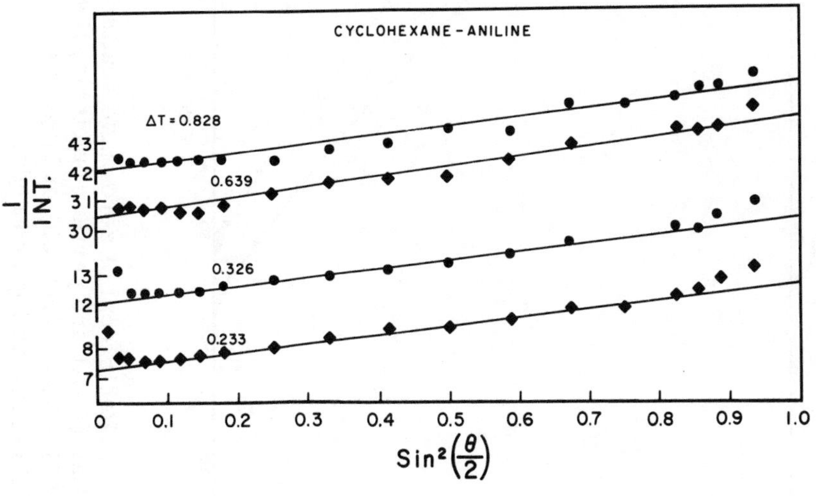

Fig. 3. Reciprocal of scattered intensity in arbitrary units as a function of $\sin^2 (\theta/2)$ for cyclohexane-aniline, T_c = 29.60 °C, at the critical concentration, 546 nm; (ref. 33).

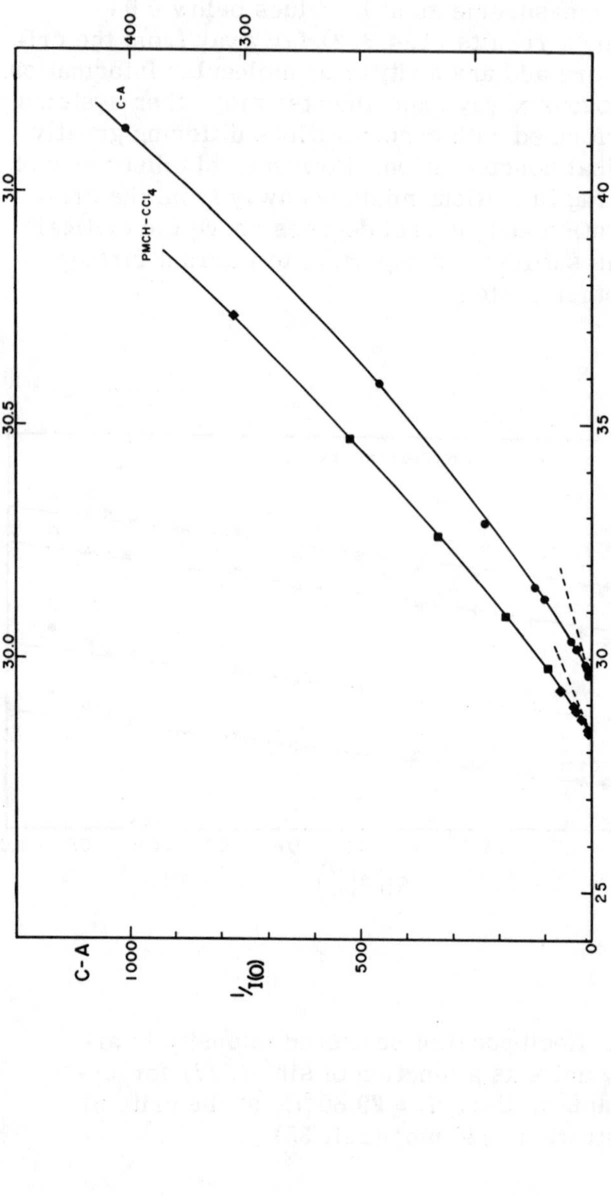

Fig. 4. Reciprocal of zero angle scattering (I_o^{-1}) for cyclohexane-aniline (C-A) and perfluoromethylcyclohexanecarbon tetrachloride (PMCH-CCl_4) (ref. 39) at large ΔT. C-A on left and bottom axes; PMCH-CCl_4 on top and right.

SCATTERING VERY NEAR THE CRITICAL TEMPERATURE

Equation 3 explicitly states the dependence of scattering at zero angle on $(dn/dc)^2$, $1/\lambda^4$, and the correlation function, G(r).

Equation 5 expresses the same result in more readily understood thermodynamic terms, where h is zero. Since the scattering must become extremely large at some small distance from the critical point, where $(\partial/\partial_c)(\pi/kT)$ is zero, and since the problem of multiple scattering will at some point begin to dominate, it is experimentally necessary to reduce the repeated scattering of primary scattered light to the primary scattering itself. There are two methods of minimizing this correction and one method to eliminate the correction. The multiple scattering can be avoided by making x-ray measurements, or reduced by using either mixtures with small (dn/dc), or cells of small path length. Each has disadvantages and advantages.

LOW ANGLE X-RAY SCATTERING

The x-ray method avoids the multiple scattering, but also avoids the possiblility of measuring the scattering at low h_o values. At its most refined instrumental development it barely overlaps the largest light scattering h_o value. Thus, it is unsuitable for any conclusive studies aimed at an experimental demonstration of the form of the long-range correlation. The data of Brady (3) and Brumberger (6) are significant, however, because they demonstrate the existence of an inaccurate extrapolation of I_o^{-1} to the separation temperature at low ΔT values ($< .03$), in a technique where multiple scattering is always known to be absent. Whether the very sharp levelling off of the I_o^{-1} plot is entirely due to the difference in the decay of the long range correlation is not known at the present time. It may represent a mixed function of a smoothly decreasing slope due to higher moments of a correlation function and a combined long range correlation.

SMALL dn/dc

To perform the light scattering measurements necessary to examine any long range correlation function very near the critical point requires both a small dn/dc and a small path length in order to eliminate multiple scattering. Chow (7) recognized the problem and believed that he had partially eliminated it. His work on aqueous mixtures (triethylamine-water, and isobutyric acid-water) is in agreement with later work on other mixtures, but his work on cyclohexane-aniline is now known to be almost completely obscured by multiple scattering. Chu (9, 12) has attempted to avoid the multiple scattering by selecting mixtures of very low dn/dc. His particular choice of mixtures allows a maximum advantage of reducing the scattering by 10 to 20 times at the same thermodynamic state. This advantage is somewhat diminished by the necessity of working within one-half degree of T_c before reliable data for the concentration fluctuations are obtained. Also the choice of mixture is limited. Finally the turbidity does increase so that the optical path, τl, where τ is the turbidity and l is the path length, becomes comparable to unity in 1 cm cells. Chu (9) has shown the angular dependence of the n-decane-ether system to follow the O-Z theory. His results are not reported at very low temperatures or low angles so that his data can not differentiate the presence of a decreased long range correlation compared to the O-Z theory. Chu (12) has also chosen a similar mixture, n-dodecane-ether, and examined the scattering from this mixture very close to the critical temperature. The results indicate a gradual bending of the O-Z plots towards the origin beginning at angles of thirty to forty degrees, and persisting at temperatures forty millidegrees from the critical temperature. An explanation for such a large angular difference between two mixtures differing only in the replacement of n-decane by n-dodecane is not clear at this time. Preliminary measurements in our laboratory of the scattering from a critical mixture of nitroethane-3-methylpentane within a few millidegrees of the critical temperature do not show a large bend in the scattering curve.

Since this mixture has an even lower difference in refractive index from the hydrocarbon-ether mixtures discussed above, it would appear that there are some unexpected chemical effects in the dodecane-ether mixture and perhaps other long chain compounds.

SMALL-PATH LENGTHS

Several years ago in an examination of the scattering from polymer solutions, we sought to avoid the multiple scattering by designing a series of cells to allow scattering measurements to be made at path lengths of 2, 1, 0.5, and 0.1 mm. Figure 5 shows a schematic diagram of the short path length cells. Several experiments were made with these cells to find out what artifacts were introduced by multiple scattering near the critical temperature. The cells were made with optical flats; the external fluid in the cylinder was chosen to closely match the quartz, and the fluid was carefully cleaned to eliminate dirt. The angular refraction corrections were easily calculated and were less than one percent since the angles greater than 65° to the normal were not measured. Since the scattering beam was never greater than 0.25 mm, and the field of view of the phototube was made only large enough to view the entire scattering volume, the cells were used only when large opalescence was present. The scattering calibration and geometry is discussed in detail elsewhere (31, 29).

The advantages of small path length cells are that all mixtures can in principle be measured. The cells are designed to rotate in order to allow measurements to be made at most angles. For the best precision it is advisable to leave the cell fixed in one position for one series of measurements. The problem of precision arises in measurements at low angles, less than 20°, where imperfections in the flat quartz windows cause large scattering. This scattering limits low angle measurements to strongly scattering systems. One unusual difficulty arose when measurements of the separation temperature of a cyclohexane-aniline mixture at the critical concentration were attempted in the 0.1

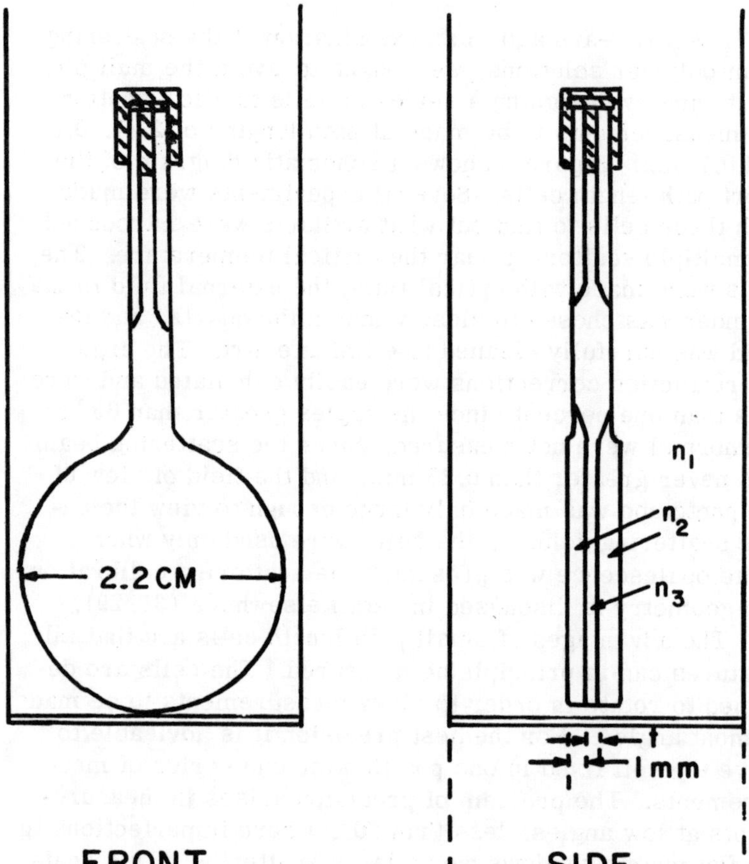

Fig. 5. Two side views of quartz light scattering cells having path lengths, t, of 2, 1, 0.5, and 0.1 mm.

mm cell. The separation temperature of the mixture in the cell was definitely higher than previously observed in larger cells and had a different opalescent behavior. Since these phenomena persisted after repeated rinsings with the critical mixture, the experiments with cyclohexane-aniline in the 0.1 mm cell had to be abandoned. Contrarily, measurements with the polystyrene-cyclohexane showed no difficulties. Several possible explanantions of surface effects particularly in the presence of polar constituents are possible, but the use of such very small cells for the study of critical phenomena with polar constituents must be examined carefully for each system.

The three most studied critical mixtures have high refractive index differences. The fluorocarbon-hydrocarbon mixtures have large refractive index differences, but they are desirable because of their very low polarity and unusually high chemical stability. Cyclohexane-aniline, which has perhaps had the most extensive study of its coexistence curve, has about the same refractive index difference. Also the polystyrene-cyclohexane system which is a binary mixture of the most widely characterized and readily available polymer has a large (dn/dc).

In Fig. 6 the scattering measurements of a critical concentration of polystyrene-cyclohexane are plotted against $\sin^2(\theta/2)$ for the three different wavelengths of light isolated from a mercury arc by filters. The cylindrical light scattering cell was one centimeter in diameter. The temperature is sufficiently removed from the critical temperature to minimize the dominant long range correlations, which might appear strongly near the critical temperature. The results strikingly demonstrate the qualitative aspects of multiple scattering, when the scattering function is mildly dependent on angle. The dangers in interpreting conformity or nonconformity with the predicted O-Z behavior are self-evident. Zero slopes and even negative slopes are possible. Interestingly, the increase of the zero angle scattering intensity due to the wavelength $(1/\lambda^4)$ change is calculated to be only a factor of five. Also, the increase in multiple scattering at these scattering intensities has an effect of inserting a maximum in the scattering curves. The maximum

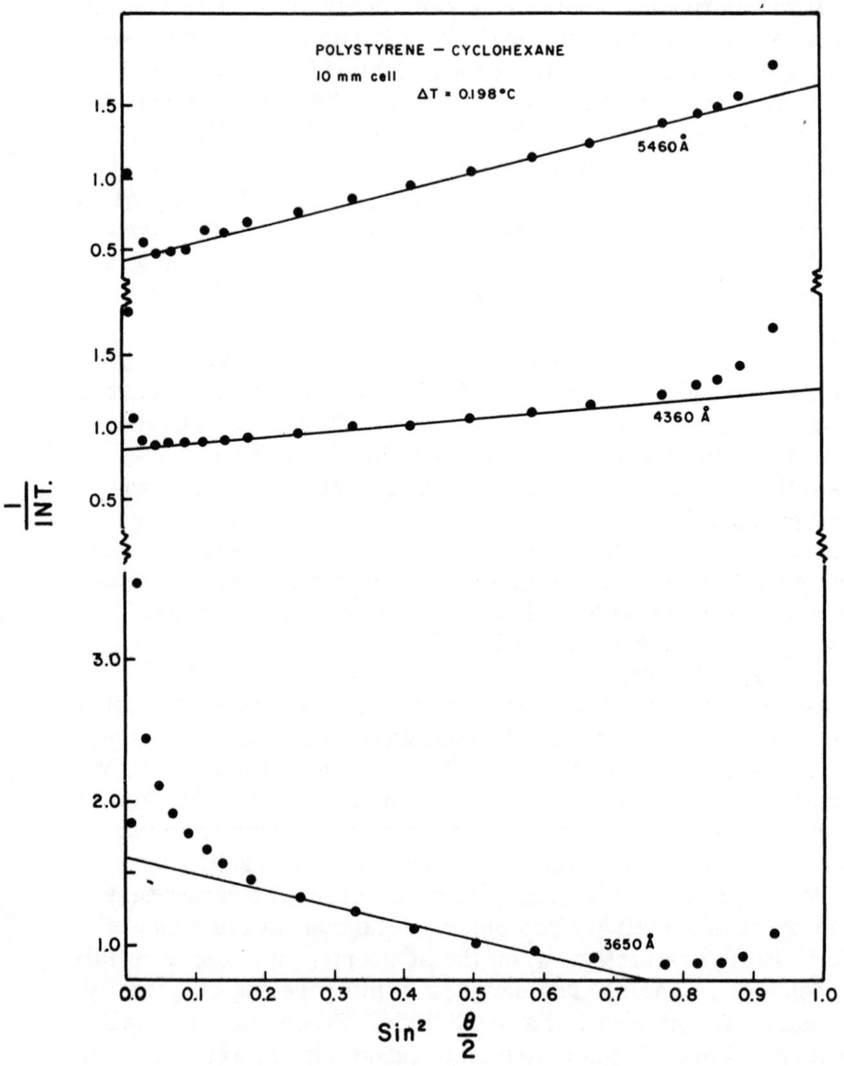

Fig. 6. Reciprocal of the angular scattering intensity of a critical concentration of polystyrene-cyclohexane as a function of wavelength, at a fixed temperature in a 1 cm cell; (ref. 33).

apparently moves towards the back scattering angles.

Fig. 7 shows the scattering measurments from the same critical concentration in the same cell at a temperature very close to the critical temperature.

A large forward scattering component begins to appear below 100 mdeg. This effect was observed and discussed earlier (32). At that time it was impossible to decide unequivocally whether this effect was due to the

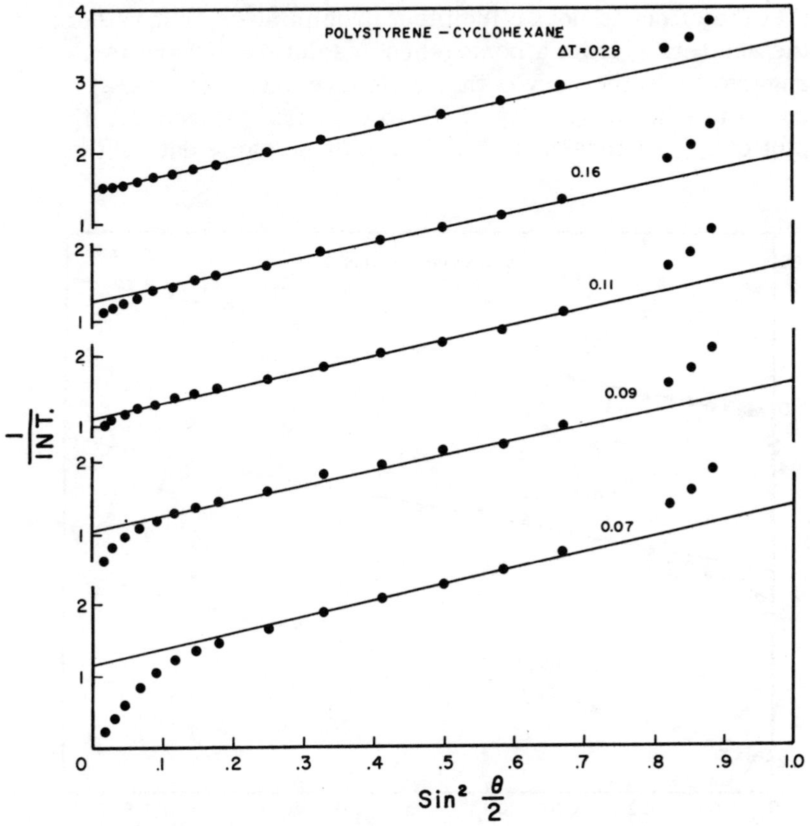

Fig. 7. Reciprocal of the angular scattering intensity for the same critical concentration of polystyrene-cyclohexane at lower temperatures in a 1 cm cell at 546 nm; (ref. 32 and unpublished work of authors).

scattering from a homogeneous solution or a spurious effect due to an unexpected precipitation of higher molecular weight components in a necessarily polydisperse polymer. The same effect can be observed in the simple binary mixture, cyclohexane-aniline, and the data are shown in Fig. 8. The cell is again one centimeter in diameter. Since it was possible to put the polymer solution in a 0.1 mm cell the scattering of the same solution used in the 1 cm cell was measured near the critical point. The results plotted in Fig. 9 clearly show that the effect is not an incipient precipitation, but rather the scattering from a homogeneous solution. There is a suggestion in the curves that the curve begins to change curvature in the vicinity of 10-15 degrees. Moreover, the plot of I_o^{-1}, expressed as $1/\tau$, for these same data shows

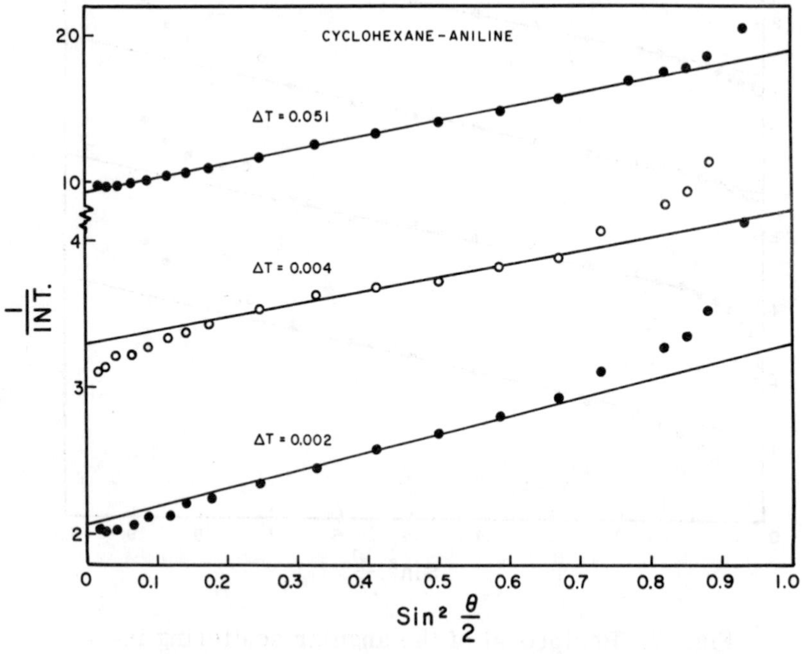

Fig. 8. Reciprocal of the angular scattering intensity at 546 nm of a critical concentration of cyclohexane-aniline in a 1 cm path length cell near the critical temperature; (ref. 33).

in Fig. 10 a clearcut inability to extrapolate adequately to the critical temperature.

It is unfortunate that the establishment of a plot like Fig. 10 is difficult when the scattering is high. But when the optical distance, τl, remains less than 0.1 as is the case with a 0.1 mm cell, some corrections like those for simple attenuation can be applied. Such a correction is applied in Fig. 10, but it is naturally arbitrary and completely avoids the difficult problem of multiple scattering. Figure 11 shows the scattering results for cyclohexane-aniline in a 0.5 mm cell. As was mentioned earlier, the 0.1 mm cell unfortunately could not be used for cyclohexane-aniline so that the extrapolation of the zero-angle scattering to the critical temperature can not be as forcefully discussed. However, the angular patterns in Fig. 11 show the elimination of the large

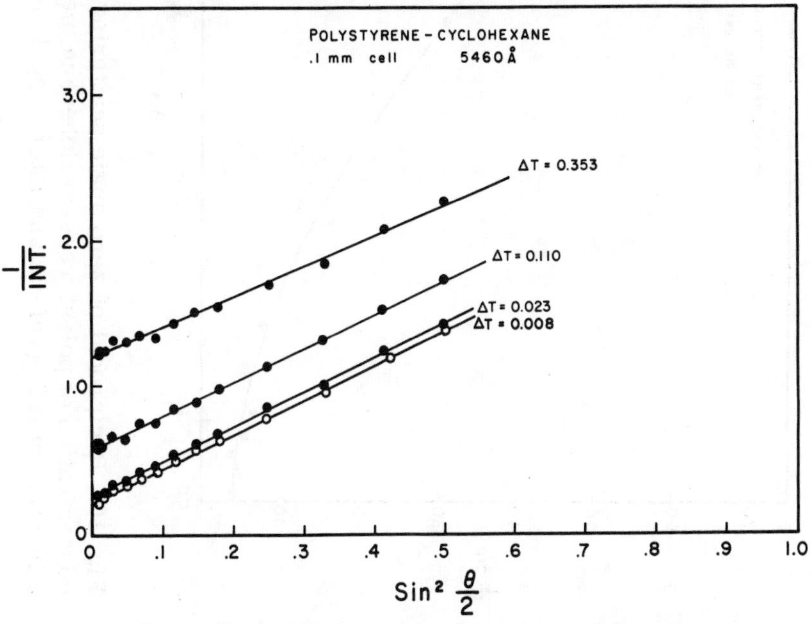

Fig. 9. Reciprocal of the angular scattering intensity at 546 nm from the same critical concentration of polystyrene-cyclohexane shown in Fig. 7, very near the critical temperature; (ref 32).

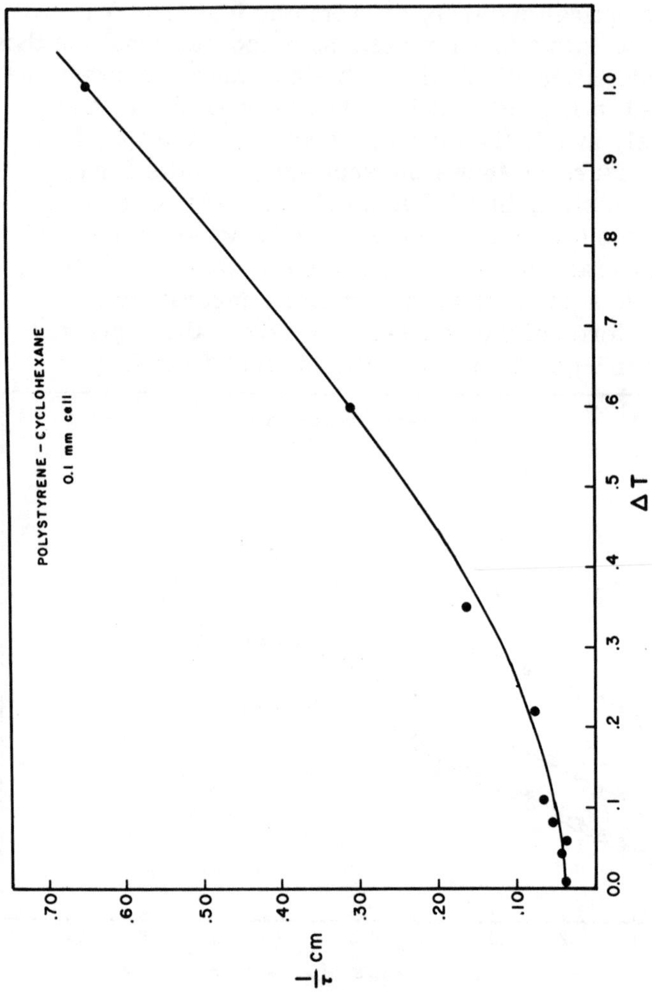

Fig. 10. Reciprocal of zero angle scattering at 546 nm for the critical concentration of polystyrene-cyclohexane measured in a 0.1 mm cell as a function of ΔT; (ref. 32 and later unpublished work of authors).

downward bend in Fig. 8, but there is a strong indication of negative deviations below 10-15 degrees of angle in an enlarged scale.

There is a reasonable explanation of these phenomena in terms of the recent theories of the correlation function near the critical point. If it is assumed that the predicted difference in the long range correlation does occur near the critical point, then the angular curves shown above demonstrate that it occurs below 10-15 angular degrees in a drastic form. Therefore, the plots of I_0^{-1} do not extrapolate properly because the intense forward scattering is not measured. It is tempting to suggest that the measured scattering from a primary scattering function that is intensely peaked in the forward direction would be smoothed due to the multiple scattering. This repeated scattering has the

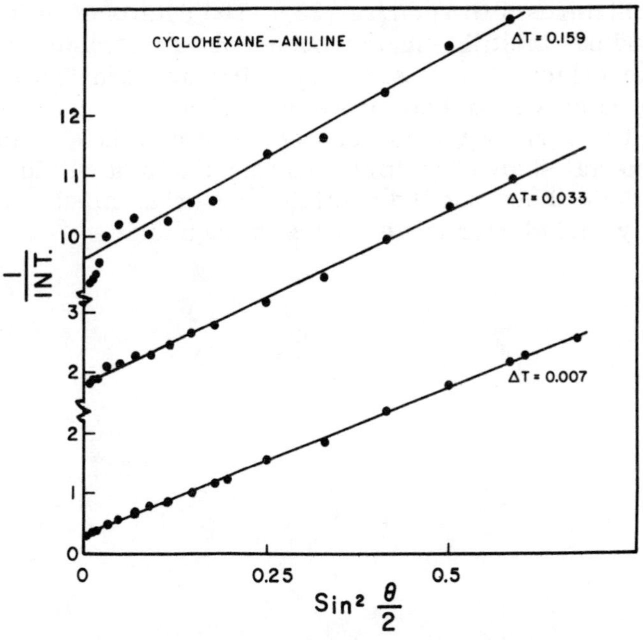

Fig. 11. Reciprocal of the angular scattering intensity at 546 nm of cyclohexane-aniline in a 0.5 mm cell near the critical temperature; (ref. 33).

experimental appearance of a more gradual curvature which appears farther back in scattering angle. Preliminary results of measurements of the perfluoroheptane-isooctane mixture at low angles have been reported by Lundberg (26). His results indicate a very steep scattering curve below one degree of angle. These results tend to make the qualitative aspects of all the scattering measurements near the critical temperature cohere in terms of the newer theories. Further investigations that scrupulously avoid multiple scattering will no doubt lead to quantitative details which do not exist now. But Lundberg's results clearly show what has heretofore been implied by the other studies.

However, there are no binary mixtures that possess all of the desirable qualitities of the critical mixture. The question of conceivable density gradients in gases and binary mixtures still remains (25). The details of technique and purity still remain troublesome on occasion, but an extension of some of the experimental techniques to other problems should not prove too difficult. Once the quantitative form of the correlation function is known, the experimental study of multiple scattering in other fields may be helped because the multiple scattering effects are so easily varied over large orders of magnitude.

REFERENCES

(1) Brady, G. W., J. Chem. Phys., **32**, 45 (1960).

(2) Brady, G. W., J. Chem. Phys., **40**, 2747 (1964).

(3) Brady, G. W. and Frisch, H. L., J. Chem. Phys., **35**, 2234 (1961).

(4) Brady, G. W. and Petz, J. I., J. Chem. Phys., **34**, 332 (1961).

(5) Brady, G. McIntyre, D., Myers, M., and Wims, A., Proceedings of Conference on Low Angle X-ray Scattering, Syracuse, 1965.

(6) Brumberger, H. and Farrar, A. C., Proceedings of the Interdisciplinary Conference on Electromagnetic Scattering, Pergamon Press, 1963, p. 403. Light Scattering results, ref. 36 in review by H. Brumberger.

(7) Chow, Q., Proc. Roy. Soc., **224A**, 90 (1954).

(8) Chu, B., J. Am. Chem. Sci., **86**, 3557 (1964).

(9) Chu, B., J. Chem. Phys., **41**, 226 (1964).

(10) Chu, B., J. Chem. Phys., **42**, 426 (1965).

(11) Chu, B., J. Chem. Phys., **42**, 2293 (1965).

(12) Chu, B., Proceedings of the Conference on Phenomena Near the Critical Point, Washington, 1965, ed. M. Green.

(13) Chu, B. and Kao, W. P., Can. J. Chem., **43**, 1803 (1965).

(14) Chu, B., Pallesen, M., Kao, W.P, Andrews, D. E., and Schmidt, P. W., private communication.

(15) Debye, P., J. Chem. Phys., **31**, 680 (1959).

(16) Debye, P., Proc. Interdisciplinary Conference on Electronmagnetic Scattering, Pergamon Press, New York, 1963, p. 393.

(17) Debye, P., Caulfield, D. and Bashaw, J. J. Chem. Phys., **41**, 3051 (1964).

(18) Debye, P., Chu, B., and Kaufman, H., J. Chem. Phys., **36**, 3373 (1962).

(19) Debye, P., Coll, H., and Woermann, D., J. Chem. Phys., **32**, 939 (1960).

(20) Debye, P., Coll, H. and Woerman, D., J. Chem. Phys., **33**, 1746 (1960).

(21) Debye, P., Chu, B. and Woerman, D., J. Chem. Phys., **36**, 1803 (1962).

(22) Debye, P., Woerman, D., and Chu, B., J. Poly. Sci., **1A**, 255, (1963).

(23) Fisher, M., J. Math. Phys., **5**, 944 (1964).

(24) Green, M. S., J. Chem. Phys., **33**, 1403 (1960).

(25) Lorentzen, H. L., Proc. Conf. on Phenomena Near the Critical Point, April 1965.

(26) Lundberg, J., private communication.

(27) Munster, A. and Schneeweiss, Ch., Z. f. Physik, Chemi NF, 37, 369 (1963).

(28) MacQueen, J. T., Meeks, F. R. and Rice, O. K., J. Phys. Chem., **65**, 1925 (1961).

(29) McIntyre, D., J. Res. Natl. Bur. Std. (U.S.) **68A**, 87 (1964)

(30) McIntyre, D., Hynne, F., Wims, A., preliminary results.

(31) McIntyre, D. and Doderer, G., J. Res. Natl. Bur. Std. (U.S. **62**, 153 (1959).

(32) McIntyre, D., Wims, A. and Green, M., J. Chem. Phys., **37**, 3019 (1962).

(33) McIntyre, D., Wims, A. and MacQueen, J., this report to be published in detail later.

(34) Ornstein, L. S. and Zernike, F., Proc. Acad. Sci., Amsterdam, **17**, 793 (1914).

(35) Pancirov, R. and Brumberger, H., J. Am. Chem. Soc., **86**, 3562 (1964).

(36) Proceedings of the Conference on Phenomena in the Neighborhood of Critical Points, April 1965, to be published by the National Burear of Standards.

(37) Thomas, J. E., and Schmidt, P. W., J. Chem. Phys., **39**, 2506 (1963).

(38) Thomas, J. E. and Schmidt, P. W., J. Am, Chem. Soc., **86**, 3554 (1964).

(39) Zimm, B. H., J. Phys. Chem., **54**, 1306 (1950).

DISCUSSION FOLLOWING PAPER BY D. McINTYRE

J. J. Hermans: The Ornstein-Zernike result for the intensity I becomes infinite when θ and ΔT become zero. The deviation from the straight line when $(1/I)_{\theta=0}$ is plotted again ΔT is in agreement with the expectation that the actual intensity remains finite. What basis do we have for the belief that this deviation should not be observed in the temperature range examined? Is it worthwhile to study mixtures of strongly polar molecules, where the range of the molecular forces is greater?

D. McIntyre: My understanding of the theories suggests that the scattering at the critical point be infinite. There might be experimental problems in its demonstration. It would be necessary to avoid attenuation and multiple scattering, while still maintaining a cell which has dimensions larger than the correlation distances. I think that both the magnitude of the deviation and the scattering intensity at which the curvature appears in our results tend to preclude this problem. It might appear very close to the critical temperature, but, even then, on the scale of $(1/I)_{\theta=0}$ it might not be evident.

R. K. Bullough: One explanation is that the optical theory breaks down. The correlation lengths become equal to the scattering volume and the optical theory collapses. However I want to show tomorrow that there is some doubt about the precise form of the functions we have variously called h^2, s^2 or n^2. I shall show tomorrow that one alternative form of this quantity is not zero at $\theta = 0$ and I does not diverge at the critical point.

Light Scattering and Small-Angle X-Ray Scattering of a Binary Liquid Mixture, N-Decane–B, B′ Dichloroethyl Ether

B. Chu
Department of Chemistry, University of Kansas
Lawrence, Kansas

ABSTRACT

When a binary liquid mixture is in the neighborhood of its critical mixing point, the osmotic work necessary to create large composition fluctuations becomes very small, zero in the critical mixing point itself. The composition fluctuations in turn produce corresponding fluctuations in the refractive index. Hence, the system is no longer optically homogeneous and it scatters light very strongly. This is the so-called critical opalescence which has been the subject of a number of recent studies. Reviews on both theory (13, 14) and experiment (3) have been presented elsewhere.

The purpose of this article is to investigate the scattering behavior of a two-component system, normal decane and β, β' dichloroethyl ether (2) over large ranges of s/λ (6), ($s = 2 \sin(\theta/2)$, λ = wave length in the medium) and over large temperature distances, including measurements at relatively small values of

s/λ and very near the critical solution temperature in the one phase region.

THEORY

Ornstein and Zernike (15, 16) developed one of the first fluctuation theories in which they stressed the importance of correlation. Among the more recent theoretical treatments, the Debye theory (9, 10) provides an excellent representation of experimental facts. Yet, we have reasons (7) to believe that, although the Debye theory works very well at intermediate temperature distances, the classical theory is likely to break down at very small temperature distances from the critical solution temperature. There are two interesting aspects to this problem. On the one hand, light scattering measurements at small values of s/λ and very near the critical point shall give us an experimental demonstration on the breakdown of the classical theory, and thus, one may obtain from the deviations proper boundary conditions for better theoretical models. On the other hand, scattering measurements by means of both light and X-rays over large ranges of s/λ and at intermediate temperature distances, where the Debye theory holds, shall enable us to get additional information on the nature of molecular interactions in binary liquid mixtures.

In putting the concepts of Debye (9, 10, 12) into quantitative form, an equation for light scattering from a critical binary liquid mixture in the one phase region can be formulated in the form:

$$I(\theta) \cong I_d(\theta) + I_c(\theta)$$

$$= I_o \frac{4\pi^2 V}{\lambda^4 r^2} \frac{1+\cos^2\theta}{2} \left[k^*T\beta\left(\frac{\rho}{n}\frac{\partial n}{\partial \rho}\right)^2 + \left(\left(\frac{c}{n}\frac{\partial n}{\partial c}\right)^2 \Big/ \left\{ \phi_2 \left[\frac{\partial}{\partial \phi_2}\left(\frac{P}{k^*T}\right)\right] + \frac{\phi_2^2}{k^*T}\left(\frac{X_{11}}{\omega_1^2} + \frac{X_{22}}{\omega_2^2} - 2\frac{X_{12}}{\omega_1\omega_2}\right) \right\} \right) \right] \quad (1)$$

where $I(\theta)$ is the intensity of light scattered at an angle θ

(between primary and secondary ray) at a large distance r from a scattering volume V, I_o is the primary intensity, I_d and I_c are scattered intensities due to density and concentration fluctuations, respectively, λ is the wave length of the light in the medium, k* is the Boltzmann constant, T is the absolute temperature, β is the compressibility, ρ is the density, n is the index of refraction, c is the concentration of the second component, ω_i is the volume occupied by molecule i, and the symbol X_{ij} represents a factor of the form:

$$X_{ij} = \int (1 - \frac{\sin ksr}{ksr}) \quad e_{ij} \quad (r) \ d\tau$$

in which e_{ij} are the three intermolecular pair potentials, $k = (2\pi/\lambda)$, and $d\tau$ is an element of volume. The integration is performed from the "point of contact" of the two molecules to infinity. Equation 1 is the generalized Debye scattering formula for binary liquid mixtures. It is not explicit that we demand a direct linear proportionality between the reciprocal of the extrapolated zero-angle scattered intensity due to composition fluctuations, $1/I_c(0)$, and the temperature distance from the critical solution temperature, $T-T_c$. In practice, we often take $\phi_2 [\partial/\partial \phi_2 (P/kT)] = \phi_2^2 [\Omega / k^*T_c - \Omega / k^*T)]$ with Ω as an averaged cohesive energy density. Then, the reduced intensity after correction for density fluctuations, $(I-I_d)/(I_{max}-I_d)$, has the form:

$$\left(\frac{I-I_d}{I_{max}-I_d}\right)^{-1} = 1 + \frac{1}{(\tau - 1)\ \Omega} \left(\frac{X_{11}}{\omega_1^2} + \frac{X_{22}}{\omega_2^2} - 2\ \frac{X_{12}}{\omega_1 \omega_2}\right) \qquad (2)$$

where $\tau = T/T_c$, and I_{max} is the scattered intensity for s= 0. Eq. 2 is very useful for studying the angular dissymmetry of the critical opalescence in binary liquid mixtures. The formula holds for light scattering as well as for small-angle scattering of X-rays.

In a strongly opalescent region, the contribution from density fluctuations becomes negligible. Then, we have $(I-I_d)/(I_{max}-I_d) \cong (I/I_{max})$. The density term, I_d, is usually negligible for angular dissymmetry studies. The approximation becomes questionable only when we want to determine the temperature dependence of the extrapolated zero-angle scattered intensity over large temperature distances. Since the calculated critical solution concentration, $(\phi_2)_{crit} = 1/[1 + (\omega_2/\omega_1)]$, (9) often deviates from the observed value, it is reasonable to expect that the expression $[1/I_c\ (0)] =$ constant $(T-T_c)$ is only approximately correct. This approximation applies in the same sense as to the theory of van der Waals. In developing sin ksr in powers of ksr, we have for small values of ks (or s/λ) the approximation:

$$\left(\frac{I}{I_{max}}\right)^{-1} = 1 + \frac{4\pi^2}{6}\,\frac{l^2}{\tau-1}\left(\frac{s}{\lambda}\right)^2 = 1 + \frac{4\pi^2}{6}\,L^2\left(\frac{s}{\lambda}\right)^2 \qquad (3)$$

where l is the range of intermolecular forces and L is the Debye persistence length. The term I_d has again been ignored.

EXPERIMENTAL

Detailed descriptions of the light scattering photometer (2, 3, 4), purification of materials (2), preparation of solutions (2, 5), phase separation temperature determinations (2, 3), and temperature controls (7) are described elsewhere. The bath temperature inside the light scattering photometer was controlled to better than ±0.0005 deg over extended periods of time. The phase separation temperature which was measured inside the photometer by means of a telescope was compared with values determined in a separate constant temperature bath. The observed phase separation temperatures agreed to within 0.001 deg for each liquid mixture.

A Kratky camera of medium resolution was adapted to a General Electric XRD-6 system (5, 6). A diagram of the collimating system for slit-shaped primary beam with corresponding slit height dimensions is shown in Fig. 1. The thermostat block (1, 11) was controlled to 0.01 deg.

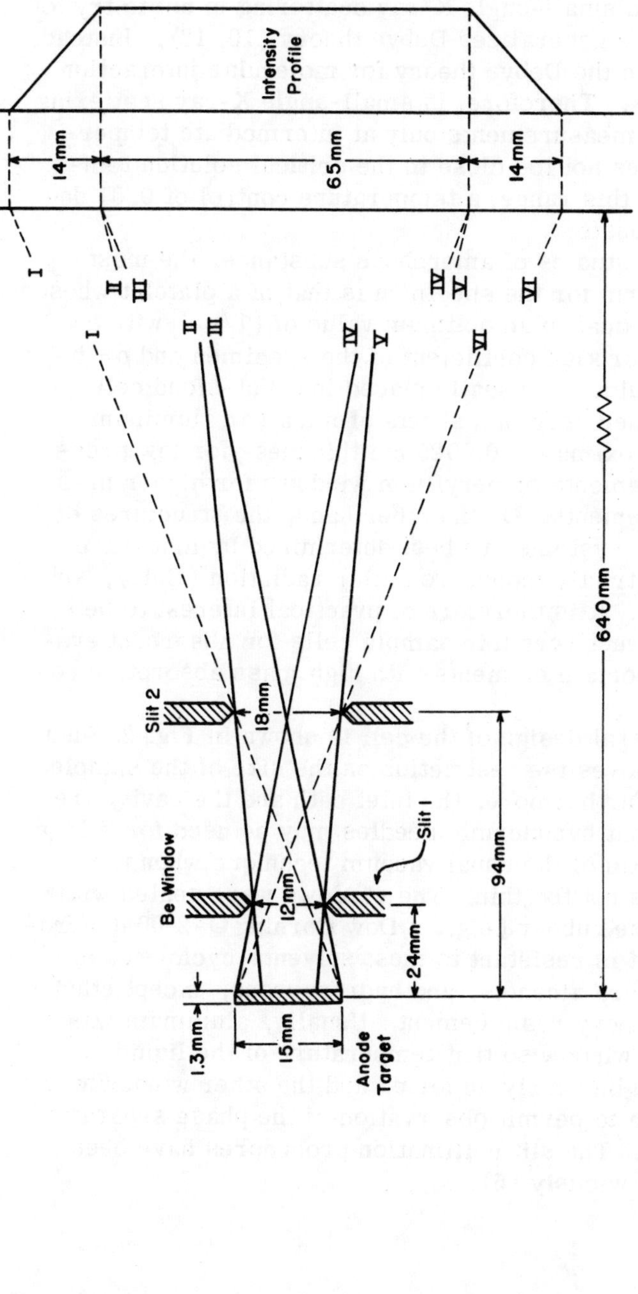

Fig. 1. Diagram of a slit height collimating system for the Kratky camera with General Electric CA7H X-ray tube.

It should be noted that our main aim in constructing a composite curve over large ranges of s/λ by means of both light scattering and small-angle X-ray scattering is not to try to break down the generalized Debye theory (10, 12). Instead, we hope to use the Debye theory for molecular interaction studies (3, 8). Therefore, in small-angle X-ray scattering we make our measurements only at intermediate temperature distances not too close to the critical solution temperature. In this range, a temperature control of 0.01 deg becomes adequate.

In X-ray studies of amorphous substance, the most convenient form for the specimen is that of a platelet whose thickness is equal to an optimum value of $(1/\mu\rho)$ with μ = the mass absorption coefficient of the specimen and ρ = its density. Liquids are usually placed in a flat-sided cell closed by either very thin sheets of mica (or aluminum foils) of approximately 0.0025 cm thickness for low pressure measurements or beryllium windows for higher pressure measurements. On the other hand, the structures of most of these systems are best determined by long wave length (and strictly monochromatic) radiation (CuK_α, or CrK_α, etc.). It is therefore of practical interest to be able to construct very thin sample cells for absorbent systems which contain elements with high mass absorption coefficients.

The general design of the cell is shown in Fig. 2. Such a design removes the restriction on the size of the sample inlet hole. Furthermore, the inlet path and the cavity are parallel so that hypodermic needles may be used for filling the cell instead of the usual vacuum technique when the X-ray path is not too thin. The windows were sealed with either silicone rubber (e.g., a Dow Corning Q-2-0046 aerospace sealant is resistant to most solvents-cyclohexane, benzene, ether, alcohols, and hydrocarbons, except ethyl acetate) or epoxy resin cement. Usually, aluminum was used for one window so that temperature of the liquid sample could be nearly uniform, and the other window was made of mica to permit observation of the phase separation temperature. The slit collimation procedures have been described previously (5).

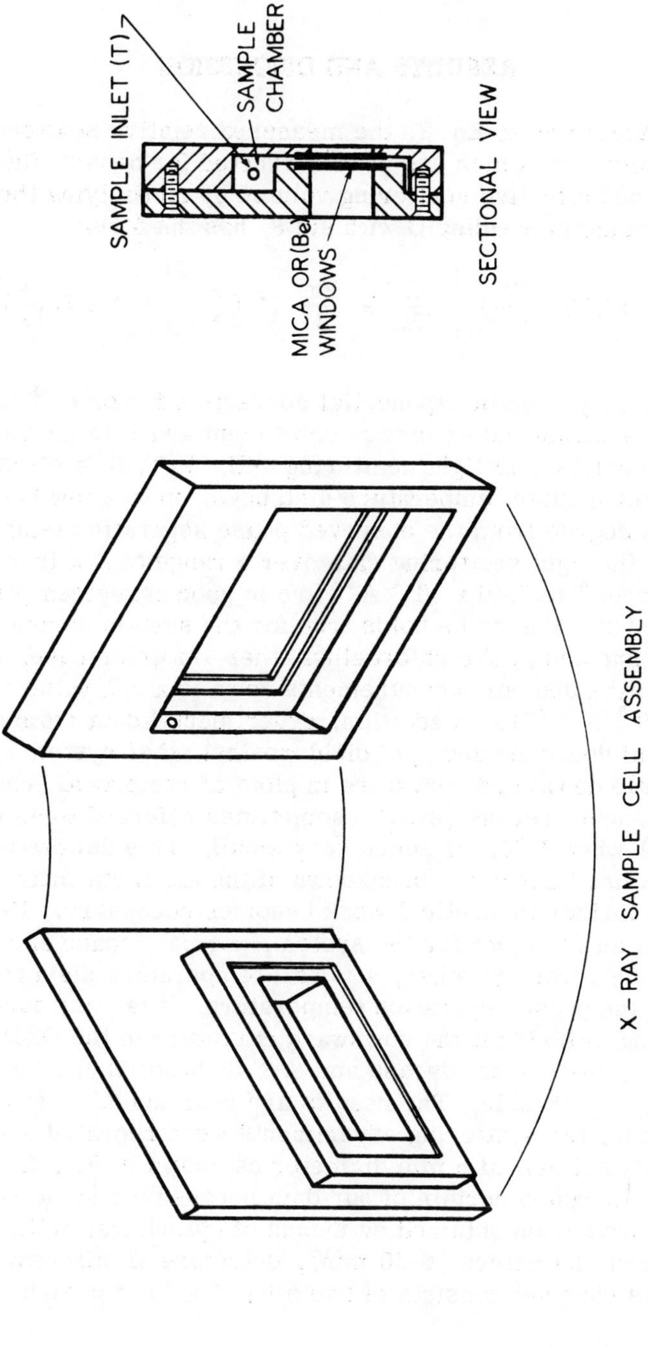

Fig. 2. Schematic sample cell.

RESULTS AND DISCUSSION

According to Eq. 3, the measured relative scattered intensity $I_c{}^*$, which has been corrected for density fluctuations and effective scattering volume by multiplying the galvanometer reading G with sin θ, has the form:

$$\frac{1}{I_c{}^*} = F'(T)\left(\frac{T_c}{T}\right)\left[\frac{\Delta T}{T_c} + \frac{2\pi^2}{3} l^2 \left(\frac{s}{\lambda}\right)^2\right] = A + B\left(\frac{s}{\lambda}\right)^2 \quad (4)$$

$F'(T)$ may contain exponential correction factor $e^{2\gamma R}$ where γ is the measured extinction coefficient and R is the radius of the cylindrical light scattering cell. $F(T, \theta) \cong e^{2\gamma R}\sin\theta 2$. At intermediate temperature distances, up to a few hundreds degree from the observed phase separation temperature, the light scattering data over a range of s/λ from 1.29×10^{-4} to 7.46×10^{-4} Å^{-1} are in good agreement with Eq. 4 (2). The same holds true for the system normal dodecane and β, β' dichloroethyl ether, in which case, we have extended our measurements down to a s/λ value of 7×10^{-5} Å^{-1} (7). In addition, experimental data from the normal dodecane and β, β' dichloroethyl ether system show a gentle downward curvature in plots of reciprocal scattered intensity versus $(s/\lambda)^2$ (sometimes referred to as OZD plots) when $T-T_P$ becomes very small. This downward curvature indicates a breakdown of the classical theory. Then further theoretical work becomes necessary. Fig. 3 shows an OZD plot for the system, normal decane and β, β' dichloroethyl ether, at small temperature distances from the phase separation temperature. It is very surprising to find that the downward curvature in the OZD plot for the normal decane and β, β' dichloroethyl ether is barely observable. The results are reproducible. In addition, the scattering experiments were repeated with a cylindrical cell of 6 mm diameter as shown in Fig. 4. We are reasonably certain of our data because the same results have been obtained by means of cylindrical cells of different diameters (6-10 mm), detectors of different slit widths (one set consists of two slits: 1 x 10 mm each and

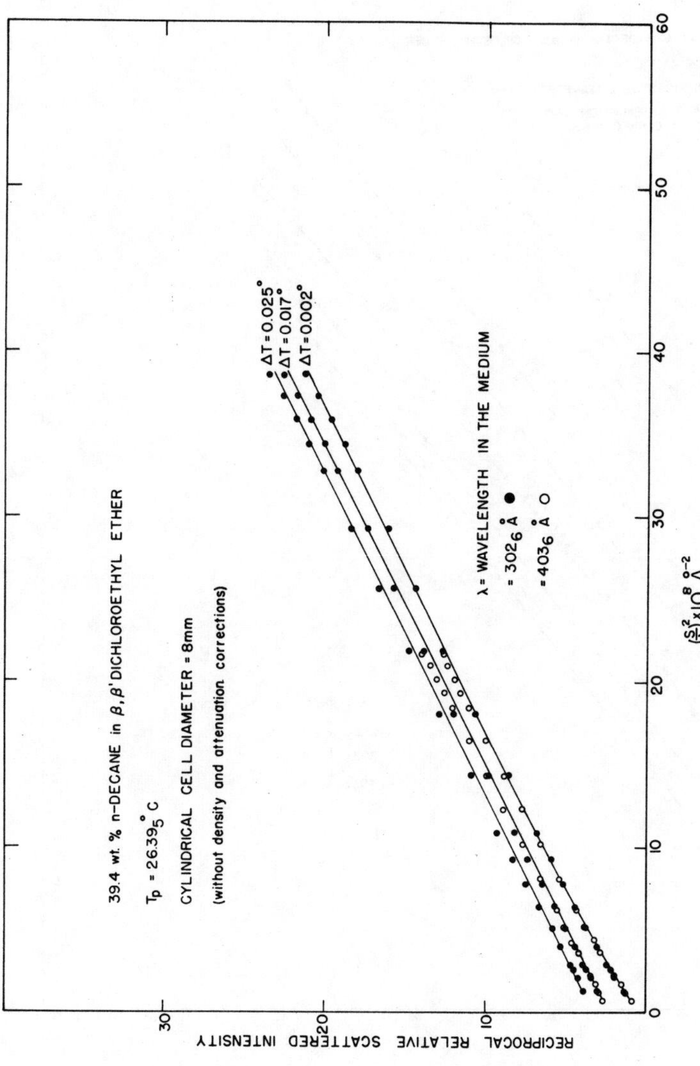

Fig. 3. Plot of reciprocal relative scattered intensity, $1/I^*$, versus $(s/\lambda)^2$.

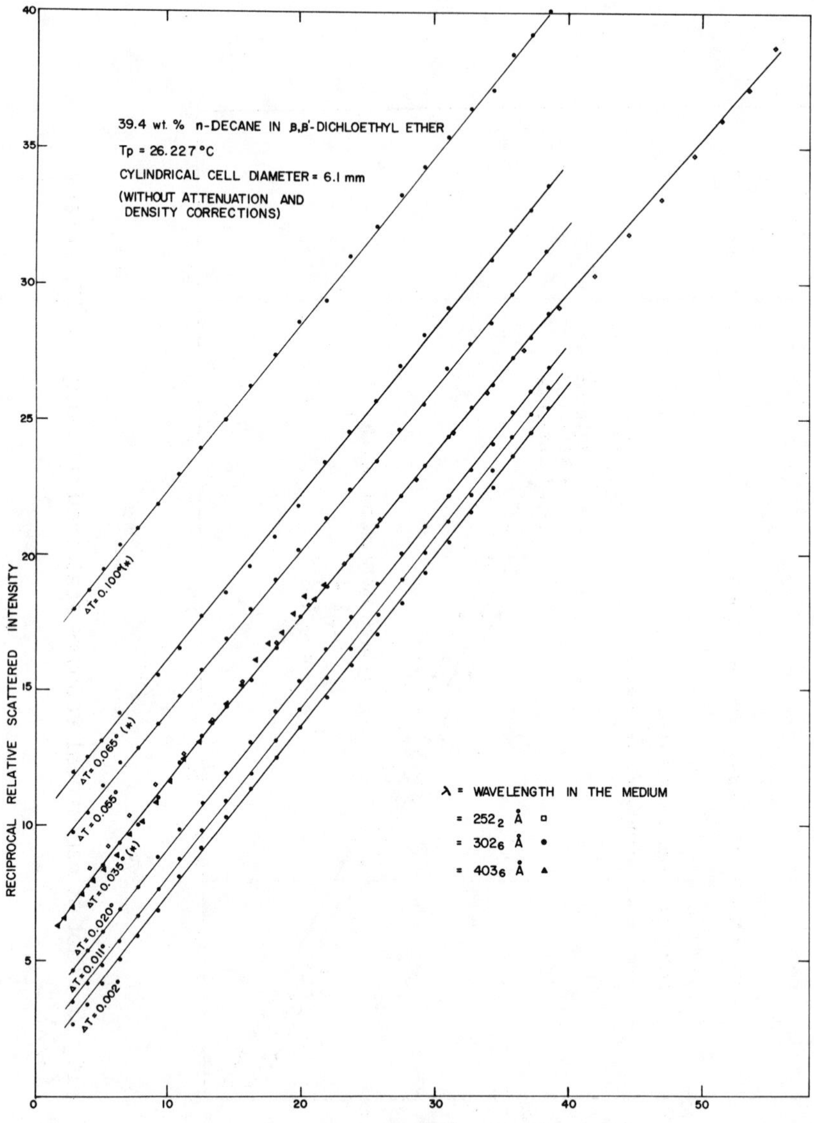

Fig. 4. Plot of reciprocal relative scattered intensity, 1/I*, versus $(s/\lambda)^2$.

20 mm apart, and the other set: 0.5 × 10 mm each and 20 mm apart) and incident light of different lengths (λ_o = 365, 436, and 578 mμ). In view of the fact that normal decane and normal dodecane belong to the same homologous series of aliphatic hydrocarbons, we feel that this downward curvature, being a small effect which appears only when the system is very close to the critical mixing point, has to be a sensitive function depending on the nature of molecular interactions of the components in the binary liquid mixture, and may vary from system to system. Closer inspection tells us that there are two minor aspects of the data which require further examination. Firstly, refractive indices of the mixture, n, at different wave lengths were calculated from molar refractions and we assumed no volume change in mixing. The error introduced by these two approximations on the calculated wave lengths in the medium, $\lambda (= \lambda_o / n)$, was estimated at less than one per cent. Yet, a superimposition of three scattering curves measured at λ_o = 365, 436, and 578 mμ and at a temperature distance of 0.035 deg showed a slight deviation for the curve measured at λ_o = 365 mμ (Fig. 4.) Secondly, the measured extinction coefficient for the system n-$C_{10}H_{22}$ and chlorex is higher than that for the system n-$C_{12}H_{26}$ and chlorex. The possibility of a detectable amount of multiple scattering in the shorter wave length region still remains.

Fig. 5 shows a plot of reciprocal extrapolated zero-angle scattered intensity, $1/I^*(0)$, versus $T-T_p$, where T_p is the observed phase separation temperature and $I^*(0)$ is the extrapolated zero-angle scattered intensity without density and attenuation corrections. Remember $I(0) = I_c(0) + I_d(0)$, and $I_c(\theta) = I_c * F'(T)$. When $T-T_p$ is small, I_c is much greater than I_d. So, $I \cong I_c$. Similarly, when $T-T_p$ is large, the attenuation correction factor, which depends on the geometry of the photometer and the light-scattering cell, can usually be neglected. The values of $I(0)$ after correction for attenuation with the exponential correction factor $e^{2\gamma R}$ are also shown in Fig. 5. A slight concave upward curvature which tends to extrapolate to a non-zero value at T_p seems to persist at very small

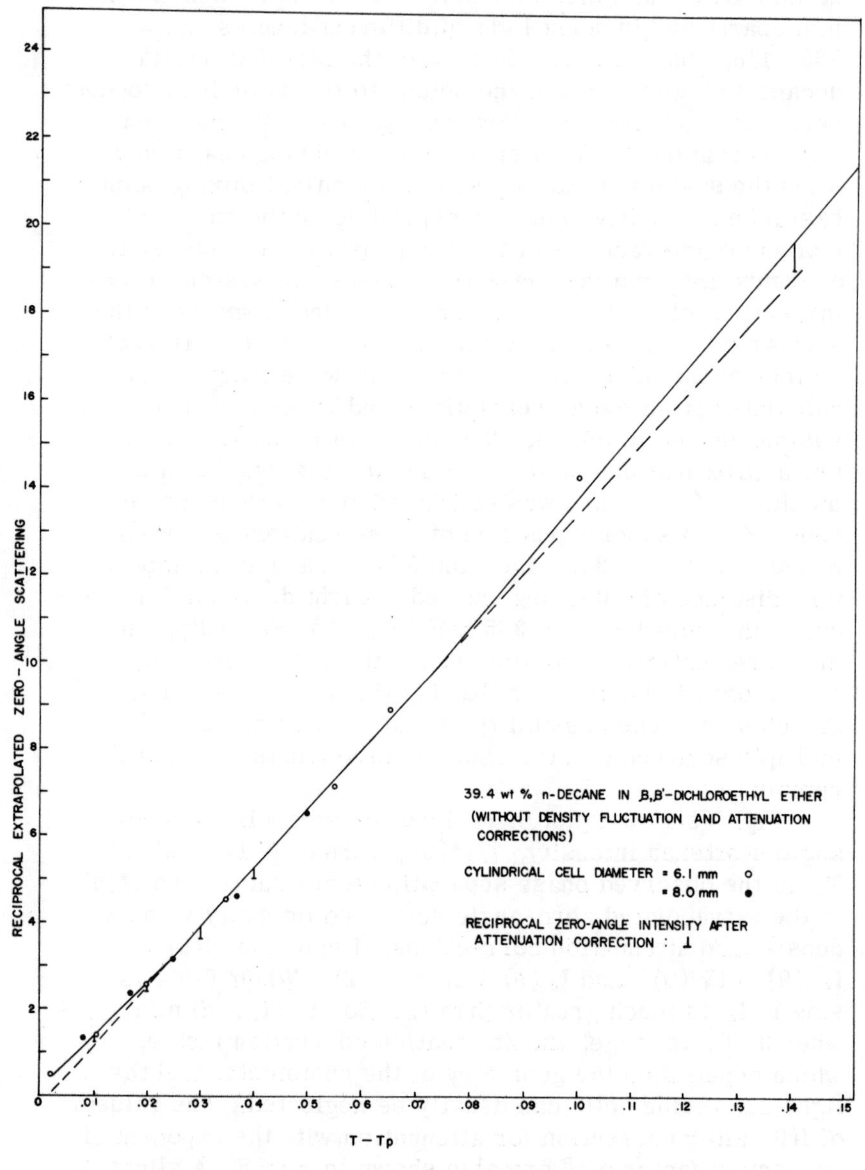

Fig. 5. Plot of reciprocal extrapolated zero-angle scattered intensity versus $(T-T_P)$.

temperature distances. However, the deviation is small and the expression $[1/I_c(0)] = \text{constant} \cdot (T-T_p)$ is a good approximation over the intermediate temperature ranges, not too close to the critical point. The values of the extrapolated zero-angle scattered intensity from an OZD plot become questionable if there is a change in the curvature of the scattering curves in the extrapolated region $[(s/\lambda) < 6.8 \times 10^{-5} \text{Å}^{-1}]$. For this reason, measurements at even lower angles ($\theta < 16°$) by means of "long-wave length" ($\lambda_0 > 578$ mμ) light scattering become interesting. At this moment, the existence of such a downward bend at small temperature distances from the critical solution temperature and at very small values of s/λ is not yet certain.

The Debye theory, which relates the angular dissymmetry to intermolecular potentials of binary liquid mixtures, holds over intermediate temperature distances. It gives us another way to examine the nature of molecular interactions in liquid mixtures in terms of deviations from the approximate Debye theory (9). Fig. 6 shows a plot of $\log [(I_{max}/I^*) - 1]$ versus $\log (s/\lambda)^2$. Logarithm was used because of the large ranges of values of both intensities and s/λ covered in the experiments. Furthermore, the connection between light and small-angle X-ray scattering can clearly be shown. Note that Eq. 3 holds over a larger range of s/λ for the system, polystyrene and cyclohexane (5) than for systems consisting of small molecules alone (6, 12). The second moment of the Debye persistence length L is defined as $L^2 = [\int C(r) r^2 d\tau / \int C(r) d\tau]$ where $C(r)$ is a correlation function (9). It is therefore within reason to expect that the curvatures observed in Fig. 6 may be expressed in terms of higher moments of the Debye persistence length L. These higher moments should contain hidden information on the microscopic nature of the fluid mixture as related to the size, shape (compactness) and molecular interactions of the components in the system. However, no quantitative explanation has yet been given. A final word of caution is also in order: at larger angles in the X-ray region, contribution of short range order to the scattering may become appreciable. The

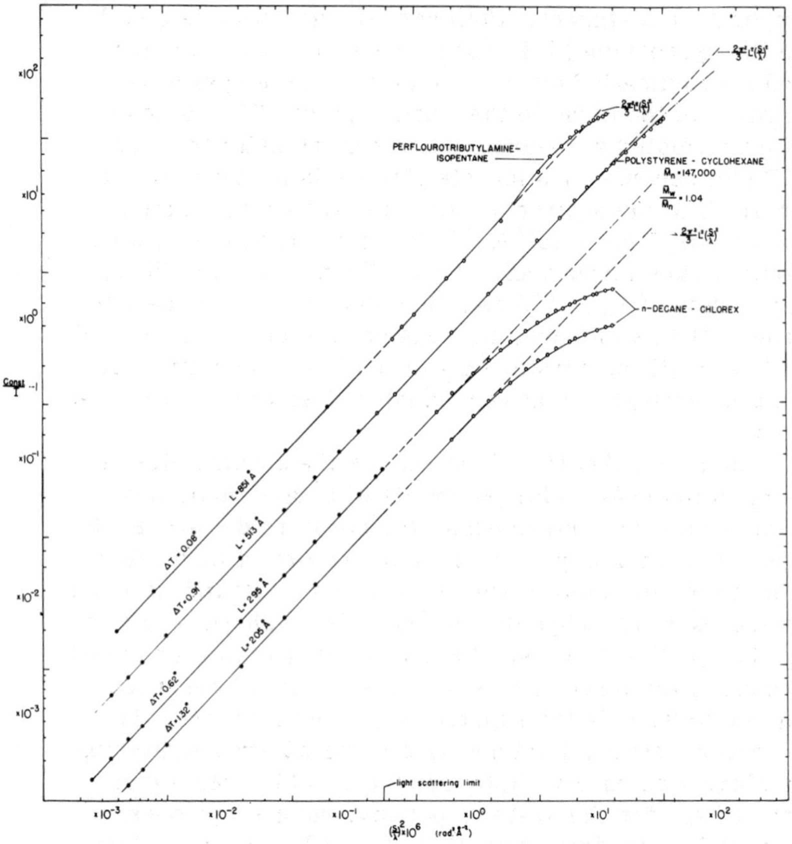

Fig. 6. Plot of log $[(I^*_{max}/I^*) - 1]$ versus log $(s/\lambda)^2$. Perfluotributyl amine and isopentane: ref. 12. Polystyrene $[\bar{M}_n = 147,000; (\bar{M}_w/\bar{M}_n) = 1.04]$ and cyclohexane: ref. 5 and P. Debye, J. Bashaw, B. Chu, and D. M. Tan Creti, J. Chem. Phys. **44**, 4302 (1966). Normal decane and β, β' dichloroethyl ether: refs. 2 and 6.

measured X-ray scattered intensity, as expressed in Fig. 6, denotes an overall sum. Therefore, in a more careful analysis on the deviations of the Debye theory at large values of s/λ in the small-angle X-ray scattering region, we should take only excess scattered intensities. Furthermore such analysis breaks down whenever contribution of short range order is present.

ACKNOWLEDGMENTS

The author gratefully acknowledges the support of the National Science Foundation and the U. S. Army Research Office (Durham). He also wishes to thank Mr. W. P. Kao who performed part of the measurements on the system normal decane and β, β' dichloroethyl ether.

REFERENCES

(1) Chu, B., J. Phys. Chem. **67**, 1969 (1963).
(2) Chu, B., J. Chem. Phys. **41**, 226 (1964).
(3) Chu, B., J. Am. Chem. Soc. **86**, 3557 (1964).
(4) Chu, B., Rev. Sci. Instr. **35**, 1201 (1964).
(5) Chu, B., J. Chem. Phys. **42**, 426 (1965).
(6) Chu, B., J. Chem. Phys. **42**, 2293 (1965).
(7) Chu, B. and Kao, W. P., J. Chem. Phys. **42**, 2608 (1965).
(8) Chu, B., J. Phys. Chem. **69**, 2329 (1965).
(9) Debye, P., in Non-Crystalline Solids, edited by C. D. Frechette, John Wiley and Sons, Inc., New York (1960) p. 1; J. Chem. Phys. **31**, 680 (1959).
(10) Debye, P., in Electromagnetic Scattering, edited by M. Kerker, The Macmillan Company, New York (1963) p. 393.
(11) Debye, P., Woermann, D. and Chu, B., J. Chem. Phys. **36**, 851 (1962).
(12) Debye, P., Caulfield, D. and Bashaw, J., J. Chem. Phys. **41**, 3051 (1964).
(13) Fisher, M. E., J. Math. Phys. **5**, 944 (1964).
(14) Fixman, M., Advan. Chem. Phys. **6**, 175 (1964).
(15) Ornstein, L. S. and Zernike, F., Proc. Acad. Sci. Amsterdam, **17**, 793 (1914); Physik Z. **19**, 134

(1918); ibid. **27**, 761 (1926).

(16) Zernike, F., Proc. Acad. Sci. Amsterdam, **18**, 1520 (1916).

Fine Structure of Rayleigh Scattered Light*

R. Pecora
Department of Chemistry, Stanford University,
Stanford, California

ABSTRACT

A discussion of the theory of the fine structure of Rayleigh scattered light with emphasis on dilute polymer solutions is presented.

I. INTRODUCTION AND THEORY

The recent development of the optical maser and associated techniques has made possible precise measurements of the fine structure of Rayleigh scattered light from thermodynamic systems (6, 5, 2). The fine structure is a measure of the spectrum of thermal motions in the system of interest, usually a fluid composed of small molecules or one composed of polymer molecules, (21, 22, 23). Cold neutron scattering (12), and Mössbauer experiments (25) also measure the spectrum of thermal motions albeit in a different frequency range from that of light. The fine structure of the Rayleigh line will, because of the small frequency shifts involved, give information only about very slow motions, motions which may usually be described by the equations of hydrodynamics. For the measurement

*Work supported by the National Science Foundation

of faster motions dependent mainly on microscopic, mechanical quantities techniques such as cold neutron, x-ray or Raman scattering must be used.

For an inelastic scattering experiment at low energies (e.g. first inelastic Born approximation scattering for cold neutrons) the scattering cross-section for the single scattering process will be proportional to the function (12).

$$S(\boldsymbol{\kappa}, \Delta\omega) = \int dt e^{-i\Delta\omega t} \left< \sum_i^N \sum_j^N \exp(-i\boldsymbol{\kappa}\cdot\mathbf{r}_i(0)) \times \exp(i\boldsymbol{\kappa}\cdot\mathbf{r}_j(t)) \right> \quad (1)$$

where $\kappa = k_0 - k_f$ the difference between the propagation vector of the incident wave and that of the scattered wave; $\Delta\omega = \omega_0 - \omega_f$, the difference between the frequencies of the incident and scattered waves. In the general case $r_i(t)$ is the Heisenberg coordinate operator of scatterer i. In this paper only the classical case is considered and $\mathbf{r}_i(t)$ simply represents the position of scatterer i at time t. The summations are over all N scatterers in the scattering medium and the angular bracketts denote an ensemble average.

The quantities in the exponential in Eq. (1) give the phase difference between the radiation scattered from scatterer i at time zero and from scatterer j at time t. The phase difference and, hence, the scattering cross-section depend explicitly on a time-displaced correlation between the positions of a pair of molecules. Equation (1) may also be written in the form (12)

$$S(\kappa, \Delta\omega) = \frac{N}{2\pi} \int\int e^{-i\Delta\omega t} e^{i\kappa\cdot\mathbf{r}} G(\mathbf{r}\, t)\, d^3r\, dt \quad (2)$$

where $G(\mathbf{r}\, t)$ is known as the space-time correlation function of the scattering medium. In the classical case $G(\mathbf{r}\, t)$ is a real function with a simple probability interpretation. $G(\mathbf{r}\, t)$ is the probability that if a scatterer is at the origin at time zero, there is one at $\mathbf{r}$ at time t. $G(\mathbf{r}\, t)$ may be written as the sum of two parts,

$$G(\mathbf{r}\ t) = G_s\ (\mathbf{r}\ t) + G_d\ (\mathbf{r}\ t) \tag{3}$$

G_s $(\mathbf{r}\ t)$, the *self* part, is the probability that the scatterer at $\mathbf{r}$, at time t is the same as that at the origin at time zero. G_d $(\mathbf{r}\ t)$, the *different* part, is the probability that the scatterer at $\mathbf{r}$ at time t is different from the one at the origin at time zero.

The simple probability interpretation of the space-time correlation function along with its decomposition into two parts is quite useful in constructing models of these functions and from these the scattering cross-sections.

If Eq. (2) is integrated over all frequency shifts

$$S(\kappa) = \int S(\kappa, \Delta\omega)\, d\Delta\omega = N \int e^{i\kappa\cdot\mathbf{r}}\ G(\mathbf{r}, o)\, d\mathbf{r} \tag{4}$$

In a liquid, $G(r, o)$ is related to the usual radial distribution function, $g(r)$, by

$$G(\mathbf{r}, o) = \delta(\mathbf{r}) + \rho g(r) \tag{5}$$

where $\delta(\mathbf{r})$ is the Dirac delta function and ρ the average density of the medium. $S(\kappa)$, the structure factor, is related by Eqs. (4) and (5) to the average spatial distribution of scatterers. It is determined by measuring the integrated (over all frequency shifts) scattering cross-section at all κ (varying scattering angles and wavelengths of radiation). If, in addition, the frequency distribution of the scattered radiation is measured, the more general function, $S(\kappa, \Delta\omega)$, conveying information about the time dependence of the fluctuations from equilibrium as well as the spatial structure is obtained.

In general, however, measurements of $S(\kappa, \Delta\omega)$ at all κ and $\Delta\omega$ and their Fourier inversion to give a $G(\mathbf{r}, t)$ valid for all $\mathbf{r}$, and t is extremely difficult. In this paper some approximations to $G(\mathbf{r}, t)$ valid in the t, $\mathbf{r}$ range appropriate to light scattering are discussed. $S(\kappa, \Delta\omega)$ is then computed in terms of thermal parameters of the medium. In the cases considered, it is hoped that measurements of $S(\kappa, \Delta\omega)$ can be used to measure the thermal parameters of the scattering medium.

II. DILUTE POLYMER SOLUTIONS

In this section a brief review of the theory of Doppler shifts in light scattered from dilute monodisperse polymer solutions is presented (21, 22). Since polymers are massive and hence move very slowly at ordinary temperatures the Doppler shifts are generally expected to be small. Only with the development of optical maser techniques has experimental exploitation of this subject become possible (6).

The theoretical problem is the evaluation of the sum in Eq. (1) in the case where the $\mathbf{r}_i(t)$ are regarded as positions of "segments" of a polymer molecule. The problem may be enormously simplified by considering only the limit of infinitely dilute solutions, that is, all correlations between segments belonging to different molecules will be ignored. Then the sum in Eq. (1) may be split into two separate sums, one containing terms with $\mathbf{r}_i(o)$, $\mathbf{r}_j(t)$ belonging to the same molecules, the other containing only terms with $\mathbf{r}_i(o)$, $\mathbf{r}_j(t)$ belonging to different molecules. Since no correlations are presumed to exist between segments on different molecules the latter term will not contribute to the scattering in other than the forward direction. The remaining sum,

$$< \sum_i \sum_j \exp\{ i\kappa \cdot [\mathbf{r}_i(o) - \mathbf{r}_j(t)]\} > \tag{6}$$

now includes in each term only segments in the same molecule.

A. Rigid Uniform Sphere

A rigid polymer with a uniform spherical distribution of segments is the simplest case that might be considered since only the translational motion of the center of mass of the sphere contributes to the Doppler shift. A new coordinate system may be defined by

$$\mathbf{r}_i(o) = \mathbf{R}(o) + S_i(o)$$

where **R** (o) is the position of the center of mass of the sphere (at time zero) and S_i (o), the position of the i th segment relative to the center of mass. The sum 6 becomes,

$$<> = < \Sigma e \exp \{ i\kappa \cdot [\mathbf{R}_i(o) - \mathbf{R}_i(t)] \} >$$

$$\times < \sum_i \sum_j \exp \{ i\kappa \cdot [S_i(o) - S_i(t) \} > \quad (7)$$

For small, rigid spheres, the second function on the right hand side of 7 may be approximated by the time independent function

$$< \sum_i \sum_j \exp \{ i\kappa \cdot [S_i(o) - S_j(o)] \} >$$

which, hence, does not contribute to the Doppler shift. Its form is, however, well known and is discussed in the literature (26).

We may define a center of mass self space-time correlation function, $G_{c.m}$ (**R**, t) corresponding to the sum

$$< \sum_i \exp \{ i\kappa \cdot [\mathbf{R}_i(o) - \mathbf{R}_i(t)] \} > = N \int G_{c.m}(\mathbf{R},t)\, e^{i\kappa\cdot \mathbf{R}} d^3 R \quad (8)$$

$G_{c.m}$(**R**, t) is the probability that if the center of mass of a given molecule is at the origin at time zero then the same molecule is at **R**, at time t. N is the total number of *molecules* in the fluid. $G_{c.m}$ (**R**, t) is easily calculated from the theory of Brownian motion of a massive particle in a fluid. The motion of the center of mass obeys the Langevin equation

$$\frac{d\vec{u}}{dt} + \beta\vec{u} = \vec{A}(t) \quad (9)$$

where $\vec{u}$ is the velocity of the center of mass; and **A**(t) a fluctuating acceleration β is the frictional coefficient per unit mass, m,

$$\beta = \frac{k_B T}{Dm} \quad (10)$$

D is the diffusion coefficient, k_B Boltzmann's constant and T the temperature. This equation may be solved for the center of mass correlation function by standard techniques (21, 24).

The resultant correlation function transformed in space and time leads to the following equation for the spectrum

$$S(\kappa, \Delta\omega) = \frac{2\kappa^2 D}{(\Delta\omega)^2 + \kappa^4 D^2} N$$

$$< \sum_i \sum_j \exp [i\kappa \cdot (S_i(o) - S_j(o)] \quad (11)$$

The spectrum consists of one Lorentzian line centered at the incident frequency with an angularly dependent half-width given by

$$\Delta \nu_{\frac{1}{2}} = \frac{\kappa^2 D}{\pi} = \frac{16\pi}{\lambda^2} D \operatorname{Sin}^2 \theta/2$$

where θ is the scattering angle and λ the incident light wavelength. For $\lambda = 6000$ Å, $D = 10^{-7}$ cm^2/sec and $\theta = 90°$ $\Delta\nu_{\frac{1}{2}} \approx 650$ cycles/sec.

Cummins, Knable and Yeh, utilizing optical heterodyne techniques have confirmed this result for small diameter polystyrene latex suspensions (6).

Calculations may also be made for rigid non-spherical polymers. In these cases, in addition to the translational Doppler shift, there will also be a shift arising from rotation of the molecule which will be proportional to the molecular rotational diffusion coefficient (21).

B. Flexible Polymers

The calculations outlined above do not include any Doppler shift due to the internal motions of a polymer molecule; that is, motions of the segments relative to each other. The short wavelength fast motions along the polymer chain will give rise to large frequency shifts (Raman Scattering). The long wavelength slower motions which include most of the polymer chain will produce much smaller Doppler shifts. These slower long wavelength motions may be described by the hydrodynamic theory as opposed to the quantum mechanical microscopic approach to the theory of Raman Scattering.

The usual ball and spring model may be used to compute the scattered light spectrum. In this model the polymer model is considered to be composed of Z gaussian segments, each of average length b, connecting Z + 1 identical optically isotropic beads. The molecule is suspended in a viscous medium with which it interacts through the beads. The beads are characterized by identical frictional coefficients and the segments are assumed to provide Hookean restoring forces to the beads. No "external" forces will be applied;however, spontaneous fluctuations will be assumed to occur, stretching the molecule to its equilibrium configuration. The return of the molecule to its equilibrium configuration is then studied. Details of this model are given elsewhere (29, 30, 31, 27). The solution of the problem is greatly simplified by the use of the Zimm-Rouse normal coordinates.

$$\mathbf{S}_j = \sum_{k=o}^{Z} Q \quad \mu_k \tag{13}$$

where μ_k are a set of normal coordinates and Q_{jk} the elements of the normal coordinate transformation matrix. With this transformation it may be shown that the Fokker-Planck equation for the bead distribution function, ψ, is diagonal and is given by (29, 30, 31)

$$\frac{\partial \Psi}{\partial t} = \sum_{k=o}^{Z} \tau_k^{-1} \left[\frac{1}{3} < \mu_k^2 >_e \nabla_k^2 \Psi + \nabla_k \cdot (\mu_k \quad \Psi) \right] \tag{14}$$

where τ_k is the relaxation time of the k_{th} normal mode, and $<\mu_k^2>_e$ is the mean square equilibrium length of the kth normal mode. In the following reference to μ_o the center of resistance diffusive mode will be omitted since it has been treated in the previous section.

If the boundary condition is imposed that at time zero the normal mode coordinates are $\mu_1^o, \mu_2^o, \mu_z^o$

$$\Psi\,(\mu_1, \mu_2, \ldots, \mu_z\,;\, \mu_1^o, \mu_2^o, \ldots, \mu_z^o \,|\, o) = \prod_{k=1}^{Z} \delta(\underline{\mu}_k - \mu_k^o) \qquad (15)$$

then $\Psi\,(\mu_1, \mu_2, \ldots, \mu_z; \mu_1^o, \mu_2^o, \ldots, \mu_z^o |\, t)$ represents the probability per unit volume that the normal coordinates are $\mu_1^o, \mu_2^o, \ldots, \mu_z^o$ at time t if they are $\mu_1^o, \mu_2^o, \ldots, \mu_z^o$ at time zero.

If $\phi\,(\mu_1^o, \ldots, \mu_z^o)$ is the probability per unit volume that the normal mode coordinates have values $\mu_1^o, \ldots, \mu_z^o$ at time zero then the average sum is given by

$$\exp\,\{ i\kappa \cdot [\mathbf{S}_l\,(o) - \mathbf{S}_j\,(t)\,]\,\}>$$

$$= \sum_{l}^{Z} \sum_{j}^{Z} \int\int \exp\,[\,i\boldsymbol{\kappa} \cdot \sum_{k} (Q_{lk}\,\mu_k - Q_{jk}\,\mu_k\,)\,]$$

$$\times\, \Psi(\mu_1, \ldots, \mu_z\,; \mu_1^o, \ldots, \mu_z^o\,|\,t)$$

$$\times\, \phi\,(\mu_1^o, \ldots, \mu_z^o) \prod_{k=1}^{Z} d\,\mu_k \;\; d\,\mu_k^o \qquad (16)$$

The solution of Eq. (14) with the boundary condition (15) is given by (24)

$$\Psi(\mu_1, \ldots, \mu_z; \mu_1^o, \ldots, \mu_z^o\,|t) =$$

$$\prod_{k=1}^{Z} \left[\frac{3}{2\pi < \mu_k^2 >_e \,[1 - \exp(-\frac{2t}{T_k})\,]}\right]^{3/2}$$

$$\times \exp\left\{ -\frac{3}{2<\mu_k^2>_e} \left[\frac{[(\mu_k - \mu_k{}^o \exp(-t/\tau_k))]^2}{[1 - \exp(-2t/\tau_k)]} \right] \right\} \quad (17)$$

Taking ϕ to be a product of gaussians in the $\mu_k{}^o$ and using Eq. (17) the sum in Eq. (16) may be evaluated,

$$< \sum_l \sum_j \exp \{ i\kappa \cdot [\mathbf{S}_l(o) - \mathbf{S}_j(t)] \} > = \sum_l \sum_j \prod_k \exp - \frac{\kappa^2}{6}$$

$$<\mu_k^2>_e [Q_{jk}{}^2 + Q_{lk}{}^2 - 2\,Q_{lk}\,Q_{jk} \exp(-{}^{t/}\tau_k)] \quad (18)$$

S (κ, $\Delta\omega$) is the time-Fourier transform of Eq. (18).

$$S(\kappa, \Delta\omega) = \sum_j \sum_l \int e^{-i\Delta\omega t} \exp \sum_k - \frac{\kappa^2}{6} <\mu_k^2>_e \quad (19)$$

$$[1Q_{jk}{}^2 + Q_{lk}{}^2 - 2Q_{jk}\,Q_{ik} \exp(-{}^{t/}\tau_k)]\ dt$$

In cases where the parameter $(\kappa^2 <\mu_k^2>_e)/6$ is small, the exponential in the exponential of Eq. (19) may be expanded in a power series in $(\kappa^2/6) <\mu_k{}^2>_1$ and the time integrations may be performed term by term. Retaining only terms up to order $(\kappa^2/6) <\mu_k^2>_e$, we obtain

$$S(\kappa\ \Delta\omega) = \sum_j \sum_l \exp \sum_k \left[-\frac{\kappa^2}{3} <\mu_k^2>_e (Q_{jk}{}^2 + Q_{1k}^2)\right] \quad (20)$$

$$\times \left[Z\delta(\Delta\omega) + \sum_k \frac{\kappa^2}{3} <\mu_k{}^2>_e Q_{lk}\ Q_{jk} \frac{2\ \tau_k}{\tau_k{}^2 \Delta\omega^2 + 1} + \ldots \right]$$

The scattering line in the above approximation is a superposition of Lorentzian's, each centered about the incident frequency. The contribution of each normal mode to the scattered intensity depends upon the parameter

$$\frac{\kappa^2}{3} < \mu_k{}^2>_e = \frac{16\pi^2}{3} \frac{<\mu_k{}^2>_e}{\lambda^2} \operatorname{Sin}^2 \theta/2$$

At a given scattering angle the contribution of each mode depends upon the ratio of the mean square equilibrium length of a mode to the square of the wavelength of the incident light. Consequently, the longer wavelength modes, corresponding to the longest relaxation times and smallest half-width, contribute most to the line intensity. The half-width due to the longest mode is

$$\Delta \nu_{\frac{1}{2}} = \frac{1}{\pi \tau_1} \tag{21}$$

The longest relaxation time τ_1, varies greatly with the type of polymer. For the free-draining model (29, 30, 31, 27)

$$\tau_1 = \frac{< 1^2 >_e}{3 \pi^2 D} \tag{22}$$

where $< 1^2 >_e$ is the mean-square equilibrium end to end length of the polymer molecule. The diffusion coefficient is usually of order 10^{-7} cm^2/sec. $< 1^2 >^{\frac{1}{2}}$, which varies greatly from polymer to polymer, will be taken to be 10^{-5} cm. Then

$$\tau_1 \sim \frac{10^{-3}}{3\pi^2}$$

and the half width

$$\Delta \nu_{\frac{1}{2}} \sim 3\pi \times 10^{-3} \sim 9 \times 10^3 \ \frac{\text{cycles}}{\text{sec.}}$$

The model presented here for the internal motion of a polymer is highly idealized. A great many more models may be made using more complicated pictures of the internal motions, especially for semiflexible molecules such as cellulose and DNA. Such theories should, however, be preceded by an experimental detection of the internal motion contribution to the Doppler shift.

III. GASES AND LIQUIDS

The theory of the fine structure of light scattered from fluids was first formulated by Landau and Placzek in 1934 (17) on the basis of a previous theory by Brillouin (3) for Debye solids and experiments by Gross (14). The measured scattered light spectrum consists of three lines, a central line peaked at the incident frequency and a doublet with peaks symmetrically situated on either side of the central line with spacing

$$\Delta \nu = \pm \cdot \frac{S|\kappa|}{2\pi} = \pm \frac{2}{\lambda} (\sin \theta/2) S \tag{23}$$

where S is the sound velocity. Measurements of $\Delta\nu$ give values for the sound velocity at hypersonic frequencies (8). The doublets were predicted by Brillouin (3) for Debye solids. They arise by diffraction of the incident light by the Debye waves; that is, the fluctuations in density produced by fluctuations in pressure at constant entropy. The central line, according to Landau and Placzek, arises from fluctuations in density produced by fluctuations in entropy at constant pressure. The central line has its origin in a "thermal" phenomenon (entropy fluctuation), while the doublet is produced by a "mechanical" phenomenon (pressure fluctuation). The ratio of the central line to the total intensity of the doublet may then be shown to be

$$\frac{I_c}{2I_d} = \frac{(C_p - C_v)}{C_v} \tag{24}$$

where C_p and C_v are the specific heats at constant pressure and volume, respectively. Since the doublets are produced by sound waves their widths are determined by the sound attenuation coefficient of the medium, which in turn is related to the viscosity and thermal conductivity (21, 16, 18).

The central line width is determined by the decay constant of an entropy fluctuation given by

$$\Delta\nu_{\frac{1}{2}} = \frac{16\pi}{\lambda^2} \sin^2 \theta/2 \quad \left(\frac{\kappa_t}{C_p\,\rho}\right) \tag{25}$$

where κ_t is the thermal conductivity of the fluid. Measurements of the line width will give values of $(\kappa_t / C_p \rho)$. This technique should be especially useful in the critical region since no thermal gradients must be imposed on the system for the measurement of $\Delta\nu_{\frac{1}{2}}$.

Experimental data for κ_t, C_p and ρ indicate a narrowing of the central line in the critical region, further facilitating measurement with optical heterodyning techniques (19, 15, 20). Corrections to Eq. (25) in the critical region have been discussed by Fixman (10).

In systems of more than one component, the three line pattern of the fine structure should remain. The central line should now, however, contain contributions from two sources: fluctuations of entropy at constant pressure and composition and fluctuations of composition at constant pressure. The doublets should arise from fluctuations of pressure at constant entropy and composition. The width of the doublets for a binary mixture should then be related to the sound attenuation coefficient in a binary mixture (16). The width of the central line will be proportional to the decay constant of a thermal fluctuation and the binary diffusion coefficient.

Since at the consulate temperature of a binary mixture, the light scattering is dominated by composition fluctuations the central line width will be determined mainly by the binary diffusion coefficient, which is expected to become small in the consulate temperature region (9, 7). Recent experiments have attempted to measure the central line width for a binary mixture at the consulate temperature (1, 28).

Light scattering has also been suggested as a tool for studying quantum liquids. Ginzburg states that the central line in liquid He^4 below the λ-point is split into a doublet due to the second sound phenomenon (11). Thus, the spectrum should consist of two doublets, one corresponding to first sound and the other to second sound. Gor'kov and Pitaevskii have presented a theory of scattering from

He^3-He^4 mixtures in the hope that experimental observation of the fine structure could be facilitated (13). Brout has suggested that light scattering might be used in the detection of zero sound in liquid He^3 (4).

REFERENCES

(1) Alpert, S. S., Yeh, Y., and Lipworth, E., Phys. Rev. Letters **14**, 486 (1965).
(2) Benedek, G. B., Lastovka, J. B., Fritsch, K., and Greytak, T., J. Opt. Soc. Am. **54**, 1284 (1964).
(3) Brillouin, L., Ann. Phys. **17**, **88** (1922).
(4) Brout, R., Unpublished Manuscript.
(5) Chiao, R. Y., and Stoicheff, B. P., J. Opt. Soc. Am. **54**, 1286 (1964).
(6) Cummins, H. Z., Knable, N., and Yeh, Y., Phys. Rev. Letters **12**, 150 (1964).
(7) Debye, P., Phys. Rev. Letters **14**, 783 (1965).
(8) Fabelinskii, I. L., Usp. Fiz. Nauk **63**, 355 (1957).
(9) Fixman, M., Adv. Chem. Phys. **6**, 175 (1964).
(10) Fixman, M., Personal Communication. See also, Botch, W., and Fixman, M., J. Chem. Phys. **42**, 199 (1965).
(11) Ginzburg, V. L., Zh. Eksperim. i Teor Fiz. **13**, 243 (1943).
(12) Glauber, R. J., in Lectures in Theoretical Physics, edited by W. E. Britten, B. W. Downs and J. Downs. (Interscience Publishers, Inc., New York, 1962), Vol. **4**.
(13) Gor'kov, L. P., and Pitaevskii, L. P., Zh. Eksperim. i Teor. Fiz **33**, 634 (1957). [Translation: Soviet Physics-JETP **6**, 486 (1958)].
(14) Gross, E., Nature **126**, 201 (1930); **129**, 722 (1932).
(15) Kestin, J., Whitelaw, J. H., and Zien, T. F., Physica **30**, 161, (1964).
(16) Landau, L., and Lifshitz, S., Fluid Mechanics (Addison Wesley Publishing Company, Inc., Reading, Massachusett, 1959).
(17) Landau, L., and Placzek, G., Physik Z. Sowjetunion **5**, 172 (1934).

(18) Mash, D. I., Starunov, V. S., and Falelinskii, I. L., Soviet Physics-JETP **20**, 523 (1965).

(19) Michels, A., Botzen, A., and Schuurman, W., Physica **23**, 95 (1957).

(20) Michels, A., Sengers, J. V., and Van der Gulik, P. S., Physica **28**, 1201, 1216, 1238 (1962).

(21) Pecora, R., J. Chem. Phys. **40**, 1604 (1964).

(22) Pecora, R., J. Chem. Phys. 43, 1562 (1965).

(23) Pecora, R., and Steele, W. A., J. Chem. Phys. **42**, 1872 (1965).

(24) See, for example, Selected Papers on Noise and Stochastic Processes edited by N. Wax (Dover Publications, New York, 1954).

(25) Singwi, K. S., and Sjolander, A., Phys. Rev. **120**, 1093 (1960).

(26) See, for instance, Stacey, K. A., Light Scattering in Physical Chemistry. (Butterworths Scientific Publications, Ltd., London, 1956) p. 27.

(27) Verdier, P. H., and Stockmayer, W. H., J. Chem. Phys. **36**, 277 (1962).

(28) Yeh, Y., Alpert, S. S., Lipworth, E., Siegel, L., and Balzarini, D.; Bull. Am. Phys. Soc. **10**, 310 (1965).

(29) Zimm, B. H., J. Chem. Phys. **24**, 269 (1956).

(30) Zimm, B. H., and Kilb, R. W., J. Poly. Sci. **37**, 19 (1959).

(31) Zimm, B. H., Roe, G. M., and Epstein, L. F., J. Chem. Phys. **24**, 279 (1956).

DISCUSSION FOLLOWING PAPER BY R. PECORA

R. Gammon: Now that the tools for discussing inelastic scattering have been presented, I would like to repeat my comment, made following J. Hijman's paper, that the so-called anisotropically scattered light from a pure liquid, i.e. the depolarized part of the scattered light, is in fact inelastically scattered light, appearing as a broad band under the triplet described in this talk.

R. Pecora: I have described here only the scattering from systems composed of spherical scatterers. In the case of systems composed of non-spherical scatterers, an additional scattering of light due to molecular anisotropy is found. Part of this "anisotropic" scattering is frequency shifted due to molecular rotations and, hence, may be called "inelastic" scattering. [See reference 23.]

Thompson Scattering Measurements of MAST Plasmas*

Richard M. Patrick
Avco-Everett Research Laboratory
Everett, Massachusetts

ABSTRACT

Measurements of Thomson scattering from the plasma electrons created by high speed shock waves in a magnetic annular shock tube (MAST) have been used to determine the electron density behind the shock waves, and some preliminary measurements of the electron velocity distribution. A Q-switched ruby laser furnished the light beam which was scattered by the plasma electrons. A rotating quartz prism furnished the Q-switching of the optical cavity for the ruby laser, and rather long Q-switched pulses were obtained (between 10^{-7} and 10^{-6} sec duration). The power level during the Q-switched pulse was between 30 and 100 megawatts.

* This work was supported by the Air Force Office of Scientific Research Office of Aerospace Research, United States Air Force under Contract No. AF 49(638)-1483.

This paper has been published in full in The Physics of Fluids 8, 1985 (1965). The abstract is reproduced here with permission of the Office of Publications of the American Institute of Physics.

Rayleigh scattering from an air sample at various pressures was used to calibrate the power output of the laser and gave a simultaneous measure of the laser output power for all of the tests, while the Thomson scattering was being measured. The measurements of the electron density using the Thomson scattering and the plasma continuum intensities agreed within the scatter of the data. The electron temperature measurements obtained with the Thomson scattering showed that the electron temperature increased with increasing shock speed for a given initial condition.

DISCUSSION FOLLOWING PAPER BY R. M. PATRICK

T. V. George: What was the laser power that you had at peak intensity?

R. M. Patrick: We've been able to obtain between 10 and a 100 megawatts at peak intensity.

T. V. George: How do your know how much of the laser beam is absorbed by the plasma?

R. M. Patrick: The calculated amount of energy that is absorbed by the plasma is small, being less than 10^{-10}. The average energy in the plasma is about 100 volts per particle and the density is roughly 10^{16} particles per cubic centimeter, and the plasma velocity is about 2×10^7 cm per sec. The laser beam was focused to approximately 1 mm diameter, the energy flux of plasma through this area is greater than 10^4 watts, so that the absorbed and scattered laser power has little effect on the plasma.

SESSION III:
MULTIPLE SCATTERING

Introduction to Multiple Scattering Problems

Zdeněk Sekera
Department of Meteorology,
University of California,
Los Angeles

ABSTRACT

The problem of radiative transfer in a plane parallel medium, illuminated by an external source of parallel illumination, is introduced and discussed as a typical problem of multiple scattering. Starting with the law of scattering which is assumed to be known, the so-called auxiliary equation is derived and its solution is indicated for the separable phase matrix, the elements of which, when expanded into harmonic series of the azimuth difference between the directions of illumination and scattering can be expressed as products of two matrices one dependent only on the directional parameters of the incident beam and the other on those of the scattered beam. The auxiliary equation is then reduced to the simple Milne equation which has for its solutions at the boundaries the X and Y matrices, completely analogue to the X and Y functions of Chandrasekhar. These matrices satisfy well-known nonlinear integral equations the solutions of which show much faster convergence of successive iterations than those of the auxiliary equation. However these solutions are not unique. These nonlinear equations, when transformed into a set of singular linear equations, allow not only the solution of the problem of uniqueness but also offer the possibility to derive asymptotic expressions of the solutions for large optical thicknesses. In addition it is possible to arrive at expressions for the intensity matrices for the internal radiation field as it is shown by Mullikin in this volume. The disscussion is concluded with a comparison of the so-called "brute force" solutions, based on numerical solution of the fundamental equations without any reductions or simplifications, with the analytical solutions the advantages of which are then enumerated.

The self-illumination of a medium consisting of a manifold of scattering centers or particles is due to the multiple scattering of the illuminating radiation originating at sources which are either external or internal to the medium. Individual scattering centers or scatterers, in addition to scattering the direct radiation from the source or sources, also scatter radiation which has already been scattered once or oftener by the neighboring scatterers. This mutual interaction makes it rather difficult to determine the diffuse radiation field due to scattering at any point inside the medium or at its boundaries. That it is indeed so is borne out by the fact that nearly a century elapsed between Rayleigh's formulation of the exact theory of scattering of light by molecular media and the solution of the fundamental equations governing the theory which took into account multiple scattering. However, even at present in many instance we are faced with difficulties same as or similar to those encountered by Rayleigh. There are still many problems which are unresolved just as they were during the time of Rayleigh. In several of the papers which have been presented at this conference, the problem of multiple scattering has been dwelt upon and some of the basic difficulties have been clearly outlined. The best way to understand or appreciate all these difficulties is to examine in greater detail the procedure of solving a typical problem of multiple scattering.

Evidently we have to start with the law of single scattering by individual scatterers. In most of the mathematical theories, the derivation of the law of scattering is based upon the concept of the illumination of the scatterer by a plane eletromagnetic wave. In none of these theories--at least to my knowledge--has it been assumed that the scatterer is illuminated by either a diverging or converging electromagnetic wave. But, in reality, the scattered radiation has the characteristics of radiation from a point source. Hence the radiation field due to scattering in a dense medium cannot be described in terms of theories of scattering, such as Mie's, based upon the concept of illumination of the scatterer by a plane electromagnetic wave because the distances between neighboring scatterers are too small to admit of the substitution of a plane wave for a spherical wave with any reasonable amount of physical validity.

With a knowledge of the instantaneous location of each scatterer and of the optical and other relevant parameters entering into the law of scattering, which is assumed to be known, it would be theoretically possible to determine the radiation field at a given point in the medium, in a given direction, resulting from the scattering of all the streams of radiation originating at all scatterers in the medium. Since all these radiational fields originate at the same source initially, the several streams scattered in any particular direction will be coherent and hence will interfere. Thus the main difficulty in any formulation of multiple scattering is the proper evaluation of phase relationships among the various individual streams which together define the resultant radiation field. It is thus evident that the mutual interaction amongst the various scatterers plays a prominent role in any such evaluation of the resultant radiation field. In the case of a solid medium, the scatterers form a well-defined lattic wherein their mutual positions are fixed and we have to consider completely the phase relationships amongst the various scattered beams. A contribution to the theory of multiple scattering in such a case will be presented in the last paper of this session. The difference between multiple scattering phenomena occurring in a medium with a well-defined, regular configuration of scatterers and in a medium with a random distribution of scatterers will be discussed in the third paper of this session. The transition from the solid to the gaseous state brings in, the additional consideration of the random motion of individual scatterers. It is tacitly assumed that this random motion destroys any phase relationship that may otherwise prevail amongst the various scattered beams (10, 11, 12). Hence the scattering process is considered incoherent and the various streams of radiation scattered in any particular direction will be independent of one another and the resultant radiation field can be evaluated by simple addition of intensities and other Stokes parameters, as opposed to the case of coherent scattering when amplitudes of the electric or magnetic vectors are to be considered. That this hypothesis of random motion of scatterers resulting in destruction of definitive phase relationships is correct has been convincingly proven in our own atmosphere. Measured values of intensity and the other Stokes parameters of radiation scattered by unit volume of air along any given direction are in good agreement with computed values based on the Rayleigh and Mie theories of scattering (5,6). The reason why considerable progress in the solution of radiative transfer in gaseous media has been made is the simplification introduced by the presence of incoherent scattering. As a prelude to the subject matter of several of the papers to be presented in this session, I would like to describe briefly some methods of solution of radiative transfer in media with incoherent scattering.

We tacitly assume that the optical properties of the individual scatterers are known, and hence also the law of scattering, which can be expressed as

$$\mathbf{E}^{(scat)}(\vec{n}) = \mathbf{S}(\vec{n} \cdot \vec{n}_0) \cdot \mathbf{E}^{(inc)}(\vec{n}_0), \quad \mathbf{E} \equiv \begin{bmatrix} E_\parallel \\ E_\perp \end{bmatrix} \qquad (1)$$

The preceding equation gives the relationship between the two orthogonal components of the electric vectors of the incident and scattered radiations. This relationship will have the simplest form when the two orthogonal directions are chosen to be parallel and normal to the plane of scattering defined by $\vec{n}$ and $\vec{n}_0$. However, when we have to add the scattereed radiations from all the scatterers in the case of multiple scattering, it is imperative that these two orthogonal directions are chosen such that they are independent of the manifold of scattering planes that are possible and also of the location of the individual scatterers. This can be done, for example, by taking the two orthogonal components along directions parallel and perpendicular to the plane defined by the direction of observation and another fixed direction, say, one normal to the boundary (if this is a plane) or the local vertical. Such a modification involves two rotations of the reference axes as indicated below:

$$\mathbf{E}^{(scat)}(\Omega) = \mathbf{R}(\pi - \beta) \cdot \mathbf{S}(\vec{n} \cdot \vec{n}_0) \cdot \mathbf{R}(-\alpha)\, \mathbf{E}^{(inc)}(\Omega_0) =$$
$$= \mathbf{L}(\Omega, \Omega_0) \cdot \mathbf{E}^{(inc)}(\Omega_0), (\Omega \equiv (\mu, \varphi)) \qquad (2)$$

where the conventional directional parameters μ and φ have been introduced. From this relationship for the components of the electric vectors of the incident and scattered radiations, it is easy to derive the corresponding relationship between the Strokes parameters (2, 4):

$$\mathbf{I}^{(scat)}(\Omega) = \mathbf{P}(\Omega, \Omega_0) \cdot \mathbf{I}^{(inc)}(\Omega_0) \qquad (3)$$

The matrix **P** for an individual scatterer is given by the Kronecker's product of the matrices **L** and their conjugates **L***, multiplied by a unitary transformation matrix **T** whose form depends on the choice of the particular set of Strokes parameters. The corresponding matrix pertaining to unit volume of the scattering medium can be conveniently called the "Invariant phase matrix", since its form is independent of the choice of the set of Stokes parameters. The elements of this matrix are obtained by summation of the corresponding elements of the matrices for the individual scatterers and hence they will in general vary with the location of the unit volume element since the particle density may vary from point to point within the medium. Therefore, we have for a single particle

$$P(\Omega, \Omega_0) = T \cdot [L \times L^*] \cdot T^{-1} = T \cdot \bar{p}(\Omega, \Omega_0) \cdot T^{-1} \tag{4}$$

and for unit volume,

$$p(\vec{r}, \Omega, \Omega_0) = \frac{1}{\beta_s(\vec{r})} \int_{a_0}^{a_1} \bar{p}(\Omega, \Omega_0)\, N(\vec{r}, a, m)\, da$$

$$P(\Omega, \Omega_0) = \beta_s(\vec{r})\, T \cdot p(\vec{r}, \Omega, \Omega_0) \cdot T^{-1} \tag{5}$$

From the definition of the invariant phase matrix, the reciprocity relationships which play a very important role in the reduction of the equation of radiative transfer can be readily derived (9) such as for, interchange of directions of observation and illumination:

$$p(\vec{r}, \Omega, \Omega_0) = \tilde{p}(\vec{r}, \Omega_0, \Omega); \tag{6}$$

reciprocity relationship for reversal of direction of observation

$$p(\vec{r}, \hat{\Omega}, \hat{\Omega}_0) = q \cdot \tilde{p}(\vec{r}, \Omega_0, \Omega) \cdot q \quad [\hat{\Omega} \equiv (-\mu, \varphi + \pi)] \tag{7}$$

where q is a diagonal matrix of the form $q \equiv (1, -1, -1, 1)$.

The fundamental task in the solution of the multiple scattering problem is the following: if the medium is illuminated by an external source of parallel radiation of net flux πF along the direction Ω_0, it is to determine the Stokes parameters of the diffuse radiation field $I(\vec{r}, \Omega)$ at any particular point defined by the position vector $\vec{r}$, and in the direction defined by the parameter Ω. For other types of illumination such as from internal sources or point sources, the solutions can be obtained by proper summation or modification of the above. Let us consider cylindrical volume element with its axis along ds and centered at the point P. Since this volume element is illuminated not only by the external source but also by the diffuse radiation scattered onto it by the neighboring scatterers, a part of the energy scattered by the elemental volume in the direction Ω appears as a kind of virtual emission which can be quantitatively expressed as $\beta_s(\vec{r})\ J(\vec{r}, \Omega)$ where the source matrix

$$J(\vec{r}, \Omega) = \frac{1}{4\pi} \int_{4\pi} p(\vec{r}, \Omega, \Omega')\ I(\vec{r}, \Omega')\ d\Omega' + \\ + \frac{1}{4}\ p(\vec{r}, \Omega, \Omega_0) \cdot F\ E(\vec{r}, \vec{r}_0, \Omega_0) \qquad (8)$$

In this and in all expressions that follow, the invariant phase matrix will be used so that in the final representation all the matrices should be multiplied by the transformation matrix **T** appropriate to the choice of the Stokes parameters. An attenuation factor whose form primarily depends on the geometry of the medium appears in the last term. When the source matrix is known, the diffuse radition field is given in terms of the source matrix integrated along the ray that passes through the point **P** in the direction Ω, the integration extending from the boundary to the point **P**.

$$I(\vec{r}, \Omega) = \int_{s_b}^{s_p} \beta_s(\vec{r}')\ J(r', \Omega)\ E(r, r', \Omega)\, ds' \qquad (9)$$

The differential form of the above expression yields the well-known equation of radiative transfer which gives the rate of change of the diffuse radiation along the elemental path ds.

Further analysis of the problem will be considerably simplified if we invoke the concept of a plane parallel medium where in it is assumed that complete homogeneity prevails along directions parallel to the boundary. As only localization parameter, the nondimensional optical thickness can be introduced which can be resolved into two parts--one due to scattering alone and the other due to absorption alone. It is also convenient to use another parameter, the albedo of single scattering defined as:

$$\omega(\tau) = \beta_s(z)/[\beta_s(z) + \beta_a(z)] = d\,\tau^{(s)}/d\tau \qquad (10)$$

The attenuation factor is then reduced to the simple exponential function

$$E(\vec{r}, \vec{r}', \Omega) = \exp[-|\tau(\vec{r}) - \tau(\vec{r}')|/\mu] \qquad (11)$$

If α and β denote the optical thicknesses at the boundaries of the medium, we can express the intensity matrix as:

$$: \mu I(\tau, +\Omega) = \int_{\tau}^{\beta} J(t, +\Omega)\, e^{-(t-\tau)/\mu}\, \omega(t)\, dt \qquad (12)$$

$$: \mu I(\tau, -\Omega) = \int_{\alpha}^{\tau} J(t, -\Omega)\, e^{-(\tau-t)/\mu}\, \omega(t)\, dt \quad \pm\Omega \equiv (\pm\mu.\varphi) \qquad (13)$$

Introduction of a convenient notation for hemispherical integration reduces the expression for the source matrix to the simple form (8):

$$J(\tau, \Omega) = \{p(\tau, \Omega, +\Omega') \cdot \mu' I(\tau, +\Omega')\} + \{p(\tau, \Omega, -\Omega') \cdot \mu' I(\tau, -\Omega')\} + \frac{1}{4} p(\tau, \Omega, -\Omega_0) \cdot F e^{-(\tau-\alpha)/\mu_0} \qquad (14)$$

where

$$\{A(\mu') \cdot B(\mu')\} = \frac{1}{4\pi} \int_0^1 \int_0^{2\pi} A(\mu') \cdot B(\mu') \frac{d\mu'}{\mu'} d\varphi' \qquad (15)$$

Solution of the problem involves solution of Eqs. 12, 13 and 14, can evidently be done either by substitution of the source matrix in the expressions for the intensity matrices or the other way around, i.e. by the substitution of the intensity matrices in the expression for the source matrix. In the latter case we arrive at the so-called auxiliary equations:

$$\mathbf{J}(\tau, \Omega) = \int_{\alpha}^{\tau} \{ \mathbf{p}(t, \Omega, -\Omega') \cdot \mathbf{J}(t, -\Omega') e^{-(\tau - t)/\mu} \} \omega(t) dt$$
$$+ \int_{\tau}^{\beta} \{ \mathbf{p}(t, \Omega, +\Omega') \cdot \mathbf{J}(t, +\Omega') e^{-(t-\tau)/\mu} \} \omega(t) dt$$
$$+ \frac{1}{4} \mathbf{p}(\tau, \Omega, -\Omega_0) \cdot \mathbf{F} e^{-\tau - \alpha/\mu_0} \qquad (16)$$

Subsequent solution of this equation depends entirely upon the form of the invariant phase matrix. Since in general the elements of the scattering matrix **S** (Eq. (1)) can be expressed as series of Legendre polynomials with the cosine of scattering angle as argument and since multiplication by the rotation matrices introduces factors expressible in terms of μ, μ' and $\varphi - \varphi'$, the elements of the invariant phase matrix can be developed into a harmonic series in $\varphi - \varphi'$. By collecting together elements involving the same multiple of $\varphi - \varphi'$ into a single matrix, the phase matrix can be expressed as:

$$\mathbf{p}(\tau, \Omega, \Omega') = \sum_{n=0}^{N} \mathbf{p}_n (\tau, \mu, \mu', n(\varphi - \varphi')) =$$
$$= \sum_{n=0}^{N} \mathbf{m}_n (\mu, \varphi) \cdot \tilde{\mathbf{m}}_n (\mu', \varphi') \qquad (17)$$

of either a finite number of terms or as infinite series. If the matrices $\mathbf{p}_n$ in this series can be written as a product of a matrix $\mathbf{m}_n$ and its transpose, either of them depending only on the directional parameters of either the incident or the scattered radiation, as will be the case in Rayleigh scattering, the solution of the problem is very much simplified. In this case of the separable matrices, it can be seen that the equations admit solutions which can be developed into similar series:

$$\mathbf{J}(\tau, \Omega) = \sum_{n=0}^{N} \mathbf{m}_n (\mu, \varphi) \cdot \mathbf{Z}_n (\tau, \mu_0) \cdot \tilde{\mathbf{m}}_n (-\mu_0, \varphi_0) \cdot \mathbf{F} \qquad (18)$$

$$\mathbf{I}(\tau, \Omega) = \sum_{n=0}^{N} \mathbf{m}_n (\mu, \varphi) \cdot \mathbf{I}_n (\tau, \mu, \mu_0) \cdot \tilde{\mathbf{m}}_n (-\mu_0, \varphi_0) \cdot \mathbf{F} \qquad (19)$$

By substituting eq. 18 for the source matrix in the auxiliary equation, we get for the matrices $\mathbf{Z}_n$ a system of auxiliary equations of a simple form (the Milne equations)

$$\mathbf{Z}_n(\tau, \mu) = e^{-\tau/\mu}\,\mathbf{E} + \int_{\alpha}^{\tau} \mathbf{K}_1^{(-)}(\tau - t) \cdot \mathbf{Z}_n(t, \mu)\,\omega(t)\,dt + \int_{\tau}^{\beta} \mathbf{K}_1^{(+)}(t - \tau) \cdot \mathbf{Z}_n(t, \mu)\,\omega(t)\,dt \tag{20}$$

where the kernel involves matrices corresponding to the Busbridge function

$$\mathbf{K}_1^{(\pm)}(t) = \int_0^1 \psi_n(\pm\mu)\, e^{-\tau/\mu} \frac{d\mu}{\mu} \tag{21}$$

and different types of scattering are taken into account by changes in the form of the characteristic f$\imath$nction

$$\psi_n(\pm\mu) = \frac{1}{4\pi} \int_0^{2\pi} \tilde{\mathbf{m}}_n(\pm\mu, n\varphi) \cdot \mathbf{m}_n(\pm\mu, n\varphi)\, d\varphi \tag{22}$$

Because of lack of time, I am unable to go into greater details of this analysis and hence I would like to mention only a special case--that of the albedo of single scattering, remaining constant throughout the entire medium. In this case it can be shown that the values of the source matrices $\mathbf{Z}_n$ at the boundaries depend only on the thickness of the medium $\beta - \alpha$ and that their transpose are identical to the **X** and **Y** matrices,

$$\tilde{\mathbf{Z}}_n(\alpha, \mu) = \mathbf{X}(\beta - \alpha, \mu), \quad \tilde{\mathbf{Z}}_n(\beta, \mu) = \mathbf{Y}(\beta - \alpha, \mu) \tag{23}$$

which satisfy a pair of non-linear integral equations, completely analogous to the well known equations for the **X** and **Y** functions of Chandrasekhar:

$$\mathbf{X}_n(\beta - \alpha, \mu) \equiv \mathbf{E} + \mu \int_0^1 [\mathbf{X}_n(\mu)\,\tilde{\mathbf{X}}_n(x) - \mathbf{Y}_n(\mu) \cdot \tilde{\mathbf{Y}}_n(x)] \cdot \psi_n(x) \frac{dx}{x + \mu}\, \mathbf{Y}_n(\beta - \alpha, \mu)$$

$$= \mathbf{E}\, e^{-(\beta - \alpha)/\mu} + \mu \int_0^1 [\mathbf{X}_n(\mu)\,\tilde{\mathbf{Y}}_n(x) - \mathbf{Y}_n(\mu) \cdot \tilde{\mathbf{X}}_n(x)] \cdot \psi_n(x) \frac{dx}{x - \mu} \tag{24}$$

When the **X** and **Y** matrices are computed from these equations, the intensity and Stokes parameters of the radiation emerging from the medium can be directly computed without any additional quadrature,

$$\mathbf{I}_n(\alpha, +\mu) = \frac{1}{4}\frac{\mu_0}{\mu_0+\mu}\left[\mathbf{X}_n(\mu)\,\tilde{\mathbf{X}}_n(\mu_0) - \mathbf{Y}_n(\mu)\cdot\tilde{\mathbf{Y}}_n(\mu_0)\right]$$

$$\mathbf{I}_n(\beta, -\mu) = \frac{1}{4}\frac{\mu_0}{\mu_0-\mu}\left[\mathbf{X}_n(\mu)\tilde{\mathbf{Y}}_n(\mu_0) - \mathbf{Y}_n(\mu)\tilde{\mathbf{X}}_n(\mu_0)\right] \tag{25}$$

It should however be mentioned that the system of non-linear integral equations for the **X** and **Y** matrices can be derived directly from the equation of radiative transfer with the use of the invariance principle (7) or its modification--the so-called invariant imbedding. When the equation of radiative transfer in its original form or the auxiliary equations are solved, for example, by successive iterations, three quadratures are to be performed for the determination of the source matrix and an additional quadrature is needed for the computation of the intensity matrix. This requires a knowledge of the source matrix for all values of μ and φ and for each value of τ in the interval $\alpha \leq \tau \leq \beta$ whereas after reduction of these equations to the **X** and **Y** matrices, only a single quadrature is required in the integral equations for the **X** and **Y** matrices. Moreover, it was observed that the method of successive iterations as applied to the auxiliary equations for the matrices $\mathbf{Z}_n$ has far slower rate of convergence for large optical thicknesses than when it is applied to the equations for the **X** and **Y** matrices. The only disadvantage of the use of non-linear equations is that their solutions may not be unique. However, it is easy to derive from the nonlinear equations a system of singular linear integral equations which can be used not only for the solution of the problem of non-uniqueness but also to develop a computational scheme wherein the iteration scheme converges faster and better for increasing optical thickness (3). It also yields very useful asymptotic expressions for large τ. It is usually cited, as a proven advantage of the solution of the problem with the use of auxiliary equations, that the radiation field inside the medium can be computed at the same time as the emergent radiations purely as a computation by-product. As will be discussed in the fourth paper of this session, the computational scheme based on the singular linear integral equations for the **X** and **Y** matrices, as developed by Prof. Mullikin can also be used for the computation of the internal field. This successful method of solution of the radiative transfer problem will be demonstrated for the simpliest case of Rayleigh scattering in a medium with random distribution of scatterers in Brownian motion. Serious complications may indeed arrive for different forms of scattering. Dr. Bullough will discuss the complication that may appear in molecular scattering and the fifth paper of this session will deal with the solution of radiative transfer for the case of strong asymmetric scattering.

I would like to conclude these introductory remarks by mentioning two points related to the problem of multiple scattering. The complexity of mathematical analysis of such problems is often used for an excuse to disregard polarization produced by scattering and the only the scalar problem of scattered intensity is solved. This procedure is fully justified if the phase matrix is reducible with respect to the first column and row, if the intensity is the first element of the matrix I. This however is never the case, even for the simplest form of scattering, like Rayleigh scattering, the phase matrix is not reducible. Therefore, as mentioned for the first time by Chandrasekhar in his treatise on Radiative Transfer (1) such procedures always lead to erroneous results. The full and complete consideration of polarization produced by scattering does lead to a quite tractable mathematical analysis and such efforts are rewarded with the knowledge of three additional parameters which then can be used to derive more informations from an analysis of the emergent radiation.

My concluding and final remark concerns the so-called 'brute force' solution of the radiative transfer problem. By this I have in mind the use of high speed computers. The basic equations in their fundamental (primitive) form are programmed, without any reduction, in such a way that quadratures are replaced by summation and differentiation by finite difference schemes and finally evaluated by the method of successive iterations. Undoubtedly such methods do yield large amount of data quickly which can even by trusted provided that careful analysis of truncation and other errors is made and published with the date. As is the case in all problems solved by such 'brute force' methods, very little is gained towards the understanding of the physics of the problem. As opposed to this, proper mathematical analysis may indeed lead to the physics of the problem. Such mathematical analysis may not only offer an easy computational scheme for diverse other quantities such as flux, radiation pressure, etc. without the necessity of additional quaderature, but also allows, in many instances, optimization of experimental methods underlying the so called 'Inversion problems', i.e. the determination of the intrinsic parameters of the medium from the measurement of emerging radiation.

For this reason, I feel we are still fully justified to continue discussions that by the supporter of the 'brute force' solution may be considered utterly useless.

REFERENCES

(1) Chandrasekhar, S., Radiative Transfer. Clarendon Press, Oxford (1950).

(2) Marathay, A. S., "Operator Formalism in the Theory of Partial Polarization." J. Opt. Soc. Am., 55, 969 (1965).

(3) Mullikin, T. W., "Uniqueness Problems in the Mathematics of Multiple Scattering," ICES (1), 559 (1963).

(4) O'Neill, E. L., Introduction to Statistical Optics. Addison-Wesley (1963).

(5) Sekera, Z., "Recent Developments in the Study of the Polarization of Skylight," Advances in Geophysics, Vol. III, 43 (1956).

(6) Sekera, Z., "Polarization of Skylight," Encyclopedia of Physics, Vol. XLVIII, 288 (1957).

(7) Sekera Z., "Radiation Transfer in a Planetary Atmosphere with Imperfect Scattering," Rand Corporation, Project

A Unified Approach to Molecular Scattering Theory

R. K. Bullough
The College of Science and Technology,
Manchester, England
and
NORDITA, Copenhagen, Denmark

ABSTRACT

The more significant conclusions that have so far emerged from a unified theory of the optical properties of condensed molecular systems are presented. The theory shows that multiple scattering can play a significant role in many optical phenomena; in particular it can modify the individual microscopic scattering processes so that they become 'screened' in a medium of refractive index $m \neq 1$. The status within the theory of Einstein's scattering formulae for small molecules is indicated and the potential importance of screening and multiple scattering in the extension of the formulae to large molecules and critical scattering is noted. The significance of excess scattering in the two component system is briefly examined in relation to both critical and (very briefly) non-critical scattering from solutions. It is noted that the 'solvation condition' introduced here permits some understanding of other environmental effects in the two component system like 'form' birefringence. The more general environmental effects due to both single and multiple scattering next briefly surveyed here can have a significant effect on the complex refractive index of both anisotropic and isotropic media; it is noted for example that one aspect of this is the modification of the absorption process displayed in the 'hypochromism' of ultra-violet absorption in polynucleotides.

I. INTRODUCTION

I want in this paper to report on some of the main results of the work on the optical properties of condensed molecular systems which I have carried out in the last few years. I shall stress two themes: first, what appears to me to be the real value of a unified approach to the theory of molecular optics, particularly in its ability to describe in a consistent way multifarious macroscopic optical phenomena by means of a theory which starts in the first instance from the interaction of individual 'optical' electrons with an electromagnetic field; and second, the significant role at 'optical' frequencies of the multiple scattering of photons between the molecules of a condensed system in the theoretical description of these macroscopic optical properties.

Although the relation of macroscopic optical phenomena to the microscopic interactions of a system's constituent particles has long been understood in principle (cf. e.g. Lorentz, 26; Ewald, 18, 19; Darwin 12),* three difficulties lie in the way of a unified theory: first, the calculation of the

*One might exclude the recent advent of the laser from this remark although in principle a description of laser emission is contained in the work on stimulated emission due to Einstein and Dirac. Points of detail still remain here however (cf. e.g. Doniach, 16).

optical properties of individual molecules still lies at the limit of our theoretical resources; second the optical interactions of what might be very simple individual molecules become in combination the interactions of very complicated many-body systems; third, even the interaction of a single pair of such simple individuals contains the not inconsiderable complications of classical electrodynamics--and in the last resort of quantum electrodynamics, but I do not attempt to consider this here. (Both the techniques and fundamental postulates of quantum field theory--notably the emphasis on Green's functions rather than on Maxwell's electromagnetic field equations—may eventually be of service in the present context; at the moment such an approach usually means the neglect of the object of interest here--the local internal field (cf. e.g. Fano, 20; Hopfield, 22; Nozieres and Pines, 28; Doniach, 16)). I shall avoid the first difficulty by dealing solely with the theory of what I shall call 'molecular' systems. On the other hand I hope to show that we are some way towards surmounting the two difficulties remaining.

I shall show that the many-body problem and the electrodynamical problem conspire to produce an old and often worked problem--that of the 'internal field' first studied by Lorentz. But, I shall deliberately maintain a 'single' and 'multiple' scattering point of view rather than an internal field one for two reasons: first, this choice will emphasize that the theory I shall describe <u>is</u> a scattering theory; secondly, although the internal field appears as a complication in molecular theories of all optical phenomena in condensed media, there seems to be no <u>unique</u> expression for the internal field which is valid in each and every context, and one aspect of the role of the multiple scattering lies in the destruction of this uniqueness. For this reason my original hope that a unified theory of optical phenomena would permit the demonstration of <u>quantitative</u> relations between the observable phenomena has largely proved abortive: nevertheless, I hope to show that such a unified theory can tell us much about the interrelation of these phenomena and much about the correlation functions which are the theory's principal structural support.

The role of multiple scattering is no better exemplified

than in the theory of the external scattering and it is this problem I shall treat in greatest detail here: the internal field in this problem proves to be different from the one one would naturally develop from the early theory of Lorentz and so it is not the one appearing in, for example, the theory of birefringence. This is one reason for the long history of criticism levelled at Einstein's (17) fundamental scattering formula.* Until the work of Fixman (21) such criticisms were always based on 'physical' interpretations of the internal field which was implicitly held to be unique. (This is the explicit assumption of Lax (24), for example, who also describes a unified multiple scattering approach to optical and other phenomena.) Now it seems that it could be possible to maintain this point of view only by changing the set of molecules to different equivalent sets of 'quasi-particles' according to the context (Bullough, 5). This has much to do with a formulation of the theory in terms of screened optical interactions which I describe as one aspect of the theory in the work below.

II. QUANTAL CONSIDERATIONS

For the starting point of the theory I assume we need dig no deeper than the Schrödinger equation. We consider a system of N molecules, for definiteness with one optical electron each, and start from the time dependent equation

$$\sum_{i=1}^{N} H_i^{(0)} \Psi + \sum_{i=1}^{N} \sum_{j \neq i}^{N} H_{ij}^{(1)} \Psi = i\hbar \frac{\partial \Psi}{\partial t}, \tag{1}$$

where the $H_i^{(0)}$ are set of Hamiltonians for each of the independent and isolated molecules. The $H_{ij}^{(1)}$ are a set of interaction Hamiltonians and will depend in our present case of interest on three things:—the incident electromag-

*For accounts of the criticisms cf. e.g. Cabannes (10), Lax (24) or Fixman (21).

netic field, interactions between the molecules due entirely to that incident field, and interactions between the molecules which would be present even in the absence of the incident field. I assume this last interaction is very small so that the system is a 'molecular' one, e.g. a molecular crystal, a fluid bound by weak intermolecular forces, and so on. This ensures that the obvious basis functions, the eigen functions of the $H_i^{(0)}$, are also physically significant ones.

The $H_{ij}^{(1)}$ are still complicated because the electromagnetic interaction can be expressed as a set of fields at molecules i due to the sets of N-1 molecules different from i and each of these fields will depend on the radiation damping (and formally at least on the self energy) of particle i itself. Thus it is not convenient to use the divergenceless vector potential and possibly zero scalar potential of Coulomb gauge (as is the usual practice in elementary treatments of the interaction of radiation and matter); we must have in the

$$\sum_{j \neq i} H_{ij}^{(1)}$$

a scalar potential

$$\phi_i = \sum_{j \neq i} \phi_{ij} \quad ,$$

and a vector potential

$$\mathbf{a}_i = \sum_{j \neq i} \mathbf{a}_{ij}$$

of the fields scattering from the N-1 molecules different from i onto i.* The ϕ_i and $\mathbf{a}_i$ are a quantal description of

*The 'unscreened' calculations described below are carried through in Lorentz gauge: the 'screened' calculations use a gauge fixed by the physical context, neither Lorentz nor Coulomb. We can actually work the 'unscreened' calculation in Coulomb gauge as long as $\phi_i \neq 0$.

the internal field: they are potentials of multiple scattering in that they depend on the positions (and, because we deal with molecules of arbitrary shape, orientations) of all the N molecules. They are unknown and their determination represents the solution of the problem of evaluating the internal field.

For our assumed 'molecular' system it both makes physical sense and offers theoretical advantage to make an intermediate step in the passage from the Schrödinger equation (1) to a theoretical description of the macroscopic optical properties of the system. We treat the $H_{ij}^{(1)}$ as perturbations on the Hamiltonian

$$\sum_{i=1}^{N} H_i^{(0)},$$

and set up a system of integral equations for the ϕ_i and $\mathbf{a}_i$ (Bullough, 6). I shall not attempt to survey this calculation here: it suffices to say that because the system is molecular in the sense described above, we can eliminate the $H_i^{(0)}$, and more precisely their eigenfunctions $\Psi_i^{(0)}$, by introducing as parameters the familiar 'multipolarisabilities' of the isolated molecules, and deal with the perturbations $H_{ij}^{(1)}$ as perturbations in terms of these parameters. Then we reach an intermediate set of molecular scattering equations.

The 'multipolarisabilities' are:- α, the dipolarisability; λ, the quadripolarisability; etc. In particular the induced dipole moment $\mathbf{P}_j$ of molecule j in a field $\mathbf{e}_j$ is

$$\mathbf{P}_j = \alpha_j \cdot \mathbf{e}_j \quad .$$

I confine attention entirely to the polarisability and the induced dipole moments here; but it is essential to realise that the local internal field can depend significantly on the multipolarisabilities of several orders (Bullough, 3, Appendix 2 a). I must add also that the use of the polarisabilities and excited state wave functions of the isolated molecules is permissible at best only because, by hypothesis, the system is a molecular one; whilst we are also obliged to neglect certain exchange terms (which are nevertheless small because of the small 'overlap' in molecular systems) and the more interesting 'electron correlation' terms which are similar in provenance and structure to the multiple scattering terms I describe below.

For relative simplicity let us look, then, at the dipole fields and ignore these other complications. Equation (1) can be reduced (Bullough, 6) to the N simultaneous equations

$$\mathbf{P}_i = \alpha_i \cdot \left\{ \mathbf{E}(\mathbf{x}_i) + \sum_{j \neq i}^{\cdot} \mathsf{T}_{ij} \cdot \mathbf{P}_j \right\} . \quad (2)$$

$\mathbf{E}(\mathbf{x}_i)$ is the electric field incident from outside onto the whole system of N molecules evaluated at the points $\mathbf{x}_i$ occupied by individual molecules i. These points are confined within a certain volume V of interest. First we treat the one component system so all the α_i are the same tensor; but these tensors will have different matrices for each of the, in general different, orientations of the molecules i. The T_{ij} are interaction tensors describing by $\mathsf{T}_{ij} \cdot \mathbf{P}_j$ the field at $\mathbf{x}_i$ when there is a dipole moment $\mathbf{P}_j$ at $\mathbf{x}_j$: thus they are fields depending on $\mathbf{x}_i$ and $\mathbf{x}_j$ and must be tensor fields because the polarising field at $\mathbf{x}_i$ is not in general in the same direction as $\mathbf{P}_j$. (Explicitly

$$\mathsf{T}_{ij} \equiv (\nabla_i \nabla_i + k_0^2 \mathsf{U})(e^{-ik_0 r_{ij}} / r_{ij})$$

where $r_{ij} = |\mathbf{x}_i - \mathbf{x}_j|$, U is the unit tensor and k_0 is the incident wave number but we shall not need this explicit form). The $\mathbf{P}_i$ are related directly to the potentials ϕ_i and $\mathbf{a}$: thus they are multiply scattered dipole moments and depend on the co-ordinates and orientations of all the molecules of the system.

Equations (2) are the 'classical scattering equations' which we have now to solve.

III. SOLUTION OF THE CLASSICAL SCATTERING EQUATIONS

To solve Eqs. (2) it is necessary either to have fixed

molecular sites $\mathbf{x}_i$ as in a cold* molecular crystal, or to treat the problem statistically as is appropriate for the molecular fluid. The first problem is considered elsewhere (Bullough 6) and I consider only the second problem here.

We introduce a statistical distribution function symbolised by $p(\mathfrak{w})$. This will be the classical grand canonical distribution function appropriate to the volume V, temperature T, and chemical potential μ of the one component. It is essential to the theory of scattering that we use the grand canonical distribution function and permit exchange of particles in V: this, however, leads us into the paradoxical situation that it is certainly most convenient, and from some points of view really desirable, to treat the optical problem as one concerned with a finite assembly of N molecules in a bounded volume V, whereas I shall show below that such a finite boundary plays a very significant role in the theory of scattering. This is one reason for attempting the so called 'screened' optical theory of the infinite system which I also describe below.

A quantity of obvious interest is the average dipole moment of particle i**

$$\overline{\mathbf{P}}_i \equiv V < \mathbf{P}_i \ \delta(\mathbf{x} - \mathbf{x}_i) \ p(\mathfrak{w}) > . \tag{3}$$

$< >$ denotes integration over the set $\mathfrak{w}$ of all co-ordinates $\mathbf{x}_i$ (and possibly orientations) of the molecules, and the δ-function simply transfers $\mathbf{x}_i$ to an arbitrary point $\mathbf{x}$: then $\overline{\mathbf{P}}_i(\mathbf{x})$ depends on the one co-ordinate $\mathbf{x}$, yet is an obvious approximation to $\mathbf{P}_i$ which depends on the N co-ordinates $\mathbf{x}_i$. We consider a homogeneous (and except briefly in §6) isotropic fluid so that all the molecular one particle functions are the same and we could simply drop

---

*The use of cold in this context disregards the zero point motion in the crystal. The effect of finite temperature is briefly noted e.g. early in Section VI.

**The factor V here is a result of the chosen 'normalisation' of $p(\mathfrak{w})$.

the subscript i on $\overline{\mathbf{P}}_i$. But in a crystal or even in a rubber-like network (Bullough, 3) we cannot so easily drop the index i, whilst here, because we use the distribution function of the grand canonical ensemble $p(\mathfrak{w})$, it is still convenient to consider instead of (3) the quantity

$$\overline{\mathbf{P}}(\mathbf{x}) \equiv n^{-1} < \sum_{i=1}^{N} \mathbf{P}_i \, \delta(\mathbf{x} - \mathbf{x}_i) \, p(\mathfrak{w}) > \qquad (3')$$

in which

$$n \equiv < \sum_{i=1}^{N} \delta(\mathbf{x} - \mathbf{x}_i) \, p(\mathfrak{w}) >$$

is the average number density of molecules in V.

Now we can express the average of (2) in the form

$$\overline{\mathbf{P}}(\mathbf{x}) = < \alpha > \cdot \mathbf{E}(\mathbf{x}) + n^{-1} < \sum_{i=1}^{N} \sum_{j \neq i}^{N} \alpha_i \cdot \mathsf{T}_{ij} \cdot \mathbf{P}_j \, \delta(\mathbf{x} - \mathbf{x}_i) p(\mathfrak{w}) >. \qquad (4)$$

Since $< >$ amounts to integration this is an implicit inhomogeneous integral equation for $\overline{\mathbf{P}}(\mathbf{x})$. We shall here simplify further by replacing both the $<\alpha>$ and the α_i by scalars α thus making the polarisabilities isotropic: the more general case has been treated (Bullough, 3). We then rewrite (4) as exactly the same equation

$$\overline{\mathbf{P}}(\mathbf{x}) = \alpha \{ \mathbf{E}(\mathbf{x}) + n^{-1} \int < \sum_{i=1}^{N} \sum_{j \neq i}^{N} \mathsf{T}_{ij} \, \delta(\mathbf{x} - \mathbf{x}_i) \delta(\mathbf{x}' - \mathbf{x}_j) p(\mathfrak{w}) > \cdot \cdot \overline{\mathbf{P}}(\mathbf{x}') \, d\mathbf{x}' \} \qquad (5)$$

$$+ \alpha n^{-1} < \sum_{i=1}^{N} \sum_{j \neq i}^{N} \mathsf{T}_{ij} \cdot (\mathbf{P}_j - \overline{\mathbf{P}}(\mathbf{x}_j)) \delta(\mathbf{x} - \mathbf{x}_i) \, p(\mathfrak{w}) > .$$

We solve this by dropping the last term on the right hand side, solving for $\overline{\mathbf{P}}(\mathbf{x})$, and then iterating with this discovered $\overline{\mathbf{P}}(\mathbf{x})$ on the last term.* It is the iteration of this last term which introduces the multiple scattering terms and causes all the trouble.

Since

$$< \sum_{i=1}^{N} \sum_{j \neq i}^{N} T_{ij}\, \delta(\mathbf{x} - \mathbf{x}_i)\, \delta(\mathbf{x}' - \mathbf{x}_j)\, p(\mathfrak{w}) > \; = n^2 g(\mathbf{x}, \mathbf{x}')\, T(\mathbf{x}, \mathbf{x}')$$

where $T(\mathbf{x}, \mathbf{x}')$ is the analogue for $\mathbf{x}$, $\mathbf{x}'$ of T_{ij} for $\mathbf{x}_i$, $\mathbf{x}_j$, and $g(\mathbf{x}, \mathbf{x}')$ is the two particle correlation function derived from the grand canonical distribution function satisfying $g(\mathbf{x}, \mathbf{x}') \to 1$ as $|\mathbf{x} - \mathbf{x}'| \to \infty$, we can derive the solution of (5) with its last term dropped

$$\overline{\mathbf{P}}(\mathbf{x}) = \mathrm{u}\, \overline{\mathrm{P}}_0\, e^{-im\mathbf{k}_0 \cdot \mathbf{x}} \tag{6}$$

when the incident field is

$$\mathbf{E}(\mathbf{x}) = \mathbf{u}\, E_0\, e^{-i\mathbf{k}_0 \cdot \mathbf{x}}$$

This solution is unique and exact providing only that the parameter m satisfies

$$\frac{m^2 - 1}{m^2 + 2} = \frac{4\pi}{3}\, n\alpha\, [1 - n\alpha J_1]^{-1} \tag{7}$$

where

$$J_1 \equiv \int_{\text{all space}} \{ g(\mathbf{x}, \mathbf{x}') - 1 \}\; \mathrm{u} \cdot T(\mathbf{x}, \mathbf{x}') \cdot \mathrm{u}\, e^{-im\mathbf{k}_0 \cdot (\mathbf{x}' - \mathbf{x})} d\mathbf{x}'. \tag{8}$$

---

*It may appear curious that by solving one integral equation we find the solution of another. The situation is a possible one in that we derive a condition for the consistency of the solution (namely equation (7)) which becomes modified by the iteration to include the multiple scattering terms. In fact, however, the multiple scattering modifies the solution for $\overline{\mathbf{P}}(\mathbf{x})$ as well as the consistency condition (Bullough, 7).

In (6), (8), and throughout, u is a unit vector in the direction of polarisation of the incident light. Because of (6), m is the refractive index which must satisfy (7): it will be the refractive index of the system when but only when (7) is modified by the multiple scattering corrections.

In (7) we have the usual Lorenz-Lorentz relation with a correction due to the pair correlation between the molecules. (It is very much worthwhile comparing the derivation of equation (7) here with the in some ways more direct argument given by Rosenfeld (30): his argument was indeed the starting point of the developments described here. For an alternative view a semi-intuitive argument based on the idea of the internal field whose intention is explanatory but which nevertheless picks up some of the points ignored here will appear in a paper entitled 'Theory of Hypochromism' (Bullough, 8). The rigorous argument for the general anisotropic system has appeared already (Bullough, 3).) Although in (7) we have obtained an extension of Lorentz's result we have not used the Lorentz sphere: nevertheless J_1 is obviously a part of Lorentz's local field and perspicuously such when (7) is put in the form

$$\frac{m^2 - 1}{m^2 + 2} = \frac{4\pi}{3} n\alpha \left[1 + n\alpha J_1 + n^2\alpha^2 J_1^2 + \ldots\ldots\right]. \tag{9}$$

From (9) we see also that the internal field will not assume any 'obvious' form:—$\mathbf{u} \cdot \mathbf{T}(\mathbf{x}, \mathbf{x}') \cdot \mathbf{u}$ is the component of the field in the direction u at **x** due to a dipole **u** at **x**': $g(\mathbf{x}, \mathbf{x}') - 1$ is the excess (or deficiency) of particles at **x**' above (or below) a uniform distribution because of correlation with a particle fixed at **x**: thus the integrand of $n\alpha J_1$ is the obvious field due to a dipole moment $\mathbf{u}(n\alpha)\,d\mathbf{x}'$ at **x**' evaluated at **x**, and the integral is the average of this field. But we see that all powers of this local field term contribute to the total local field.

J_1 is a single scattering term since it depends only on the field at **x** due to a source at **x**' : it is in some cases the most interesting part of the local field and in suitably generalised form provides a theoretical description of observable optical phenomena as various as external scattering (Rosenfeld, 30; Bullough, 4, 5), optical rotation (Bullough, 3, § 7 and Appendix 2(b)), birefringence (Bullough, 2), frequency splitting in crystals (Bullough, 6), hypochromism (i.e. the variation of the absorption intensity with the state of denaturation of polymers like DNA) (Bullough, 8, 9) and so on*. The special significance of J_1 is, however, to some extent imposed upon us by the fact that it depends only on the pair correlation function $g(\mathbf{x}, \mathbf{x}')$ and we have some hope of calculating this for real fluids (cf e.g. De Boer, 14; Brout, 1). I shall now suggest that for an adequate theory of most optical phenomena it will not be sufficient to consider J_1 alone.

We remember from (5) that the multiple scattering adds to the single scattering term containing $g(\mathbf{x}, \mathbf{x}')$: the result is to add a multiple scattering series to $n\alpha J_1$ and $n\alpha J_1$ is replaced by

$$\sum_{r=1}^{\infty} (n\alpha)^r J_r \qquad \text{(say)}.$$

Thus although the local field term as it is expressed in (9) can also be given in closed form the multiple scattering series apparently cannot. This series apparently does not converge as fast as is often implicitly assumed: if $m \sim 1{\cdot}5$, $n\alpha \sim 1/16$, but with sufficient molecular correlation the J_r can apparently approach magnitudes near to Lorentz's own internal field term $4\pi/3$ so that the series goes roughly as $(1/4)^r$. In the theory of scattering this last figure is apparently too low an estimate: in the theory of the refractive index of those isotropic systems like the sequence of paraffins which satisfy the Lorenz-Lorentz relation to 0.1 per cent $(n\alpha)^r J_r \sim (1/16)^r$ is a much better approximation.

The J_r are complicated. Here are the first three:

$$J_1 \equiv \int \mathbf{u} \cdot \mathsf{T}(\mathbf{x}, \mathbf{x}') \cdot \mathbf{u}\, e^{-imk_0 \cdot (\mathbf{x}' - \mathbf{x})} \{ g(\mathbf{x}, \mathbf{x}') - 1 \} d\mathbf{x}' \;;$$

*Several phenomena are discussed in terms of J_1 in § 7 of my paper (3).

$$J_2 \equiv \int u \cdot T(x, x') \cdot T(x', x'') \cdot u \, e^{-imk_0 \cdot (x''-x)}$$

$$\{ g_{123}(x, x', x'') - g_{12}(x, x') g_{23}(x', x'') \} \, dx'' dx'$$

$$+ \frac{1}{n} \int u \cdot T(x, x') \cdot T(x', x) \cdot u \, g_{12}(x, x') \, dx' \; ; \; g_{12}(x, x') \equiv g(x, x');$$

$$J_3 \equiv \int u \cdot T(x, x') \cdot T(x', x'') \cdot T(x'', x''') \cdot u \, e^{-imk_0 \cdot (x'''-x)}$$

$$\{ g_{1234}(x, x', x'', x''') - g_{12}(x, x') g_{234}(x', x'', x''')$$

$$- g_{123}(x, x', x'') g_{34}(x'', x''')$$

$$+ g_{12}(x, x') g_{23}(x', x'') g_{34}(x'', x''') \} \, dx''' dx'' dx'$$

$$+ \frac{1}{n} \int u \cdot T(x, x') \cdot T(x', x'') \cdot T(x'', x') \cdot u \, e^{-imk_0 \cdot (x'-x)}$$

$$\{ g_{123}(x, x', x''.) - g_{12}(x, x') g_{23}(x', x'') \} \, dx'' dx'$$

$$+ \frac{1}{n} \int u \cdot T(x, x') \cdot T(x', x) . T(x, x'') \cdot u \, e^{-imk_0 \cdot (x''-x)}$$

$$\{ g_{123}(x, x', x'') - g_{12}(x, x') g_{23}(x, x'') \} \, dx'' dx'$$

$$+ \frac{1}{n} \int u \cdot T(x, x') \cdot T(x', x'') \cdot T(x'', x) \cdot u \, g_{123}(x, x', x'') \, dx'' dx'$$

$$+ \frac{1}{n^2} \int u \cdot T(x, x') \cdot T(x', x) \cdot T(x, x') \cdot u \, e^{-imk_0 \cdot (x'-x)} g_{12}(x, x') \, dx' .$$

It is plain that J_r depends on the configurations of $(r + 1)$ molecules and so contains correlation functions of order $r + 1$: further it contains the tensor fields scattered between these particles and it is for this reason that we can call the J_r multiple scattering terms when $r > 1$.

J_1 is a single scattering term which we can symbolize by such a Mayer diagram (Brout, 1; Mayer and Mayer, 27) as is displayed in (a) of Fig. 1. The dumb-bell structure indicates the tensor $T(x, x') e^{-imk_0 \cdot (x'-x)}$ (in the summations of Fig. 3 α times T alone, however) and the cross shows that the correlation function g_{12} entirely 'covers' that tensor: the integration is over all co-ordinates but that of '1' at **x**, and we take the uu-component of the tensor. In the same way we can display J_2 and J_3 as in (b) and (c) of Fig. 1.

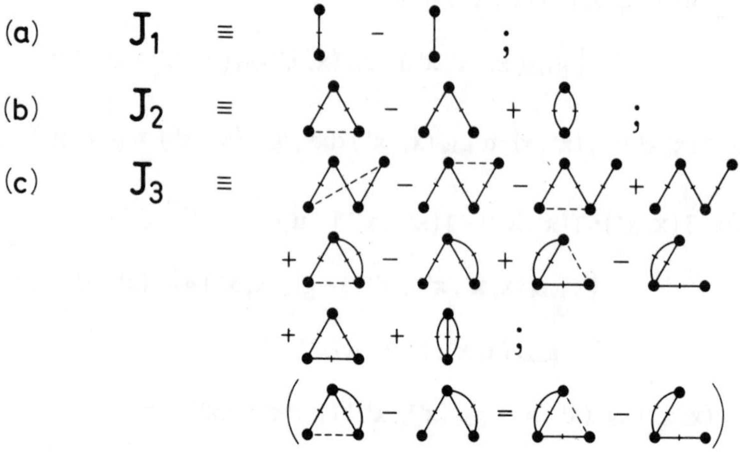

Fig. 1. Diagrams for J_1, J_2 and J_3.

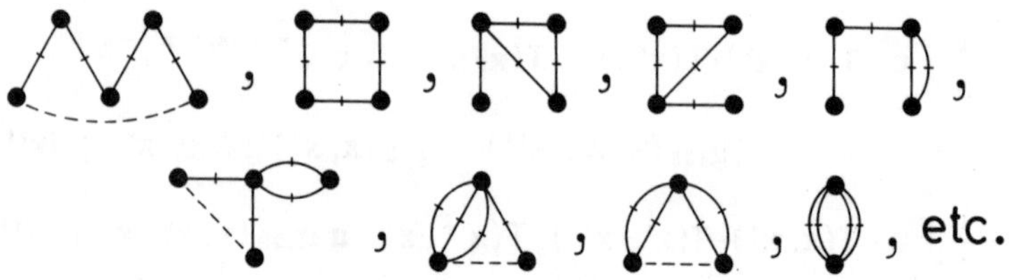

Fig. 2. Some diagrams contributing to J_4.

Some of the diagrams contributing to J_4 appear in Fig. 2.

It is not my purpose in this paper to discuss the structure of this multiple scattering series in detail (and in any case I still have much to do on it). Those who are familiar with the virial expansion for a dilute non-ideal gas will, however, already see formal similarities. For example, it is possible to infer that the term $(n\alpha)^r J_r$ of arbitrary order r contains terms in n^r, n^{r-1}, ..., n and it is therefore possible to convert the multiple scattering series in the J_r to one of the virial type*

---

*In practice one would use the mass density (instead of n) as a manifestly small parameter at a small enough mass density.

$$\sum_{s=1}^{\infty} n^s K_s$$

where the K_s now depend on α : in particular we have formal results like those of Fig. 3 in which

$$\equiv \int u \cdot T(x, x')\, e^{-imk_0 \cdot (x' - x)} \cdot [U - \alpha^2 T(x, x') \cdot T(x', x)]^{-1} \cdot ug_{12}(x, x')\, dx' \tag{11a}$$

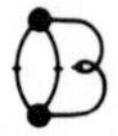

$$\equiv \int u \cdot T(x, x') \cdot T(x', x) \cdot [U - \alpha^2 T(x, x') \cdot T'(x', x)]^{-1} \cdot ug_{12}(x, x')\, dx' \tag{11b}$$

where U is the unit tensor, and as noted earlier we have summed on αT rather than $T e^{-imk_0 \cdot (x' - x)}$.

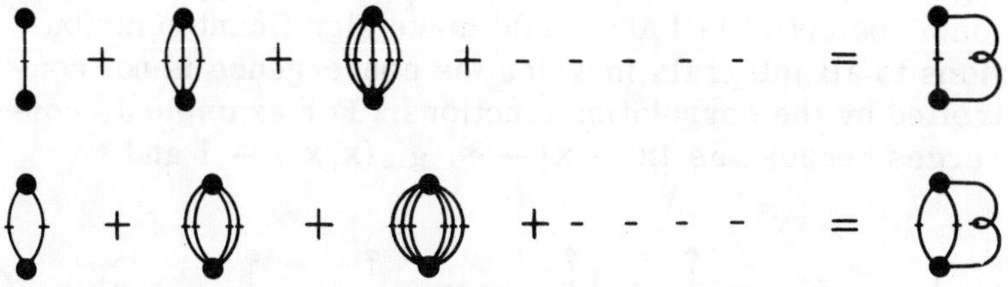

Fig. 3. Examples of diagram summation: the sums are defined in Eqs. (11).

However, the multiple scattering series is much more complicated than the virial series in that it is necessary to retain both irreducible and reducible clusters, and it is also necessary to distinguish the combinations of the correlation functions which appear in the integrands. Fortunately the series has one great advantage over the virial series: the coefficient $(n\alpha)^r$ of J_r is, as we have seen, about $(1/16)^r$ in a condensed system ($m \approx 1.5$) so that in the sense of the virial expansion the system is moderately 'dilute'. This seems to be too simple a point of view in some contexts, however, particularly in the theory of the external scattering which we now consider.

IV. THEORY OF EXTERNAL SCATTERING

To see the complications in the theory of the external scattering we must look carefully at the correlation functions in the integrands of the J_r: for example, J_2 contains the combination

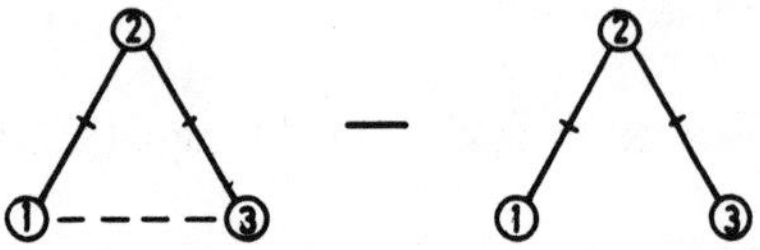

The tensor $\mathsf{T}(\mathbf{x}, \mathbf{x}')\ e^{-imk_0 \cdot (x'-x)}$ symbolised by the dumb-bell in 1 and 2 describes the field at particle 1 at $\mathbf{x}$ due to scattering from source 2 at $\mathbf{x}'$ (together with an additional exponential factor): part of this field is a radiation field falling asymptotically as $|\mathbf{x} - \mathbf{x}'|^{-1}$. This is a typical 'Coulomb' potential tail and would make significant contributions to all integrals in which the convergence is not controlled by the correlation functions. For example J_1 converges because as $|\mathbf{x}' - \mathbf{x}| \to \infty$, $g_{12}(\mathbf{x}, \mathbf{x}') \to 1$ and *

as $|x' - x| \to \infty$.

(12)

However, if we apply the same argument to J_2 we find that the term which would be in n^2 behaves as follows when $|\mathbf{x} - \mathbf{x}'| \to \infty$ and $|\mathbf{x} - \mathbf{x}''|$ stays small:

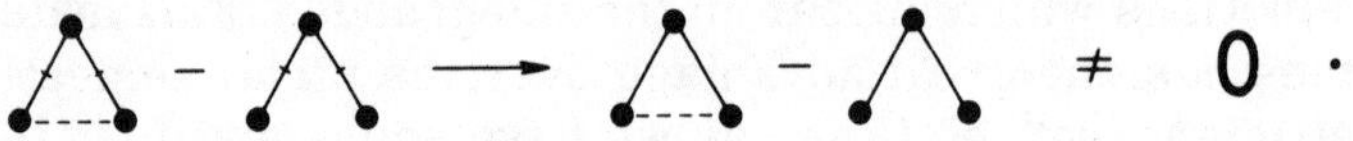

(13)

*We here use the diagrams to describe the integrands rather than the integrals.

Thus the integral depends on the Coulomb tail, it must be evaluated over a finite volume V (since it could be divergent oscillatory for a spherical V for example when $V \to \infty$) and so it depends on the shape of the volume V containing the molecules.*

As far as I can see at the moment this sort of thing happens in all terms in n^s, $s > 1$. It also seems that the result is peculiar to the theory of refractive index, and the theory of dielectric constant we obtain by putting $k_0 = 0$ has all integrals convergent. It is certain, for example, that exactly the situation of (13) occurs in the dielectric theory; but because there is now no Coulomb tail the integrals converge through the $T(\mathbf{x}, \mathbf{x'})$ and not through the correlation functions (Compare e. g. Stecki (31)). This special feature of the refractive index theory is just what we should expect since the scattering does depend on the shape of the scattering volume (Carr and Zimm, 11). What one would scarcely expect is the way this property influences the expression for the complex refractive index.

Let us first compute the turbidity τ due to scattering from the imaginary part of the refractive index using the relations

$$m = \mu + i\,\delta, \qquad \tau = -\,2\,k_0\,\delta\,.$$

---

*That shape dependence can be mild for points well inside V. Although I have chosen to speak of a 'Coulomb tail' to emphasize the long-range character of the tensor $\mathbf{T}$, the tail is more precisely $\sim \exp(-ik_0 r)/r$. Thus the integral is divergent oscillatory when $\mathbf{x}$ lies at the center of a spherical V, but when V is the parallel sided slab $-c < z < +d$ (say), with $\mathbf{x} = (x, y, z)$, the integral is of order $A + B(c+z)^{-1} \exp\{-2ik_0(c+z)\}$ (plus a similar term in $(d-z)$) and converges for large enough $(c+z)$ and $(d-z)$. The behavior near the boundary of the slab is different and must describe the passage of the scattered light across the surface. It is the slab rather than the sphere which is the (relatively) simple and sensible choice for V.

First we perform the calculations upto single scattering alone retaining only J_1 and get

$$\tau = \frac{8\pi^3}{3\lambda^4}\left(n\frac{\partial m^2}{\partial n}\right)^2 \frac{9}{m(m^2+2)^2}\,\kappa\, k'\, T; \qquad (14)$$

k' = Boltzmann's constant, T = Temperature, κ = compressibility. As a check we compute τ from the scattered intensity also and get exactly the same answer: this is a very satisfactory consistency, but we differ from the generally accepted Einstein (17) result by $9/m(m^2+2)^2 \sim 1/2$ for $m = 1\cdot 5$. The discrepancy is due to multiple scattering terms which are scarcely negligible here!

Write (13) as

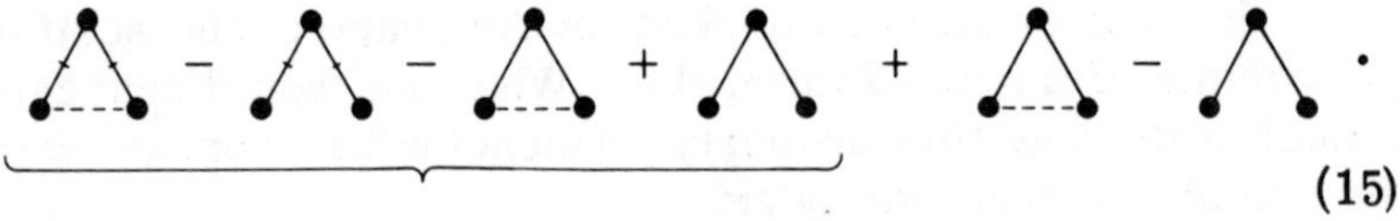

(15)

The bracketed terms $\to 0$ as $|\mathbf{x}' - \mathbf{x}| \to \infty$ and $|\mathbf{x}'' - \mathbf{x}|$ is small: thus this combination is shape independent. The remaining terms are shape dependent: they may be split into two types of term*, one describing that shape dependence and the other contributing directly to the refractive index. These second contributions are in their contribution to τ, the first terms (of order $n\alpha$) in the power series for $(m^2+2)^2/9$, and as the next terms (of order $n^2\alpha^2$) can be found in J_3 by the same process (Bullough, 7) the factor $9(m^2+2)^{-2}$ really should be out. Thus ignoring the shape dependent terms and some additional complication from the depolarisation which comes from those J_n for which $n \geq 3$** the formula is

---

*I have performed this split only on the imaginary part of these terms.

**The Cabannes factor precisely describes the depolarisa- from J_3 but must in principle be modified by some of the multiple scattering terms of higher order.

$$\tau = \frac{8\pi^3}{3\lambda^4} \left(\frac{n\partial m^2}{\partial n}\right)^2 \frac{1}{m} \kappa k' T \tag{16}$$

upto second order in the multiple scattering (and third order in the scattering). You will see that the complicated molecular theory has reduced to the simple phenomenological result of Einstein (17) except for the m^{-1}.

It is easy to give an argument in favor of the factor m^{-1}. The transmitted Poynting vector in the medium is ($\mathbf{H}^*$ is the complex conjugate of the magnetic field $\mathbf{H}$ and $\overline{\mathbf{E}}$ and $\overline{\mathbf{H}}$ are the average Maxwell fields (compare Bullough, 3))

$$\frac{1}{8\pi} \overline{\mathbf{E}} \wedge \overline{\mathbf{H}}^* = \frac{1}{8\pi} |E_0|^2 \, m \hat{k}_0; \quad \hat{\mathbf{k}}_0 = \mathbf{k}_0 / |\mathbf{k}_0| = \mathbf{k}_0 k_0^{-1};$$

(we can ignore the small imaginary part of m here (Bullough, 5). If we use Gaussian units, for example, for $\mathbf{E}$ and $\mathbf{H}$ we also need an additional factor c, the velocity of light in vacuo, but factors of this type we can also ignore.) Normalisation of the scattered intensity against this introduces a factor m^{-1} into τ in full agreement with the calculation from the imaginary part δ of m.

Unfortunately, there is the important calculation of the scattered intensity due to Fixman (21). He found (16) upto order $(n\alpha)^4$, i.e. upto our J_3 or upto second order in the multiple scattering, or third order in the scattering, without the m^{-1}. Fixman's calculation was exciting and certainly the best calculation upto 1955, but he was careless with phase factors and never permitted his m to be complex: if one extends his calculation of m (which was actually a review of the earlier calculation of Yvon (32)) one gets exactly (16) again, and this result from the extinction is apparently inconsistent with Fixman's own calculation from the scattered intensity by a factor $m \sim 1 \cdot 5$.

It would seem a simple matter to decide whether such a simple factor should be included or not: unfortunately this view seems to be misleading, for I believe that this simple factor is representing symbolically the other shape dependent factors we have so far omitted. If these are included I believe they will explicitly eliminate the m^{-1} but at the same time they undoubtedly replace this factor by a complicated function of m, α, the molecular correlation functions, and the shape of V. In this way these shape dependent terms will describe the refraction and reflection of the scattered beam at the boundary of V. But, there is no evidence yet that one can apply the usual Fresnel transmission coefficients to the emergent scattered light: instead it looks as though the theory is good enough to yield an exact scattering envelope appropriate to the particular scattering volume V under consideration. It is unfortunate that this will apparently depend on the unknown correlation functions,* but at least we can see the significant role here of the multiple scattering terms.

It is of course playing with words to 'eliminate' m^{-1} only to replace it by a complicated function: but it can be explicitly removed from the formulae in the following way. My calculations so far described calculate the scattered intensity in vacuo outside the scattering region V or calculate the extinction due to this scattering. The individual scattering processes described by the tensors $\mathsf{T}(\mathbf{x}, \mathbf{x}')$ take place in vacuo and depend on the wave number k_0, but their collective effect is to transmit the dipole wave $\overline{\mathbf{P}}(\mathbf{x})$ of (6) which has wave number mk_0. There is apparently no evidence that the scattered light on its passage through the medium has any wave number other than k_0 and this is very important when we attempt to investigate molecular shapes and sizes by light scattering.

If we calculate the scattered intensity upto single scattering we actually get (at a distance $\mathcal{R}$ from the scattering cell from the assumed incident amplitude E_0)

---

*The integral studied in greatest detail has been expressed in terms of the macroscopic compressibility rather than the molecular correlation functions however. It is interesting to speculate whether we can otherwise use this 'unfortunate' situation to obtain information about the higher order correlation functions.

$$i(\theta) = I(\theta)\ (n\frac{\partial m^2}{\partial n})^2\ \frac{9}{(m^2+2)^2}$$

$$\times\ \frac{1}{n}\{1 + n\int[g_{12}(\mathbf{x},\ \mathbf{x}') - 1]j_0(k_u(\theta)\,r)\ d\mathbf{r}\} \tag{17}$$

$$\mathbf{s}\ = \text{scattering direction},\ I(\theta) \equiv \frac{\pi}{8\lambda^4}\ \frac{E_0^2\,V}{\mathcal{R}^2}\,[1 - (\mathbf{u}\cdot\mathbf{s})^2],$$

$$k_u(\theta) \equiv (1 - 2\,m\cos\theta + m^2)^{1/2}\ k_0, \tag{17'}$$

in which $j_0(\xi) = (\sin\xi)/\xi$. We now 'understand' the factor $9(m^2+2)^{-2}$ and expect it will be eliminated by the multiple scattering (the evidence is that it is still explicitly eliminated even in the presence of the additional complications due to long correlation lengths which we now discuss), but we see that our theory tells us to compute the effect of the correlation length of g_{12} on $i(\theta)$ using $k_u(\theta)$ * and not

$$k_s(\theta) \equiv (m^2 - 2\,m^2\cos\theta + m^2)^{1/2}k_0 = 2m(\sin\tfrac{1}{2}\theta)\,k_0. \tag{18'}$$

On the other hand if we use Fixman's approach and carefully restore his discarded phase factors we get upto single scattering

$$i(\theta) = I(\theta)\ (n\frac{\partial m^2}{\partial n})^2\ m\times\frac{1}{n}\{1+n\int[g_{12}(\mathbf{x},\mathbf{x}') - 1]j_0(k_s(\theta)r)d\mathbf{r}\} \tag{18}$$

Fixman's calculation amounts to a regrouping of the terms in our multiple scattering series in such a way that some of them are used in what is apparently a single scattering expansion explicitly to cancel the 'macroscopic' factor $9(m^2+2)^{-2}$: we do not now need to sum some of our multiple scattering series—the summation is automatic. Moreover, we see the extra factor m in (18) which will exactly cancel the m^{-1} in the turbidity. But we also see that $k_u(\theta)$ of (17') has been replaced by $k_s(\theta)$ of (18') in (18).

*The quantity $k_u(\theta)$ was first obtained in this context by Rosenfeld (30).

From this analysis it is evident that the scattering envelope depends on the multiple scattering: but the question arises "Is $k_s(\theta)$ more correct than $k_u(\theta)$?". Unfortunately I have so far been unable to decide this question: the evidence is that neither expression is any better than the other. To see this last point notice that we now have three calculations of the turbidity, one from the extinction, one from the scattered intensity, whilst the third comes from Fixman's (21) calculation of the scattered intensity: the first two calculations have been carried out in terms of an 'unscreened' scattering tensor $\mathsf{T}(\mathbf{x}, \mathbf{x}')$ appropriate to single scatterings in vacuo and depending on the vacuum wave number k_0, the third, when the phase factors are restored to Fixman's calculation, proves to depend at the single scattering approximation on a scattering tensor $\tilde{\mathsf{T}}(\mathbf{x}, \mathbf{x}')$ depending on mk_0 (although the multiple scattering development depends on T *): the tensor $\tilde{\mathsf{T}}$ is 'screened' in the sense that individual molecules scatter with effective wave number mk_0 in a medium of refractive index m. Evidently a calculation is missing—that of the extinction computed with $\tilde{\mathsf{T}}$ instead of T.

I have managed to carry out this calculation (Bullough, 7), but so far have only evaluated the expressions explicitly upto first order in multiple scattering: the calculation is still incomplete but I do already find a multiple scattering series which so far seems to have very much the same structure as before. I find

$$(m^2 - 1) = 4\pi n\alpha \left[1 - \sum_{r=1}^{\infty} (n\alpha/m^2)^r \tilde{J}_r \right]^{-1}$$

which is exactly the form of (7) with its multiple scattering series included except only that inverse powers of m^2 appear in this 'screened' multiple scattering series and the $\tilde{J}_r$ differ from the J_r as comparison of Fig. 4 with Fig. 1

*This is the form adopted in Bullough (5) also: the development in $\tilde{\mathsf{T}}$ has only been done for the extinction (Bullough, 7), i.e., in that calculation described here.

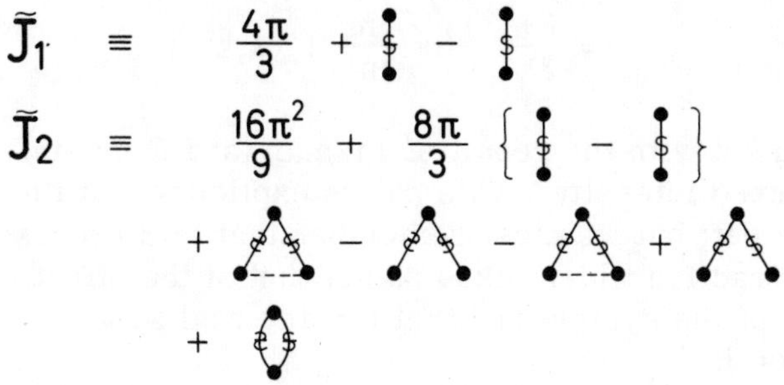
$\tilde{J}_1 \equiv \frac{4\pi}{3} +$ … $-$ …
$\tilde{J}_2 \equiv \frac{16\pi^2}{9} + \frac{8\pi}{3}$ { … $-$ … }
$+$ … $-$ … $-$ … $+$ …
$+$ …

Fig. 4. Diagrams for $\tilde{J}_1$ and $\tilde{J}_2$. The bracketed term in $\tilde{J}_2$ is actually more complicated but will yield a correct expression for its imaginary part.

shows: in particular the 'tilde' across the dumb-bell in Fig. 4 indicates $\tilde{T}(x, x')$ rather than $T(x, x')$. Note in this comparison that, if (7) is expressed in the form of (19), J_1 in Fig. 1 must have $4\pi/3$ added to it.

There are still difficulties associated with the radiation reaction field which here is modified by the term

 ,

but otherwise we see that a comparison of the three particle part of $\tilde{J}_2$ with the corresponding part (15) of J_2 shows that the shape dependent terms have been eliminated and this calculation both defines and provides an expression for a shape independent refractive index. For this reason it is, however, less relevant to the experimental situation than the unscreened one, whilst we see a nasty complication in the factors m^{-2r} in the screened multiple scattering series.

I have still much work to do on this series: for our purposes it is sufficient to say that by computing $\delta = \text{Im}(m)$ upto first order in multiple scattering I find (with certain qualifications about the radiation reaction field) that for small correlation distances

$$\tau = \frac{8\pi^3}{3\lambda^4} \left(n \frac{\partial m^2}{\partial n}\right)^2 \kappa k' T \qquad (20)$$

in agreement with the result of Fixman (and Einstein) from the scattered intensity. This shows explicitly that the m^{-1} should be out; but we must remember that this expression is an abstraction which takes no account of the effect of the boundary of the system and that for any real system the true expression is

$$\tau = \frac{8\pi^3}{3\lambda^4} \left(n \frac{\partial m^2}{\partial n}\right)^2 \kappa k' T \times \{\text{surface factor}\} . \qquad (21)$$

The surface factor has been defined to absorb the m^{-1} and can in principle be calculated by the 'unscreened' calculation.

Thus we see we have essentially two types of calculation: one is with unscreened T and is relevant to the real situation in making a concession to the boundary; the other is with screened $\tilde{T}$ and the system has no boundary.* We see that there is a multiple scattering series <u>in each case</u> and that in the case of small molecules and correlation lengths the multiple scattering series in each of the turbidities τ_u and τ_s collapse to the Einstein phenomenological formula. However, when the correlation distances are of order k_0^{-1} there is no such collapse:

---

*The screened calculation can and should be applied consistently to the limiting case of infinite volume: the unscreened calculation necessarily describes the scattering from a finite system in which the scattering is observed <u>in vacuo</u> and outside the scattering volume, and this volume V can be taken to infinity only if the surface factor described here is isolated before taking the limit.

we must apparently take the multiple scattering series term by term*, and if we try to work from single scattering formulae like (17) or (18) we do not know whether we should use

$$j_0(k_s(\theta)\, r) \qquad \text{or} \qquad j_0(k_u(\theta)\, r).$$

Thus there is doubt about the precise form of our scattering envelope, of the observable dissymmetry, and hence about the measurement of particle size. The discrepancies are about 10 % for $m = 1{\cdot}5$ and $\theta = \pi/3$: - $k_u(\pi/3) = 1{\cdot}33\ k_0$, $k_s(\pi/3) = 1{\cdot}50\ k_0$. These become about 17 % when $\theta = 2\pi/3$. This complication could be very relevant to critical scattering where the correlation lengths become very long: in so far as very long correlation lengths are experimentally investigated at small scattering angles note that $k_u(\theta)$ and $k_s(\theta)$ become equal for some $\theta > 0$ and that, whilst $k_s(0) = 0$, $k_u(0) = (m - 1)\ k_0 > 0$.

To get a clear idea of the possible numerical significance of the multiple scattering it seems to me sufficient to look again at the expressions for τ computed upto <u>single</u> scattering. These can be written in the forms

$$\tau_e = (8\pi^3/3\lambda^4)(n\partial m^2/\partial n)^2\, \kappa\, k'\ T \tag{22a}$$

$$\tau_u = (8\pi^3/3\lambda^4)(m^2 - 1)^2\, \kappa\, k'\, T \times \{\text{surface factor}\}$$

$$= \{9/(m^2 + 2)^2\} \times \{\text{surface factor}\} \times \tau_e^{(0)} \tag{22b}$$

$$\tau_s = (8\pi^3/3\lambda^4)(m^2 - 1)^2\, \{m^2 + 2)^2/9\}\, \kappa\, k'\, T = \tau_e^{(0)} \tag{22c}$$

---

*In view of the spectacular collapse of the multiple scattering series in the case of short correlation lengths it would perhaps be safer to say here that the methods which demonstrate that collapse have proved insufficient to demonstrate a similar collapse when the correlation lengths are of order k_0^{-1}.

where τ_e is Einstein's phenomenological τ, and $\tau_e^{(0)}$ is τ_e evaluated explicitly from the Lorenz-Lorentz relation–itself evaluated only upto single scattering. Recall that all three expressions become the same, except for the surface factor, when multiple scattering upto second order is included. Carr and Zimm (11), Table V, quote the following figures for CCl_4

$$\frac{1}{4}(n\,\partial m^2/\partial n)^2_{\text{experimental}} = 0.448;\ \frac{1}{4}(m^2 - 1)^2 = 0.325;$$

$$\frac{1}{4}\left[(m^2 - 1)(m^2 + 2)/3\right]^2 = 0.618;$$

and similar figures for several other pure liquids. It is plain that multiple scattering in either the unscreened or the screened formulation has to account for about 30% of the scattering from small molecules and that neither formulation offers computational advantage over the other. For larger correlation lengths it is then obvious that (until we know very much more) either $k_s(\theta)$ or $k_u(\theta)$ must be an equally good expression for the 'angular wave number' and that (17) and (18) are equally good single scattering approximations to the scattered intensity. Remember that when we include multiple scattering we must no longer use $(n\,\partial m^2/\partial n)^2$ as we have used it in these single scattering expressions but must evaluate the multiple scattering series term by term explicitly.

As a final illustration we look at the critical scattering formulae: using the Ornstein-Zernike formula (Zernike, 33; Ornstein and Zernike, 29)

$$g(r) - 1 = A\,\chi^2 e^{-\chi r}/4\pi r,$$

where $\chi^{-2} = n^2\,\overline{l^2}\,F\,\kappa k'T$; $A = \kappa k'T - n^{-1}$; and F depends on the pair interaction energy, whilst $\overline{l^2}$ is a 'direct' mean square correlation length; we find upto single scattering (unscreened)

$$i_u(\theta) = I(\theta)16\pi^2 \left|\frac{m^2+2}{3}\right|^2 n^2 \alpha^2 \left[\frac{1 + n\overline{l^2}\, F\, k_u^2(\theta)}{(\kappa k' T)^{-1} + n^2 \overline{l^2}\, F k_u^2(\theta)}\right] + \begin{Bmatrix}\text{multiple}\\ \text{scattering}\\ \text{terms}\end{Bmatrix} \tag{23a}$$

and (screened)

$$i_s(\theta) = I(\theta)\, 16\pi^2 \left|\frac{m^2+2}{3}\right|^4 mn^2 \alpha^2 \left[\frac{1 + n\,\overline{l^2}\, F\, k_s^2(\theta)}{(\kappa\, k' T)^{-1} + n^2 \overline{l^2}\, F k_s^2(\theta)}\right] + \begin{Bmatrix}\text{multiple}\\ \text{scattering}\\ \text{terms}\end{Bmatrix} \tag{23b}$$

Close to the critical point $(\kappa\, k' T)^{-1} \propto |T - T_c|^{\gamma}$, where $\gamma \sim 1{\cdot}0$, so that the forms of the denominators in the two square brackets are important: the terms in $k_u^2(\theta)$ and $k_s^2(\theta)$ in the numerators can be dropped since they are small compared with unity $((\overline{l^2})^{1/2} \sim$ an intermolecular distance.) On the other hand, the multiple scattering terms can only be computed from $g_{123}(\mathbf{x}, \mathbf{x}', \mathbf{x}'')$, $g_{1234}(\mathbf{x}, \mathbf{x}', \mathbf{x}'', \mathbf{x}''')$ etc. We have shown in the case of small correlation lengths that multiple scattering terms make a very significant contribution just sufficient, however, to yield a single scattering formula: now we can expect that they will be relatively much more important and at the same time we cannot expect to obtain a single scattering formula.

V. TWO COMPONENT SYSTEMS

A general optical theory of these has been given (Bullough, 3): all the difficulties described above in the theory of the external scattering from the one component system reappear in the theory for the binary system, but in addition the scattering (which is always quadratic or worse in the molecular polarisabilities) is not additive either for small molecules (Bullough, 4, 5) or for different reasons for large ones (Bullough, 5). I here illustrate the case of critical scattering from a binary system. By taking the 'solvation' conditions

$$n_a v_a (g_{aa} - 1) + n_b v_b (g_{ab} - 1) = f_a, \quad r \text{ outside } v_a$$
$$= f_a - 1, \quad r \text{ inside } v_a \qquad (24a)$$

$$n_a v_a (g_{ba} - 1) + n_b v_b (g_{bb} - 1) = f_b, \quad r \text{ outside } v_b$$
$$= f_b - 1, \quad r \text{ inside } v_b \qquad (24b)$$

where (definition) f_a, f_b are short range satisfying $\int f_a(r)\, d\mathbf{r} = \int f_b(r)\, d\mathbf{r} = \kappa k' T$ (and the reasons for adopting this condition are discussed in (Bullough, 5)), I have obtained by an extension of Ornstein's and Zernike's arguments the following formula for the scattering from critical mixtures

$$i_s(\theta) = I(\theta)\; m\Big\{ \Big| n_b \left(\frac{\partial m^2}{\partial n_b}\right)_{p,T} \Big|^2 n_b^{-1} B(\theta) + \Big|\kappa^{-1} \left(\frac{\partial m^2}{\partial p}\right)_{T,n_b} \Big|^2 \kappa k' T + \Big[n_b \left(\frac{\partial m^2}{\partial n_b}\right)_{p,T} \kappa^{-1} \left(\frac{\partial m^2}{\partial p}\right)^*_{Tn_b} + \text{c. c.} \Big] \kappa k' T \Big\} \qquad (25)$$

where

$$B(\theta) \equiv \frac{1 + \frac{1}{6}(1 + n_b Q_{bb})\, n_b v_b^2 \left\{ \overline{l^2_{bb}}\, v_b^{-2} F_{bb} - \overline{l^2_{ab}}\, v_a^{-1} v_b^{-1} F_{ab} \right\}}{(1 + n_b G_{bb})^{-1} + \frac{1}{6} n_b v_b^2 \left\{ \overline{l^2_{bb}}\, v_b^{-2} F_{bb} - \overline{l^2_{ab}}\, v_a^{-1} v_b^{-1} F_{ab} \right\}} \cdot \frac{[1 + v_a^{-1} \kappa k' T n_b F_{ab}]^{-1} k_s^2(\theta)}{[1 + v_a^{-1} \kappa k' T n_b F_{ab}]^{-1} k_s^2(\theta)} . \qquad (26)$$

In (24), (25), and (26) v_a and v_b are partial molar volumes; but this is not the place to discuss these formulae at length and I shall not further define the individual terms adding only that the calculation is screened and taken no further than single scattering. If multiple scattering is included we cannot expect to use $\partial m^2/\partial n_b$ and $\partial m^2/\partial p$ in the formulae but need the molecular polarisabilities explicitly. The solvation conditions (24) are assumed and without them we cannot expect to isolate the excess scattering (the term in $B(\theta)$) from the 'density fluctuation' term (the first term in $\kappa k'T$): if multiple scattering is included we need extensions of the solvation condition to three and more particle correlations (Bullough, 5). On the other hand the formula agrees well with that given by Debye (15): when κ is put equal to zero we can choose $f_a \equiv f_b \equiv 0$ and then find that we have eliminated all but the excess scattering (for we can expect $\kappa^{-1}(\partial m^2/\partial p)_{T, n_b}$ to remain finite) and that

$$n_b^{-1} B(\theta) \approx \frac{k'T}{(n_b(\partial \Pi/\partial n_b)) + n_b^2 v_b^2 H k_s^2(\theta))} \qquad (27)$$

In (27),

$$H = \frac{1}{12}\{\overline{l^2}_{bb} v_b^{-2} W_{bb} + \overline{l^2}_{aa} v_a^{-2} W_{aa} - (\overline{l^2}_{ba} W_{ba} + \overline{l^2}_{ab} W_{ab}) v_a^{-1} v_b^{-1}\}$$

in which the various symbols refer to the similar quantities defined by Debye (so that H is actually one half of Debye's H) and Π is the osmotic pressure. When $Hk_s^2(\theta) \approx 0$ for all θ, and the correlation lengths are small whilst $n_b \partial \Pi/\partial n_b$ is relatively large, (25) reduces to the Einstein formula without appeal to any solvation conditions like (24)– except that we have the factor m (for the reasons discussed earlier) and the additional 'cross term' in $\kappa k'T$, and depending on n_b, reported already (Bullough, 4, 5). There are two such terms in the three component system as well as a natural cross-term like that first described by Kirkwood and Goldberg (23). Note however, that our thermodynamic variables are not quite those adopted by these particular authors. It is in fact possible to show that the additional cross-terms vanish when the thermodynamic variables I use here are replaced by those of Kirkwood and

Goldberg; but the choice of variables I have made here seems to me to be the physically more significant one.*

VI. FINAL REMARKS

There is no opportunity here to discuss other applications of this unified theory. I can add only that the theory has been applied to the birefringence of rubber-like polymers (Bullough, 2, 3), infra-red dichroism (Bullough, 3, §7), optical rotation (Bullough, 3, Appendix 2(b)), birefringence of polymer solutions (Bullough, 2), and the hypochromism of ultra-violet absorption in polymers (Bullough 8, 9): much work remains to be done on these topics because of the difficulty of calculating even the two-particle correlation functions. One result of some interest here is that a variant of the solvation condition (24) is needed to abstract the 'form' birefringence (an excess term) from the single scattering environmental birefringence terms J_{aa}, J_{ab}, etc. in a binary system (Bullough, 2). One advantage of the unified theory is that interacting optical phenomena can be treated together: thus, for example, true absorption and

---

*Both this statement and the relation between Kirkwood's and Goldberg's formulae and the two- or multi-component scattering formulae of my papers (4) and (5) must be discussed elsewhere. Unfortunately my paper (4) implies that these cross-terms are additional to the Kirkwood-Goldberg cross-term. This is not correct, although the one cross-term derived from equation (25) above is certainly additional to the usual formulations of the two-component formula. The fact that this term is implicitly contained in Kirkwood's and Goldberg's (23) formula has been obscured by these authors' only comment on their two-component formula that it is the 'usual expression' which 'has been extensively used in light scattering studies'. This remark does not seem to me to be consistent with the published literature and the significance of the proper form of the two or more component scattering formulae still does not seem to be sufficiently widely realised.

resonance scattering, which can interact significantly (cf. e.g., Leach and Scheraga, 25) and then non-linearly, can be treated together (Bullough, 8).

All these phenomena are complicated by the appearance of the multiple scattering series: the evidence is that multiple scattering terms are significant in the theory of each. One example where the series will not occur is the theory of the optical properties of cold crystals: Equation (2) has been rederived from Equation (1) in this context and has been shown (Bullough, 6) to embrace (and indeed replace) the 'static exciton' theory of the molecular crystal given by Davydov (13). Equation (2) has been solved for the refractive index of a molecular crystal of arbitrary lattice and formulae for the refractive index obtained (Bullough, 6). If phonon interactions are included the complications of the multiple scattering series re-appear but they are presumably numerically much less important here.

I have related the theory presented here to the framework of our current knowledge of theoretical optics: now to finish I ought to indicate its relation to some of the topics which have been or will be specifically described in this conference. I have pointed out the importance of the multiple scattering in the theory of the observable scattering at optical frequencies. In this sense the work reported here is an integral part of this conferences discussion of the multiple scattering problem (Session III). But I believe I have cast the argument in a form which relates it most closely to that group of papers discussed under the heading of 'Nonparticulate Scattering' (Session II). Certainly the theory of correlation functions there discussed by, for example, Drs. W. Prins and Frisch is an essential feature of the approach I describe here. Indeed Dr. Frisch's 'double scattering' (which I would however call 'triple scattering' since it is describable by a diagram like that of J_3 in Fig. 1) is contained within the theory, and it is certainly a potential source of depolarization (even from isotropically polarizable particles) as he has described. In principle all J_n with $n \geq 3$ contribute to the depolarization.

I should also draw attention to the importance of carefully executed experimental work like that of Dr. Hymans and his collaborators in establishing the correct form of the scattering formulae for two component systems on which I make some comment in Section 5.* The work I briefly report on critical mixtures is naturally relevant to the papers of Drs. McIntyre and Chu: the present theory suggests that multiple scattering is always a significant feature of scattering at optical frequencies but we can expect it to become overwhelmingly important near the critical point (How near remains to be seen). This should not be the case at x-ray frequencies although the theory of single scattering in the two cases is very similar—a point I hope to take up elsewhere. The very interesting contribution of Dr. Pecora who uses Van Hove's two particle correlation function is strictly speaking outside the range of the theory reported here but the extension of the theory to cover this time dependent case should be fairly straightforward. Because of the significant multiple scattering, however, it appears that we shall need more than just the two-particle Van Hove correlation function. For this reason it will be interesting to see what additional information such sophisticated theoretical and experimental techniques will enable us to extract from observations of scattering envelopes and their spectra. I would also like to point to the obvious connections between the theory presented here and the scattering problems discussed by Professor Keller at the end of this conference: his approach may provide a simpler route to a shape independent unscreened theory, though I believe some of the difficulties are intrinsic here. A major problem associated with the molecular theory reported here is in the passage from that theory to the phenomenological theory in which the scattering power is vested in a refractive index and not in a molecular polarizability. I have indicated here that it is possible to establish a remarkably close connec-

---

*I am actually greatly indebted to Dr. Hymans for jogging my recollection that Kirkwood and Goldberg (23) do not use the 'usual' thermodynamical variables as noted in section V. Can I make a special plea that when authors quote current light scattering formulae they always quote explicity which variables are constant when partial derivatives are taken?

tion between Einstein's phenomenological theory and the molecular theory: it is very desirable to establish some similar connection between the molecular theory and, for example, the phenomenological interpretation of the very beautiful results reported by Professor Stein on scattering from solid polymer films.

ACKNOWLEDGEMENT

I should like to take this opportunity of acknowledging a profound debt of thanks to Professor Rosenfeld. By no means the smallest part of this lies in my gratitude for his book Theory of Electrons in which his very elegant presentation of the optical theory which lies at the heart of that described here first stimulated my interest in this field; but I must also thank him more personally for his continued interest, displayed in countless discussions, in the work reported here. I should also like to thank Nordita for the generous hospitality and support which has both enabled me to write this paper and earlier enabled me to carry out much of the work described within it.

REFERENCES

(1) Brout, R. H., Phase Transitions (New York: W. A. Benjamin Inc., 1964) Chap. 3.
(2) Bullough, R. K., J. Poly. Sci. **46**, 517 (1960).
(3) Bullough, R. K., Phil. Trans. Roy. Soc. A **254**, 397 (1962).
(4) Bullough, R. K., Proc. Roy. Soc. A **275**, 271 (1963).
(5) Bullough, R. K., Phil. Trans. Roy. Soc. A **258**, 387 (1965).
(6) Bullough, R. K., In preparation (1965b).
(7) Bullough, R. K., Unpublished (1965c). (This work is the basis of the theory of external scattering reported here: I note in the text that it is still incomplete).

(8) Bullough, R. K., Intended for publication in Det Kgl. Danske Vidensk. Selskab, Mat. fys. Medd. (1965d).
(9) Bullough, R. K., J. Chem. Phys. **43**, 1927 (1965e).
(10) Cabannes, J., La Diffusion Moléculaire de la Lumière (Paris: Presses Universitaires de France, 1929).
(11) Carr, C. I. and Zimm, B. H., J. Chem. Phys. **18**, 1616 (1950).
(12) Darwin, C. G., Trans. Camb. Phil. Soc. **23**, 137 (1924).
(13) Davydov, A. S., Theory of Molecular Excitons (New York: McGraw Hill Book Co. Inc., 1962).
(14) De Boer, J., Rept. Progr. Phys. **12** , 305 (1948).
(15) Debye, P., J. Chem. Phys. **31**, 680 (1959).
(16) Doniach, S., Polarons and Excitons (Edinburgh: Oliver and Boyd, 1963) p. 191.
(17) Einstein, A., Ann. Phys., Lpz. **33**, 1275 (1910).
(18) Ewald, P. P., Thesis: Munich (1912).
(19) Ewald, P. P., Ann. Phys., Lpz. **1**, 117 (1916).
(20) Fano, U., Phys. Rev. **103**, 1202 (1956).
(21) Fixman, M., J. Chem. Phys. **23**, 2074 (1955).
(22) Hopfield, J. J., Phys. Rev. **112**, 1555 (1958).
(23) Kirkwood, J. G. and Goldberg, R. J., J. Chem. Phys. **18**, 54 (1950).
(24) Lax, M., Rev. Mod. Phys. **23**, 287 (1951).
(25) Leach, S. J. and Scheraga, H. A., J. Am. Chem. Soc. **82**, 4790 (1960).
(26) Lorentz, H. A., The Theory of Electrons (Leipzig: Teubner, 2nd edition, 1916; reprinted by Dover Publications (New York), 1952).
(27) Mayer, J. E. and Mayer, M. G., Statistical Mechanics (New York: John Wiley, 1940) Chap. 13.
(28) Nozieres, P. and Pines, D., Il Nuovo Cimento, X 9, 470 (1958).
(29) Ornstein, L. S. and Zernike, F., Physik Z. **27**, 761 (1926).
(30) Rosenfeld, L., Theory of Electrons (Amsterdam: North Holland Publishing Co., 1951) Chaps V and VI.
(31) Stecki, J., Advances in Chemical Physics Vol. VI (New York: Interscience Publishers Inc., 1964) p. 428.

(32) Yvon, J., Actualités Scientifiques et Industrielles (Paris: Hermann et Cie, 1937) Nos. 542, 543.

(33) Zernike, F., Proc. Acad. Sci. Amsterdam 18, 1520 (1916).

DISCUSSION FOLLOWING PAPER BY R. K. BULLOUGH

J. B. Keller: What is the logical basis for the use of the screened scattering tensor?

R. K. Bullough: There is no logical basis. Well that is perhaps a silly remark! What I mean is that we can choose the screening parameter more or less as we wish. Essentially the choice amounts to a change of the electromagnetic gauge; as one moves m, one shifts the gauge as one wants. There are, however, at least two natural choices for m, namely m = 1, and m equal to the refractive index of the system. In the second case it is clear that the screened T, $\tilde{T}$, is screened in the sense that it is the dipole scattering tensor in a medium whose refractive index is m. Of course both the screened and unscreened formulations give multiple scattering. Whether there is a gauge transformation which will eliminate the multiple scattering is another question.

J. M. Greenberg: This is a question of clarification. Does your "screening" amount to (1) the use of an index of refraction m for the "medium" in which a scatterer finds itself (2) adding up the scatterings from all of the scatterers in this medium (3) finally defining - self consistently - this same "m" as an outgrowth of the multiple scattering?

R. K. Bullough: No, I would not describe the situation in quite this way. The essential situation is that we can formulate the individual scattering process in at least two ways: both are essentially (but as it turns out) not quite exactly equivalent. Both formulations produce, for example, the average macroscopic Maxwell field variables in the medium, and, with qualifications about the boundary and restriction to short correlation lengths, the same turbidity. Initially, however, we must treat the m in $\tilde{T}$ as a parameter which we can subsequently fix self-consistently within the calculation. One possible choice is m = 1; this is the unscreened calculation. Another possible choice is m is equal self-consistently to that quantity which we can subsequently interpret to be the true refractive index of the system. There may yet be a better choice of the parameter m which eliminates more of the multiple scattering series.

These comments are no more than a slightly different view of my answer to the previous question.

S. Levine: Could you explain why your results differ from those of Fixman? Presumably you both begin with the same principles of statistical mechanics.

R. K. Bullough: Yes, I use the same principles of statistical mechanics although there is one difficulty in the application of these to the 'unscreened' formulation of the theory which I shall raise in a minute. The reasons for any discrepancy with Fixman are that the 'unscreened' formulation is not dealing with quite the same system or boundary conditions as Fixman's, and it is unfortunately the case that boundary effects in this problem are very important: one has only to remember the factors of order m which the experimentalist uses to 'correct' his data to realize that the finite boundary and definite shape of the scattering cell are important. The theoretical form of corrections to be used by the experimentalist has been deduced on the basis of geometrical optics (see for example Carr and Zimm, 1950).

In my talk I tried to show that the 'unscreened' formulation took into account the fact that the scattered light was observed in vacuo and thus (for a simply connected medium!) necessarily outside a finite medium with definite boundary. In this the formulation may be considered to be very relevant to the experimental situation. One consequence of this formulation is the factor m^{-1} in τ: this is apparently peculiar to the unscreened formulation and in a certain sense is demonstrably connected with the existence of a boundary to the system. At the same time combinations of the correlation functions different from those indicated by Fixman appear in the multiple scattering series and these complications are also connected with the existence of a boundary. I suggest in the text of this talk that these terms will explicitly eliminate the factor m^{-1} in τ, but this may be slightly overstating the case. What seems pretty certain is that all these terms, including whatever part of the m^{-1} which is not explicitly eliminated by the multiple scattering terms, are representing the effective transmission and reflexion coefficients of the scattered beam at the boundary of the system; but because the scattered beam is not really a beam we cannot expect to (and so far do not) find the usual Fresnel coefficients for these quantities. It seems that the unscreened formulation is describing the exact scattering pattern from the finite system (I assume a finite slab and normal incidence since this is the simplest cell geometry and incidence direction to handle theoretically); there is no appeal to geometrical optics. I have not yet been able to discover how well the usual corrections based on geometrical optics approximate to these surface dependent terms in the unscreened theory and I expect the problem to be a rather difficult one.

One complication of the unscreened theory is that multiple scattering terms appear in the expression for m, that is in the generalization of the Lorenz-Lorenz relation. I find that the usual plane wave Maxwell field vector within the medium is accompanied by a family of plane waves induced by multiple scattering and representing the total effect of that multiple scattering: these waves are unimportant if the scattering is small enough but become vitally important close to the critical point (for example) where the scattering is very large. In terms of our discussion these waves are associated with transmission of the scattered fields across the boundary of the scattering region V and so must still play a significant role under normal conditions when, compared to critical scattering, the scattered intensity is relatively small. Each wave is a source of scattered radiation and is transmitted with a complex refractive index. This is a complicated situation outside the range of Fixman's approach so that it is again not surprising that the unscreened theory of τ throws up points of discrepancy with Fixman: the oddest thing about the situation is that up to single scattering and short correlation lengths the two theories differ by the simple, clean factors m^{-1} - which even has the 'simple' interpretation I described in my talk - and $9(m^2 + 2)^{-2}$.

However, Fixman's theory is really comparable with the 'screened' formulation of the problem. Here the boundary conditions assumed are the 'natural' ones to take within the theory but are not so easy to describe here: they are chosen essentially to ensure self-consistency of the situation

With these boundary conditions it is apparently possible to describe an infinite system which can transmit a single monochromatic wave with a well-defined complex refractive index: there are no shape or volume dependent terms in this refractive index. When summed up to first order in multiple scattering (which is as far as I have gone) this refractive index yields exactly Fixman's (and Einstein's) expression for τ but it is not in Fixman's form term by term. In the second point it is very different from the unscreened formulation where the multiple scattering series for both scattered intensity and τ calculated from Im (m) agree term by term as well as in sum. It also differs from the unscreened formulation in that the factor m^{-1} is eliminated - although here I still have a difficulty associated with the radiation reaction field.

In fact the term by term discrepancy from Fixman is not surprising because Fixman, although he was the first to indicate how we might set up what I have called the screened theory, uses in his calculation of the screened scattered intensity a theory of refractive index, due to Yvon, which is related more to the unscreened than the screened theory. Thus from a logical point of view I think it is fair to say that Fixman is using two incompatible sets of boundary conditions within the same calculation: in particular, as I suggest in the text, the extension of his refractive index from pure real to complex form yields the 'unscreened' τ incompatible with that he obtained explicitly from the integrated scattered intensity.

Nevertheless, we can still expect his derived formula to be to all intents and purposes equal to the result of a consistently screened calculation - essentially because calculations of τ based on complex m always work at what is in a certain sense one 'order' higher in the scattering process than do those based on scattered intensity: thus Im (m) is more strongly influenced by the choice of boundary conditions than is the scattered intensity. Therefore we can expect that Fixman's theory should be essentially equivalent to the screened theory and differ from it only in those usually exceptionally small corrections to the scattered intensity due to the fact that where m appears within the theory it is itself a complex quantity. I have only carried out the consistently screened theory for the complex refractive index, and when I calculated the scattered intensity from the two component system (Bullough, (5) in what I called the screened* formulation it should really be described as a mixed 'screened-unscreened' formulation open to criticism on logical grounds just as is Fixman's argument. I believe the conclusions of the argument are nevertheless significant for the reasons I have just indicated; but it is worth remembering this logical criticism if only to see how difficult is an entirely self-consistent theory of the scattering from a thermally agitated fluid.

I have I hope long since answered Dr. Levine's question, but it has seemed to me useful to use this answer to elaborate on some of the difficulties and complexities which I have found within this theory. On this account it might be useful finally to expose to the collectors gaze two other nasty little points. I have said in effect that the screened formulation, although more difficult to carry through than the unscreened, has the merit of yielding a well-defined volume and shape independent refractive index. Because of the somewhat sophisticated nature of the boundary conditions one is, however, still obliged to ask "What does this particular refractive index mean"! In this connection it is perhaps a sobering thought that we are ultimately dealing with a transmitted plane monochromatic wave which is being attenuated all the way from $-\infty$. This difficulty of interpretation seems to me a valid criticism of the screened theory.

On the other hand, the unscreened formulation does seem to be dealing with the practical problem of a finite scattering medium and, for example, shows remarkable term by term consistency between the two routes for τ within it. There is, however, the difficulty I mentioned at the beginning of this "answer" - and which is already referred to at the beginning of the printed text of my paper:

---

*I actually used the much clumsier phrase "in the medium" rather than "screened" in the paper (5).

I have used for the statistical mechanics of the theory always the theory of the grand canonical ensemble. One way, of introducing the grand canonical ensemble is to associate it with an open region within a larger region describable by the canonical ensemble. But this means that in the unscreened formulation we are really dealing with a finite bounded optical scattering region which nevertheless can exchange particles with a material and heat bath outside whose particles are incapable of scattering light. This is by no means the explicit representation of the experimental situation we desire. After studying this scattering problem over the last few years one thing has become quite clear to me: inadequacies in the precise description of the system always show up in inconsistent answers. It therefore seems to me desirable to carry out the unscreened theory consistently in terms of the theory of the canonical, rather than the grand canonical, ensemble. I have made no attempt to do this so far if only because I expect this theory to be still more difficult. The asymptotic behavior of the canonical correlation functions is less simple than that of the grand canonical correlation functions.*

May I finally add that in my paper I have been reporting on what is still very much unfinished work. In particular some of the apparently general results on, for example, the structure of the multiple scattering series have been inferred from the terms I have studied in detail so far. Thus not all the details I have reported may stand up to the discoveries of later work. I believe, however, that the interpretation I have made of the relation of the screened and unscreened formulations of the scattering problem both in my paper and more immediately here will be one of the features which will survive any discoveries from further work on this problem.

---

*If this fact is not taken into consideration the external scattering is actually zero upto single scattering: there are no density fluctuations admissible in the canonical ensemble.

Theory and Microwave Measurements of Higher Statistical Moments of Randomly Scattered Fields

Victor Twersky
Sylvania Electronic Systems
Mountain View, California

ABSTRACT

We measure phase quadrature components X and Y of the instantaneous field for scattering of millimeter waves by dynamic gas-like distributions of large tenuous spheres and average them over time electronically to obtain the mean values $\langle X \rangle$ and $\langle Y \rangle$. From these we construct $x = X - \langle X \rangle$ and $y = Y - \langle Y \rangle$, generate the time-averages $\langle x^n y^m \rangle$ electronically for $0 < n + m \leq 4$ (i. e., up to the fourth central moments of the ensemble of signals), and compare these time averages with scattering theory for the analogous averages over the ensemble of configurations. In general, the fundamental scattering parameters and the distances of the transmitting and receiving apertures from the scattering region enter differently into various terms of the different moments. With increasing distances the central moments reduce to those of an uncorrelated Gaussian distribution. However, the distance dependence can be exploited to isolate different combinations of fundamental scattering parameters than obtained by conventional average intensity and coherent phase measurements. In particular for sparse unknown concentrations ρ of identical scatterers with scattering amplitude f, we show how all three unknowns (Ref, Imf, ρ) are determined by forward scattering data for $\langle X \rangle$, $\langle Y \rangle$, and $\langle xy \rangle$. Nonvanishing values of $\langle xy \rangle$ correspond to a correlated signal distribution; the fact that we also measure $\langle x^3 \rangle$ shows that the distribution is more general than the correlated bivariate Gaussian. For non-gas-like distributions, the n-particle distribution functions may be obtained in principle from scattering data for the n-th moments (even in ranges of the parameters where only single scattering is significant). Analogous measurement techniques and the same data reduction procedures could be used for a coherent light source to obtain similar optical data on naturally occurring distributions.

I. INTRODUCTION

To consider scattering of waves by random distributions, we may start with the solution for a fixed configuration, define an ensemble of configurations in terms of an appropriate probability distribution function (which specifies the relative weights of the individual configurations), and then seek the average of the field and of related functions [7, 14, 21, 18, 20]. We may also proceed phenomenologically and consider a set of functions in time, define an appropriate ensemble of such signals, and seek various time-averages [13, 9, 6, 15, 19]. Experimentally, we perform time-averages of measurements (3, 1, 4, 10, 12]. For present purposes, we consider situations where the time constants of the motion are large compared to the period of the incident wave and small compared to the time interval for the measurement; the time interval for the averaging is long enough, and the random

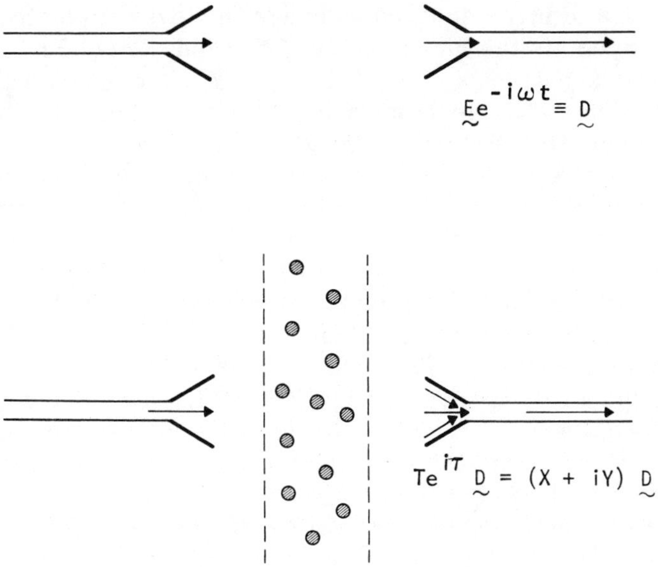

Fig. 1. Top of figure is sketch of free-space situation; the direct field at the receiver is **D**. Bottom of figure shows air path between transmitter and receiver interrupted by slab region of randomly moving scatterers: the field at the receiver is $Te^{i\tau}$ **D** with $T = |T(t)|$ and $\tau = \tau(t)$. Equivalently, we have $Te^{i\tau} = X + iY$, where X is the field component in phase with **D**, and Y is 90° ahead of phase.

process stationary enough, so that all of the above averaging procedures may be regarded as equivalent.

We write the normalized instantaneous field for the scattering problem as $X(t) + iY(t)$, where X is the component in phase with the direct field at the receiver in the absence of scatterers, and Y is the component 90° ahead of phase; see Fig. 1.

We measure phase quadrature components $X(t)$ and $Y(t)$

for scattering of millmeter waves by dynamic random distributions of large spheres, and average over time electronically to obtain the mean values $<X>$ and $<Y>$. From these we construct $x = X - <X>$, $y = Y - <Y>$, and various products $x^n y^m$ electronically. Then we average the products over time electronically to obtain $<x^n y^m>$ for $0 < n + m \leq 4$ (i. e., up to the fourth central moments of the ensemble of signals), and compare these time averages with scattering theory for the analogous averages over the ensemble of configurations. Measurements on second moments were reported originally by Beard 1], and the theory [19] for the various moments was substantiated up to fourth moments by Kays and Twersky [12].

In general, the fundamental scattering parameters and the distances (d_t and d_r) of the transmitting and receiving apertures from the scattering region enter differently into various terms of the amplitudes and phases of the different moments. With increasing distances the central moments reduce to those of an uncorrelated Gaussian distribution. However, the distance dependence can be exploited to isolate different combinations of fundamental scattering parameters than obtained by conventional average intensity and coherent phase measurements. In particular, for sparse unknown concentrations ρ of identical scatterers with forward scattering amplitude f (the forward value of the angular function in the usual far-field form of an isolated scatterer), we show that all three unknowns (Ref, Imf, ρ) can be obtained from forward scattering data for $<X>$, $<Y>$, and $<xy>$. Non-vanishing values of $<xy>$ correspond to a correlated signal distribution; the fact that we also measure $<x^3>$ shows that the distribution is more general than the correlated bivariate Gaussian. For non-gas-like distributions, the n-particle distribution functions may be obtained in principle from scattering data for the n-th moments (even in ranges of the parameters where only single scattering is significant).

Today with incoherent light, one measures an intensity function $<X^2> + <Y^2>$ directly, and obtains a phase function arctan $(<Y>/<X>)$ by using an interferometer. However, the measurement techniques and data reduction procedures we use for millimeter wavelengths can be carried over (in terms of appropriate instruments and a coherent light source) to obtain analogous optical data on naturally occurring distributions of scatterers. The microwave aspect of our measurements enters essentially only in that the frequency of 58×10^9 cps determines the wavelength for the scattering problem, i. e., only the 'sensors' of our scattering facility are microwave devices: we use a superheterodyne-interferometer system and process the scattering information via a low beat-frequency signal of 420 cps.

In the following, we describe our millimeter wave measurement facility and procedures, summarize general relations [19] that exist among the averages, and illustrate these relations explicitly with measured data and with simplified theory for sparse random distributions of large tenuous spheres of styrofoam (radii very large compared to wavelength and index of refraction close to unity). The data given here is a selection of that obtained recently [10, 12] by T. H. Kays and the writer, and more complete results will be published subsequently.

The discussion in Sec. II emphasizes aspects fundament to the measurement procedure in an attempt to stimulate the development of an analogous optical scattering facility. We give typical experimental data in graphical form to illustrate many of the new scattering functions as they are introduced, and to indicate the inadequacy of oversimplified treatments of the ensemble of signals.

II. SIGNAL STATISTICS

We write the total field for a fixed collection of scatterers as $\Psi e^{-i\omega t}$,

$$\Psi(\mathbf{r}) = \psi_i(\mathbf{r}) + U(\mathbf{r}) = \psi_i(\mathbf{r}) + \sum_s u_s(\mathbf{r} - \mathbf{r}_s) \quad , \qquad (1)$$

where ψ_i represents the incident field (say the electric **E** field) at a point **r**; the total scattered field is U, and u_s

represents the multiple-scattered contribution of the scatterer fixed at r_s. The field is a complex valued function of the configuration (the set of vectors $\mathbf{r}_s$), the parameters of the individual scatterers, etc. We may define an ensemble of configurations in terms of an appropriate probability distribution function which specifies the relative weights of the individual configurations, and then seek the average of Ψ and of related functions [7, 14, 21, 18, 20].

We may also consider a function $Te^{i\tau} e^{-i\omega t}$,

$$Te^{i\tau} = |T| e^{i|\tau|} , \qquad (2)$$

to represent one of a set of functions in time, define an appropriate ensemble of such signals, and seek various averages [13, 9, 6, 15, 19].

For present purposes we are interested in the above in connection with time-averages of measurements on dynamic collections of scatterers. The time constants of the motion are large compared to the period of the incident wave and small compared to the time interval for the measurement; the time interval for the averaging is long enough to include an adequate sample of the realizable configurations, and we may assume that we are dealing with a stationary random process. We therefore regard Ψ and $Te^{i\tau}$ as equivalent, and use one symbol ($< >$, such that $\ll \gg = < >$) to represent any of the averages we are concerned with. Essentially as in Fig. 1, we work with

$$\Psi = Te^{i\tau} = X + iY , \qquad (3)$$

where X and Y are real. The phase of the incident field ψ_i at the observation point (the 'direct field' at the receiver in the absence of scatterers) provides the reference phase for τ and for all other phase functions in the problem. Initially we assume this reference phase to be zero so that the real part of Ψ corresponds to the component of the field in phase with the direct field, and the imaginary part to the component 90° ahead of phase; subsequently we change the direct phase from zero (i. e., rotate the coordinate frame X, Y) and discuss any two phase quadrature components of the field.

II.1 Description of Experiment

We measure X and Y on our 5-mm microwave facility [1, 4, 10, 12] for scattering by distributions such as the dynamical model of a 'large scale gas' of spheres shown in Fig. 2 (and described elsewhere [3] in detail). The model consists essentially of a slab-region styrofoam container (practically transparent to microwaves) whose top and bottom are grids which allow for the passage of turbulent air streams, but serve to confine light-weight scatterers; a system of blowers, turbulence-creating wedges, honeycombed grids, and collision processes produce the 'randomness'. The significant dimensions of the container are approximately 10" × 20" × 24", and the scatterers of present interest are styrofoam spheres with diameters ranging from 2a = 0.7" to 1.4" (very large compared to the incident wavelength) and relative indices of refraction between η = 1.015 and 1.03. The time constants of the distribution may be inferred from Fig. 3, which shows strips of movie film taken at 60 frames per second; we may regard the scatterers as fixed for say 0.01 second. The relatively sparse cases on the left are the ones of present interest; the number (N) and volume of the scatterers are such that the fractional volume is less than 0.05.

The essential geometry of present interest is sketched in Fig. 1. We start from the free-space situation shown at the top for which the received field is completely known, insert the distributuion of scatterers to correspond to the bottom sketch, and seek to measure the scattering functions of (3) over a short time interval during which X(t) and Y(t) are practically constant. The actual setup for measurements is drawn in Fig. 4, and a corresponding photograph is shown in Fig. 5.

Since most of the features of our millimeter-wave facility have been described previously [3, 1, 4, 10, 12] we mention only the essentials of the system and highlight some recent innovations. The system was developed

Fig. 2. Large scale dynamical distribution of scatterers. The Lucite panels in the faces of the 10" × 20" × 24" container are replaced by styrofoam panels when microwave measurements are in progress, and an expansion 'chimney' is added to help stabilize the distribution.

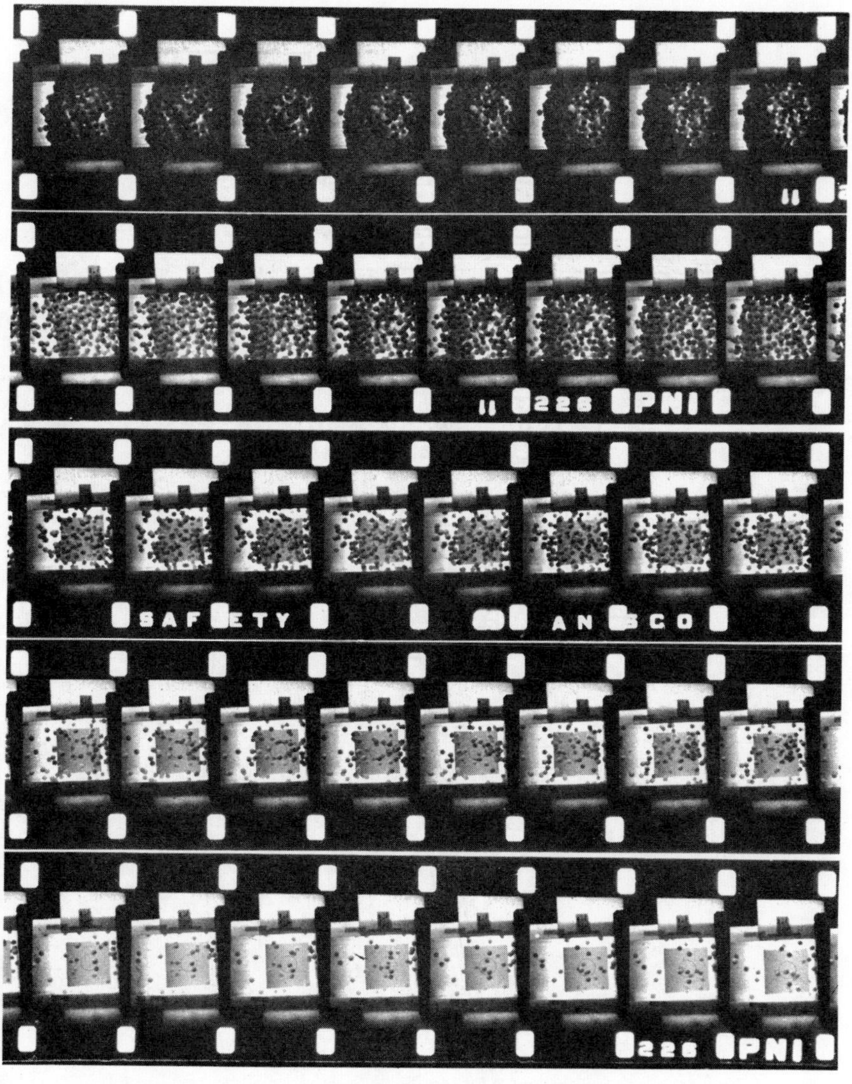

Fig. 3. Strips of movie films of different concentrations (different number N of spheres in the container) taken at 60 frames per second. The present paper deals with the 'gas-like' cases at the left with fractional volumes less than 0.05.

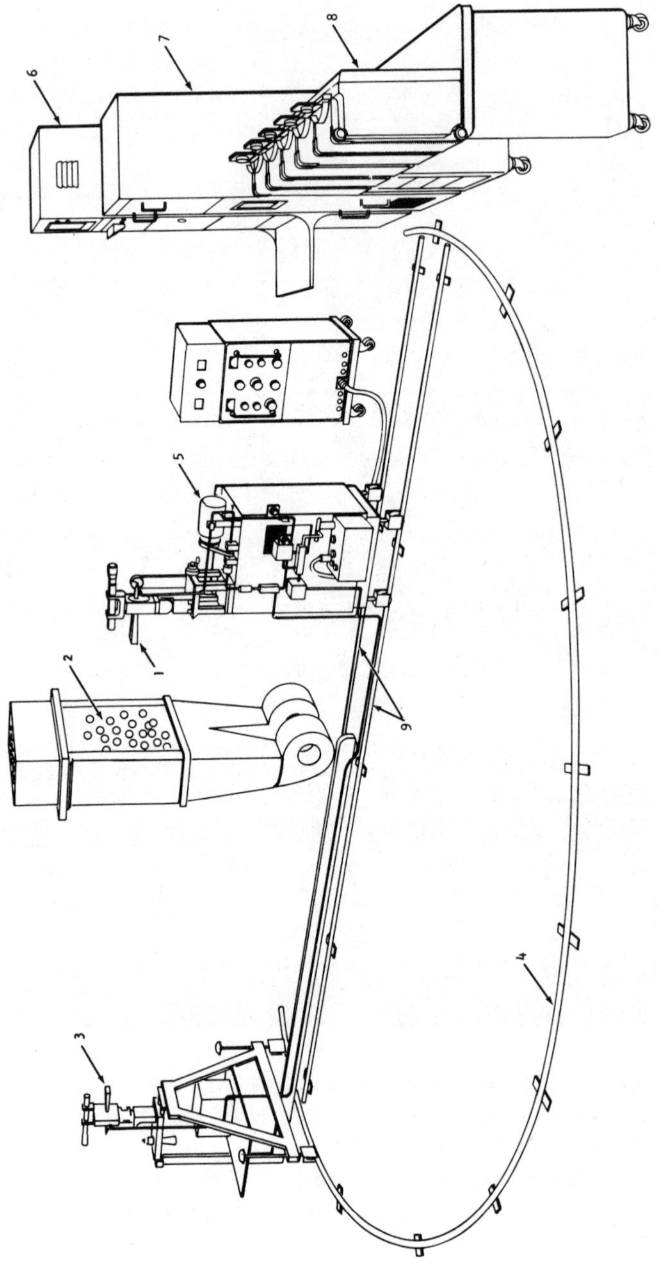

Fig. 4

to measure X and Y directly for various problems of either fixed or moving scatterers. The field at the receiver in the absence of scatterers is proportional to $E_0 = e^{-i\omega t}$ ($\omega/2\pi = 58 \times 10^9$ cps), and if the air path is interrupted by scatterers the transmitted field is $E = Te^{i\tau} e^{-i\omega t}$. Ideally, we would isolate $\text{Re}E = T\cos(\omega t - \tau) = X\cos\omega t + Y\sin\omega t$, multiply by $\text{Re}E_0 = \cos\omega t$, and integrate over half a period (the smallest interval over which the trigonometric functions are orthogonal) to obtain X, and similarly use $\text{Im}E_0 = \sin\omega t$ to get Y. This is impractical: the very high frequency (ω) waves corresponding to the short wavelengths ($\lambda \approx$ 5-mm) we require to make the many body scattering study feasible cannot be handled in this fashion.

However, essentially the same problem arises for the somewhat lower radio frequencies (RF) in conventional radio circuits and is resolved by the superheterodyne system: the information carried originally by a wave of high frequency ω (say in the form $T \exp(i\tau - i\omega t) = E$) is transferred to a wave of lower frequency Ω (the intermediate frequency, IF) by first forming $E^1 = T\exp[i\tau - i(\omega+\Omega)t]$ and then 'mixing' (beating) E^1 with a signal $E_0 = e^{-i\omega t}$. generated by a local oscillator; the significant output of the

---

Fig. 4. Drawing of 5-mm microwave setup for forward scattering measurements. The transmitter horn (1) illuminates the distribution (2) and part of the field is intercepted by the receiver horn (3); the horns (26 db) are face to face and their polarizations (vertical **E**) are parallel. [The receiver carriage can be moved around the 18-foot diameter track (4), and the transmitter carriage can be moved along parallel tracks (9).] The auxillary equipment includes the rotary phase shifter (5), the demodulator (6), the electronic analog computer (7), and recorders (8). The distances of the phase centers of the transmitter and receiver apertures from the center of the scattering region are d_t = 27.5" and d_r = 104" respectively. The wavelength for the present work is 0.205". Horn patterns are given in last paper of ref. 3.

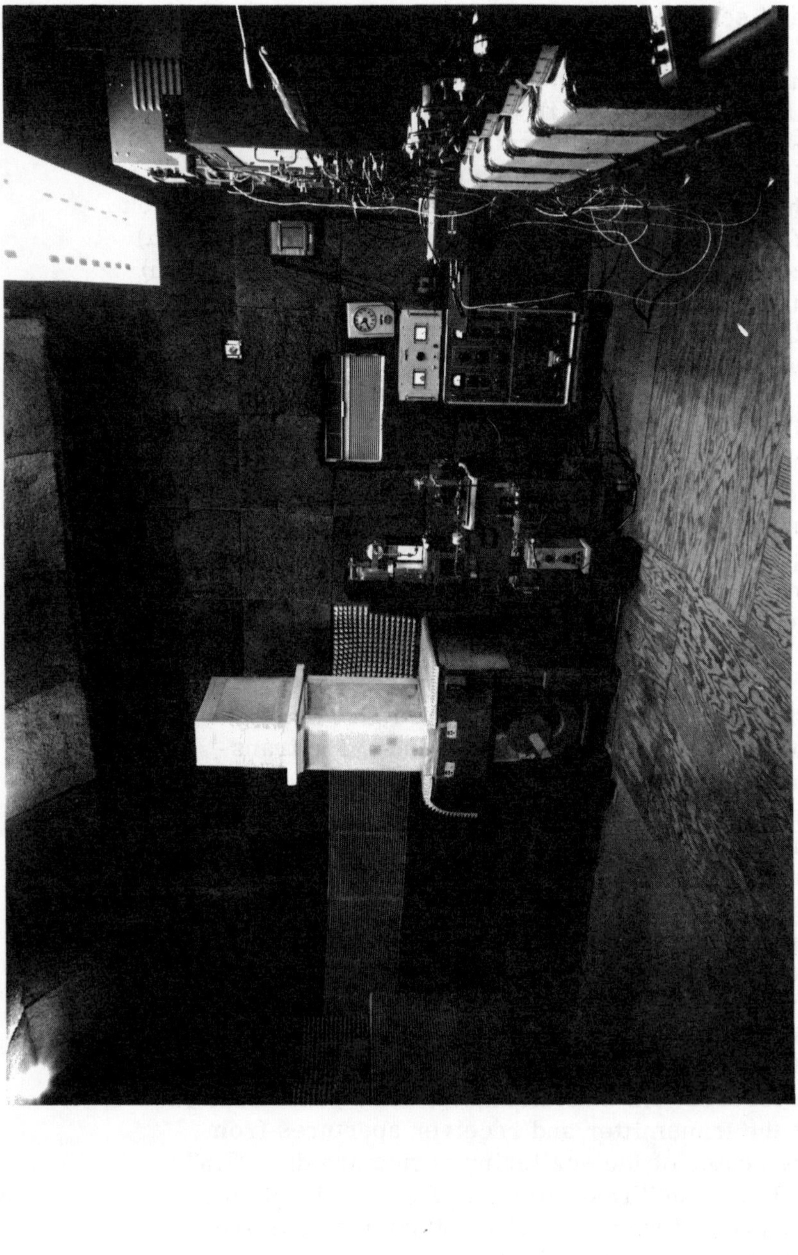

Fig. 5. Photograph of scattering facility. The faces of the carriages, and the walls and ceiling are covered by microwave absorbing material.

mixer is proportional to Tcos $(\Omega t - \tau)$ (essentially the oscillating term of $|E_0 + E^1|^2$), so that the information is carried by a wave at the lower beat frequency Ω. The superheterodyne principle has been carried over to the microwave region by Ring [16] and Yaw [25], by using a continuously rotating Fox-type phase-shifter [8] as the 'intermediate frequency oscillator': a linearly polarized wave proportional to $e^{-i\omega t}$ (the TE_{01} mode of a rectangular guide first converted to a TE_{11} mode in a circular guide by a tapered transition) passes through the microwave analog of a quarter-wave plate (an appropriate length of tapered elliptical guide), then through the rotating analog of a half-wave plate, through another quarter-wave device, and emerges essentially as $\exp[-i(\omega + \Omega)t]$, where $\Omega / 2\pi$ is twice the frequency of rotation of the device. Our unit rotates at 210 cps, and our frequency shift is 420 cps—a very low 'audio frequency' convenient for conventional circuit operations.

The circuit of our microwave system shown in Fig. 6 consists of two bridges (interferometers) isolated from each other: a reference bridge (the minor bridge I) whose outputs are $\cos \Omega t \equiv \mathcal{C}$ and $\sin \Omega t \equiv \mathcal{S}$, and a measurement bridge (the major bridge II) whose output is essentially $T\cos(\Omega t - \tau) = X\cos \Omega t + Y\sin \Omega t \equiv \mathcal{T}$. From the figure we see that the input signal (essentially $e^{-i\omega t} = E_0$) from the klystron to each bridge is split in two: one part is unchanged and plays the role of a 'local oscillator signal', and the other part has its frequency raised by the rotating 'intermediate frequency oscillator' so that it becomes essentially $\exp[-i(\omega + \Omega)t] = E_0^1$. In the reference bridge, E_0^1 and E_0 are mixed in a bolometer to yield an output proportional to $\mathcal{C}$, and half of this is then shifted in phase by $90°$ to provide a second reference signal $\mathcal{S}$. In the measurement bridge, the signal proportional to E_0^1 emerges from a rectangular horn, encounters the slab-region distribution of scatterers, and part of the resultant field enters a rectangular receiving horn as $T\exp[i\tau - i(\omega+\Omega)t] = E^1$. At the receiver, E^1 is mixed with E_0 (which arrives there via a waveguide); the output $\mathcal{T}$ of the bolometer detector then enters a demodulating device. The reference signals

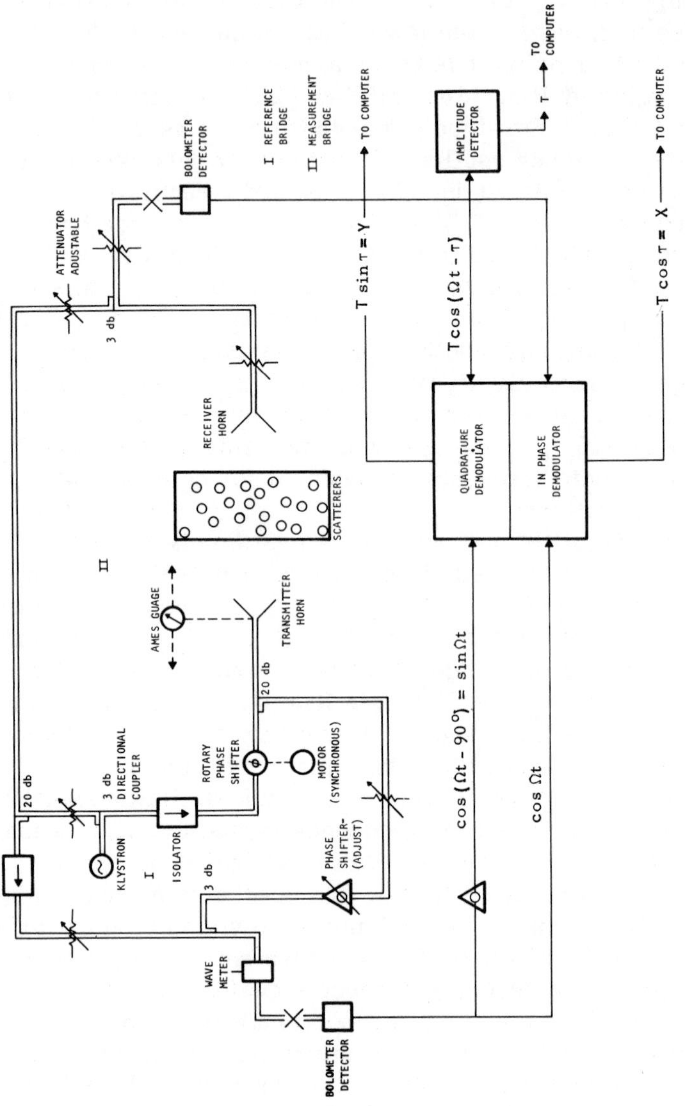
BOLOMETER DETECTOR
ATTENUATOR ADUSTABLE
3 db
I REFERENCE BRIDGE
II MEASUREMENT BRIDGE
TO COMPUTER
TO COMPUTER
TO COMPUTER
AMPLITUDE DETECTOR
T
T sin τ = Y
T cos (Ωt - τ)
T cos τ = X
RECEIVER HORN
SCATTERERS
QUADRATURE DEMODULATOR
IN PHASE DEMODULATOR
II
AMES GUAGE
TRANSMITTER HORN
20 db
ROTARY PHASE SHIFTER
MOTOR (SYNCHRONOUS)
20 db
3 db DIRECTIONAL COUPLER
KLYSTRON
I
ISOLATOR
3 db
PHASE SHIFTER- (ADJUST)
cos (Ωt - 90°) = sin Ωt
cos Ωt
WAVE METER
BOLOMETER DETECTOR

Fig. 6

$\mathcal{C}$ and $\mathcal{S}$ are amplified and clipped to provide the time bases for two phase-sensitive demodulators which operate on $\mathcal{G}$ to produce essentially X and Y. (This demodulation procedure is more accurate than integrating $\mathcal{C}\mathcal{G}$, and $\mathcal{S}\mathcal{G}$; however either procedure requires that X(t) be essentially constnat over half a cycle, i.e., over 1/840 of a second as is fulfilled experimentally.) The bandwidth of the audio part of the circuit is 420 cps ± 200 cps which appears adequate for the measurements: decreasing the half-bandwidth from 200 to 100 cps has no effect, and a decrease to 50 cps changes X and Y by about 3%. (The minor bridge system replaces the previously [1, 4] described 420 cps tachometer generator which was driven by the rotationg phase shifter; the present system provides time bases that are relatively independent of klystron drift, i.e., both bridges are afftected equally.) Figure 6 also shows a separate channel for isolating the magniture T; we use this data for checking purposes.

Figure 7 shows photographs of 0.45 second oscilloscope traces of X, Y relative to the magnitude D of the direct signal (for 100 spheres of diameter 2a = 1.36" and index of refraction $\eta = 1.016$). The function X(t) that we isolate as above represents the component of the field in phase with the field at the receiver in the absence of scatterers, and

Fig. 6. Schematic diagram of waveguide circuitry. The klystron frequency is $\omega/2\pi = 58\times 10^9$ cps, and the frequency shift introduced by the rotating Fox-type phase-shifter is $\Omega/2\pi = 420$ cps. The reference circuit I combines a wave of frequency ω with one of frequency $\omega + \Omega$ to produce an output at the beat-frequency Ω. The measurement circuit II differs from I in that the path of the frequency shifted wave is interrupted by the scattering region where it acquires an amplitude and phase change $Te^{i\tau} = X + iY$. Thus the X, Y data carried originally at a microwave frequency is 'transferred' to a low audio-frequency wave, and then isolated by phase sensitive demodulators driven by the beat-frequency references. The two-bridge system is relatively insensitive to klystron drift.

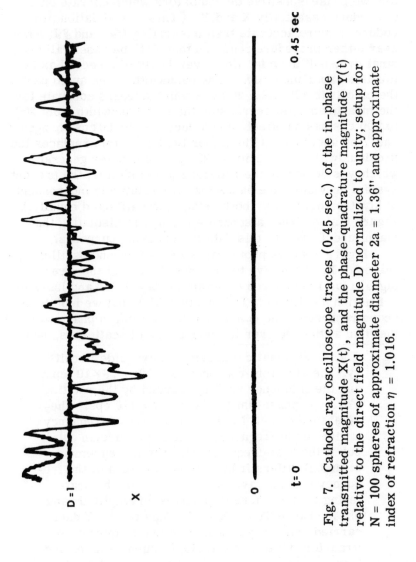

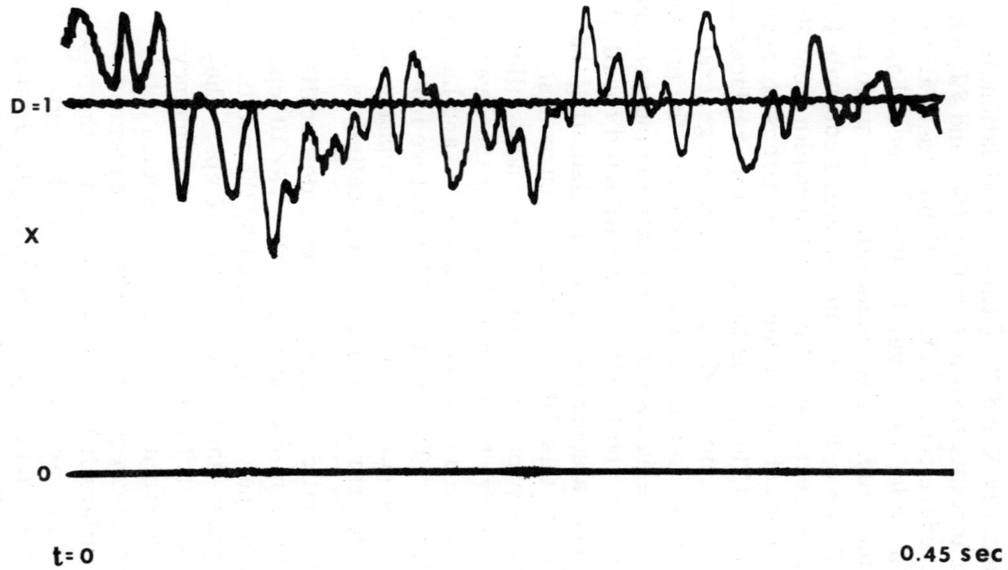

Fig. 7. Cathode ray oscilloscope traces (0.45 sec.) of the in-phase transmitted magnitude $X(t)$, and the phase-quadrature magnitude $Y(t)$ relative to the direct field magnitude D normalized to unity; setup for $N = 100$ spheres of approximate diameter $2a = 1.36''$ and approximate index of refraction $\eta = 1.016$.

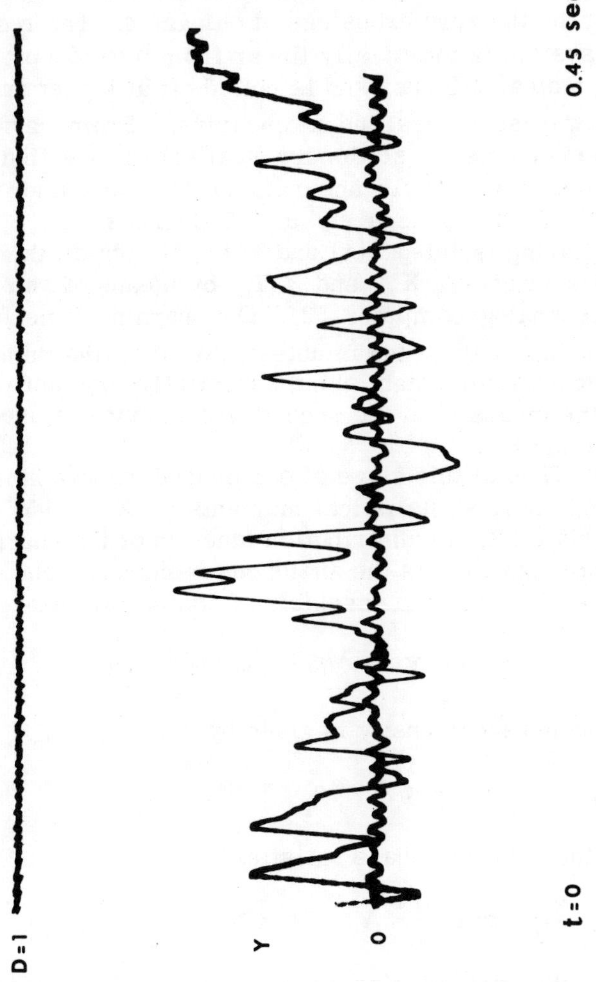

Fig. 7 (continued)

the function Y(t) is 90° ahead of the direct phase; in our circuit we insure this by means of the reference bridge, i. e., by the zero crossings of our gates. The response of our system is practically linear from 0 to 80 cps; it is down by 4.5 db at 210 cps, and is rolled off at higher frequencies by low-pass filters and attenuators. From various measurements on stationary scatterers, we find that $T^2 = (X^2 + Y^2)/D^2$ is accurate to 1%, and that $\tau = \tan^{-1}(Y/X)$ is accurate to 0.5 degrees.

Having isolated X(t) and Y(t), we obtain their time-averages $\langle X \rangle$ and $\langle Y \rangle$ by means of an electronic analog computer [2]. Our running time for this setup is about ten minutes: the first five minutes is adequate for establishing essentially constant values for the means, and the second five minutes is used for confirmation.

Thus at this stage of our procedure, we have determined the first statistical moments ($\langle X \rangle$, $\langle Y \rangle$) of the bivariate (X, Y) distribution function of the ensemble of signals, as well as the analogous 'coherent field'–the average of Ψ over the ensemble of configurations:

$$\langle X \rangle + i \langle Y \rangle = \langle T e^{i\tau} \rangle = \langle \Psi \rangle \equiv C e^{i\alpha} . \qquad (4)$$

The coherent intensity is given by

$$C^2 = \langle X \rangle^2 + \langle Y \rangle^2 , \qquad (5)$$

and the coherent phase satisfies

$$\tan \alpha = \langle Y \rangle / \langle X \rangle . \qquad (6)$$

We could also average X^2 and Y^2 to provide the second moments ($\langle X^2 \rangle$, $\langle Y^2 \rangle$) and the average total intensity

$$\langle X^2 \rangle + \langle Y^2 \rangle = \langle T^2 \rangle = \langle |\Psi|^2 \rangle . \qquad (7)$$

In practice, we obtain $\langle T^2 \rangle$ more directly by squaring the output of the T-channel of Fig. 6, and then averaging T^2.

From X, Y, and their means, we form the departures

$$x = X - \langle X \rangle , \qquad y = Y - \langle Y \rangle . \tag{8}$$

Then we construct $x^n y^m$ with $n + m \leq 4$ and determine $\langle x^n y^m \rangle$ by an additional ten minute run (five minutes to establish the averages, and five for confirmation); see Fig. 8 for computation sequences. The first central moments $\langle x \rangle$ and $\langle y \rangle$ are zero by construction, and the variances are of the form $\langle x^2 \rangle = \langle (X - \langle X \rangle)^2 \rangle = \langle X^2 \rangle - \langle X \rangle^2$. Thus we may rewrite (7) as

$$\langle T^2 \rangle = C^2 + \langle I^2 \rangle , \quad \langle I^2 \rangle \equiv \langle x^2 \rangle + \langle y^2 \rangle , \tag{9}$$

where $\langle I^2 \rangle$ is the 'incoherent intensity'. The value of $\langle T^2 \rangle$ that we determine by this procedure is checked by the value obtained from our separate channel for T. The usual optical photometric measurements on a similar geometry yield $\langle T^2 \rangle$ directly near the forward direction, and $\langle T^2 \rangle \approx \langle I^2 \rangle$ for off-forward angles; α is obtained directly by means of an interferometer.

In addition to the variances $\langle x^2 \rangle$ and $\langle y^2 \rangle$, we also obtain the covariance $\langle xy \rangle$ to complete the set of second central moments. These provide the standard statistical parameters for the bivariate distribution function of the ensemble of signals, i. e., the standard deviations σ_x, σ_y, and the correlation coefficient μ:

$$\sigma_x^2 = \langle x^2 \rangle , \quad \sigma_y^2 = \langle y^2 \rangle , \quad \mu = \langle xy \rangle / \sigma_x \sigma_y . \tag{10}$$

It is often assumed (at least implicitly), both for the scattering problem and for the analogous radiation problem, that x and y are uncorrelated and specified by Gaussian functions having equal standard deviations, i. e., that the bivariate distribution function factors into a product of normal distributions

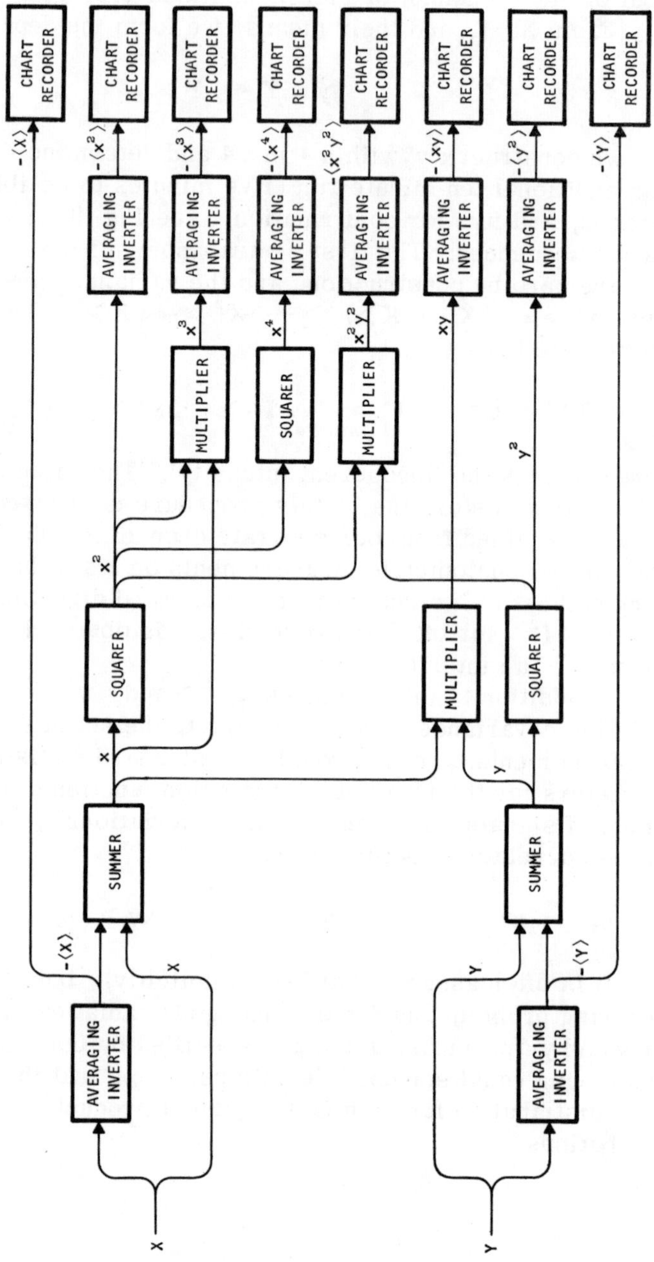

Fig. 8. Computer schematic for determining higher moments.

$$\mathcal{W}(x, y)\, dxdy = W_G(x;\sigma)\; W_G(y;\sigma)\, dxdy \;,$$
$$W_G(x;\sigma) = \frac{1}{\sigma\sqrt{2\pi}} \exp\left(-x^2/2\sigma^2\right) \;, \tag{11}$$
$$\sigma^2 = \langle x^2 \rangle = \langle I^2 \rangle / 2 \;.$$

For the very special situations where (11) holds, the ensemble of signals around the mean is specified completely by the one parameter σ, i. e., if this simple model holds then all non-vanishing higher central moments can be expressed simply in terms of σ:

$$\langle x^n y^m \rangle = \iint_{-\infty}^{\infty} x^n y^m W_G(x)\, W_G(y)\, dxdy \;, \tag{11a}$$

so that, e. g.

$$\begin{aligned} &\langle x^2 \rangle = \langle y^2 \rangle = \sigma^2 \;; \quad \langle xy \rangle = 0 \;; \\ &\langle x^3 \rangle = \langle y^3 \rangle = \langle xy^3 \rangle = \langle x^2 y \rangle = 0 \;; \\ &\langle x^4 \rangle = \langle y^4 \rangle = 3\sigma^4/4,\; \langle x^2 y^2 \rangle = \sigma^4/4, \\ &\qquad \langle xy^3 \rangle = \langle x^3 y \rangle = 0 \;. \end{aligned} \tag{11b}$$

It is convenient to write

$$Ie^{i\varphi} \equiv x + iy = Te^{i\tau} - Ce^{i\alpha} = \Psi - \langle \Psi \rangle ,\; \langle Ie^{i\varphi} \rangle = 0, \tag{12}$$

where $Ie^{i\varphi}$ is sometimes called the 'random field' or incoherent field'; we call $Ie^{i\varphi}$ the variant field. The interrelations of the functions of (8) and (12) are shown in Fig. 9.

We have $W(I, \varphi)\, Id\, Id\varphi = \mathcal{W}(x, y)\, dxdy$, and for the special case corresponding to (11),

$$W(I, \varphi)\, Id\, Id\varphi = W_R(I)\, W_U(\varphi)\, dId\varphi = W_R(I)\, dId\varphi \;;$$
$$W_R(I) = \frac{2I}{\langle I^2 \rangle} \exp\left(-I^2/\langle I^2 \rangle\right) = \frac{I}{\sigma^2} \exp\left(-I^2/2\sigma^2\right),$$
$$W_U(\varphi) = 1/2\pi, \tag{13}$$

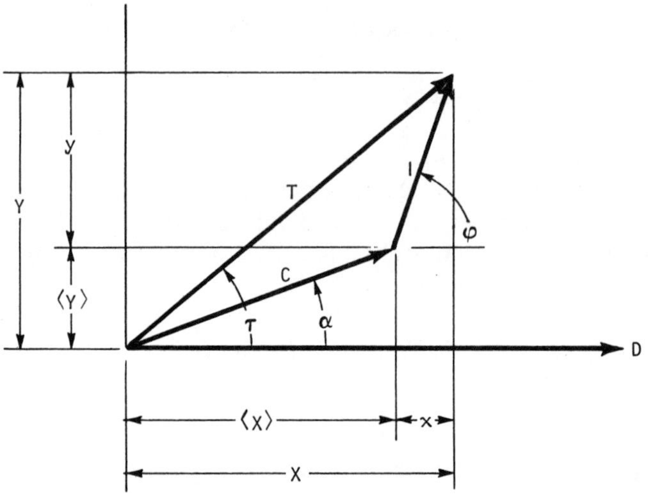

Fig. 9. Argand diagram for instantaneous field $Te^{i\tau} = Ce^{i\alpha} + Ie^{i\varphi}$.

where I is Rayleigh distributed and φ is uniformly distributed. If we apply (13) to determine

$$<I^n e^{im\varphi}> = \int_0^\infty \int_0^2 I^n e^{im\varphi} W_R(I) dI d\varphi \ , \qquad (13a)$$

we obtain

$$<I^{2n}> = n! <I^2>^n = n! \ 2^n \sigma^{2n} \ ; \ n = 1, 2, 3 \cdots , \qquad (13b)$$

and all other averages vanish.

Were (11) or equivalently (13) applicable, then photographs of an oscilloscope trace of $Ie^{i\varphi}$ (obtained by applying $x(t)$ to the horizontal deflection plates and $y(t)$ to the verticle) would become more and more circularly symmetrical as the exposure time was increased. However, the series of time exposures of Fig. 10 (2 seconds to 4 minutes) corresponding to the same run as X, Y of Fig. 7, show that the situation is considerably more complicated: the shape approached is a rough oval. Were the long exposure results actually elliptical, then the simplest corresponding ensemble of x, y would be specified by the bivariate normal distribution function

$$\mathcal{W}(x, y)\,dxdy =$$

$$= \frac{dxdy}{2\pi\sigma_x\sigma_y\sqrt{1-\mu^2}} \exp\left\{-\frac{1}{2(1-\mu^2)}\left[\frac{x^2}{\sigma_x^2} - \frac{2\mu xy}{\sigma_x\sigma_y} + \frac{y^2}{\sigma_y^2}\right]\right\}$$

$$= \frac{dxdy}{2\pi[\langle x^2\rangle\langle y^2\rangle - \langle xy\rangle^2]^{\frac{1}{2}}} \exp\left\{-\frac{x^2\langle y^2\rangle - 2xy\langle xy\rangle + y^2\langle x^2\rangle}{2[\langle x^2\rangle\langle y^2\rangle - \langle xy\rangle^2]}\right\} \quad (14)$$

in terms of either the three standard statistical parameters of (10) or the set of moments. However, we show shortly that (14) or any other function specified solely by second moments is inadequate for the problems we consider: the third central moments do not vanish (i. e., the distribution is skewed), and the fourth moments cannot be specified solely by the second (the distribution is peaked differently than (14)).

We now consider interrelations of the moments that follow from elementary considerations, substantiate these with experimental data, and then go on to discuss the scattering function representations of the various moments.

II.2 Interrelations of Second Moments

We could make the relations between the second moments explicit by rotating the coordinate frame an angle ν and dealing with

$$x_\nu = x\cos\nu + y\sin\nu, \qquad y_\nu = -x\sin\nu + y\cos\nu, \qquad (15)$$

where x and y correspond to $\nu = 0$. However, the interrelations are more conveniently exhibited in terms of $Ie^{i\varphi}$ of (12). Squaring $x = I\cos\varphi$, $y = I\sin\varphi$, and averaging to obtain $\langle x^2\rangle = \langle I^2\cos^2\varphi\rangle$, $\langle y^2\rangle = \langle I^2\sin^2\varphi\rangle$, we see that $\langle I^2\rangle$ of (9), which was a definition, follows from

$$\langle x^2\rangle + \langle y^2\rangle = \langle I^2(\cos^2\varphi + \sin^2\varphi)\rangle = \langle I^2\rangle \equiv 2\sigma^2, \quad (16)$$

where we introduced σ (an 'average' standard deviation) for subsequent use. In addition, by trigonometry, we have

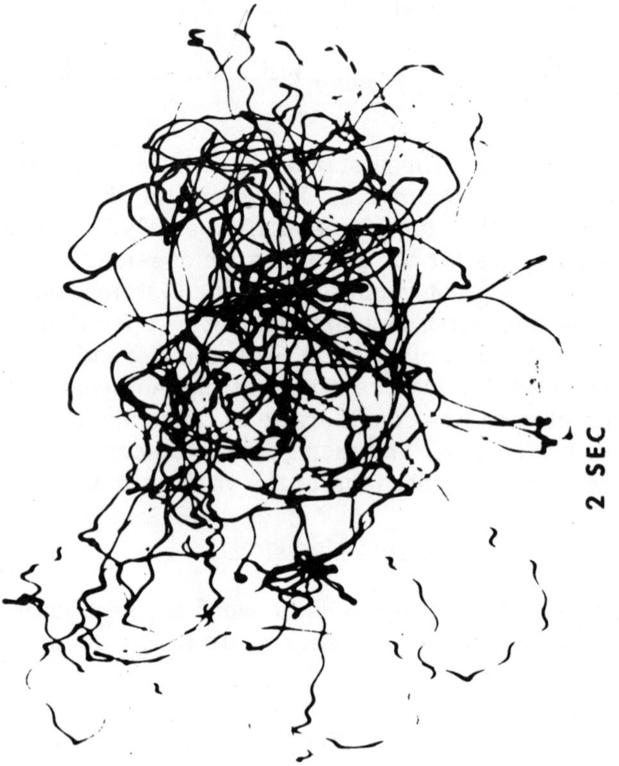

Fig. 10. Oscilloscope patterns of trace of $Ie^{i\varphi} = x(t) + iy(t)$ (corresponding to Fig. 7) obtained with x on horizontal deflection plates and y on vertical plates.

5 SEC

Fig. 10 (Cont'd)

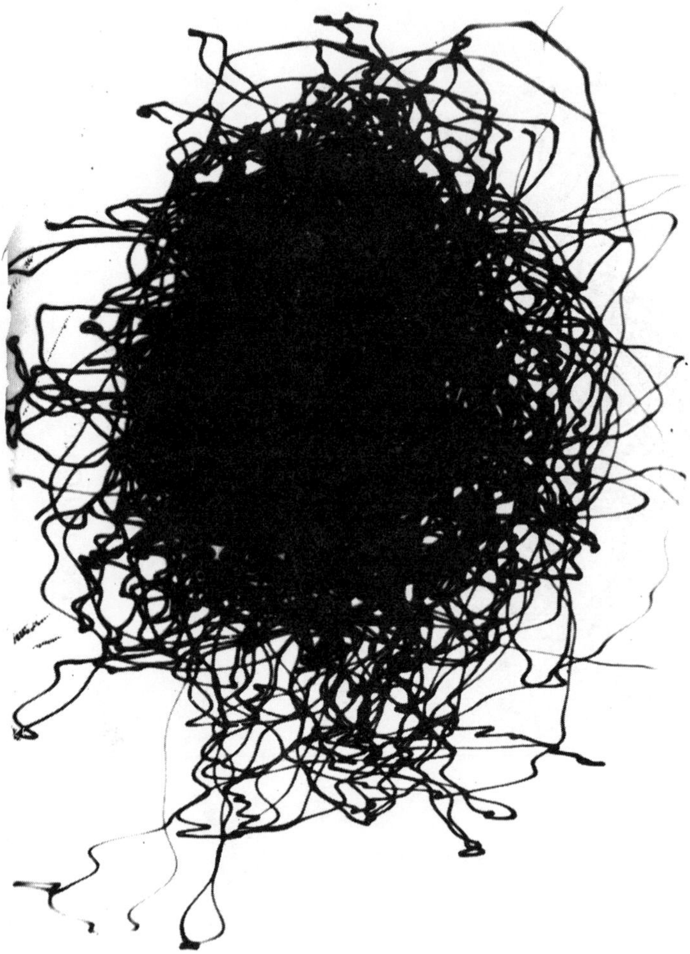

15 SEC

Fig. 10 (Cont'd)

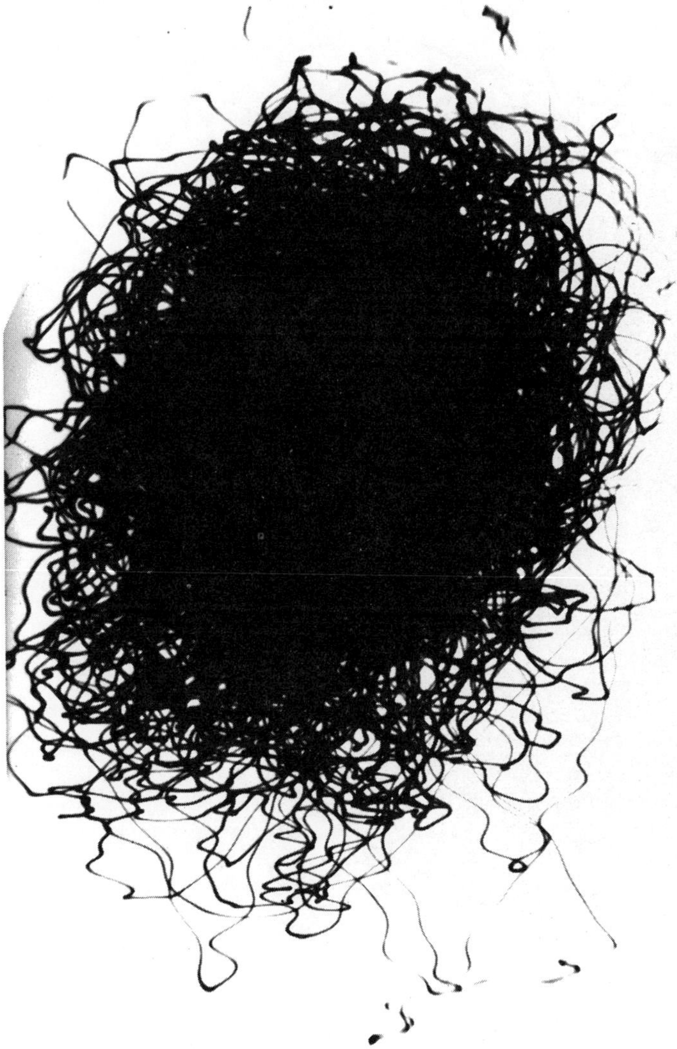

30 SEC

Fig. 10 (Cont'd)

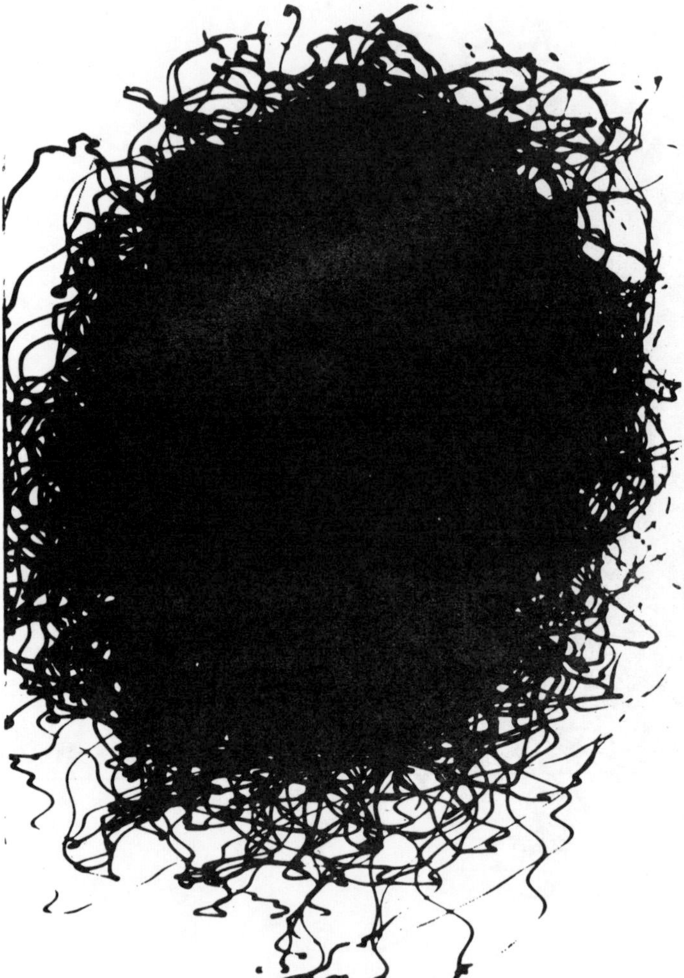

1 MIN

Fig. 10 (Cont'd)

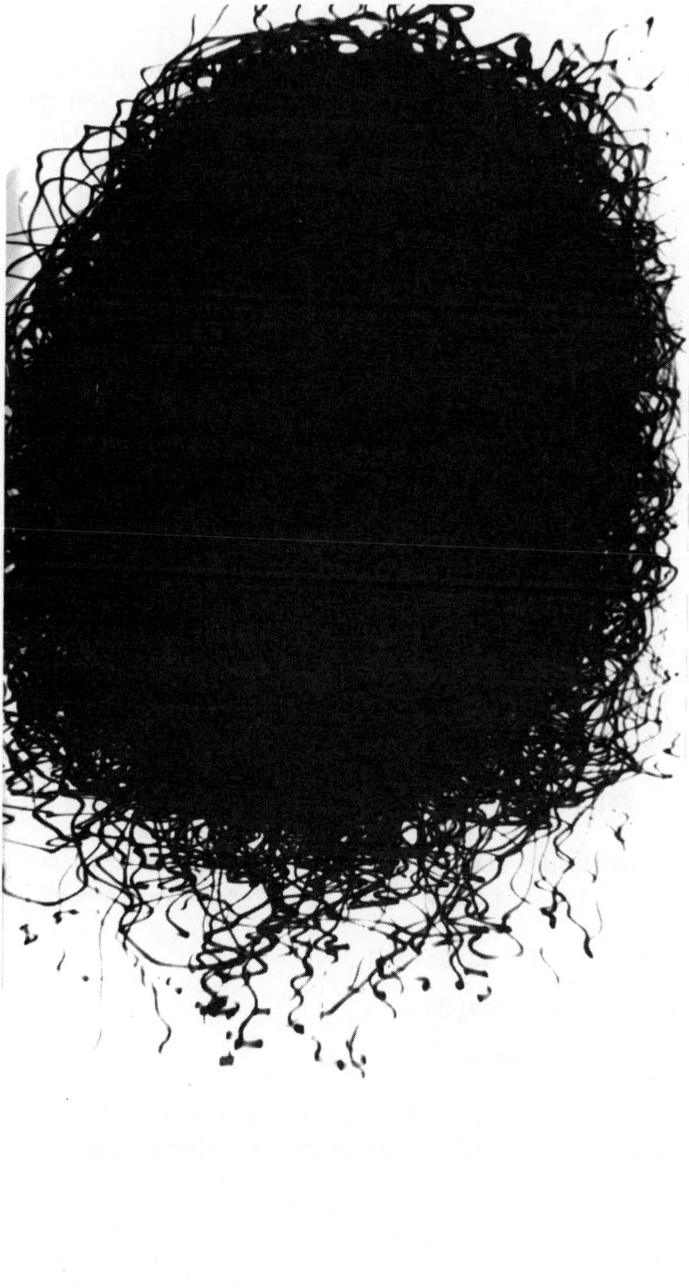

4 MIN

Fig. 10 (Cont'd)

$$<x^2> = <I^2 \cos^2\varphi> = \tfrac{1}{2}<I^2> + \tfrac{1}{2}<I^2 \cos 2\varphi>,$$
$$<y^2> = <I^2 \sin^2\varphi> = \tfrac{1}{2}<I^2> - \tfrac{1}{2}<I^2 \cos 2\varphi>, \qquad (17)$$
$$<xy> = <I^2 \cos\varphi \sin\varphi> = \tfrac{1}{2}<I^2 \sin 2\varphi>.$$

Thus the two variances are always equally displaced above and below the value of half the incoherent intensity, and the covariance is simply this same displacement shifted 90°.

To make the relations more explicit, we introduce

$$2S^2 e^{i2s} \equiv <I^2 e^{i2\varphi}> = <(Te^{i\tau} - Ce^{i\alpha})^2> = <T^2 e^{i2\tau}> - C^2 e^{i2\alpha}, \qquad (18)$$

where the relation of the phase s to the variant phase φ is roughly analogous to the relation of the coherent phase α to the instantaneous phase τ. The function S^2 is the maximum value of the covariance; from (17), we have $0 \le S^2 \le <I^2>/2 = \sigma^2$. We call S the <u>covariant magnitude</u>, and s the <u>covariant phase</u>. Using (16) and (18) we rewrite (17) as

$$<x^2> = \sigma^2 + S^2 \cos 2s, \quad <y^2> = \sigma^2 - S^2 \cos 2s, \quad <xy> = S^2 \sin 2s. \qquad (17a)$$

Because of the factor $e^{i2\varphi}$ in the core of $S^2 e^{i2s}$, a rotation of the coordinate frame by an angle ν as in Fig. 11 introduces a factor $e^{i2\nu}$. Thus for arbitrary ν,

$$\frac{1}{2}<I^2 \exp[i2(\varphi-\nu)]> = S^2 \exp[i(2s-2\nu)] \qquad (19)$$

and consequently the second moments corresponding to $Ie^{i(\varphi-\nu)} \equiv x_\nu + iy_\nu = (x\cos\nu + y\sin\nu) + i(-x\sin\nu + y\cos\nu)$ are

$$<x_\nu^2> = \sigma^2 + S^2\cos(2s-2\nu),$$
$$<y_\nu^2> = \sigma^2 - S^2\cos(2s-2\nu), \qquad (20)$$
$$<x_\nu y_\nu> = S^2\sin(2s-2\nu),$$

i.e., the period of all second moments as ν is varied is π. These results hold for all bivariate distributions. The

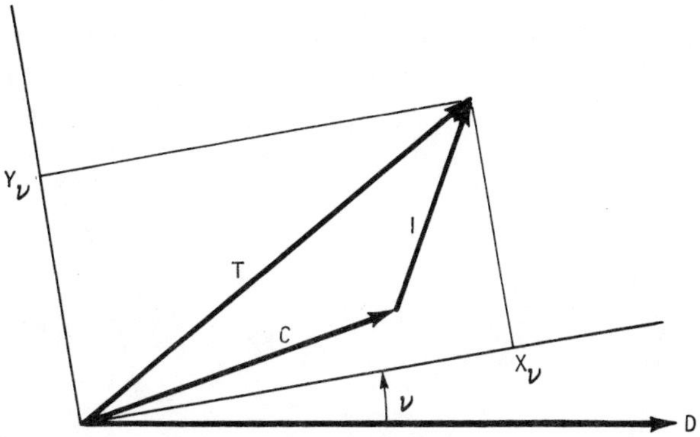

Fig. 11. Rotation of coordinate frame of Fig. 9. Note that the phase of the direct field (**D**) provides the permanent reference for τ, α, φ, and other phase angles that arise in averaging.

average of $<x_\nu^2>$ or $<y_\nu^2>$ over a period in ν is σ^2, and the average of $<x_\nu y_\nu>$ over ν is zero.

The real axis of our original coordinate system X, Y of Fig. 9 is determined by the phase of the direct field at the receiver in the absence of scatterers; Fig. 9 is our permanent reference system for τ, α, φ, s, and any other phase angles that arise in averaging. In order to transform to the coordinate system of X_ν, Y_ν of Fig. 11, we temporarily change our reference phase by ν. For measurement purposes, we vary the phase of the reference gates that provide the time bases for the demodulators.

As ν is varied, the first moments $<X_\nu> = C\cos(\alpha-\nu)$ and $<Y_\nu> = C\sin(\alpha-\nu)$ are periodic in 2π as shown in Fig. 12, and the second moments are periodic in π as shown in Fig. 13. (Such second moment data was first reported by Beard [1], and additional results are given in ref. 12). The figures show data for gas-like distributions of 50 and 100 scatterers having similar physical parameters; the distribution for N = 100 corresponds essentially to that for which we obtained the oscilloscope traces of Figs. 7 and 10.

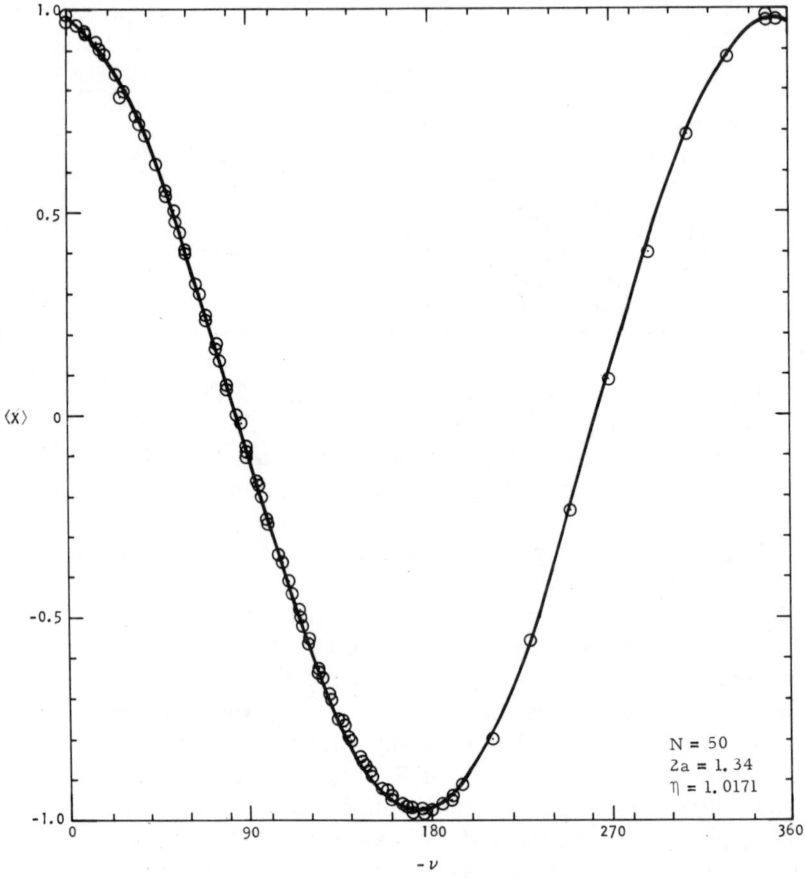

Fig. 12. Plots of quadrature components $<X_\nu>$ and $<Y_\nu>$ of coherent field (normalized by division with direct signal magnitude D) versus reference phase $-\nu$ (in degrees) for gas distributions of 50(a, b and 100(c, d) spheres with similar parameters: the N = 100 set corresponds

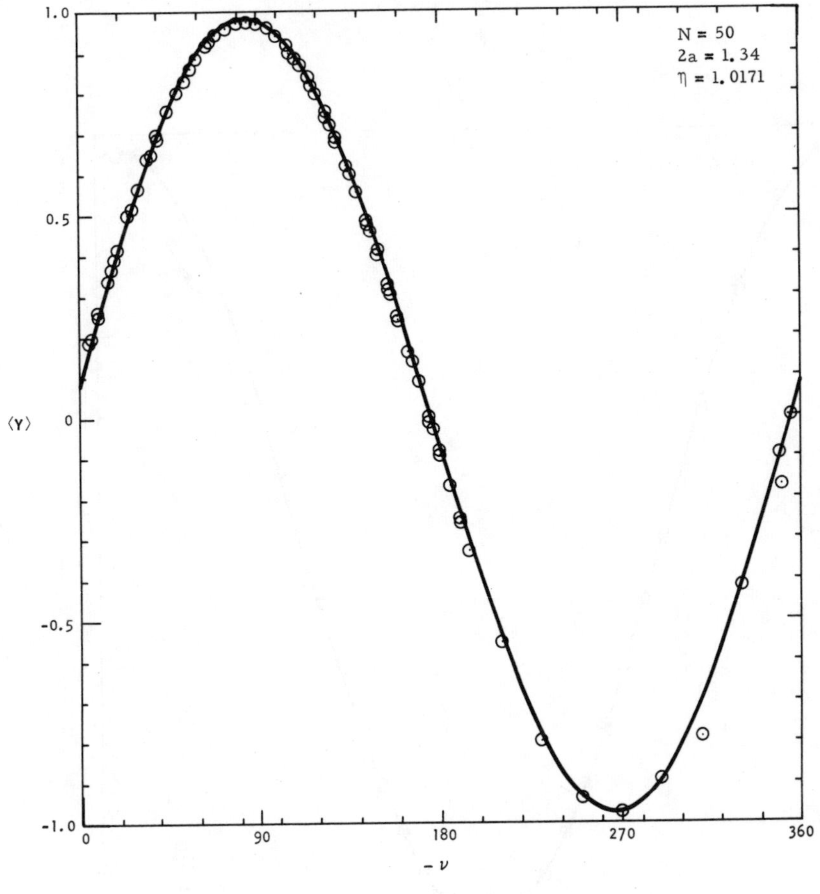

essentially to Figs. 7 and 10. Curves are of the form C cos (α-ν) and C sin (α-ν); theory for C and α will be discussed subsequently. We may obtain C from the amplitudes of the sinusoidal cata, and α from the positions of the extrema (i.e., α - ν = 0, 90°, 180°, etc.).

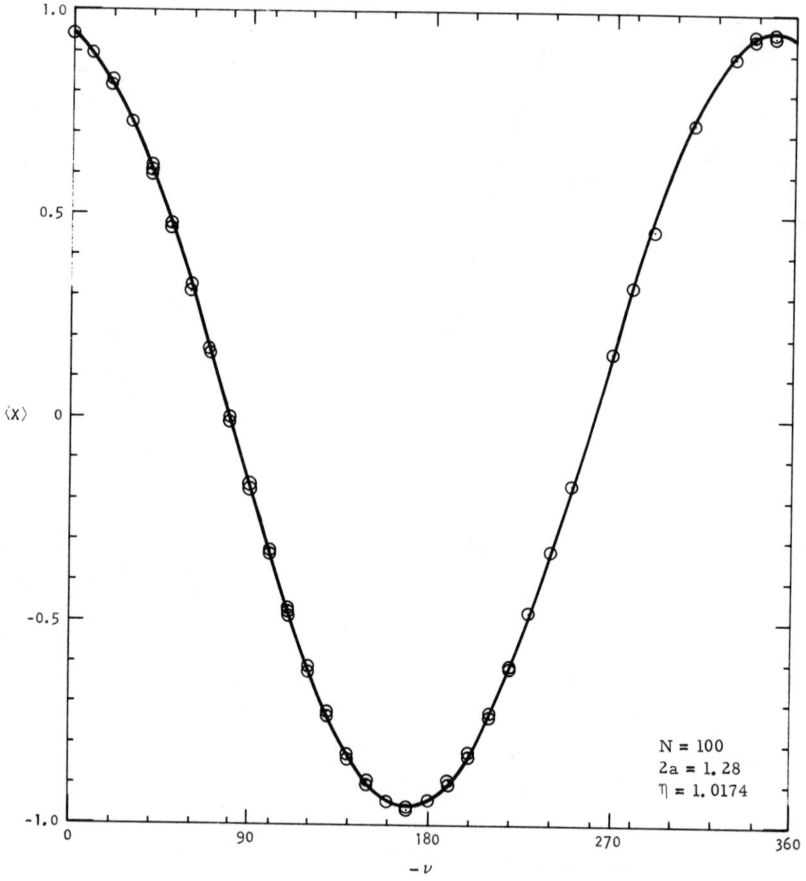

Fig. 12 (Cont'd)

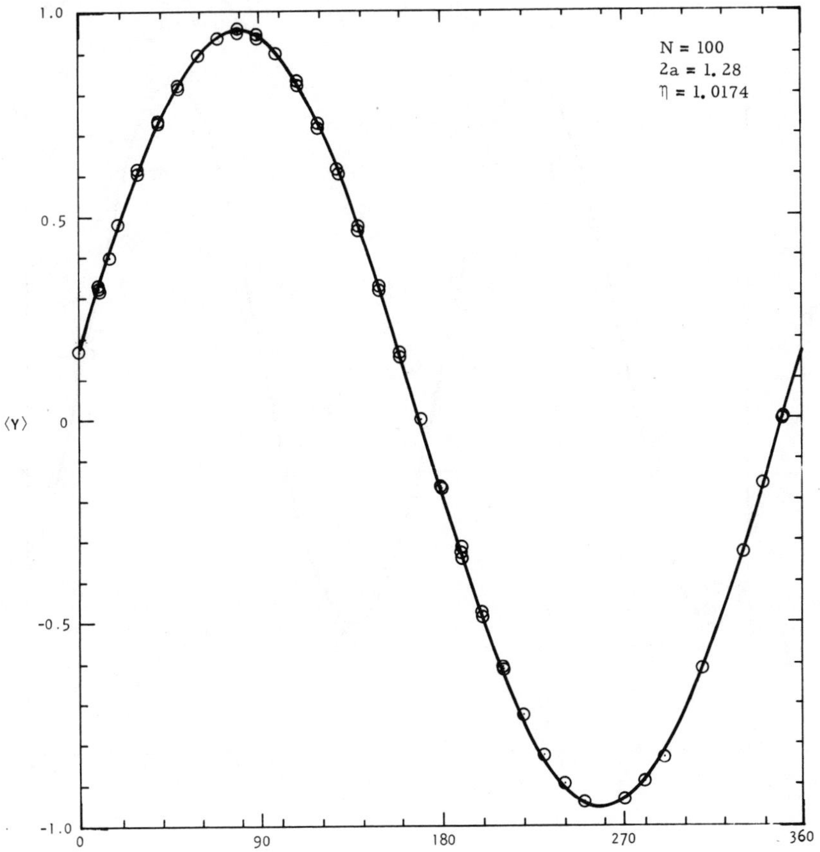

Fig. 12 (Cont'd)

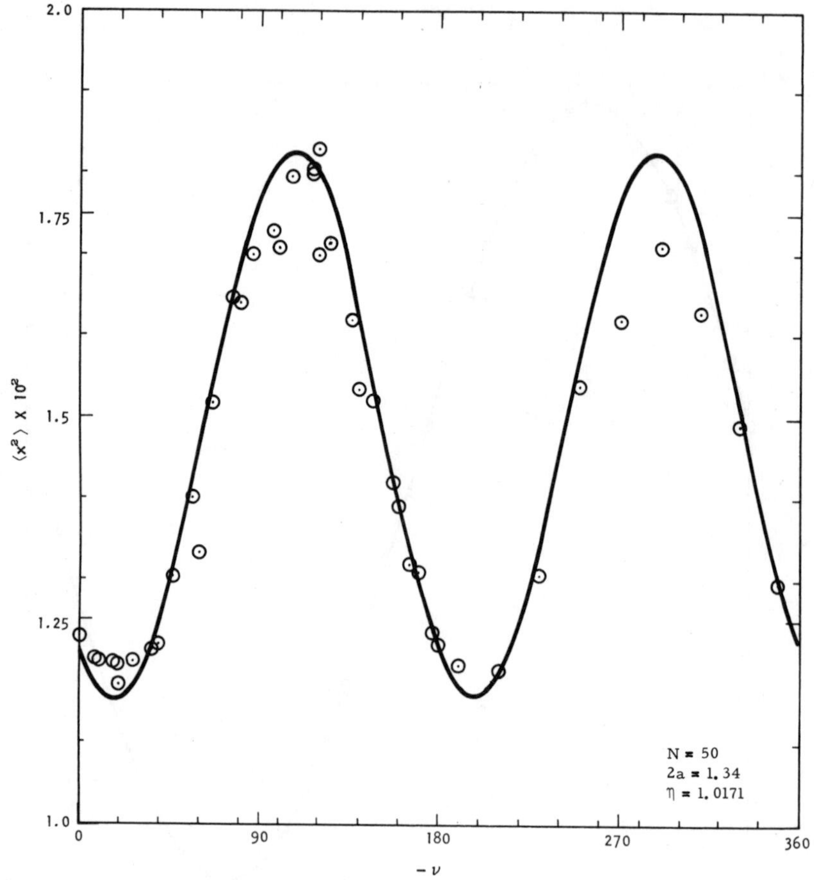

Fig. 13. Data for variances $<x_\nu^2>$ and covariance $<x_\nu y_\nu>$ (normalized by division with D^2) versus ν (in degrees) corresponding to Fig. 12. Curves are $\sigma^2 + S^2 \cos(2s-2\nu)$ and $S^2 \sin(2s-2\nu)$. Analogous data for $<y_\nu^2>$ fits $\sigma^2 - S^2 \cos(2s-2\nu)$. We may obtain S^2 from the amplitudes of the

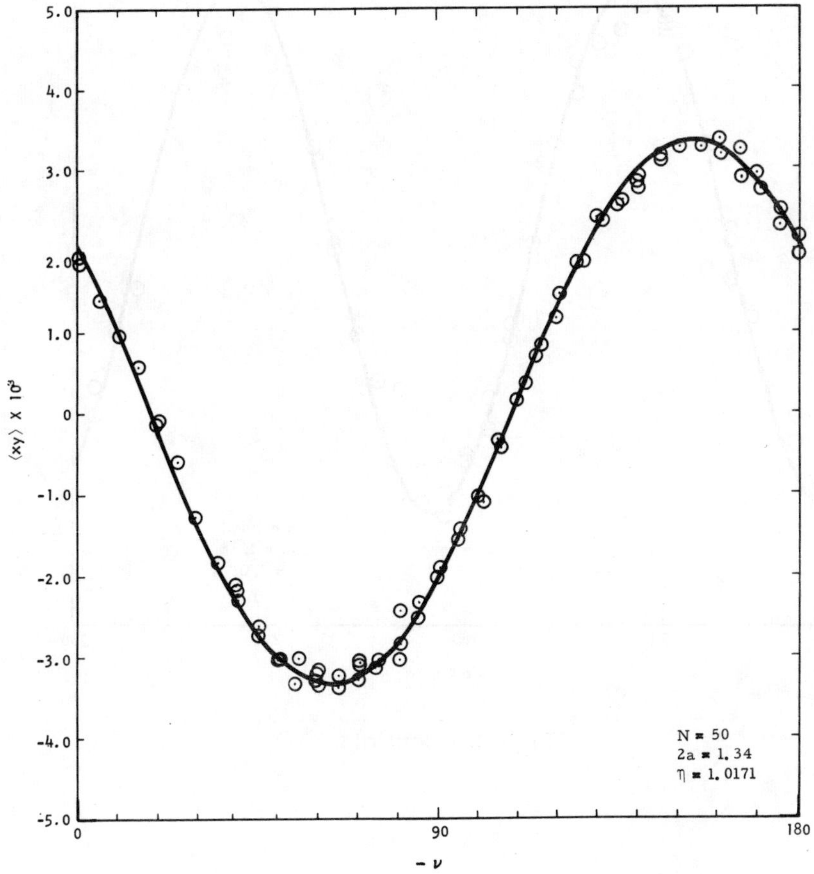

sinusoidal data, and $\sigma^2 = < I^2 > /2$ from the average value (over ν) of $<x_\nu^2>$. The phase s may be obtained from the positions of the extrema of $<x_\nu^2>$ or $<x_\nu y_\nu>$, i. e., from $2s-2\nu=0$, $90°$, $180°$, etc. Scattering theory for $<I^2>$, S, and s will be discussed subsequently.

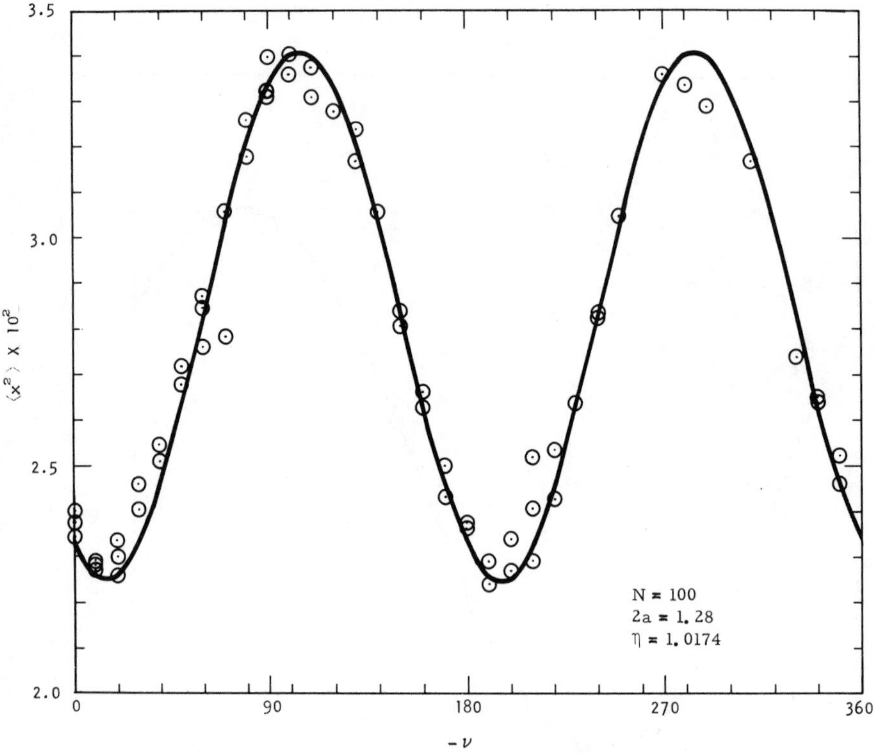
3.5
3.0
2.5
2.0
$\langle x^2 \rangle \times 10^2$
0
90
180
270
360
$-\nu$
N = 100
2a = 1.28
η = 1.0174

Fig. 13 (Cont'd)

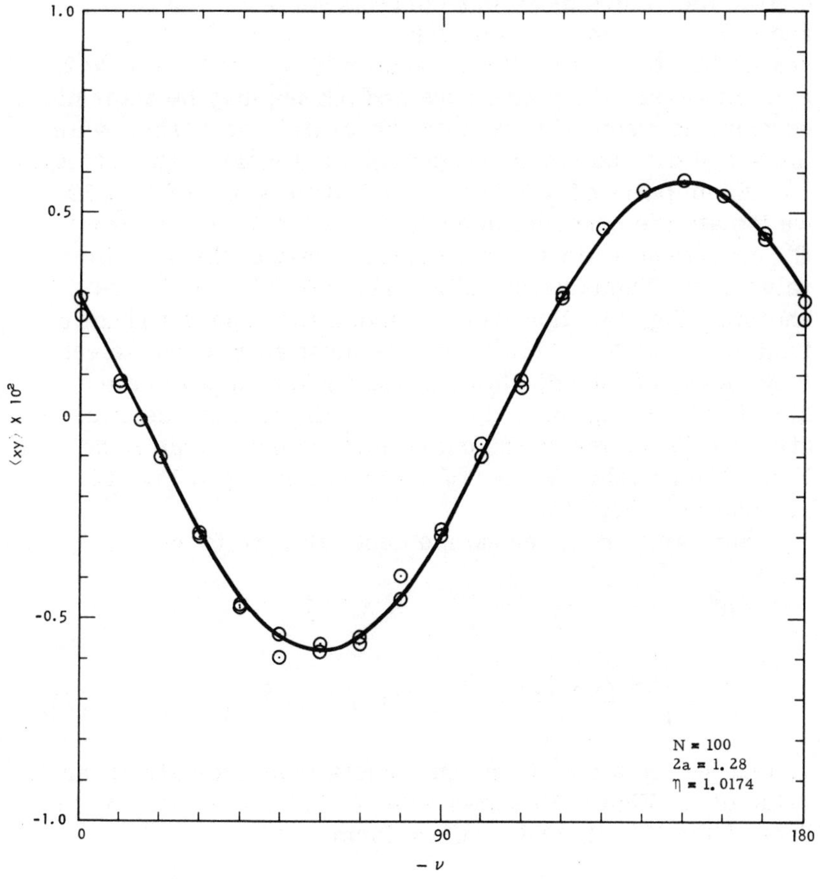

Fig. 13 (Cont'd)

One could determine C from the magnitudes of the maxima of $<X_\nu>$ and $<Y_\nu>$ of Fig. 12 with variation of ν; similarly the early measurements [4] sought to isolate S^2 by determining the magnitudes of the extrema of the second moments, e. g., from the amplitudes of such sinusoidal records as in Fig. 13. The values of ν for which the extrema occur determine the corresponding phases. Thus we could obtain α from the values $\alpha - \nu = 0, \pi$ corresponding to $|<X_\nu>| = C$ and $<Y_\nu> = 0$, and s from $2(s - \nu) = \pi/2,\ 3\pi/2$ corresponding to $|<x_\nu y_\nu>| = S^2$ and $<x_\nu^2> = <y_\nu^2> = <I^2>/2$, etc. However, the magnitudes and phases may be determined more conveniently and more accurately by working with the set of data points corresponding to a single value of ν.

From pairs of $<X_\nu>$ and $<Y_\nu>$ data points of Fig. 12 we isolate the coherent intensity $C^2 = <X_\nu>^2 + <Y_\nu>^2 = C^2[\cos^2(\alpha-\nu) + \sin^2(\alpha-\nu)]$ independently of the specific value of ν. The corresponding values of $2\beta = \ln C^2$ are shown in Fig. 14. However, to obtain the coherent phase α from $<Y_\nu>/<X_\nu> = \tan(\alpha - \nu)$, we must know ν; we select ν by means of the adjustable phase shifter shown in the $\sin\Omega t$ path in Fig. 6, and check it in the free-space situation by the values on the output meters that monitor the X and Y channels. Values of α corresponding to Fig. 12 are shown in Fig. 15.

Similarly from second moment data, we form

$$S^2 = \left\{\left[\frac{<x_\nu^2>-<y_\nu^2>}{2}\right]^2 + <x_\nu y_\nu>^2\right\}^{\frac{1}{2}}$$

$$= \left\{\frac{2S^4\cos^2(2s-2\nu)}{2} + S^4\sin^2(2s-2\nu)\right\}^{\frac{1}{2}}, \qquad (21)$$

so that we isolate S^2 from data points independently of the value of ν. Figure 16 shows values of S^2 corresponding to data of Fig. 13. In addition, we form

$$\tan(2s-2\nu) = \frac{2<x_\nu y_\nu>}{<x_\nu^2>-<y_\nu^2>}, \qquad (22)$$

and since we always know 2ν, we isolate the covariant phase s as in Fig. 17.

Physical Meaning of Covariant Field Se^{is}:

The familiar 'coherent field' $Ce^{i\alpha} = \langle\Psi\rangle$ has perhaps acquired its label because C and α can be isolated by an interferometer method, i. e., by essentially the same techniques that one can use to determine the amplitude and phase change introduced by a homogeneous sample of material. Thus we could convert [3] our facility to the microwave analog of an optical interferometer by using only the 'measurement bridge' II of Fig. 6 and disconnecting the rotary phase shifter, i. e., we add a reference field from the klystron to the field (proportional to $Te^{i\tau} = Ce^{i\alpha} + Ie^{i\varphi}$) entering the receiver horn, and apply the sum (say P) to a square-law detector. With no scatterers in the container, we vary the air-path phase (by moving the transmitter horn) and adjust the magnitude of the reference signal until a null reading is obtained in the detector output (i. e., until the direct and reference fields have equal magnitude D and are 180° out of phase). With the scatterers in motion in the container, the transmitter horn is moved to obtain a minimum time-average detector output; the coherent field is then 180° out of phase with the reference field. The shift in transmitter horn position (Δ) multiplied by $k = 2\pi/\lambda$ is the phase difference α between the coherent and direct fields. At this position ($k\Delta = \alpha$), we have $\langle P^2\rangle_{min} = (D-C)^2 + \langle I^2\rangle$. If the transmitter horn is then moved by $\lambda/2$ (i. e., at $k\Delta = \alpha + \pi$), we obtain $\langle P^2\rangle_{max} = (D+C)^2 + \langle I^2\rangle$. Consequently $C/D = [\langle P^2\rangle_{max} - \langle P^2\rangle_{min}]/4D^2$. Thus, at least in principle, an interferometer method yields the normalized magnitude of the coherent field as well as the coherent phase. Were we dealing with one fixed configuration (as is usually only of interest for a periodic spatial array), then the averaging procedure would not change anything and this measurement procedure would yield $Ce^{i\alpha} = \Psi$.

We now seek a fuller picture of the 'covariant field' Se^{is} introduced in (18) in the above. We have seen that the covariant magnitude S can be isolated from the extremum value of the covariance $\langle x_\nu y_\nu\rangle$ and that the covariant phase can be determined from the nulls of $\langle x_\nu y_\nu\rangle$ versus ν. (The 'bridge-circuits' of Fig. 6 plus the associated computer corresponding to Fig. 8 constitute a generalized interferometer for determining the nulls and

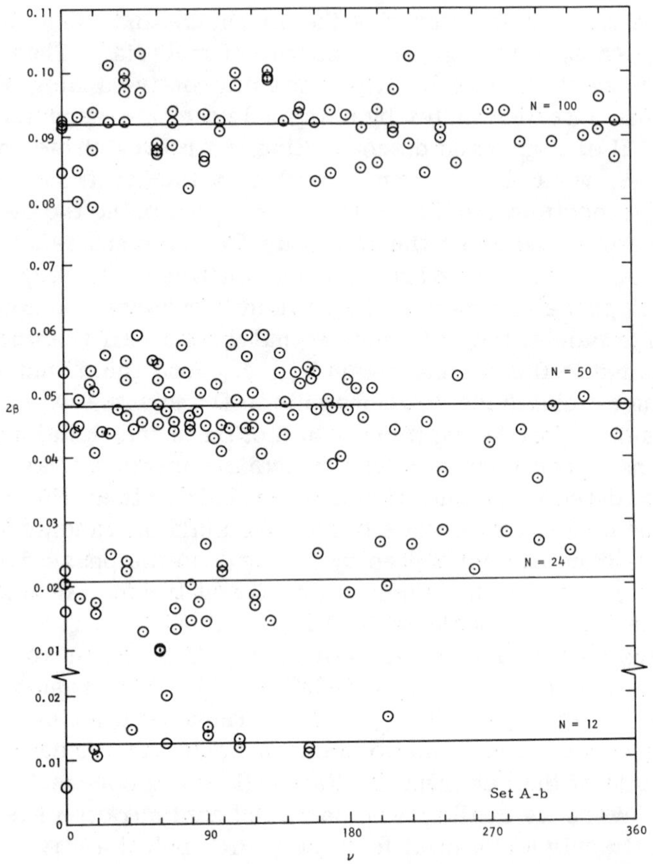

Fig. 14. Data for coherent attenuation coefficient $2\beta = -\ln C^2$ corresponding to N = 50, 100 of Fig. 12 and for two additional sets (N = 12, 24) of similar spheres. Our results for say N< 50 are not always consistent with those for N>50, partly because of the difficulty in maintaining a uniform spatial distribution of a small number of scatterers in the 'gas-model', but primarily because the effects of slight variations in shape, size, and index of refraction among the individual scatterers are more significant when we deal with a small number.

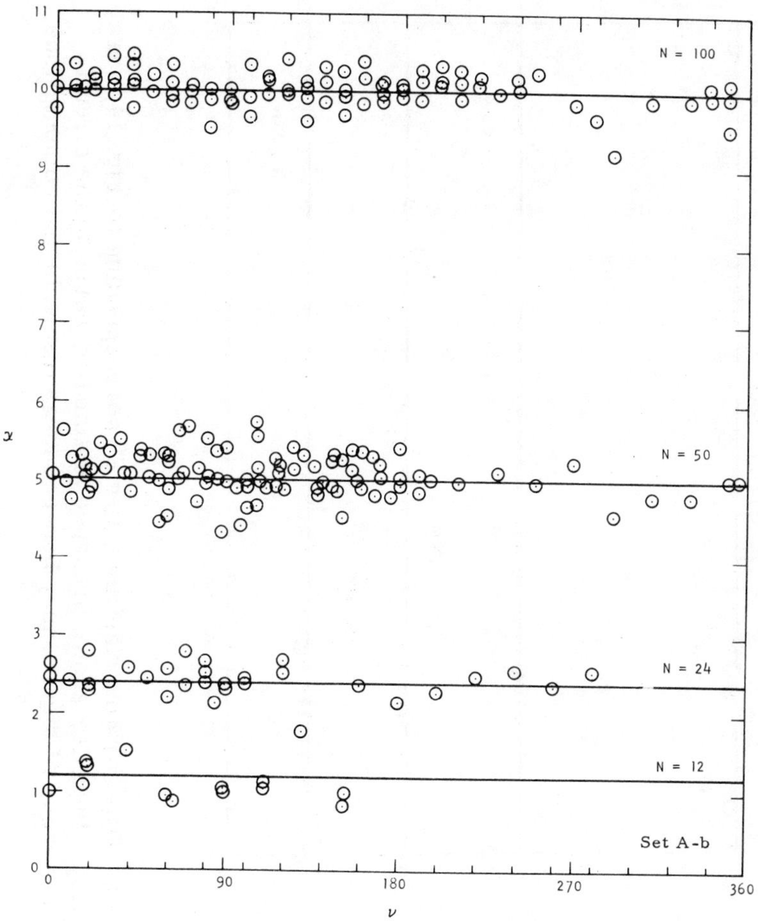

Fig. 15. Data points for coherent phase α (in degrees) corresponding to Fig. 14.

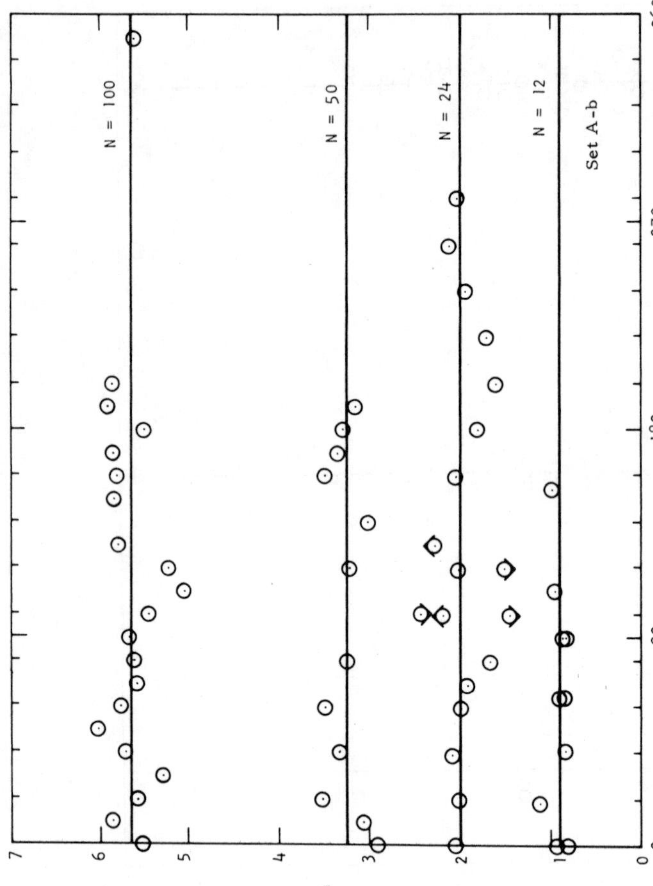

Fig. 16. Data for covariant intensity S^2 corresponding to Fig. 14; quasiperiodic behavior shows presence of standing waves in the circuit—a major cause of discrepancy between measurements and computations.

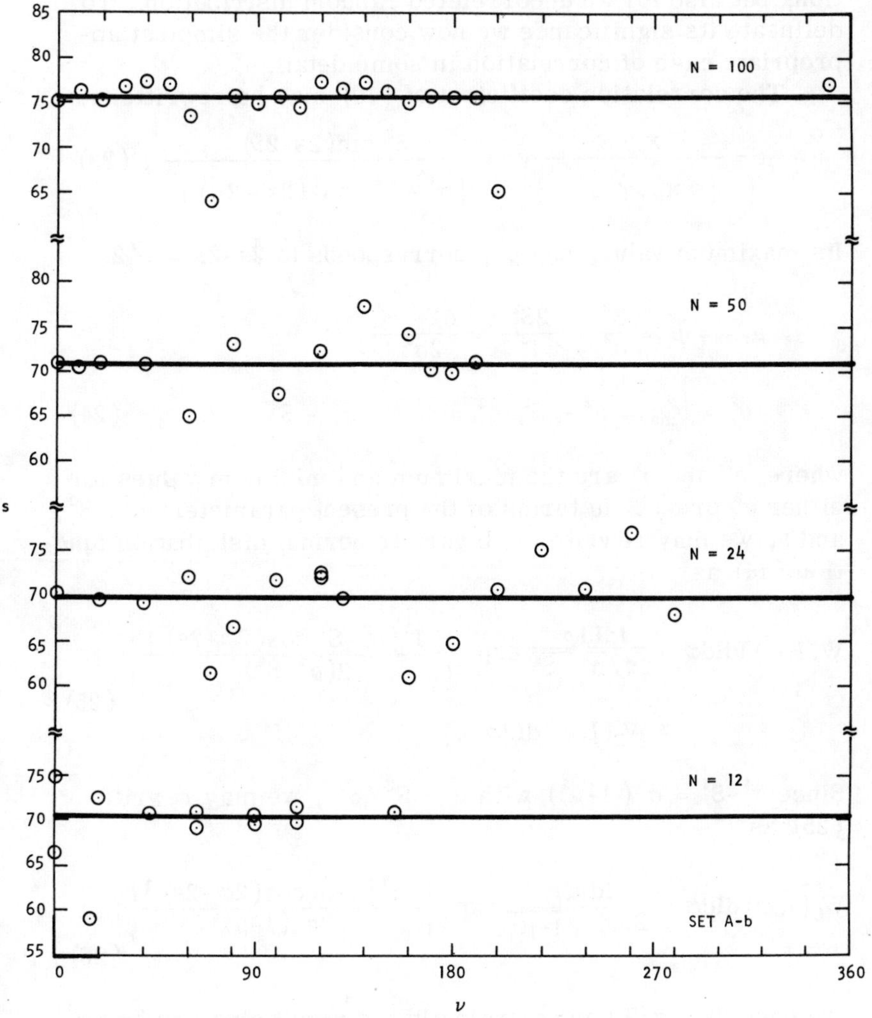

Fig. 17. Value of the covariant phase s (in degrees) corresponding to Fig. 16.

extrema of $<x^n y^m>$ with variation of the reference phase ν.) The covariant field vanishes not only for a fixed configuration, but also for an uncorrelated random distribution. To delineate its significance we now consider the simplest appropriate case of correlation in some detail.

The correlation coefficient of (10) may be rewritten as

$$\mu = \frac{<x_\nu y_\nu>}{[<x_\nu^2><y_\nu^2>]^{\frac{1}{2}}} = \frac{S^2 \sin(2s-2\nu)}{[\sigma^4 - S^4 \cos^2(2s-2\nu)]^{\frac{1}{2}}} . \quad (23)$$

Its maximum value, say μ , corresponds to $2s-2\nu = \pi/2$:

$$\mu_{max} = \mu_\wedge = \frac{S^2}{\sigma^2} = \frac{2S^2}{<I^2>} = \frac{\sigma_\wedge^2 - \sigma_\vee^2}{2\sigma^2} \quad ;$$

$$\sigma_\wedge^2 = \sigma_{max}^2 = \sigma^2 + S^2, \; \sigma_\vee^2 = \sigma_{min}^2 = \sigma^2 - S^2 \quad . \quad (24)$$

where $\sigma_\wedge^2$ and $\sigma_\vee^2$ are the maximum and minimum values for either σ_x^2 or σ_y^2 . In terms of the present parameters σ^2, S^2, and s, we may rewrite the bivariate normal distribution function (14) as

$$W(I, \varphi)\, IdId\varphi = \frac{IdId\varphi}{2\pi\sqrt{\sigma^4 - S^4}} \exp\left\{- \frac{I^2[\sigma^2 - S^2\cos(2\varphi - 2s)]}{2(\sigma^4 - S^4)}\right\}$$
$$\equiv W_E(I, \varphi)\, dId\varphi \quad . \quad (25)$$

Since $\sigma^4 - S^4 = \sigma^4(1-\mu_\wedge^2)$ with $\mu_\wedge = S^2/\sigma^2$, we may rewrite (25) as

$$W_E(I, \varphi)\, dId\varphi = \frac{IdId\varphi}{2\pi\sigma^2\sqrt{1-\mu^2_\wedge}} \exp\left\{- \frac{I^2[1-\mu_\wedge\cos(2\varphi-2s)]}{2\sigma^2(1-\mu_\wedge^2)}\right\}; \quad (26)$$

the case $2s = \pi/2$ (or equivalently the result obtained by replacing $2\varphi - 2s$ by $2\varphi' - \pi/2$) is of the form obtained previously by Wheelon [24] for identical variances $\sigma_x^2 = \sigma_y^2 = \sigma^2$. Similarly since $\sigma^4 - S^4 = (\sigma^2 - S^2)(\sigma^2 + S^2) = \sigma_\wedge^2 \cdot \sigma_\vee^2$, and $\sigma^2 = (\sigma_\wedge^2 + \sigma_\vee^2)/2$, $S^2 = (\sigma_\wedge^2 - \sigma_\vee^2)/2$, we may rewrite (25) as

$$W_E(I,\varphi)\,dId\varphi = \frac{IdId\varphi}{2\pi\sigma_\wedge\sigma_\vee}\exp\left\{-\frac{I^2\left[\sigma_\vee^2\cos^2(\varphi-s)+\sigma_\wedge^2\sin^2(\varphi-s)\right]}{2\sigma_\wedge^2\sigma_\vee^2}\right. . \tag{27}$$

The case s = 0 (or equivalently the result obtained by replacing φ - s by φ') is of the form obtained previously by Beckmann [5] for zero correlation and variances $\sigma_x = \sigma_\wedge$ and $\sigma_y = \sigma_\vee$.

The first derivatives of $W_E(I,\varphi)$ with respect to I and to φ vanish simultaneously for the values

$$\varphi = s,\quad s+\pi\ ;\quad I^2 = \frac{1}{2(b-c)} = \sigma^2 + S^2 = \sigma_\wedge^2\ , \tag{27-}$$

$$\varphi = s+\pi/2,\quad s+3\pi/2;\quad I^2 = \frac{1}{2(b+c)} = \sigma^2 - S^2 = \sigma_\vee^2\ . \tag{27+}$$

From the corresponding second derivatives, we find that $W_E(I,\varphi)$ has maxima for the values of (27-):

$$W_E(I,\varphi)\,|_{max} = \frac{e^{-1/2}}{2\pi\sigma_\vee}\ ;$$

$$I = \sigma_\wedge = \sqrt{\sigma^2 + S^2} = \sqrt{\tfrac{1}{2}<I^2>+S^2}\ ; \tag{28}$$

$$\varphi = s,\quad s+\pi\ .$$

The value $W = e^{1/2}/2\pi\sigma_\wedge$ corresponding to (27+) is neither a maximum nor a minimum. From (28) we see the significance of the covariant magnitude S and the covariant phase s we introduced. Since W_E of (28) is a maximum, the values s and s + π are the most probable values of the variant phase φ; the corresponding most probable value of I depends not only on the incoherent intensity $<I^2> = 2\sigma^2$ but also on the covariant intensity S^2.

The curves of equal probability corresponding to (25) are ellipses determined by constant values of the exponent, say constant L in the form e^{-L}. From Eq. (27) we see that the major axis is along φ = s, and that its length is $\sigma_\wedge\sqrt{2L}$; the minor axis is $\sigma_\vee\sqrt{2L}$, and the focii are at $\pm$ 2S. Since the area of an ellipse is $\pi\sigma_\wedge\sigma_\vee 2L$, its differential (the area of an elliptic ring) is $\pi\sigma_\wedge\sigma_\vee 2dL$, and we may rewrite (27) (or any of its alternatives) as $W(L)\,dL = e^{-L}dL$; this is the probability that the point x, y is in the ring between the ellipses L and L + dL.

If we integrate (25) over all values of φ, we obtain the distribution function for I:

$$W_E(I) = \int_0^{2\pi} W_E(I,\varphi)\,d\varphi = \frac{I}{\sqrt{\sigma^4 - S^4}} \exp\left\{-\frac{I^2\sigma^2}{2(\sigma^4 - S^4)}\right\} J_0\left\{i\frac{I^2 S^2}{2(\sigma^4 - S^4)}\right\}$$
$$= \frac{I}{\sigma^2\sqrt{1-\mu_\wedge^2}} \exp\left\{-\frac{I^2}{2\sigma^2(1-\mu_\wedge^2)}\right\} J_0\left[i\frac{I^2\mu_\wedge}{2\sigma^2(1-\mu_\wedge^2)}\right]. \tag{29}$$

where the modified Bessel function $J_0(iX)$ is real. Similarly integrating W_E of (25) over I from 0 to ∞ yields

$$W_E(\varphi) = \int_0^{\infty} W_E(I,\varphi)\,dI = \frac{\sigma\sqrt{\sigma^2 - S^2}}{2\pi[\sigma^2 - S^2\cos(2\varphi - 2s)]}$$
$$= \frac{\sqrt{1-\mu_\wedge^2}}{2\pi[1-\mu_\wedge\cos(2\varphi-2s)]}, \tag{30}$$

whose extrema for $\sin(2\varphi - 2s) = 0$ (the same values as in (27±)) give the maxima and minima of $W_E(\varphi)$.

It is of interest to note that for an uncorrelated distribution with equal standard deviations, i. e., $S^2 = 0$, we have simply

$$\langle T^2 e^{i2\tau}\rangle = C^2 e^{i2\alpha} \quad \text{if } S^2 = 0\,. \tag{31}$$

Thus for the symmetrical case (illustrated, for example, by φ uniformly distributed and I Rayleigh distributed) the average of the squared instantaneous wave is simply the square of the coherent wave.

The second moments also appear in expansions of other averages of physical interest. To second order terms, we have

$$
\begin{aligned}
<T> &= C + [\sigma^2 - S^2 \cos(2s-2\alpha)]/2C + \cdots, \\
<\tau> &= \alpha - (S^2/C^2)\sin(2s-2\alpha) + \cdots, \\
<T^2> &= <T>^2 + [\sigma^2 + S^2\cos(2s-2\alpha)] + \cdots, \\
<\tau^2> &= <\tau>^2 + [\sigma^2 - S^2\cos(2s-2\alpha)]/C^2 + \cdots.
\end{aligned} \tag{32}
$$

where $\sigma^2 = <I^2>/2$. To second order, we have

$$
\frac{<T>^2 - C^2}{C^2} \approx <(\tau-\alpha)^2> \approx <\tau^2> - <\tau>^2 \approx \sigma^2 - S^2\cos(2s-2\alpha), \tag{33}
$$

which stresses that the variance of the departure in phase quadrature with the coherent field provides the first approximation that links several other averages of interest. See ref. 19 for additional results.

If the phase quadrature components of the departure are uncorrelated, then $<\tau> \approx \alpha$; for this case, the average of the instantaneous phase equals the coherent phase. If in addition, the quadrature components have equal standard deviations σ (i. e., if S=0), then $<\tau> \approx \alpha^2 + \sigma^2/C^2$. These special relations and corresponding distributions are considered by Bremmer [6].

II. 3 Higher Moments

Once we have determined the departures x and y, we form various products $x^n y^m$, and average the products electonically essentially as shown on Fig. 8. (Our total running time to obtain up to fourth moments is 20 minutes for a specific distribution: the first 10 minutes to establish $<X>$ and $<Y>$, and the second 10 minutes to obtain all the rest.) To discuss the higher moments, we begin by restating the primary resul's for the second moments in a generalized notation.

For the second moments, we consider essentially two relations

$$<I^2 e^{i2\varphi}> = <(x+iy)^2> \equiv Q_{22}\exp(iq_{22}) ,$$
$$<I^2> = <x^2+y^2> = <|x+iy|^2> \equiv Q_{20} . \qquad (34)$$

The first subscript gives the power of I and the second of $e^{i\varphi}$. Separating real and imaginary parts, we obtain the fundamental linear combinations

$$<x^2> - <y^2> = Q_{22}\cos q_{22} , \qquad 2<xy> = Q_{22}\sin q_{22} ;$$
$$<x^2> + <y^2> = Q_{20} . \qquad (35)$$

Thus for a reference phase angle ν, we have the separated moments

$$2<x_\nu^2> = Q_{20} + Q_{22}\cos(q_{22}-2\nu) , \quad 2<y_\nu^2> = Q_{20} - Q_{22}\cos(q_{22}-2\nu) ,$$
$$2<x_\nu y_\nu> = Q_{22}\sin(q_{22}-2\nu) . \qquad (36)$$

These moments are specified by a steady term and terms of period 180° in ν. See Fig. 13.

For third moments we consider the two relations

$$<I^3 e^{i3\varphi}> = <(x+iy)^3> \equiv Q_{33}\exp(iq_{33}) ,$$
$$<I^3 e^{i\varphi}> = <|x+iy|^2(x+iy)> = Q_{31}\exp(iq_{31}) . \qquad (37)$$

The real and imaginary parts give the fundamental forms

$$<x^3> - 3<xy^2> = Q_{33}\cos q_{33} , \qquad 3<x^2 y> - <y^3> = Q_{33}\sin q_{33} ,$$
$$<x^3> + <xy^2> = Q_{31}\cos q_{31} , \qquad <x^2 y> + <y^3> = Q_{31}\sin q_{31} ,$$
$$(38)$$

Solving for the individual moments and introducing ν, we obtain

$$\begin{aligned} 4<x_\nu^3> &= 3Q_{31}\cos(q_{31}-\nu) + Q_{33}\cos(q_{33}-3\nu) , \\ 4<x_\nu y_\nu^2> &= Q_{31}\cos(q_{31}-\nu) - Q_{33}\cos(q_{33}-3\nu) , \\ 4<x_\nu^2 y_\nu> &= Q_{31}\sin(q_{31}-\nu) + Q_{33}\sin(q_{33}-3\nu) , \\ 4<y_\nu^3> &= 3Q_{31}\sin(q_{31}-\nu) - Q_{33}\sin(q_{33}-3\nu) . \end{aligned} \qquad (39)$$

The third moments have no steady component; they consist of two terms with fundamental periods of 120° and 360° in ν. Data for $<x_\nu^3>$ for the same distributions as in Fig. 12 are given in Fig. 18.

For fourth moments, we consider the relations

$$
\begin{aligned}
<I^4 e^{i4\varphi}> &= <(x+iy)^4> \equiv Q_{44}\exp(iq_{44}) \ , \\
<I^4 e^{i2\varphi}> &= <(x^2+y^2)(x+iy)^2> \equiv Q_{42}\exp(iq_{42}) \ , \\
<I^4> &= <(x^2+y^2)^2> \equiv Q_{40} \ .
\end{aligned}
\tag{40}
$$

The real and imaginary parts give

$$
\begin{aligned}
<x^4> - 6<x^2y^2> + <y^4> &= Q_{44}\cos q_{44} \ , \\
4<x^3y> - 4<xy^3> &= Q_{44}\sin q_{44} \ ; \\
<x^4> - <y^4> &= Q_{42}\cos q_{42} \ , \\
2<x^3y> + 2<xy^3> &= Q_{42}\sin q_{42} \ ; \\
<x^4> + 2<x^2y^2> + <y^4> &= Q_{40} \ .
\end{aligned}
\tag{41}
$$

Thus, for arbitrary ν, the moments equal

$$
\begin{aligned}
8<x_\nu^4> &= 3Q_{40} + 4Q_{42}\cos(q_{42}-2\nu) + Q_{44}\cos(q_{44}-4\nu) \ , \\
8<x_\nu^3 y_\nu> &= 2Q_{42}\sin(q_{42}-2\nu) + Q_{44}\sin(q_{44}-4\nu) \ , \\
8<x_\nu^2 y_\nu^2> &= Q_{40} - Q_{44}\cos(q_{44}-4\nu) \ , \\
8<x_\nu y_\nu^3> &= 2Q_{42}\sin(q_{42}-2\nu) - Q_{44}\sin(q_{44}-4\nu) \ , \\
8<y_\nu^4> &= 3Q_{40} - 4Q_{42}\cos(q_{42}-2\nu) + Q_{44}\cos(q_{44}-4\nu) \ ,
\end{aligned}
\tag{42}
$$

which involve a steady term, and terms period in 180° and 90° in ν. Data for $<x_\nu^4>$ for the same distributions as in Fig. 12 are given in Fig. 19, and Fig. 20 shows $<x_\nu^2 y_\nu^2>$.

The generalization of the above is straighforward. For moments of order n, we consider the set of functions corresponding to $<|Te^{i\tau} - Ce^{i\alpha}|^{2m}(Te^{i\tau} - Ce^{i\alpha})^{n-2m}>$, i. e.,

$$
\begin{aligned}
<I^n\exp[i(n-2m)\varphi]> &= <(x^2+y^2)^m(x+iy)^{n-2m}> \\
&\equiv Q_{n(n-2m)}\exp[iq_{n(n-2m)}] \ ,
\end{aligned}
\tag{43}
$$

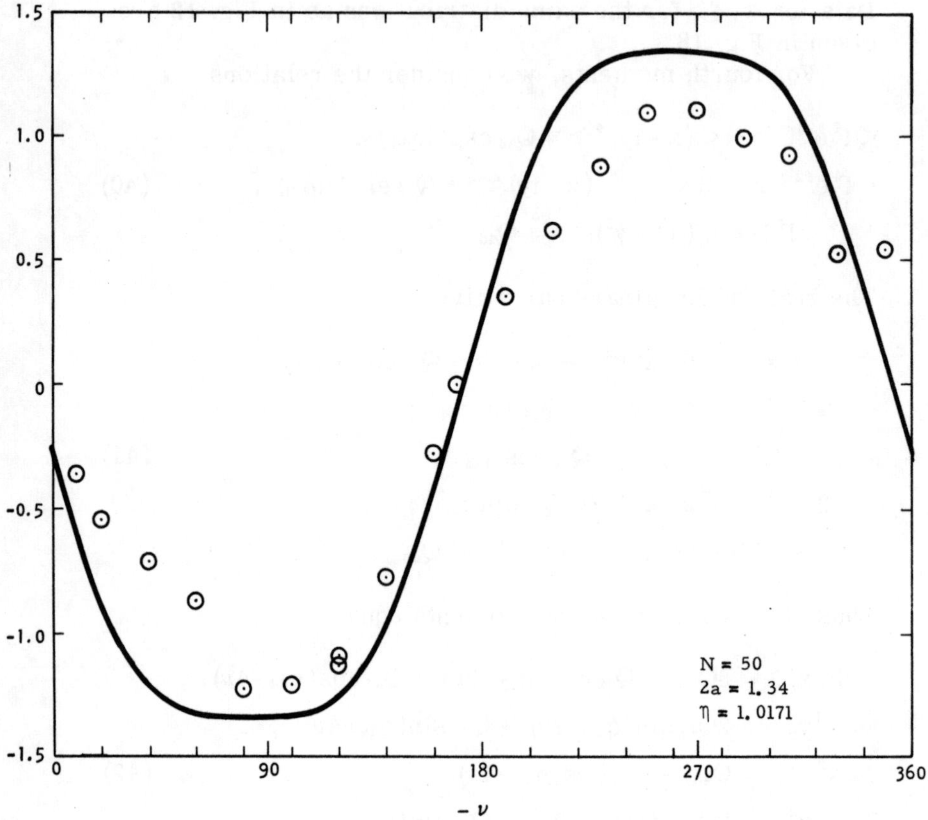

Fig. 18

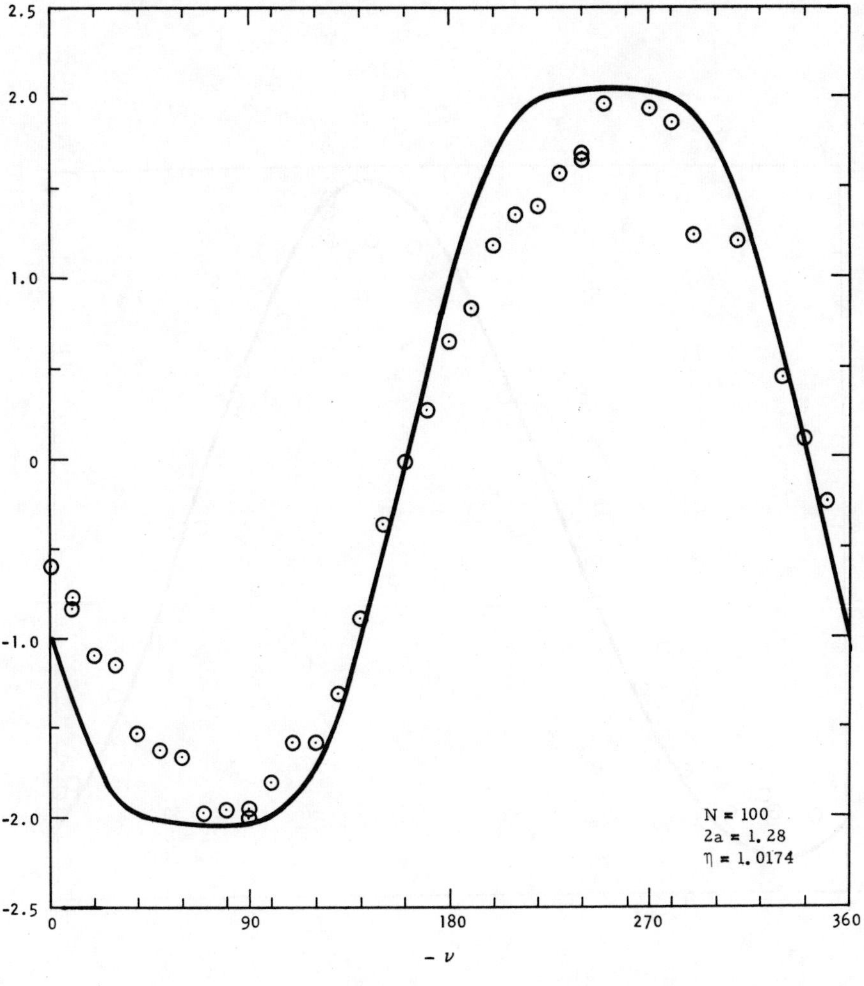

Fig. 18. Data for $< x_v^3 >$ normalized by division with D^3) corresponding to distribution of Figs. 12 and 13. Curves are of the form $A[9 \sin(\nu - \Phi) + \sin 3(\nu - \Phi)]$; theory for A and $\Phi = s - 45^\circ$ will be discussed subsequently.

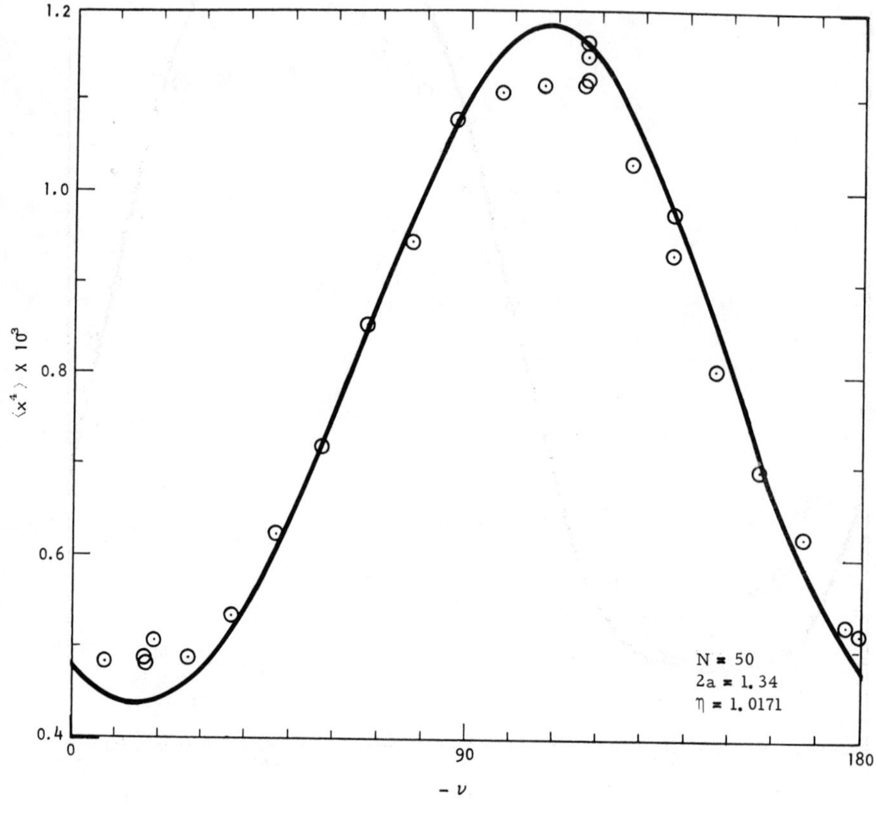

Fig. 19. Data for $<x_v^4>$ (normalized by division with D^4) corresponding to Figs. 12, 13, and 18 versus ν (in degrees). Curves are of the form

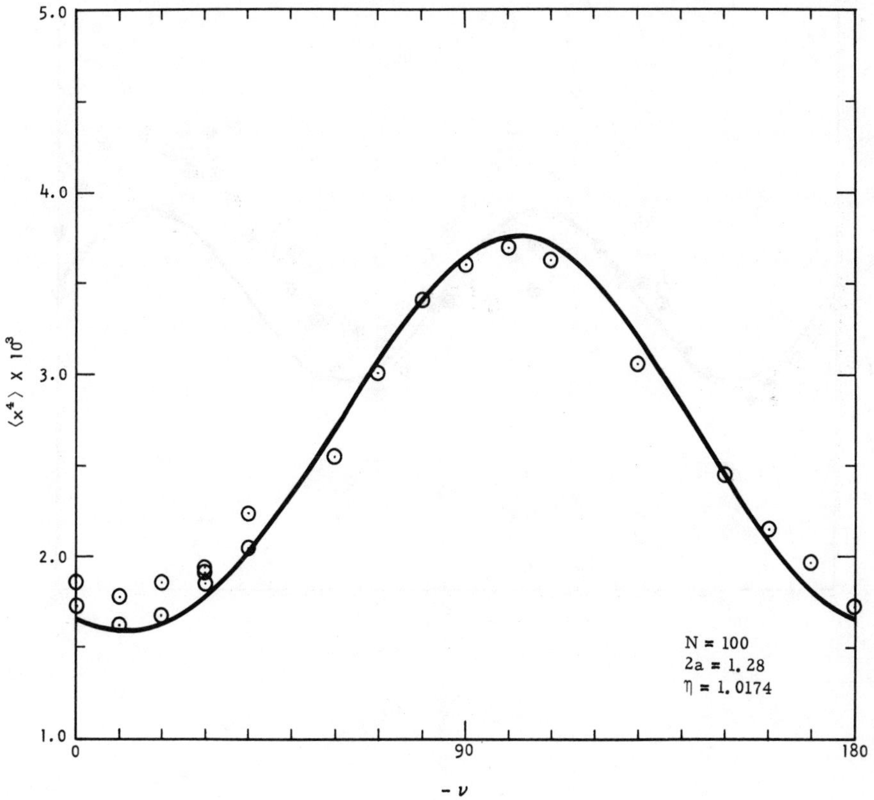

A' + B' sin $2(\nu - \Phi)$ + C' sin $4(v - q)$ where A', B', C', and q will be discussed subsequently.

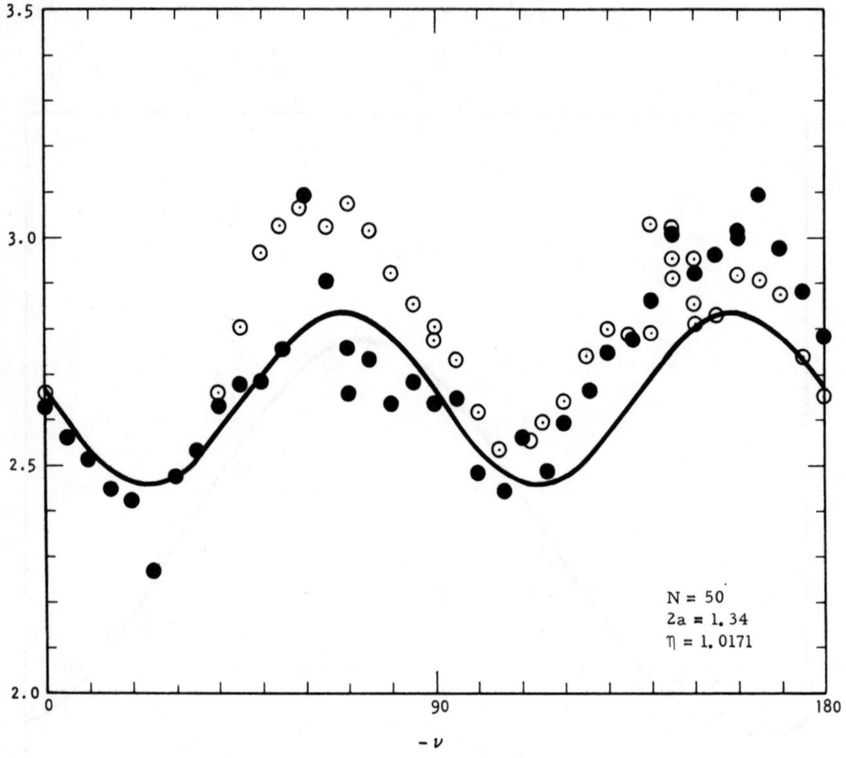

Fig. 20

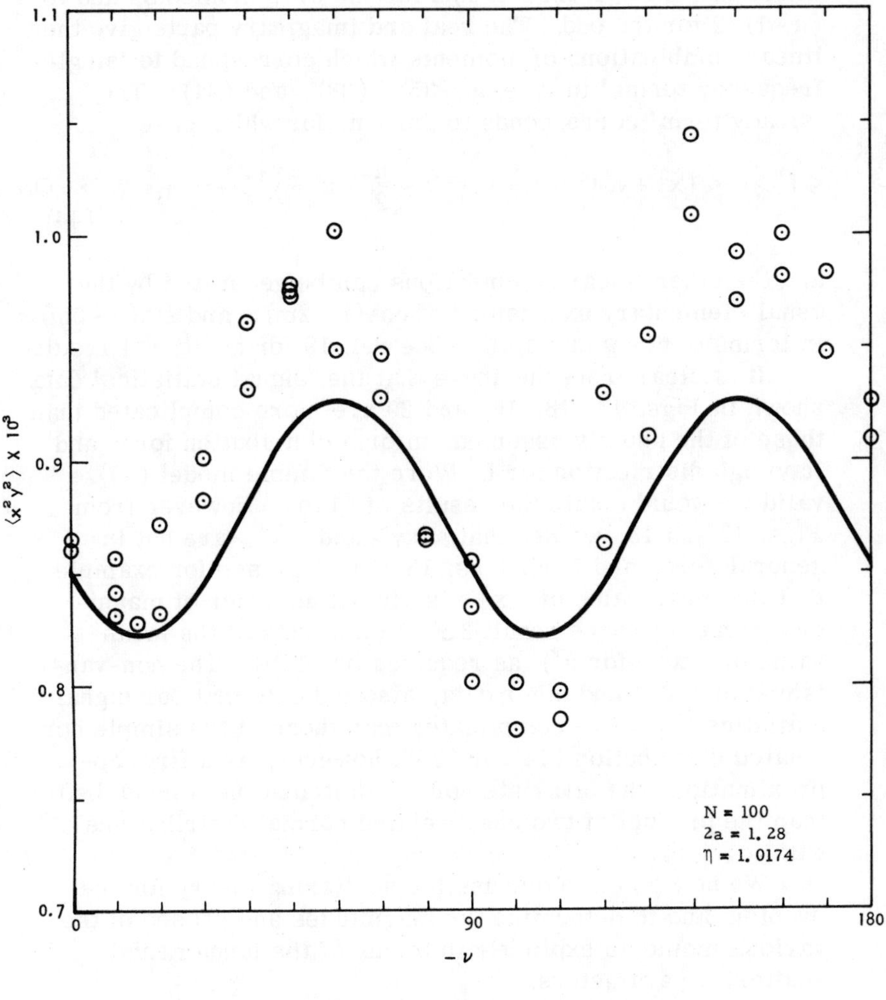

Fig. 20. Data for $< x_\nu^2 y_\nu^2 >$ (normalized by division with D^4) corresponding to Figs. 12, 13, 18, and 19 versus ν (indegrees). The two sets of points for N = 50 correspond to two sequences of runs several months apart; the major discrepancies are believed to be due to standing wave effects. Curves are $(A'/3) - C' \sin 4(\nu - q)$.

where m ranges from 0 to n/2 for the even moments, and to (n - 1)/2 for the odd. The real and imaginary parts give the linear combinations of moments which correspond to 'single-frequency terms' in ν, e. g. (35), (38), and (41). The 'steady term' corresponds to 2m = n, for which case

$$<I^n> = <(x^2 + y^2)^{n/2}> = <x^n> + \frac{n}{2} <x^{n-2} y^2> + \cdots + <y^n> = Q_{n0}, \quad (44)$$

and the other linear combinations can be generated by the usual elementary expansions of $\cos(n - 2m)\varphi$ and $\sin(n - 2m)\varphi$ in terms of $\cos\varphi$ and $\sin\varphi$. See ref. 19 for additional results.

It is clear from the above that the 'signal statistics' data shown in Figs. 13, 18, 19, and 20 are more complicated than those of the usually assumed uniform distribution for φ and Rayleigh distribution for I. Were the simple model (11) valid we would obtain the results of (11b). However from Figs. 13 and 18, we see that $<xy>$ and $<x^3>$ are not in general zero, and from Figs. 13 and 19 we see for example that the mean value of $<x^4>$ is almost an order of magnitude larger than the result $3\sigma^4/4$ (in terms of the mean value of $<x^2>$ for σ^2) as required by (11b). The non-vanishing of $<x^3>$ and other data, also indicate that our signal statistics are more complicated than those of the simple correlated distribution (14) or (25); however, as a first approximation, the bivariate normal distribution is much better than the product of two uncorrelated normal distributions with $\sigma_x = \sigma_y$.

We now go on to discuss the scattering theory for the problem and to determine the magnitudes and phases of the various moments explicitly in terms of the fundamental scattering parameters.

III. SCATTERING THEORY

We begin with notation and certain definitions for scattering of an electromagnetic wave by an isolated scatterer, and then consider scattering by a 'gaslike' random distribution. We obtain simple approximations for the various statistical moments discussed in Section II for cases where the back scattering is negligible.

III. 1 One Scatterer

We consider a plane wave (**E** field)

$$\psi_i \hat{\mathbf{x}} = e^{ikz} \hat{\mathbf{x}}, \qquad k = 2\pi/\lambda, \qquad \hat{\mathbf{x}} = \mathbf{x}/x, \tag{45}$$

incident on a scatterer at the origin $\mathbf{r} = 0$. The far-field scattered wave is written as

$$v \sim \frac{e^{ikr}}{r} f(\hat{\mathbf{r}}, \hat{\mathbf{z}}), \qquad \hat{\mathbf{z}} = \mathbf{z}/z, \qquad \hat{\mathbf{r}} = \mathbf{r}/r. \tag{46}$$

where f is the scattering amplitude, and $\hat{\mathbf{z}}$ and $\hat{\mathbf{r}}$ stand for directions of incidence and observation. We have

$$4\pi \operatorname{Im} \mathbf{f}(\hat{\mathbf{z}}, \hat{\mathbf{z}}) \cdot \hat{\mathbf{x}}/k = \sigma = \sigma_a + \sigma_s, \qquad \sigma_s = \int_\pi |\mathbf{f}(\hat{\mathbf{r}}, \hat{\mathbf{z}})|^2 d\Omega(\hat{\mathbf{r}}), \tag{47}$$

where the total cross-section is the sum of the absorption (σ_a) and scattering (σ_s) cross-sections, and where $\int_\pi d\Omega$ is the integral over all directions of observation with respect to $\hat{\mathbf{z}}$. The intensity scattered into a cone of half-angle γ around the forward direction $\hat{\mathbf{z}}$ is given by

$$G(\gamma) = \int_\gamma |\mathbf{f}|^2 d\Omega, \qquad G(\pi) = \sigma_s, \tag{48}$$

and the fraction of σ_s received by the cone γ is

$$g(\gamma) = G(\gamma)/G(\pi) = \int_\gamma |\mathbf{f}|^2 d\Omega \Big/ \int_\pi |\mathbf{f}|^2 d\Omega = \int_\gamma |\mathbf{f}|^2 d\Omega / \sigma_s \,. \tag{49}$$

For lossless scatterers, we have $\sigma = \sigma_s$ and (49) reduces to

$$g(\gamma) = k \int_\gamma |\mathbf{f}|^2 d\Omega / 4\pi \operatorname{Im} \mathbf{f} \cdot \hat{\mathbf{x}} \,. \tag{50}$$

For the case of a distant spherical source located at $\mathbf{z}_t$ whose field at the scatterer may be written as

$$\psi(|\mathbf{z}_t - \mathbf{r}|)\hat{\mathbf{x}} = \frac{\exp(ik|\mathbf{z}_t - \mathbf{r}|)}{|\mathbf{z}_t - \mathbf{r}|} \hat{\mathbf{x}}, \qquad |\mathbf{z}_t - \mathbf{r}| \sim |\mathbf{z}_t| - \mathbf{r} \cdot \hat{\mathbf{z}}, \tag{51}$$

the corresponding scattered field may be written

$$\psi(|z_t|)\, v(r) = \frac{\exp(ik|z_t|)}{|z_t|}\, v(r) \sim \frac{\exp[ik(|z_t|+r)]}{|z_t|\, r} f(\hat{r}, \hat{z}). \tag{52}$$

The scattering amplitude f in the above is the primary scattering function of interest. Although we defined f by the far-field form (46), we may represent the field v practically everywhere in space as a series of derivatives of f, or as an integral [22].

As an illustration, we specialize the above to the case of large tenuous spheres. For a dielectric sphere (relative magnetic parameter equal to unity) with radius a large compared to wavelength λ (i. e., $ka = 2\pi a/\lambda \gg 1$), and with index of refraction k'/k near unity, we may use a WKB procedure to approximate the forward scattered amplitude by [23, 17]

$$f(\hat{z}, \hat{z}) = f(0)\, \hat{x}, \qquad f(0) = \frac{i(K'+k)\, a^2}{2}\left[\frac{1}{2} - F(\delta)\right],$$
$$F(\delta) \equiv \frac{e^{i\delta}}{i\delta} + \frac{1-e^{i\delta}}{(i\delta)^2}, \qquad \delta = 2a(K'-k) \quad . \tag{53}$$

Similarly in the back scattered direction,

$$f(-\hat{z}, \hat{z}) = f(\pi)\, \hat{x}, \qquad f(\pi) = \frac{(K'-k)\, a^2}{i2}\, [F(2K'a) - F(2ka)] \tag{54}$$

For small δ the forward scattered value to second power in $(K'-k)a$ reduces to

$$f(0) = (\mathcal{V}/2\pi)\, k(K'-k)\, [1+i(K'-k)\, b], \qquad \mathcal{V} = 4\pi a^3/3, \quad b = 3a/4 \tag{55}$$

which also holds for a non-spherical scatterer [18] in terms of the appropriate $\mathcal{V}_s$ and b. Since $ka \gg 1$, we have $|f(0)/f(\pi)|^2 \propto (ka)^4$, and we may neglect the back scattering. (For large perfect conductors the corresponding ratio is $(ka)^2$.)

In other directions, to a first approximation in $(K'-k)$, we use the Rayleigh-Born approximation [23, 17]

$$f(\hat{r}, \hat{z}) = f(\theta)\, e, \qquad f(\theta) = (\mathcal{V}| 2\pi)\, k(K'-k)\, J(\Gamma)\ , \qquad e = \hat{x} - \hat{r}(\hat{r}\cdot\hat{x}),$$

$$J(\Gamma) = 3(\sin\Gamma - \Gamma\cos\Gamma)/\Gamma^3, \qquad \Gamma = 2ka\sin(\theta/2),$$

$$\cos\theta = \hat{r}\cdot\hat{z}\ . \tag{56}$$

If the direction of observation $\hat{r}$ is in the plane perpendicular to the incident direction of polarization $\hat{x}$ (i. e., if $\hat{r}$ is in the 'H-plane'), then $e = \hat{x}$ and the scattered field has the same polarization as the incident filed. For large values of Γ we have $J^2 \sim 9/\Gamma^4$, and consequently

$$|f(\theta)|^2 \sim |(\mathcal{V}/2\pi)\, k(K'-k)|^2\, 9/\Gamma^4 \tag{57}$$

falls off rapidly in angle. Practically all of the scattered radiation goes into the forward half space. Thus for lossless scatterers (real K') we use $|f|^2$ of (56) and Im f(0) of (55) in (50) to obtain

$$\begin{aligned} g(\gamma) &= (2ka/3)^2 \int_0^{\gamma} J^2 \sin\theta d\theta \\ &= \left[2(\cos 2\Gamma - 1) + 4\Gamma\sin 2\Gamma - (2\Gamma)^2 + (2\Gamma)^4/4\right] \Big/ (2\Gamma)^4/4 \\ &\equiv g_s(\gamma),\ \ \Gamma = \Gamma(\gamma)\ . \end{aligned} \tag{58}$$

For large ka we see that $g_s(\pi) \sim 1 - 1(2ka)^2 \sim 1$; because of this, we may also use (58) even for lossy scatterers, i. e.,

$$g(\gamma) \approx \int_0^{\gamma} J^2 \sin\theta d\theta \Big/ \int_0^{\pi} J^2 \sin\theta d\theta = g_s(\gamma)/g_s(\pi) \sim g_s(\gamma)\ . \tag{59}$$

This function is plotted versus $\Gamma(\gamma) = 2ka\sin(\gamma/2)$ in a subsequent figure (Fig. 21 for g_2).

In the following, we restrict consideration to 'forward type scatterers' whose radiation is significant only near the forward scattered direction (i. e., as illustrated by the above).

III. 2 Sparse Distribution of Scatterers

We consider a symmetrical random distribution of N identical scatterers each of volume $\mathcal{V}$ in a volume V, specified

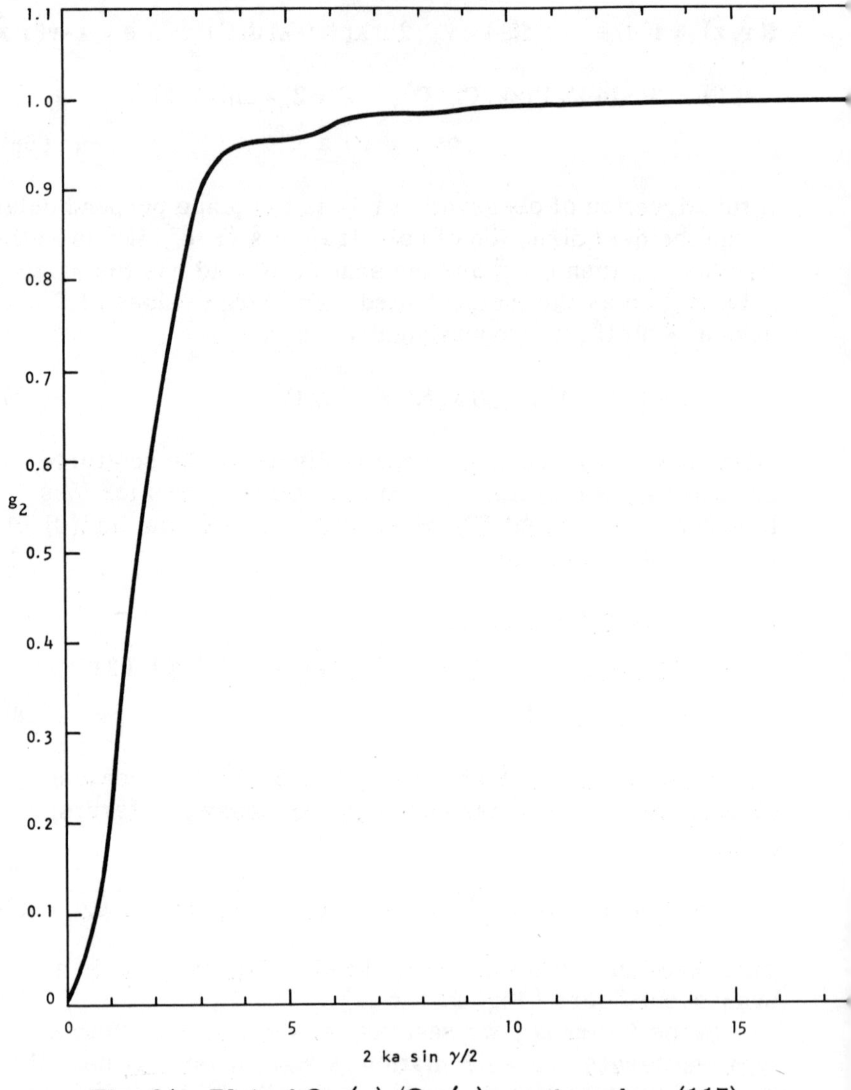

Fig. 21. Plot of $Q_{20}(\gamma)/Q_{20}(\pi) = g_2$ based on (117) versus $2ka \sin \gamma/2$. For present range of parameters, g_2 is also $g(\gamma)$ and g_s of (58) and (59).

by an average density function $\rho = N/V$, with fractional volume $w = \rho \mathcal{V}$ close to zero; the ensemble of configurations of scatterers is that of a 'homogeneous rare gas'. We are interested in practical approximations corresponding to a narrow beam transmitter with axis perpendicular to a slab region of scatterers, and similar receiver aimed at the source (to measure the field in the forward scattered direction); the receiver's and transmitter's cones are coaxial, and the polarization of the two horns is parallel. For simplicity, we start with a scalar formalism and an incident plane wave, and then generalize the results.

The total field for a fixed configuration of N scatterers as in (1) is a function of N sets of vectors, say **1**, **2**, ⋯, **N**, such that **1** stands for all properties of scatterer 'one' that are to be varied, etc.; thus **1** includes the location of its 'center' (the center of the smallest sphere circumscribing the scatterer), its electromagnetic parameters, shape, size, etc. A given configuration is specified by the values of **1**, **2**, ⋯, **N**. The corresponding field is determined by the usual wave equations plus any of the usual conditions at the scatterers, plus the usual conditions at large distances. Assuming that we know the solutions of the scattering problem for each scatterer in isolation $(\psi_i + v_s)$, we express [22] the solution for the configuration $\Psi = \psi_i + U = \psi_i + \Sigma_s u_s$ in terms of v_s.

We may write the 'compact form' of the solution at a point $\mathbf{r}_a$ symbolically as

$$\Psi^a = \psi_i^a + \sum_s v_s^a \Psi_e^s \,, \qquad \Psi_e^s = \psi_i^s + \sum_t{}' v_t^s \cdot \Psi_e^t \,, \tag{60}$$

where the superscript indicates the observation point, the prime means $t \neq s$, and where Ψ_e^s is the multiple scattered excitation of the scatterer at $\mathbf{r}_s$. In general, (60) is an operational form in terms of complex integrals of plane waves (spectral representations) for Ψ_e^s, etc. If we iterate (60) and eliminate Ψ_e^s, we obtain the series of 'orders of successive scattering' essentially in powers of v. The expanded solution (subject to any restrictions required for convergence) may be written symbolically as

$$\Psi^a = \psi_i^a + \sum_s v_s^a \psi_i^s + \sum_s \sum_t{}' v_s^a v_t^s \cdot (\psi_i^t + v_s^t \psi_i^s + v_s^t v_t^s v_i^t + \cdots)$$
$$+ \sum_s \sum_t{}' \sum_m{}'' v_s^a v_t^s v_m^t \cdot (\psi_i^m + v_t^m \psi_i^t + v_s^m \psi_i^s + \cdots) + \cdots, \quad (61)$$

where the prime means $t \neq s$ the double prime means $m \neq t$ and $m \neq s$, etc. In general, (61) is an operational form in which the plane wave representation for the isolated scatterer function v_t^s is to be used [22]. For the present class of 'near-forward scatterers', however, we may use (61) with the asymptotic form for v_t^s, and drop the terms which involve back scattering, e. g., we drop the terms $v_s^a v_t^s v_s^t$ arising from the third-order of scattering, as well as all other 'chains' of v's having two or more subscripts in common. Thus for finite N, (61) reduces to the finite sequence

$$\Psi^a = \psi_i^a + \sum_s v_s^a \psi_i^s + \sum_s \sum_t{}' v_s^a v_t^s \psi_i^t + \sum_s \sum_t{}' \sum_m{}'' v_s^a v_t^s v_m^t \psi_i^m + \cdots, \quad (62)$$

which terminates with the single term of the Nth order of scattering, i. e., in (62) each scatterer is used only once in any order of scattering.

An ensemble of configurations is specified by an appropriate probability distribution function $W(1, 2, \cdots, N)$, such that $W d1 \cdots dN$ is the probability of finding the scatterers in a configuration in the 'volume element' around $1, 2, \cdots, N$. The ensemble average of Ψ (the coherent field) is determined by multiplying Ψ by W and integrating over all variables

$$\langle \Psi \rangle = \int \cdots \int \Psi(1, 2, \cdots, N) \cdot W(1, 2, \cdots, N)\, d1 d2 \cdots dN, \quad (63)$$

and similarly for the intensity $|\Psi|^2$, and for other scattering functions. We may work with the expanded forms of Ψ, $|\Psi|^2$, etc., carry out the integrations, and then reduce the final results to compact forms; or we may first average the compact form of Ψ, etc., proceed heuristically to construct simplified average equations , and then seek their solutions. The simple case we consider corresponds to

$$W = (1/V)^N = (\rho/N)^N , \quad (64)$$

where N is in general large. (However, for the scatterers we deal with our explicit results will also hold down to $N \Rightarrow 1$.) We assume ρ to be small, and treat the scatterers essentially as points confined to a slab region $0 < z < d$. We treat the scatterers as identical, but the results also apply if f represents an appropriate average over isolated scatterer parameters.

III.3 The Coherent Field

As discussed elsewhere [21] in detail, the average of (62) obtained by using (63) subject to (64) is equivalent to the solution of the integral equation approximation

$$< \Psi(\mathbf{r})> = \psi_i(\mathbf{r}) + \rho \int v(|\mathbf{r} - \mathbf{r}_s|)< \Psi(\mathbf{r}_s)> d\mathbf{r}_s,$$

$$\psi_i = e^{ikz} = e^{ik\hat{z}\cdot\mathbf{r}}, \quad d\mathbf{r}_s = dx_s\, dy_s\, dz_s. \tag{65}$$

Foldy [7] obtained (65) for monopoles by averaging the compact form (60) and approximating the average of Ψ_e^s over all variables but **s** by $<\Psi>$; his procedure was generalized by Lax [14].

For a slab region perpendicular to z with entrance face at $z = 0$, and exit face at $z = d$ (and infinite along x and y), the average internal field for the case of negligible back scattering is given [18] by

$$<\Psi(z)> = e^{ikz} + \rho \int \frac{f(\hat{\mathbf{s}}, \hat{\mathbf{z}})}{|\mathbf{z} - \mathbf{r}_s|}\, e^{ik|z - r_s|} <\Psi(z_s)> d\mathbf{r}_s$$

$$\approx e^{ikz}[1 + \Delta \int_0^z e^{-ikz_s}<\Psi(z_s)> dz_s] = \psi_i(z)e^{i\Delta z};$$

$$\Delta = K - k = 2\pi\rho f/k \tag{66}$$

where K, the propagation factor for the medium associated with coherent propagation, is specified essentially by the forward scattered amplitude $f(\hat{z}, \hat{z})$ of one scatterer in isolation. (For finite transverse dimensions x and y, the corresponding integrals can be evaluated by the method of stationary phase; the integrals have two stationary points, but the restriction to large tenuous scatterers allows us to neglect the one corresponding to geometrical reflection and to keep only the forward scattering contribution.)

In the transmitted region, $z > d$, we have $\langle\Psi\rangle/\psi_i = e^{i\Delta d} = Ce^{i\alpha}$ with

$$e^{i\Delta d} = Ce^{i\alpha} \equiv \exp(-\beta + i\alpha), \quad \alpha \equiv (2\pi\rho d/k)\mathrm{Re}\, f \equiv M\, \mathrm{Re}\, f,$$

$$2\beta = (4\pi\rho d/k)\ \mathrm{Im}\, f = 2M\ \mathrm{Im}\, f = \rho\, \sigma d, \tag{67}$$

where $e^{i\Delta d}$ is also the corresponding ratio $Ce^{i\alpha}$ for the vector case, and also for the case of an incident diverging wave for observation along the cone axis $\hat{z}$; for other angles θ_t with respect to $\hat{\mathbf{z}}\ (\theta = 0)$, we multiply d by $\sec\theta_t$. Thus for the present restrictions on the parameters, the average coherent transmitted field is determined by ray tracing along a single path from transmitter to receiver through an appropriate thickness of uniform slab medium specified by K.

Scattering measurements on distributions are often undertaken to determine essentially

$$f(\hat{\mathbf{z}}, \hat{\mathbf{z}}) \cdot \hat{\mathbf{x}} = f = \mathrm{Re}\, f + i\, \mathrm{Im}\, f = |f|e^{i\, \mathrm{arc}\, f}. \tag{68}$$

From (51) we see that the measurements of the coherent phase α and of the 'coherent attenuation coefficient' β for the present sparse concentration serve to determine the far-field phase for one scatterer:

$$\mathrm{arc}\, f = \tan^{-1}(\mathrm{Im}\, f/\mathrm{Re}\, f) = \tan^{-1}(\beta/\alpha)$$

$$= \tan^{-1}\left\{\frac{-\frac{1}{2}\ln\left[\langle X\rangle^2 + \langle Y\rangle^2\right]}{\tan^{-1}\left[\langle Y\rangle/\langle X\rangle\right]}\right\} \tag{69}$$

where the final form is in terms of first moments of Section II. However, β and α do not determine Re f and Im f unless we know $M = 2\pi\rho d/k$ explicitly. Thus one reason for considering the higher moments is to seek additional combinations of Re f and Im f and M in order to eliminate M from β and α.

We note that the average of the series form (62) gives [21] directly

$$<\Psi> = \psi_i (1 + i\Delta z/N)^N \tag{70}$$

by a procedure which is valid even for N = 1. The limit of (70) for $N \to \infty$ is the continuum form $<\Psi> = \psi_i e^{i\Delta z}$ of (66). However, for our present restrictions there is no practical error in using either (66) or (70) for any low value of N.

III.4 Average Intensity

In general we are concerned with two kinds of real squared functions: the normalized 'energy density' $|\Psi|^2$ and the normalized energy flux $\mathbf{P} = \mathrm{Re}\,(\Psi^* \nabla \Psi/ik)$. The flux normal to the slab (i.e., $\mathbf{P} \cdot \hat{z}$) differs from $|\Psi|^2$ by trigonometric factors which are slowly varying around the forward direction. For present purposes we restrict attention to a narrow cone receiver with axis along $\hat{z}$, and use $\mathbf{P} \cdot \hat{z}$ and $|\Psi|^2$ interchangeably.

As shown elsewhere [21], the average of $|\Psi|^2$ obtained from (62) subject to (64) is equivalent to the solution of the integral equation

$$<|\Psi|^2> = |<\Psi>|^2 + \rho \int |\mathcal{U}|^2 <|\Psi^s|^2> d\mathbf{r}_s, \tag{71}$$

where the inhomogeneous term is the absolute square of the coherent field, and where $\mathcal{U}$ is an average one-scatterer, multiple-scattered function determined by

$$\mathcal{U}_s = \mathcal{U}(\mathbf{r} - \mathbf{r}_s) = v(\mathbf{r} - \mathbf{r}_s) + \rho \int v(\mathbf{r} - \mathbf{r}_t)\mathcal{U}(\mathbf{r}_t - \mathbf{r}_s)\, d\mathbf{r}_t, \tag{72}$$

i.e., $\mathcal{U}$ satisfies the same integral equation as the coherent field but the source term is now the isolated scatterer function.

In particular, for a slab region of large scatterers and negiligible back scattering we have

$$\mathcal{U}(\mathbf{r} - \mathbf{r}_s) = v(\mathbf{r} - \mathbf{r}_s) \exp(i\Delta_s |\mathbf{r} - \mathbf{r}_s| \sim f(\hat{\mathbf{s}}, \hat{\mathbf{z}}) \frac{e^{iK_s|\mathbf{r}-\mathbf{r}_s|}}{|\mathbf{r} - \mathbf{r}_s|},$$
$$K_s - k = \Delta_s = \frac{2\pi\rho f(\hat{\mathbf{s}}, \hat{\mathbf{s}})}{k}, \quad \mathbf{s} = \frac{\mathbf{r} - \mathbf{r}_s}{|\mathbf{r} - \mathbf{r}_s|}. \tag{73}$$

Thus $\mathcal{U}$ is related to v essentially as the coherent field $<\Psi>$ is to ψ_i. Substituting (73) and $|<\Psi>|^2 = \exp(-2 \text{ Im } \Delta z) = \exp(-\rho\sigma d)$ into (71), we obtain

$$<|\Psi(r)|^2> = \exp(-2 \text{ Im } Kz) + \rho \int \frac{|f(\hat{s}, \hat{z})|^2}{|r - r_s|^2} <|\Psi(r_s)|^2> \exp(-2 \text{ Im } K_s |r - r_s|) dx_s dy_s dz_s. \tag{74}$$

Using $dx_s dy_s = |r - r_s|^2 \sec\theta_s d\Omega(\hat{s})$ and $|r - r_s| = |z - z_s| \sec\theta_s$, with $\cos\theta_s = \hat{z}\cdot\hat{s}$, we may rewrite (74) as

$$<|\Psi(r)|^2> = \exp(-2 \text{ Im } Kz) + \rho \int_{\pi/2} |f(\hat{s}, \hat{z})|^2 \sec\theta_s d\Omega \int_0^z <|\Psi(r_s)|^2> \exp[-2 \text{ Im } K(z - z_s)\sec\theta_s] dz_s \tag{75}$$

where we dropped the negligible back-scattered terms and replaced K_s by K. Since $|f(\hat{s}, \hat{z})|^2 \exp[-\rho\sigma(z - z_s)\sec\theta_s]$ falls off very rapidly with increasing θ_s, we drop the sec θ_s factor, and approximate the integral over the forward hemisphere

$$\rho \int_{\pi/2} |f|^2 d\Omega$$

by σ_s; we obtain

$$\begin{aligned} <|\Psi(z)|^2> &= \exp(-2 \text{ Im } Kz)\left[1 + \rho\sigma_s \int_0^z <|\Psi(z_s)|^2> \exp(-2 \text{ Im } Kz_s) dz_s\right] \\ &= \exp(-2 \text{ Im } Kz + \rho\sigma_s z) = \exp[-\rho(\sigma - \sigma_s)z] \\ &= \exp(-\rho\sigma_a z). \end{aligned} \tag{76}$$

Thus to the present approximation, the average total internal field $\exp(-\rho\sigma_a z)$ (which involves only the absorption cross-section) reduces to unity for lossless scatterers as required by energy considerations.

For an external point ($z > d$), we replace z by d in (74), substitute (76), and integrate from $z_s = 0$ to $z_s = d$; the average total intensity into a cone of half-angle γ around the forward direction (i.e., with axis normal to the slab) is thus

$$<|\Psi|^2> = \exp(-\rho\sigma d)$$
$$+\rho \exp(-\rho\sigma d) \int_\gamma |f|^2 d\Omega \int_0^d \{\exp[-\rho(\sigma - \sigma_s) z_s]\} \exp(\rho\sigma z_s) dz_s$$
$$= \exp(-\rho\sigma d) + \exp(-\rho\sigma d)\, \rho d \int_\gamma |f|^2 d\Omega \frac{[\exp(\rho\sigma_s d) - 1]}{\rho\sigma_s d}. \tag{77}$$

Using the symbols of Section II,

$$\Psi = Te^{i\tau} = Ce^{i\alpha} + Ie^{i\varphi} = <\Psi> + Ie^{i\varphi},\ Ie^{i\varphi} = \sum_s (u_s - <u_s>),$$
$$<|\Psi|^2> = <T^2> = C^2 + <I^2>, \tag{78}$$

we write the coherent intensity as

$$C^2 = e^{-\rho\sigma d} = e^{-2\beta} \tag{79}$$

and the corresponding incoherent itensity $<I^2>$ as

$$<I^2> = e^{-\rho\sigma d} g(\gamma)(e^{\rho\sigma_s d} - 1) = g(\gamma)\, e^{-\rho\sigma_a d}(1 - e^{-\rho\sigma_s d}), \tag{80}$$

with $g(\gamma)$ as the fraction of the scattering cross-section of an isolated scatterer that is collected by the receiver. The corresponding discrete form of the average total intensity is (21)

$$<|\Psi|^2> = (1 - \rho\sigma d/N)^N + g(\gamma)\,[(1 - \rho\sigma_a d/N)^N - (1 - \rho\sigma d/N)^N]. \tag{81}$$

For an incident narrow conical beam of half-angle γ_t, and a corresponding coaxial receiving beam of half-angle γ_r, we suppress aperture factors and write the 'direct intensity' at the receiver in the absence of scatterers as

$$|\Psi_0|^2 = D^2 = 1/(d_t + d_r)^2, \tag{82}$$

where d_t and d_r, the fixed distances of the phase centers of the transmitter and receiver from the scatterer, can be determined with high accuracy and are assumed to be known. We write the coherent intensity for the present case as

$$D^2 e^{-2\beta} \equiv D^2 C^2, \tag{83}$$

so that we reserve C^2 for the normalized value as in (79). We write the corresponding incoherent intensity as

$$D^2 \langle I^2 \rangle = \rho \int_{\gamma_t, \gamma_r} \frac{|f(\hat{r}, \hat{t})|^2 \exp[-\rho\sigma(d - z_s)] \langle |\Psi|^2 \rangle d\mathbf{r}_s}{(\mathbf{z}_t - \mathbf{r}_s)^2 (\mathbf{z}_r - \mathbf{r}_s)^2}, \tag{84}$$

where $|\mathbf{z}_r - \mathbf{r}_s|$ and $|\mathbf{z}_t - \mathbf{r}_s|$ are the distances from the transmitter and receiver to a point $\mathbf{r}_s$ in V, and $\hat{\mathbf{t}}$ and $\hat{\mathbf{r}}$ are the corresponding directions. We can reduce (84) to

$$D^2 \langle I^2 \rangle = \tag{85}$$

$$D^2 [\exp(-\rho\sigma d)] \rho \int_{\gamma_t + \gamma_r} |f(\hat{\mathbf{s}}, \hat{\mathbf{z}})|^2 d\Omega \int_0^d \exp(\rho\sigma z_s) \langle |\Psi_s|^2 \rangle dz_s .$$

Thus substituting (76), we obtain

$$\langle I^2 \rangle = q(\gamma) \exp(-\rho\sigma d) [\exp(\rho\sigma_s d) - 1],$$

$$\gamma = \gamma_t + \gamma_r , \tag{86}$$

so that the normalized incoherent intensity (i.e., normalized by division with the direct intensity D^2) is of the same form as (80) in terms of a cone angle equal to the sum of those of the transmitter and receiver. For a given experimental set-up, the quantity $q(\gamma)$ ranges from 0 to unity as determined by f. Although it can be isolated by measurements, we discount $q(\gamma)$ as fundamental because it depends on the transmitter and receiver patterns and on the specific laboratory geometry.

The above scattering functions (coherent phase, coherent and incoherent intensities) are still inadequate to determine Re f and Im f without additional information on ρd. We now show that the scattering representation for the covariant intensity S^2 of Section II enables us to eliminate ρd.

III.5 Average Squared Field

As shown elsewhere [21], the average of Ψ^2 satisfies the analogous integral equation as $< |\Psi|^2 >$ of (71), i.e.,

$$<\Psi^2> = <\Psi>^2 + \rho \int \mathcal{U}^2 <\Psi^2> d\mathbf{r}_s, \qquad (87)$$

where $<\Psi> = \psi_i \exp(i\Delta z)$ as in (66), and where $\mathcal{U}$ is given in (73). Proceeding as for (74) to (76), with the previous $-2 \text{ Im } K$ and $|f|^2$ replaced by $i2K$ and f^2 we reduce (87) to

$$<\Psi^2(z)> = e^{i2Kz}[1 + \rho p \int_0^z e^{-i2Kz_s} <\Psi^2(z_s)> dz_s]$$

$$= \exp(i2Kz + \rho pz),$$

$$p = \int_{\pi/2} f^2(\hat{\mathbf{s}}, \hat{\mathbf{z}}) d\Omega. \qquad (88)$$

Substituting (88) in (87) we obtain the transmitted value for $z > d$:

$$<\Psi^2> = e^{i2\Delta d}\psi_i^2 + \rho \int \frac{f^2(\hat{\mathbf{s}}, \hat{\mathbf{z}})}{(z - r_s)^2} e^{i2k|\mathbf{z} - \mathbf{r}_s|} \exp i2\Delta[|d - \mathbf{r}_s|]$$

$$\exp(i2Kz_s + \rho pz_s) d\mathbf{r}_s$$

$$= <\Psi^2> + <I^2 \exp(i2\varphi)> = \psi_i^2 \; [C^2 \exp(i2\alpha) + 2S^2 e^{i2s}], \qquad (89)$$

where $[|d - \mathbf{r}_s|]$ is that part of $|\mathbf{z} - \mathbf{r}_s|$ that lies within the slab region. The final forms follow from (18).

From here on our procedure for $2S^2 e^{i2s}$ is no longer analogous to our previous one for $<I^2>$: because of the presence of the phase factors we may now evaluate the integral over xy by the method of stationary phase and obtain results independent of horn factors. Thus, essentially as for (74) (and as in ref. 21, where, however, we approximated the internal field by only its first iteration e^{i2Kz_s}), we obtain

$$\psi_i^2 \, 2S^2 e^{i2s} = \psi_i^2 \frac{i\pi\rho f^2}{k} \int_0^d \frac{e^{i2kz_s} e^{i2\Delta(d - z_s)} e^{i2Kz_s + \rho pz_s}}{z - z_s} dz_s$$

$$= \psi_i^2 \; e^{i2\Delta d} \frac{i\pi\rho f^2}{k} \int_0^d \frac{e^{\rho pz_s}}{z - z_s} dz_s . \qquad (90)$$

Since we assume $z \gg d$ we neglect z_s in the denominator and obtain

$$2S^2 e^{i2s} = \frac{i\pi\rho f^2}{kz} d \exp(i2\Delta d) \left[\frac{\exp(\rho p d) - 1}{\rho p d}\right]. \quad (91)$$

Similarly for a transmitter and receiver at distances d_t and d_r from the center of the distribution (or equivalently at distances $|z_t| = d_t - d/2$ and $z_r = d_r + d/2$ from the entrance face $z = 0$), we have

$$\psi_D 2S^2 e^{i2s} = \rho \int \frac{f^2(\hat{s}, \hat{z}) \exp i2\{k|z_r - r_s| + \Delta[|d - r_s|] + k|z_t - r_s|}{(z_t - r_s)^2 (z_r - r_s)^2}$$

$$+ \frac{(\Delta + \rho p/2i)[|o - r_s|]\}}{(z_t - r_s)^2 (z_r - r_s)^2} dr_s \quad (92)$$

where $\psi_D = e^{ik(d_t+d_r)}/(d_t + d_r) \equiv \psi_i D$; here $[|d - r_s|]$ is the portion of the ray from r_s to z_r within the slab and similarly $[|o - r_s|]$ is the portion of the ray from z_t to r_s within the slab. Integrating over xy by the method of stationary phase (ignoring the variation of the Δ terms), we obtain

$$\psi_D^2 2S^2 e^{i2s} \approx \psi_i^2 D^2 \frac{i\pi\rho f^2(\hat{z}, \hat{z})}{k} \left\{(|z_t| + z_r) \int_0^d \frac{e^{\rho p z_s}}{(|z_t| + z_s)(z_r - z_s)} dz_s \right\}, \quad (93)$$

where we used $D^2 = (d_t + d_r)^{-2} = (|z_t| + z_r)^{-2}$. For $|z_t|$ and $z_r \gg d$ we neglect z_s in the denominator to obtain

$$2S^2 e^{i2s} \approx \frac{i\pi\rho f^2 \exp(i2\Delta) d}{kZ} \left[\frac{\exp(\rho p d) - 1)}{\rho p d}\right], \quad \frac{1}{Z} \equiv \frac{1}{d_t} + \frac{1}{d_r}, \quad (94)$$

which differs from (91) only in that z^{-1} is replaced by $Z^{-1} \equiv d_t^{-1} + d_r^{-1}$.

For lossless tenuous scatterers for which we use the Born approximation as in (56), we also have

$$f^2(\theta) \approx |f(\theta)|^2 \approx [\mathrm{Re} f(\theta)]^2, \quad (95)$$

and consequently the parameter p of (88)ff reduces simply to

$$p = \int_{\pi/2} f^2 \, d\Omega \approx \int_{\pi} |f|^2 \, d\Omega \approx \sigma_s. \quad (96)$$

Thus (94) reduces to

$$2S^2 e^{i2s} = \left[\frac{\pi|f|^2}{k\sigma_s Z}(1 - e^{-\rho\sigma_s d})\right] \exp[i(2\alpha + 2\,\text{arc}\,f + \pi/2)], \tag{97}$$

which satisfies essentially the same relations in terms of C^2 as does $<I^2>$.

The maximum value of the correlation coefficient as in (24) for the present lossless 'gas' is thus simply

$$\mu = \frac{2S^2}{<I^2>} = \frac{\pi|f|^2}{kg(\gamma)\ \sigma_s Z} = \frac{\pi|f|^2}{kZ\int_\gamma |f|^2 d\Omega}. \tag{98}$$

The covariant phase is given by

$$s = \alpha + \text{arc}\,f + \pi/4. \tag{99}$$

The results for the variances ($<x^2>$, $<y^2>$) and covariance ($<xy>$) of the phase quadrature components obtained by using (86) and (97) in (20) give good agreement with the analogous measured [3, 1, 4, 10] data on 'gases' of spheres. In particular, we note that S^2 of (97) vanishes as the distances $d_t \to \infty$ and $d_r \to \infty$, i.e., the standard deviations of the quadrature components become equal and the distribution of signals becomes uncorrelated with increasing separation of transmitter and receiver from the slab. See corresponding data by Beard [3], who stresses the dependence of the magnitudes on $(1/d_t) + (1/d_r)$, and also stresses the insensitivity to distance factors of the values of ν corresponding to the zeros $[\nu = s - (n - 1)\ \pi/2]$ and extrema $[\nu = s - (2n + 1)\pi/4]$ of the correlation coefficient.

The phase s of (99) provides an additional determination of arc f and serves to check (69). The function $2S^2$ together with α and β of (67) enables us to determine Re f and Im f without prior knowledge of $M = 2\pi\rho d/k$. Thus for very sparse concentrations

$$2S^2 \approx \frac{\pi|f|^2\rho d}{kZ} = \frac{M}{2}\left(\frac{1}{d_t} + \frac{1}{d_r}\right)|f|^2, \tag{100}$$

and consequently,

$$\frac{\alpha^2 + \beta^2}{2S^2} = 2M \Big/ \left(\frac{1}{d_t} + \frac{1}{d_r}\right). \tag{101}$$

Since d_t and d_r are known accurately, we may isolate $M = 2\pi\rho d/k$ by using (101) and then use α and β of (67) to determine Re f and Im f.

If we cannot neglect z_s in the denominator of (93), then we rewrite the function in braces as

$$\{\,\} = e^{\delta/2}(\epsilon_t + \epsilon_r) \int_{-\frac{1}{2}}^{\frac{1}{2}} \frac{e^{\delta\eta}\, d\eta}{(1 + \epsilon_t \eta)(1 - \epsilon_r \eta)},$$

$$\delta = \rho p d, \quad \epsilon_t = \frac{d}{d_t}, \quad \epsilon_r = \frac{d}{d_r}. \tag{102}$$

Since $1/(1 - \epsilon_r \eta) = 1 + \epsilon_r \eta + \ldots$, and since $\epsilon_r \eta e^{\delta\eta} = \epsilon_r \partial\, e^{\delta\eta}$ with $\partial = \partial/\partial\delta$, we obtain

$$\{\,\} \doteq (\epsilon_t + \epsilon_r) e^{\delta/2} \left(\frac{1}{1 - \epsilon_r \partial}\right)\left(\frac{1}{1 + \epsilon_t \partial}\right)\left[\frac{e^{\delta/2} - e^{-\delta/2}}{\delta}\right] \tag{103}$$

$$= (\epsilon_t + \epsilon_r) e^{\delta/2}[1 - (\epsilon_t - \epsilon_r)\partial + (\epsilon_r^2 + \epsilon_t^2 - \epsilon_r \epsilon_t)\partial^2 + \ldots]$$

$$\times \left[\frac{e^{\delta/2} - e^{-\delta/2}}{\delta}\right].$$

Thus to third order in ϵ, we have replaced approximation (94) by

$$2S^2 e^{i2s} = (94) \left\{1 - (\epsilon_t - \epsilon_r)\left[\frac{e^{\delta} + 1}{2(e^{\delta} - 1)} - \frac{1}{\delta}\right]\right.$$

$$\left. - (\epsilon_r^2 + \epsilon_t^2 - \epsilon_r \epsilon_t)\left[\frac{1}{4} + \frac{2}{\delta^2} - \frac{1}{\delta}\left(\frac{e^{\delta} + 1}{e^{\delta} - 1}\right)\right]\right\} \tag{104}$$

which is useful to determine corrections if d_t and d_r are not particularly large with respect to d. If $\delta = \rho p d \to 0$, then we use

$$\{\,\} = (\epsilon_t + \epsilon_r) \int_0^1 \frac{d\zeta}{(1 + e_t \zeta)(1 - e_r \zeta)} = \ln\left(\frac{1 + e_t}{1 - e_r}\right),$$

$$e_t = \frac{d}{d_t - d/2}, \quad e_r = \frac{d}{d_r + d/2}, \tag{105}$$

i.e., we would use (105) instead of its limit Z^{-1} in (100).

As a simple illustration, we apply the above to the scattering amplitude of (55). We write the propagation function K' for the isolated scatterer as

$$K' = k(\eta + i\,\xi), \tag{106}$$

where η is the real index of refraction of the material and ξ is the absorption coefficient (for conversion of microwave energy to Joule heat or to radiation at other frequencies), or a coefficient for very fine-scale scattering if the individual scatterers are inhomogeneous (e.g., cellular stryofoam spheres). In microwave notation we write $\xi = \eta \tan(x/2)$ where tan x is the loss tangent. We assume in general that $\eta - 1$ and ξ are small positive numbers less than unity and that ξ is of the order of $(\eta - 1)^2$. Substituting (55) in terms of (106) into (67) we obtain to lowest orders in $\eta - 1$ and ξ,

$$\alpha = M(2a^3/3)k^2(\eta - 1) \approx N\mathfrak{V}k(\eta - 1)d/V = w(\eta - 1)kd,$$

$$2\beta = 2M(\mathfrak{V}/2\pi)k^2[\xi + (\eta - 1)^2 kb] = 2NVkd/\mathfrak{V})[\xi + (\eta - 1)^2 kb]$$

$$= 2wkd[\xi + (\eta - 1)^2 kb], \tag{107}$$

where $w = NV/\mathfrak{V}$ is the fractional volume (the fraction of the significant volume occupied by scattering material). We have

$$\sigma = \sigma_a + \sigma_s = \operatorname{Im} f\, 4\pi/k, \quad \sigma_a = 2\mathfrak{V}k\xi, \quad \sigma_s = 2\mathfrak{V}k(\eta - 1)^2 kb, \tag{108}$$

and we may write 2β as

$$2\beta = 2\beta_a + 2\beta_s, \quad 2\beta_a = 2wkd\xi, \quad 2\beta_s = 2wkd(\eta - 1)^2 kb. \tag{109}$$

Thus where these limiting forms are valid, measurements of β and α as for (69) give directly

$$\frac{\beta}{\alpha} = \frac{\xi + (\eta - 1)^2 kb}{\eta - 1} = \tan(\operatorname{arc} f) \approx \operatorname{arc} f, \tag{110}$$

which reduces to $(\eta - 1)kb \approx \text{arc}\, f$ for lossless scatterers.

Similarly, we may determine all the previous functions explicitly, e.g., for $\xi = 0$, we may approximate $2S^2$ of (100) by

$$2S^2 \approx \frac{\pi\rho d}{kZ}\,[(\mathcal{V}/2\pi)k^2(\eta - 1)]^2 = \frac{w\mathcal{V}k^3(\eta - 1)^2 d}{4\pi Z}. \quad (111)$$

If loss is present, then the Rayleigh-Born form yields

$$f^2(\theta) = |f(\theta)|^2 (K' - k)^2 / |K' - k|^2$$

$$\approx |f(\theta)|^2 [1 + 2i\xi/(\eta - 1)],$$

and similarly p of (96) is to be replaced by $\sigma_s[1 + 2i\xi/(\eta - 1)]$. However, this does not affect the first approximation (111).

Note that the form f(0) of (55) holds not only for spheres but for arbitrary large tenuous scatterers of volume $\mathcal{V}$ and length parameter b specified by

$$b = \frac{1}{\mathcal{V}}\int_{z_0}^{z_1} (z^1 - z_0)\, d\mathcal{V}(x^1, y^1, z^1)$$

$$= \frac{1}{\mathcal{V}}\int_0^{z_1 + |z_0|} \xi\, d\mathcal{V}(x^1, y^1, \zeta), \quad (112)$$

where z_0 and z_1 are the entrance and exit points for a ray $\hat{\mathbf{z}}$ traversing the scatterer. Geometrically, if we translate the volume elements of the original shape parallel to the direction of incidence ($\hat{\mathbf{z}}$) to generate a new shape having a flat face perpendicular to $\hat{\mathbf{z}}$ (as we have done in the second integral), then b is the distance of the centroid of this new shape from its flat face.

The above development applies for $w \approx 0$. For larger values of w, ('dense gas'), we modify the above by replacing V in ρ by an 'available volume' $V_a = V - N\mathcal{V}$, and by using a 'mixed space' scattering amplitude (18)

$$f_m(k\hat{\mathbf{z}}, K\hat{\mathbf{z}}) = (\mathcal{V}/2\pi)k(K' - K)[1 + i(K' - k)b]. \quad (113)$$

instead of the isolated scattering amplitude (55). Using (113) in $K = k + 2\pi\rho f_m/k$ essentially as in (66), we obtain

$$\alpha = k(\eta - 1)dw, \quad 2\beta_a = 2\xi kdw, \quad 2\beta_s = 2k^2(\eta - 1)^2 bdw(1 - w),$$

$$f_m(\theta) = f(\theta)(1 - w\cos^2\theta), \tag{114}$$

where α and $2\beta_a$ are the same as in (107) and (109), and β_s has a parabolic shape around $w = 1/2$. Eq. (114) appears appropriate [3,4] for a gas-like 'linear compression process' (up to say $w \sim 1/4$) in which w increases linearly with N, and for which the concentration is homogeneous throughout the slab region. More general distributions are considered elsewhere [20,4].

III. 6 Higher Moments for Sparse Concentrations

For very sparse concentrations, to first order in ρ (or N), we may approximate the higher moments by

$$< I^n \exp[i(n-2m)\varphi] > \sim \rho \int |v|^{2m} v^{n-2m} dr_s$$

$$\sim \frac{\rho d |f|^n \, 2\pi i \exp[i(n-2m)\Phi]}{k(n-2m) Z^{n-m}}; \tag{115}$$

$$0 \le 2m < n; \qquad \Phi \equiv \operatorname{arc} f(\hat{i}, \hat{i}) + \alpha;$$

$$< I^{2n} > \sim \rho \int |v|^{2n} dr_s \sim \frac{\rho d}{Z^{2(n-1)}} \int |f(\theta)|^{2n} d\Omega, \tag{116}$$

where we suppressed the fields ψ_i and ψ_D from the start; (115) is normalized by division with

$$D^n \exp[ik(n-2m)(d_t + d_r)],$$

and (116) by division with $D^{2n} = |d_t + d_r|^{-2n}$. (To the present order in ρ we should drop α from Φ; we keep it because the phase is usually more sensitive than the magnitude.) The corresponding phases when the reference angle is ν are $(n - 2m)(\Phi - \nu) + \pi/2$. The terms of (115) follow from a stationary phase procedure and are significant only in the near-forward scattering region $\hat{r} \approx \hat{z}$; succeeding terms of

(115) and also of (116) (with f as in (56)) are more sharply peaked around $\hat{\mathbf{r}} = \hat{\mathbf{z}}$.

Thus for the second moments (34)ff, the above yields the leading terms of the results of Sections III.4 and III.5:

$$Q_{20} = \rho d \int_{\gamma} |f(\theta)|^2 d\Omega, \quad Q_{22} = \frac{\pi \rho d |f(0)|^2}{kZ}, \qquad (117)$$

$$q_{22} = \frac{\pi}{2} + 2\Phi.$$

(A normalized version of Q_{20} is plotted in Fig. 21.) Consequently (36) gives

$$2 < x_v^2 > = Q_{20} + Q_{22} \sin(2\nu - 2\Phi),$$
$$2 < y_v^2 > = Q_{20} - Q_{22} \sin(2\nu - 2\Phi), \qquad (118)$$
$$2 < x_v y_v > = Q_{22} \cos(2\nu - 2\Phi).$$

For the third moments (37)ff, we have

$$Q_{33} = \frac{1}{3} Q_{31} = \frac{\rho d |f|^3 2\pi}{3kZ^2}; \quad q_{31} = \frac{\pi}{2} + \Phi, \quad q_{33} = \frac{\pi}{2} + 3\Phi. \qquad (119)$$

Consequently (39) gives

$$4<x_v^3> = Q_{33}\,[9 \sin(\nu - \Phi) + \sin 3(\nu - \Phi)],$$

$$4<x_v y_v^2> = Q_{33}[3 \sin(\nu - \Phi) - \sin 3(\nu - \Phi)],$$

$$4<x_v^2 y_v> = Q_{33}\,[3 \cos(\nu - \Phi) + \cos 3(\nu - \Phi)],$$

$$4<y_v^3> = Q_{33}\,[9 \cos(\nu - \Phi) - \cos 3(\nu - \Phi)]. \qquad (120)$$

Thus, if $\nu = \Phi$, we have $<x_\Phi^3> = <x_\Phi y_\Phi^2> = 0$, $<y_\Phi^3> = 2Q_{33} = 2<x_\Phi^2 y_\Phi>$, etc.

For the fourth moments, and now indicating the first order approximations in ρ by a superscript 1, we have

$$Q_{40}^1 = \frac{\rho d}{Z^2} \int_{\gamma} |f(\theta)|^4 d\Omega; \quad Q_{44}^1 = \frac{1}{2} Q_{42}^1 = \frac{\rho d |f|^4 2\pi}{kZ^3 4};$$

$$q_{42}^1 = \frac{\pi}{2} + 2\Phi, \quad q_{44}^1 = \frac{\pi}{2} + 4\Phi. \qquad (121)$$

(A normalized version of Q_{40}^{1} is plotted in Fig. 26.) Consequently (42) gives

$$\begin{aligned} 8\langle x_\nu^4 \rangle &= 3Q_{40}^1 + Q_{44}^1[8 \sin 2(\nu - \Phi) + \sin 4(\nu - \Phi)] \\ 8\langle x_\nu^3 y_\nu \rangle &= Q_{44}^1 [4 \cos 2(\nu - \Phi) + \cos 4(\nu - \Phi)], \\ 8\langle x_\nu^2 y_\nu^2 \rangle &= Q_{40}^1 - Q_{44}^1 \sin 4(\nu - \Phi), \\ 8\langle x_\nu y_\nu^3 \rangle &= Q_{44}^1 [4 \cos 2(\nu - \Phi) - \cos 4(\nu - \Phi)], \\ 8\langle y_\nu^4 \rangle &= 3Q_{40}^1 - Q_{44}^1[8 \sin 2(\nu - \Phi) - \sin 4(\nu - \Phi)]. \end{aligned} \tag{122}$$

Thus for $\nu = \Phi$, we have $\langle x_\Phi^4 \rangle = 3\langle x_\Phi^2 y_\Phi^2 \rangle = \langle y_\Phi^4 \rangle = 3Q_{40}^1/8$, and $8\langle x_\Phi^3 y_\Phi \rangle/5 = 8\langle x_\Phi y_\Phi^3 \rangle/3 = Q_{44}^1$, etc.

The approximations (115) and (116) are merely to first order in ρ. Since ρ is only one parameter of the problem, and since the higher order terms in ρ may involve lower order terms in Z^{-1}, additional terms may be required for a specific measurement setup. (In out setup, the values of d and Z are such that departures from the small-ρ forms show up in fourth moment data as in Figs. 19 and 20; the theoretical curves of these figures are based on the more complete forms we shortly derive.) In addition, we see that except for Q_{20} all of the above approximations for Q_{nm} vanish if $Z \to \infty$. Thus, discounting a specific laboratory setup, it is of interest to isolate the terms of $\langle I^n \exp[i(n - 2m)\varphi] \rangle$ and $\langle I^{2n} \rangle$ that do not vanish as $Z \to \infty$; these non-vanishing terms can depend only on powers of $Q_{20} = \langle I^2 \rangle$ and should therefore provide the moments of the Rayleigh distribution for I.

Proceeding systematically, and seeking approximations for the various moments to the lowest order in ρ that retains the non-vanishing terms for $Z \to \infty$, we start with the initial forms of (78) and introduce

$$\Psi - \langle \Psi \rangle = I e^{i\varphi} = \sum_s (u_s - \langle u_s \rangle) \equiv \sum_s V_s, \tag{123}$$

where V_s is the departure of the multiple scattered contribution u_s of scatterer s from its average value $\langle u_s \rangle$. From its definition, we have

$$\langle V_s \rangle = \langle u_s - \langle u_s \rangle \rangle = 0, \tag{124}$$

which enables us to simplify subsequent manipulations. In addition, the present 'gas' case corresponds to uncorrelated scatterer statistics in the sense that

$$\langle V_s V_t \rangle = \langle V_s \rangle \langle V_t \rangle . \qquad (125)$$

Thus from (124), we have $\langle V_s V_t \rangle = \langle V_s V_t V_m \rangle = 0$, etc., but of course $\langle V_s^2 \rangle, \langle V_s^3 \rangle, \langle V_s^2 V_t^3 \rangle$, etc., do not in general vanish. However, from (124) and (125) we see that an average involving at least linear factor vanishes:

$$\langle V_s^2 V_t \rangle = \langle V_s^2 \rangle \langle V_t \rangle = 0, \langle V_s^2 V_t^2 V_n \rangle = \langle V_s^2 V_n V_m \rangle = 0,$$
etc. (126)

Using (123), (124), and (125), we obtain directly

$$\langle (\Psi - \langle \Psi \rangle)^2 \rangle = \langle I^2 e^{i2\varphi} \rangle = Q_{22} e^{iq_{22}} = \Sigma\Sigma \langle V_s V_t \rangle$$
$$= \Sigma \langle V_s^2 \rangle + \Sigma\Sigma' \langle V_s V_t \rangle = \Sigma \langle V_s^2 \rangle =$$
$$= \rho \int \langle V_s^2 \rangle_s \, d\mathbf{r}_s , \qquad (127)$$
$$\langle |\Psi - \langle \Psi \rangle|^2 \rangle = \langle I^2 \rangle = Q_{20} = \Sigma \langle |V_s|^2 \rangle = \rho \int \langle |V_s|^2 \rangle_s d\mathbf{r}_s ,$$

where the final forms follow on replacing $\sum_{s=1}^{N}$ by N, and making the integration over $\mathbf{r}_s$ explicit by using $\langle \rangle = \int \langle \rangle_s d\mathbf{r}_s / V$ with $\langle \rangle_s$ as the average over all variables but $\mathbf{r}_s$. The final forms may be converted to the integral equations of Secs. III.4 and III.5 by proceeding as in ref. 21, or to the approximations of (88) by replacing $\langle V_s^2 \rangle_s$ by v_s^2. Similarly

$$\langle (\Psi - \langle \Psi \rangle)^3 \rangle = Q_{33} e^{iq_{33}} = \Sigma_3 \langle V_s V_t V_m \rangle$$
$$= \Sigma \langle V_s^3 \rangle + 3\Sigma_2' \langle V_s V_t^2 \rangle + \Sigma_3' \langle V_s V_t V_m \rangle$$
$$= \Sigma \langle V_s^3 \rangle = \rho \int \langle V_s^3 \rangle_s \, d\mathbf{r}_s ,$$
$$\langle |\Psi - \langle \Psi \rangle|^2 (\Psi - \langle \Psi \rangle) \rangle = Q_{31} e^{iq_{31}} = \Sigma \langle |V_s|^2 V_s \rangle$$
$$= \rho \int \langle |V_s|^2 V_s \rangle_s \, d\mathbf{r}_s , \qquad (128)$$

which reduce to (119) if we replace $\langle V_s^3 \rangle_s$ by v_s^3, etc. Here and in the following, for brevity, we use $\Sigma_3 \equiv \Sigma\Sigma\Sigma$, $\Sigma_2' \equiv \Sigma\Sigma'$, and $\Sigma_3' \equiv \Sigma\Sigma'\Sigma''$, etc.

On the other hand, for the fourth moments, we have

$$\langle (\Psi - \langle \Psi \rangle)^4 \rangle = Q_{44} e^{iq_{44}} = \Sigma_4 \langle V_s V_t V_m V_n \rangle$$

$$= \Sigma \langle V_s^4 \rangle + 4\Sigma_2' \langle V_s^3 V_t \rangle + 3\Sigma_2' \langle V_s^2 V_t^2 \rangle$$

$$+ 6\,\Sigma_3' \langle V_s^2\, V_t V_m \rangle + \Sigma_4' \quad \langle V_s V_t V_m V_n \rangle$$

$$= \Sigma \langle V_s^4 \rangle + 3\,\Sigma \langle V_s^2 \rangle \cdot \Sigma' \langle V_t^2 \rangle$$

$$= \rho \int \langle V_s^4 \rangle_s \, d\mathbf{r}_s + \frac{3(N-1)}{N} \rho^2 \left[\int \langle V_s^2 \rangle_s \, d\mathbf{r}_s\right]^2,$$

$$\langle |\Psi - \langle \Psi \rangle|^2 (\Psi - \langle \Psi \rangle)^2 \rangle = Q_{42} e^{iq_{42}} =$$

$$\rho \int \langle |V_s|^2 V_s^2 \rangle_s \, d\mathbf{r}_s$$

$$+ \quad \frac{3(N-1)}{N} \rho^2 \int \langle |V_s|^2 \rangle_s \, d\mathbf{r}_s \cdot \int \langle V_t^2 \rangle_t \, d\mathbf{r}_t,$$

$$\langle |\Psi - \langle \Psi \rangle|^4 \rangle = Q_{40} = \rho \int \langle |V_s|^4 \rangle_s \, d\mathbf{r}_s$$

$$+ \frac{2(N-1)}{N} \rho^2 \left[\int \langle |V_s|^2 \rangle_s \, d\mathbf{r}_s\right]^2$$

$$+ \frac{N-1}{N} \rho^2 \left| \int \langle V_s^2 \rangle_s d\mathbf{r}_s \right|^2. \qquad (129)$$

Labeling the explicit terms of (129) that are of first order in ρ by a superscript 1, i.e.,

$$Q_{44}^1 e^{iq_{44}^1} \equiv \rho \int \langle V_s^4 \rangle_s \, d\mathbf{r}_s, \; Q_{42}^1 e^{iq_{42}^1} \equiv \rho \int \langle |V_s|^2 V_s^2 \rangle_s \, d\mathbf{r}_s,$$

$$Q_{40}^1 \equiv \rho \int \langle |V_s|^4 \rangle_s \, d\mathbf{r}_s, \qquad (130)$$

we rewrite (129) in terms of (128) and (130) as

$$Q_{44} e^{iq_{44}} = Q_{44}^1 \; e^{iq_{44}^1} + 3\mathcal{N}(Q_{22} e^{iq_{22}})^2, \; \mathcal{N} \equiv \frac{N-1}{N},$$

$$Q_{42} e^{iq_{42}} = Q_{42}^1 \; e^{iq_{42}^1} + 3\mathcal{N} Q_{20} Q_{22} \; e^{iq_{22}}, \qquad (131)$$

$$Q_{40} = Q_{40}^1 + 2\mathcal{N}(Q_{20})^2 + \mathcal{N}(Q_{22})^2.$$

For large N we would replace $\mathcal{M} = (N-1)/N$ by unity; however, since we are interested in the full range of N down to N = 1, we keep the ratio as is.

To obtain the simplified forms for the Q^1's and q^1's corresponding to (115) and (116), we require essentially that the long dimensions of the slab be very large compared to λ, and also that the face area of the slab be large compared to λZ, i.e., we regard the slab as practically infinite. (Equivalently the present evaluation of the integrals of (115) corresponds to the near field situation of the corresponding slab region.) To emphasize these restrictions, we show how (117) follows from (127). If we replace $V_s = u_s - \langle u_s \rangle$ by the single scattering approximation $v_s - \langle v_s \rangle$, we have

$$\Sigma \langle V_s^2 \rangle \approx N[\langle v_s^2 \rangle - \langle v_s \rangle^2] = \frac{\rho d f^2 2\pi i}{2kZ}\left[1 - \frac{i4\pi d}{kV} Z\right], \quad (132)$$

where we use $\langle v_s \rangle = i2\pi f d/kV$ as obtained from the single-scattering approximation for (66) and (67). The term in brackets equals $1 - i2\lambda Z/\mathcal{A}$ where $\mathcal{A} = V/d$ is the face area of the slab region; for our setup we have $[\,] - 1 \approx -i0.02$, so that (in general) we disregard the correction. Similarly we have

$$\Sigma \langle |V_s^2| \rangle \approx N[\langle |v_s|^2 \rangle - |\langle v_s \rangle|^2]$$

$$\approx \rho d \int_\gamma |f|^2 d\Omega \left[1 - \frac{d\lambda^2}{V} \frac{|f|^2}{\int_\gamma |f|^2 d\Omega}\right], \quad (133)$$

so that the correction is of order $d\lambda^2/V = \lambda^2/\mathcal{A}$ (about 10^{-4} for our setup).

Using the approximations of (130) given in (121), and the approximations of the Q^1's of (117), we construct the analogous approximations of the amplitudes and phases of (131):

$$Q_{44} \approx [(Q_{44}^1)^2 + 9\mathcal{M}^2 (Q_{22})^4]^{\frac{1}{2}},$$

$$q_{44} = \frac{\pi}{2} + 4\Phi + \tan^{-1}[3\mathcal{M}(Q_{22})^2/Q_{44}^1],$$

$$Q_{42} = Q_{42}^1 + 3\mathcal{M}Q_{20}Q_{22}, \quad q_{42} = q_{42}^1 = q_{22} = \frac{\pi}{2} + 2\Phi,$$

$$Q_{40} = Q_{40}^1 + 2\mathcal{M}(Q_{20})^2 + \mathcal{M}(Q_{22})^2. \quad (134)$$

Thus, for example, in terms of (134), we obtain from (42),

$$8\langle x_\nu^4\rangle = 3[Q_{40}^1 + 2\mathcal{M}(Q_{20})^2 + \mathcal{M}(Q_{22})^2]$$
$$+ 8[Q_{44}^1 + 3\mathcal{M}Q_{20}Q_{22}/2] \sin[2\nu - \Phi]$$
$$+ [(Q_{44}^1)^2 + 9\mathcal{M}^2(Q_{22})^4]^{\frac{1}{2}}$$
$$\sin\{4(\nu - \Phi) - \tan^{-1}[3N(Q_{22})^2/Q_{44}^1]\} \quad (135)$$

from which the other four moments may be obtained by inspection.

If we consider the explicit form of say Q_{40}, i.e.,

$$Q_{40} = \frac{\rho d}{Z^2} \int_\gamma |f(\theta)|^2 d\Omega + \frac{2(N-1)}{N} \rho^2 d^2 [\int_\gamma |f(\theta)|^2 d\Omega]^2$$
$$+ \frac{N-1}{N} \frac{\pi^2 \rho^2 d^2}{k^2 Z^2} |f(0)|^4, \quad (136)$$

we may determine ranges of parameters for which the various terms predominate. Thus if $Z \to \infty$ (i.e., $d_t \to \infty$ and $d_r \to \infty$), then

$$Q_{40} \to \frac{2(N-1)}{N} \left[\rho d \int_\gamma |f(\theta)|^2 d\Omega\right]^2 = \frac{2(N-1)}{N} (Q_{20})^2, \quad (137)$$

and similarly $Q_{44} \to 0$ and $Q_{42} \to 0$. For $N \to \infty$, (137) corresponds to the moment of a Rayleigh distribution. Thus for $Z \to \infty$, and $N \to \infty$, we have

$$\langle x^4\rangle \to \langle y^4\rangle \to 3(Q_{20})^2/4, \quad \langle x^2 y^2\rangle \to (Q_{20})^2/4,$$
$$\langle xy^3\rangle \to \langle x^3 y\rangle \to 0. \quad (138)$$

Similarly the third moments all vanish, $\langle x^n y^m\rangle|_{n+m=3} \to 0$, and the second moments reduce to $\langle x^2\rangle \to \langle y^2\rangle \to Q_{20}/2$. Thus $\langle x^4\rangle \to 3\langle x^2\rangle^2$, $\langle x^2 y^2\rangle \to \langle x^2\rangle\langle y^2\rangle$, etc., and our more general results for the gas reduce to the special values of (11b).

Referring back to (136), we may consider angles of observation away from the forward scattered direction $\theta = 0$.

For angles outside the coherent beam, we drop all terms of the moments arrived at by a stationary phase evaluation of integrals. Thus we have

$$Q_{40} \approx \frac{\rho d}{Z^2} \int |f|^4 d\Omega + \frac{2(N-1)}{N} (Q_{20})^2,$$

$$Q_{20} = \rho d \int_{\gamma} |f(\theta)|^2 d\Omega, \tag{139}$$

where Q_{20} was considered previously [3] in detail for large tenuous spheres. In the range where (139) is valid, we also have

$$Q_{44} \approx Q_{42} \approx Q_{33} \approx Q_{31} \approx Q_{22} \approx 0, \tag{140}$$

and of course $< \Psi > \approx 0$, so that only Q_{40} and Q_{20} survive up to fourth moments. We see from Figs. 21 and 22 that the integral over $|f|^4$ is in general more tightly peaked around $\theta = 0$ than the integral over $|f|^2$, and since these normalized integrals lie between zero and unity, the $|f|^4$ integral is even more tightly peaked than $[\int |f|^2 d\Omega]^2$ of (139); thus provided $2Z^2\rho d$ is not too small, the second term of (140) becomes dominant with increasing θ and we obtain the Rayleigh distribution. For θ relatively close to zero, except for $Z \to \infty$, or for $\rho \to 0$, both terms of (139) must be considered.

We may extend the above directly. Thus, from

$$\begin{aligned} <|\Psi - <\Psi>|^6> = \Sigma <|V_s|^6> + \Sigma_2' <V_s^3>^* <V_t^3> \\ + \Sigma_2' <|V_s|^2><|V_t|^4> \\ + \Sigma_3' <|V_s|^2><|V_t|^2><|V_m|^2>, \end{aligned} \tag{141}$$

we obtain

$$Q_{60} = Q_{60}^1 + \mathcal{N}(Q_{31})^2 + 3\mathcal{N}Q_{20}Q_{40}^1 + 6\mathcal{N}\mathcal{N}'(Q_{20})^3, \tag{142}$$

where $\mathcal{N} = (N-1)/N$ and $\mathcal{N}' = (N-2)/N$. For $Z \to \infty$, all Q_{6m} for $m \neq 0$ vanish, and (142) reduces to

$$Q_{60} \to 6\mathcal{N}\mathcal{N}'(Q_{20})^3 = \frac{3!N!}{N^3(N-3)!} (Q_{20})^3. \tag{143}$$

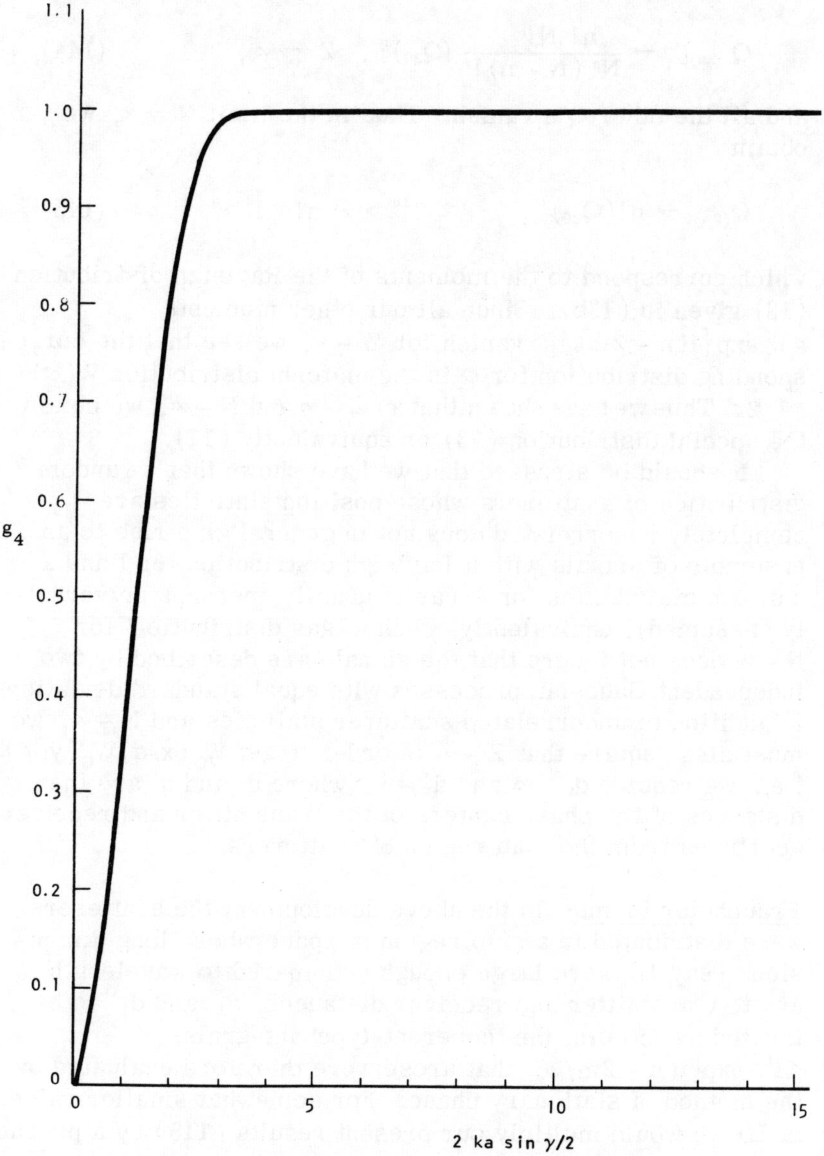

Fig. 22 Plot of $Q^1_{40}(\gamma)/Q^1_{40}(\pi) = g_4$ based on (121) versus 2 ka sin $\gamma/2$.

Generalizing the above, we have

$$Q_{(2n)0} \rightarrow \frac{n!\,N!}{N^n\,(N - n)!}\,(Q_{20})^n, \quad Z \rightarrow \infty, \tag{144}$$

and all the other Q's vanish. Thus in the limit $N \rightarrow \infty$, we obtain

$$Q_{(2n)0} \rightarrow n!(Q_{20})^n, \qquad \langle I^{2n} \rangle \rightarrow n!\,\langle I^2 \rangle^n, \tag{145}$$

which correspond to the moments of the Rayleigh distribution (13) given in (13b). Since all our other moments $\langle I^n \exp[i(n - 2m)\varphi] \rangle$ vanish for $Z \rightarrow \infty$, we see that the corresponding distribution for φ is the uniform distribution $W(\varphi) = 1/2\pi$. Thus we have shown that as $Z \rightarrow \infty$ and $N \rightarrow \infty$, we obtain the special distribution (13) or equivalently (11).

It should be stressed that we have shown that a random distribution of scatterers whose position statistics are completely uncorrelated does not in general give rise to an ensemble of signals with a Rayleigh distribution for I and a uniform distribution for φ (as is usually, perhaps universally, assumed); equivalently, such a 'gas distribution' for $N \rightarrow \infty$ does not insure that the signals are described by two independent Gaussian processes with equal standard deviations. In addition to uncorrelated scatterer statistics and $N \rightarrow \infty$, we must also require that $Z \rightarrow \infty$ in order to get $W_G(x; \sigma) W_G(y; \sigma)$, i.e., we require $d_t \rightarrow \infty$ and $d_r \rightarrow \infty$, where d_t and d_r are the distances of the phase centers of the transmitter and receiver apertures from the slab region of scatterers.

Fraunhofer forms: In the above development the scatterers were distributed in a slab region of space whose long dimensions (say L) were large enough (compared to wavelength and to transmitter and receiver distances, d_t and d_r) to be treated as infinite; the 'coherent-type' integrals $\langle I^n \exp[i(n - 2m)\varphi \rangle$ that arose were therefore evaluated by the method of stationary phase. For somewhat smaller values of L, we would multiply our present results (115) by a product of Fresnel integrals to take into account the edge effects of the bounded distribution. Similarly if kL were very much smaller than kd, we would work with the analogous Fraunhofer forms. In particular for a spherical scattering region of radius L, the integrals of (115) reduce to

$$\rho \int |v|^{2m} v^{n-2m} d\mathbf{r}_s \approx \frac{|f(\theta)|^n}{Z^n} \exp[i(n-2m)\operatorname{arc} f(\hat{\mathbf{r}}, \hat{\mathbf{z}})] \\ NJ([n-2m]\, 2kL \sin\frac{\theta}{2}), \tag{146}$$

where J is the Rayleigh-Born sphere function as in (56). As previously, we have normalized by division with

$$D^n \exp[i(n-2m)k(d_t + d_r)],$$

and have used $1/Dd_t\, d_r = (d_t + d_r)/d_t\, d_r = (1/d_t) + (1/d_r) = 1/Z$. Since the angular width of the main lobe of J is determined by $[(n-2m)2kL]^{-1}$, we see that corresponding terms of the higher moments are more tightly peaked around the forward direction $\theta = 0$. In the forward direction, we may use a WKB type procedure as for (53) and obtain (146) with $f(\theta)$ replaced by $f(0)$, and J replaced by

$$J \Rightarrow \frac{i3}{\delta}\left[\frac{1}{2} - F(\delta)\right], \qquad \delta = 2L[(n-2m)\operatorname{Re}(K-k)], \tag{147}$$

where (inIm K) was dropped from the brackets for δ to obtain the analog of (115); the approximation corresponding to (55) is

$$J \Rightarrow [1 + i\delta\, 3/8]. \tag{148}$$

Similarly the integrals of (116) reduce to

$$\rho \int |v|^{2n} d\mathbf{r}_s \approx \frac{N|f(\theta)|^{2n}}{Z^{2n}}, \tag{149}$$

where we normalized by division with D^{2n}. We may use (149) for different directions θ provided that d_t and d_r are kept fixed, and provided that $D = 1/(d_t + d_r)$ is maintained as the magnitude received in the absence of scatterers with the receiver in the position for forward scattering measurements. We have assumed uniform and finely collimated beams enveloping the spherical region in order to suppress horn factors, etc.

The most significant difference between the present results for the completely bounded spherical scattering region and the previous ones for the slab region are the additional factors in Z: the present phase-bearing terms involve Z^{-n} instead of the previous Z^{-n+1}, and the others involve Z^{-2n} instead of the previous Z^{-2n+2}. However, we may still obtain the Rayleigh distribution in an appropriate range of parameters.

Equations (146) and (149) are the Fraunhofer approximations of the integrals of (115) and (116), but they are not in general the analogous approximations of the moments $\langle I^n \exp[i(n-2m)\varphi]\rangle$ and $\langle I^{2n}\rangle$: the present case requires more careful consideration of $\langle v_s\rangle$ in the single scattering approximation $V_s \approx v_s - \langle v_s\rangle$. We now have

$$\langle v_s\rangle = \frac{1}{V}\int v_s \, d\mathbf{r}_s = \frac{f(\theta)}{Z} J(\Gamma_L), \quad \Gamma_L \equiv 2kL \sin\frac{\theta}{2}, \tag{150}$$

where we again normalized by division with ψ_D. Thus corresponding to (132), we obtain from (146) and (150),

$$Q_{22} e^{iq_{22}} = \Sigma \langle V_s^2\rangle \approx N[\langle v_s^2\rangle - \langle v_s\rangle^2]$$

$$= N\frac{f^2(\theta)}{Z^2}[J(2\Gamma_L) - J^2(\Gamma_L)], \tag{151}$$

which vanishes in the forward direction $\theta = \Gamma_L = 0$, $J(0) = 1$. (Similarly if we use the WKB form (148), we replace the function in the square brackets by $1 + i\delta\, 3/8 - (1 + i\delta\, 3/16)^2$ which vanishes to first order in δ.) The analogous results hold for

$$Q_{20} = \Sigma \langle |V_s|^2\rangle \approx N[\langle |v_s|^2\rangle - |\langle v_s\rangle|^2]$$

$$= \frac{N|f(\delta)|^2}{Z^2}[1 - J^2(\Gamma_L)]. \tag{152}$$

Similarly, all other central moments reduce to zero in the forward direction, for which case Ψ reduces to $\langle\Psi\rangle$ subject to the present restrictions.

However, although Q_{20} vanishes in the forward direction, it may be approximated in other directions by

$$Q_{20} \approx \frac{N|f(\theta)|^2}{Z^2} \quad \text{for } \theta \neq 0. \tag{153}$$

Similarly in the range of angles where $J(\Gamma_L)$ (and consequently $J(n\,\Gamma_L)$) is negligible, we may neglect (152) as well as all other terms of the moments which involve (146). Thus the analog of (139) is now

$$Q_{40} = Q^1_{40} + \frac{2(N-1)}{N}(Q_{20})^2 \approx \frac{N}{Z^4}|f(\theta)|^4 + \frac{2(N-1)}{N}\left[\frac{N|f(\theta)|^2}{Z^2}\right]^2$$

$$= \frac{N|f(\theta)|^4}{Z^4}[1 + 2(N-1)]. \qquad (154)$$

Thus for large N, we have $Q_{40} \rightarrow 2(Q_{20})^2$, and similarly proceeding as for (142) to (145), we obtain $Q_{(2n)0} \rightarrow n!(Q_{20})^n$,

$$\langle I^{2n} \rangle \rightarrow n!\langle I^2\rangle^n, \quad \langle I^2\rangle = \frac{N|f(\theta)|^2}{Z^2} = N|f(\theta)|^2\left(\frac{1}{d_t} + \frac{1}{d_r}\right)^2. \qquad (155)$$

Thus except for the forward direction (for which the central moments and the variant field vanish), the magnitude of the variant field becomes Rayleigh distributed and its phase becomes uniformly distributed as $N \rightarrow \infty$.

<u>Correlated distributions</u>: In the sets of average (127), (128), and (129), we gave the complete form in V_s for only one member of each set; for the other members we wrote only the forms appropriate for the uncorrelated (rare-gas) distribution. For correlated distributions (dense gas or liquid state position statistics), we supplement (127), (128), and (129) with

$$Q_{20} = \Sigma_1\langle |V_s|^2\rangle + \Sigma_2'\langle V_s V_t^*\rangle, \qquad (127s)$$

$$Q_{31}e^{iq_{31}} = \Sigma\langle |V_s|^2 V_s\rangle + \Sigma_2'\langle 2|V_s|^2 V_t + V_s^2 V_t^*\rangle$$
$$+ \Sigma_3'\langle V_s V_t V_m^*\rangle, \qquad (128s)$$

$$Q_{42}e^{iq_{42}} = \Sigma\langle |V_s|^2 V_s^2\rangle + \Sigma_2'\langle 3|V_s|^2 V_s V_t + V_s^3 V_t^*$$
$$+ 3|V_s|^2 V_t^2\rangle \qquad (129s)$$
$$+ \Sigma_3'\langle 3|V_s|^2 V_t V_m + 3V_s^2 V_t V_m^*\rangle + \Sigma_4'\langle V_s V_t V_m V_n^*\rangle,$$

$$Q_{40} = \Sigma\langle |V_s|^4\rangle + \Sigma_2'\langle (V_s^* V_t)^2 + 2|V_s V_t|^2$$
$$+ 4|V_s|^2\,\mathrm{Re}(V_s^* V_t)\rangle + \Sigma_3'\langle 4|V_s|^2 V_n V_m^*$$
$$+ 2\,\mathrm{Re}(V_s^2 V_n^* V_m^*)\rangle + \Sigma_4'\langle V_s V_t V_n^* V_m^*\rangle.$$

In the single scattering approximation, the various averages would be of the form

$$<F(s)> = \int p(s)F(s)d\mathbf{r}_s ,$$

$$<F(s, t)> = \int p(s, t)\, F(s, t)d\mathbf{r}_s\, d\mathbf{r}_t , \qquad (156)$$

$$<F(s, t, \ldots n)> = \int p(s, t, \ldots n) F(s, t, \ldots n)d\mathbf{r}_s\, d\mathbf{r}_t \ldots d\mathbf{r}_n ,$$

where p(s), p(s, t), etc. are the one-, two-, etc., particle distribution functions. Thus in the same sense that one inverts single scattering experimental data for $<T^2>$ to isolate the pair distribution function [11], one can also seek to isolate the n-particle distribution functions from higher moment data.

IV. COMPARISON OF DATA AND THEORY

Detailed comparison of data records and numerical computations based on the theory of Sec. III, will be published elsewhere [10, 12]. Here we consider primarily the determination of the isolated scatterer function f(0) without prior knowledge of the concentration, and discuss the additional parameters required to construct the periodic curves of the various moments shown in Figs. 12, 13, 18, 19, and 20.

IV. 1 Determination of Scattering Parameters

Initially we illustrate the procedure for determining Re f and Im f based on

$$\alpha = \nu + \tan^{-1}\frac{<Y>}{<X>} = M\,\mathrm{Re}\,f, \quad M = \frac{2\pi\rho d}{k} = \frac{\lambda d}{V} N, \qquad (157)$$

$$2\beta = -\ln[<X>^2 + <Y>^2] = 2M\,\mathrm{Im}\,f, \qquad (158)$$

$$S^2 = |<xy>|_{max} = \left\{\left[\frac{<x^2> - <y^2>}{2}\right]^2 + <xy>^2\right\}^{\frac{1}{2}} = \frac{M|f|^2}{4Z}, \qquad (159)$$

where ν and Z = 21.75" are known, but M, Re f, and Im f are not.

Figure 15 shows the data points α obtained for four different concentrations of similar spheres (four different values of N--the number of spheres in the container) for different values of the reference angle ν. [The spheres were all cut from the same styrofoam log and were practically identical at the start. However, they are worn down and become slightly compacted and misshapen with use; since newly cut spheres wear most rapidly, we use worn-in spheres and sort them regularly by means of sieves to reject those that have become too small or too misshapen [3]. The material is cellular with cell widths of the order of $\lambda/7$, and the compaction is not uniform throughout a sphere. The data was collected under a variety of conditions (and the primary reason for varying the reference angle ν was to obtain oscillating data on the periodic results predicted for the higher moments).] Discounting a few isolated cases, and independently of N, all data points are within 0.5 degrees of $C_1 N = 1.75 \times 10^{-3} N$ (the horizontal lines).

Figure 14 shows corresponding data for $2\beta = -\ln |\langle\Psi\rangle/D|^2 = -\ln C^2$, where D^2 is the measured intensity in the absence of scatterers; the fitted horizontal lines may be compared with $C_2 N = 9.17 \times 10^{-4} N$, where C_2 is an overall average of the results for the present and for an additional procedure that we discuss subsequently; with decreasing N, the four cases give $2\beta \times 10^4 / N = 9.17,\ 9.65,\ 8.7,\ 10.42$. As indicated by these numbers, our results for a specific small gas-like set of spheres are not always consistent with those for a larger gas-like set: this arises partly because of the difficulty in maintaining a uniform spatial distribution at low-N, but primarily because the effects of slight variations in shape, size, and index of refraction of the individual scatterers are more significant for low-N (i.e., we do not have a big enough sample for such effects to cancel).

Figure 16 shows corresponding data points for S^2 divided by D^2; the horizontal lines are fitted to the data. The departures of the horizontal lines from $C_3 N = 6.71 \times 10^{-5} N$, where C_3 is an overall average of the results for the present and for two additional procedures to be mentioned shortly, arise primarily from differences in the average sphere parameters for the different cases; with decreasing N, the four cases give $S^2 \times 10^5 /N = 5.65, 6.5, 8.33, 7.5$. The quasi-periodic behavior in Fig. 16 shows the presence of standing waves in the microwave circuit (probably in the receiver bolometer system); such waves appear to be a major cause of internal discrepancies among the measured data presented for a constant value of N. [In our current work, in order to eliminate the effects of standing waves, we repeat each data collecting run; on the second pass we introduce a 90° phase shift in both bridges of our circuit, i.e., we do so in both bridges in order to maintain the same value of reference phase ν for both passes.]

If we substitute the values of α, 2β, S^2, obtained by fitting in Figs. 15, 14, and 16 into (157)-(159), we can eliminate M and solve for Re f and Im f. Comparing f with Fig. 23 (based on Eq. (53)) we isolate the corresponding radius a and index η. (First we form arctan (Re f/Im f) and compare with arc f of Fig. 23c to isolate $\delta = 2\,ka\,(\eta - 1)$ and then we determine a from say Fig. 23b.) The values of a and η given in Figs. 13, 13, 18, 19, and 20 were obtained by this procedure.

As an illustration, substituting the values $C_1 N$, $C_2 N$, and $C_3 N$ called out in the above text into (157)-(159) we obtain Re f = 3.075 and Im f = 0.808. Comparison with the plots of Fig. 23 yields 2a = 1.36" and $\eta = 1.0163$. [This diameter is essentially the average radius of the spheres we sought to maintain by sifting (2a = 1.36" ± 0.02), and the value of η is within the range 1.016 to 1.017 we obtained by interferometer measurements on slabs of styrofoam cut from the same log as the spheres.] From the above constants, we also obtain $M = (\lambda d/V) N = 5.59 \times 10^{-4} N$; since $\lambda = 0.205"$, this yields $V/d = 366$ in.^{2} as the face area of the slab region corresponding to the measurements. Since d = 10.25", the fractional volume for N = 100 is w = 0.035, and the other cases correspond to smaller values of w.

In addition to the above ' constant concentration procedure', we may vary the concentration and determine the constants from the slopes of straight lines fitted to the data. In Fig. 24a we show α versus N, and the straight line $C_1 N$ (with C_1 as above); the vertical lines correspond to the spread of the points shown in Fig. 15. Figure 24b shows 2β versus N, and the straight line $C_2 N$; the vertical lines correspond to the spread of the points shown in Fig. 14. Figure 24c shows data points for S^2, a dashed line obtained by fitting for $N \leq 60$, a solid line $C_3 N$, and vertical lines corresponding to the spreads of the points of Fig. 16. In addition, Fig. 24c shows four squares; these squares, which represent a third procedure for determining S^2, were obtained by fitting data points of $\langle x_\nu y_\nu \rangle$ versus ν (as in Fig. 13) to the oscillating curve $S^2 \cos(2s - 2\nu)$ predicted by theory. The value C_3 used to determine Re f and Im f for the case illustrated in the text is essentially an average of the results obtained for all three procedures. (The discrepancies at low-N may arise from clumping; see Refs. 20 and 4.)

To substantiate the above procedures, some of the measurements were repeated for smaller spheres cut from the same styrofoam log. Figure 25 shows data points for α, β, S^2, versus N; the solid lines are the theoretical values for $2a = 0.74''$ and $\eta = 1.0163$. The bands of α and β points at $N = 400$ and 800 correspond to the values obtained by varying ν. In terms of fractional volume $w = N\mathcal{V}/V$ (the essential parameter for the linear-in-N theory) about 624 of the present small spheres correspond to 100 of the larger ones; the fractional volume for $N = 800$ is $w = 0.045$. Similarly, Fig. 26 shows data and straight line theory for α, 2β, and S^2 versus N for spheres the same size as those used in Fig. 24, but with a value of $\eta - 1$ roughly twice as large.

For completeness we include here additional data corresponding to the spheres of Fig. 24. Thus Fig. 27 gives $\langle I^2 \rangle$; the solid line corresponds to

$$\langle I^2 \rangle = \rho d \int_\gamma |f(\theta)^2| d\Omega = \frac{kM}{2\pi} \int_\gamma |f(\theta)|^2 d\Omega, \qquad (160)$$

for the parameters of Fig. 24 and a 'horn angle' $\gamma = 5.72°$ obtained as an overall average by fitting (160) (and such forms as $\langle T^2 \rangle$ and $\langle I^2 \rangle/(1 - C^2)$) to data for different N, η, and a, and then using Fig. 21 to determine γ (a fixed parameter for our specific horns and distances d_t and d_r provided that (160) with (58) is applicable). Figure 28 compares data for $\langle T^2 \rangle$ obtained by two methods with theory for the parameters of Figs. 24 and 27. The empty circles are time averages of the square of the output of the T-channel of Fig. 6;

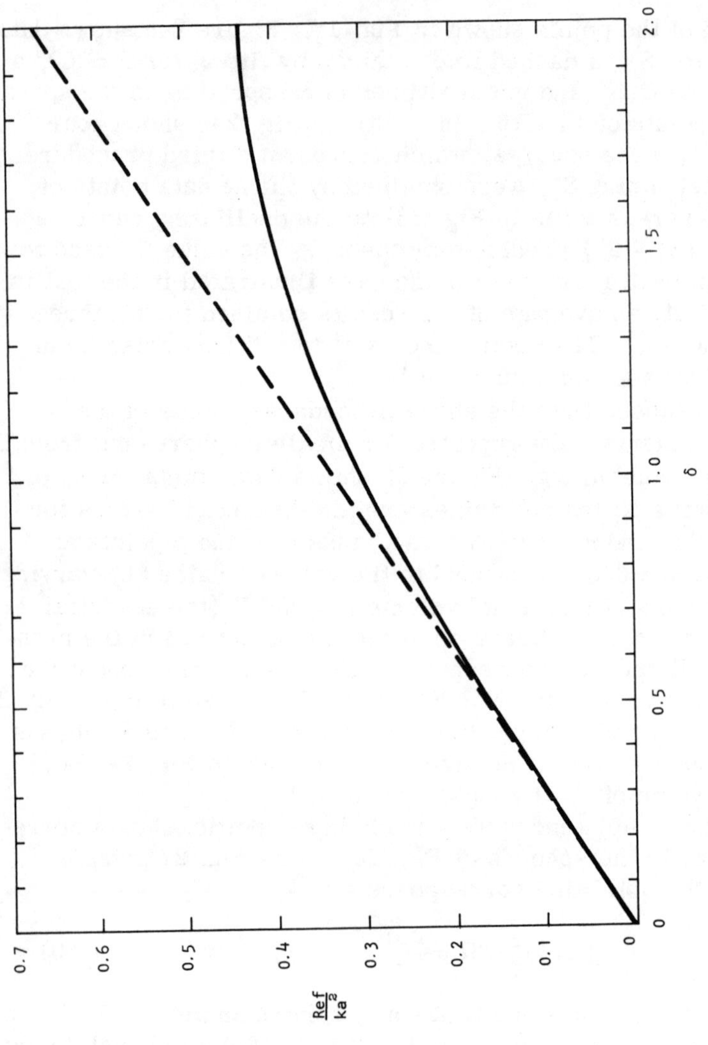

Fig. 23a.

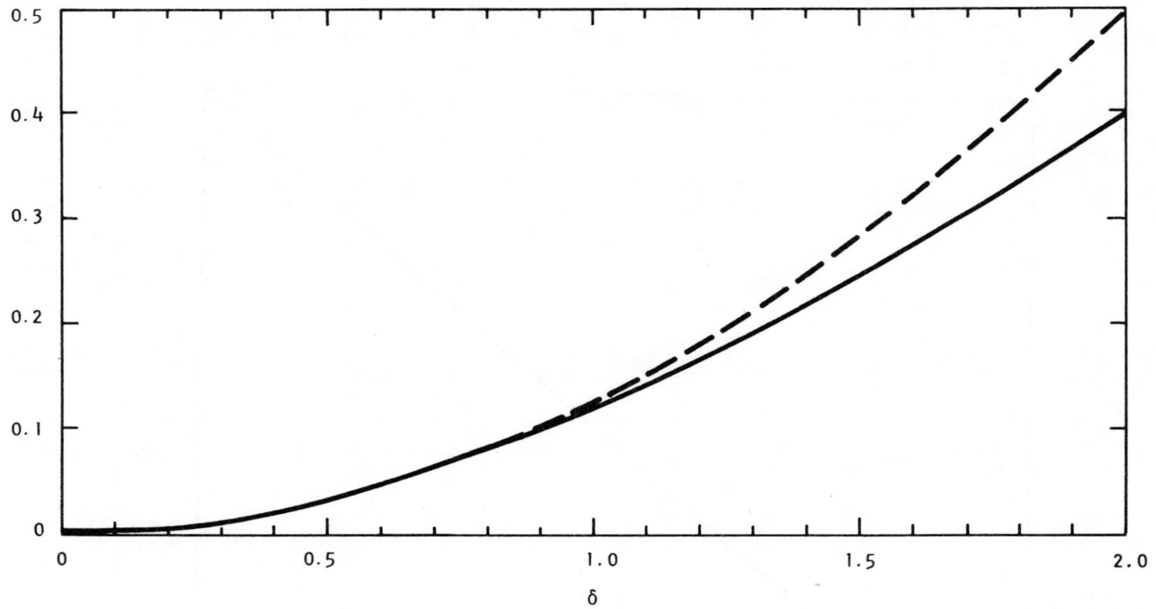

Fig. 23b.

Fig. 23. Solid lines are plots of $\mathrm{Re}\,f/ka^2$, $\mathrm{Im}\,f/ka^2$, arc f, and $|f|^2/k^2a^4$ versus $\delta = 2ka(\eta - 1)$ obtained from Eq. (53); dashed lines are approximations based on (55).

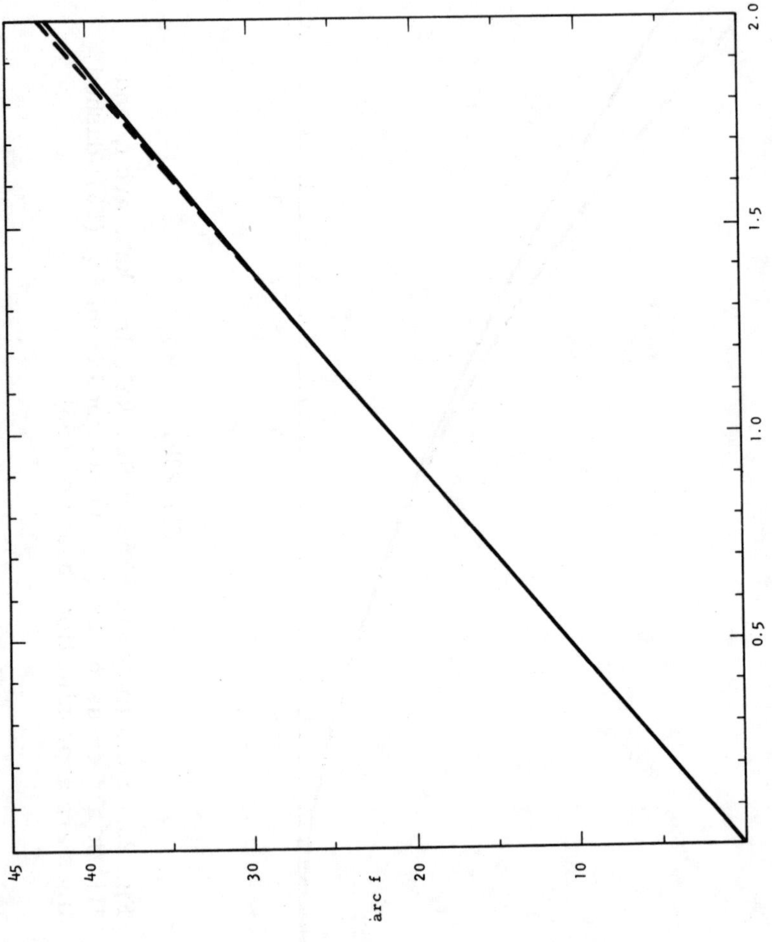

Fig. 23c.

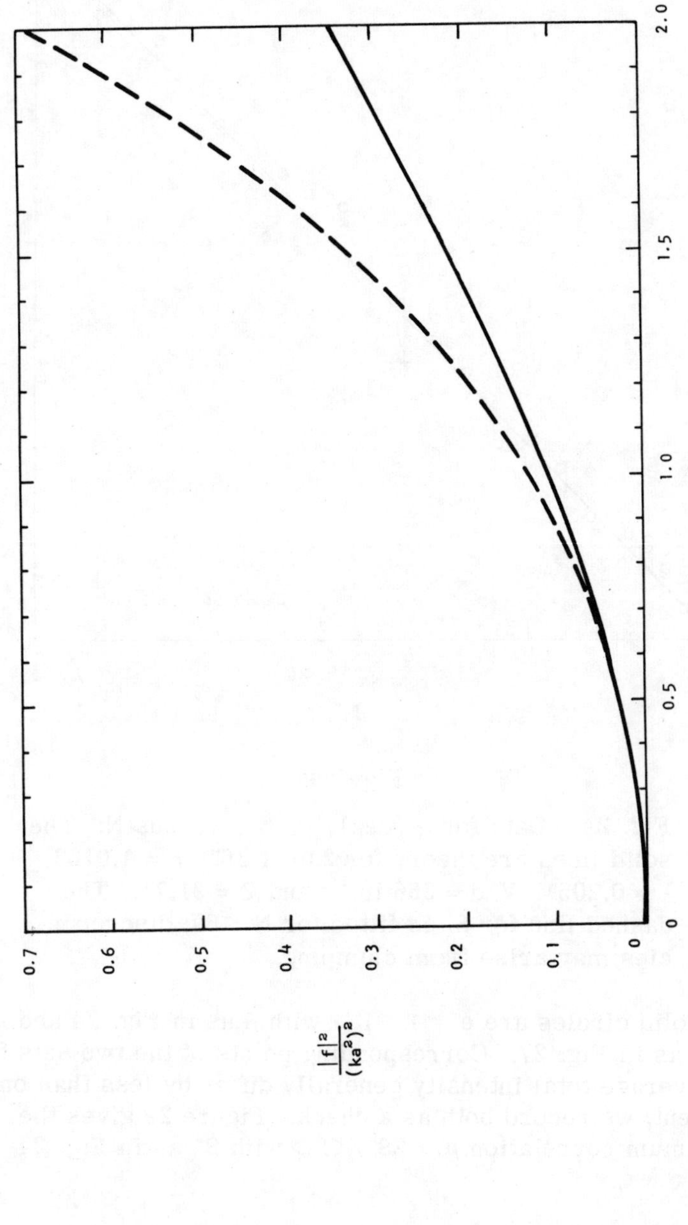

Fig. 23d.

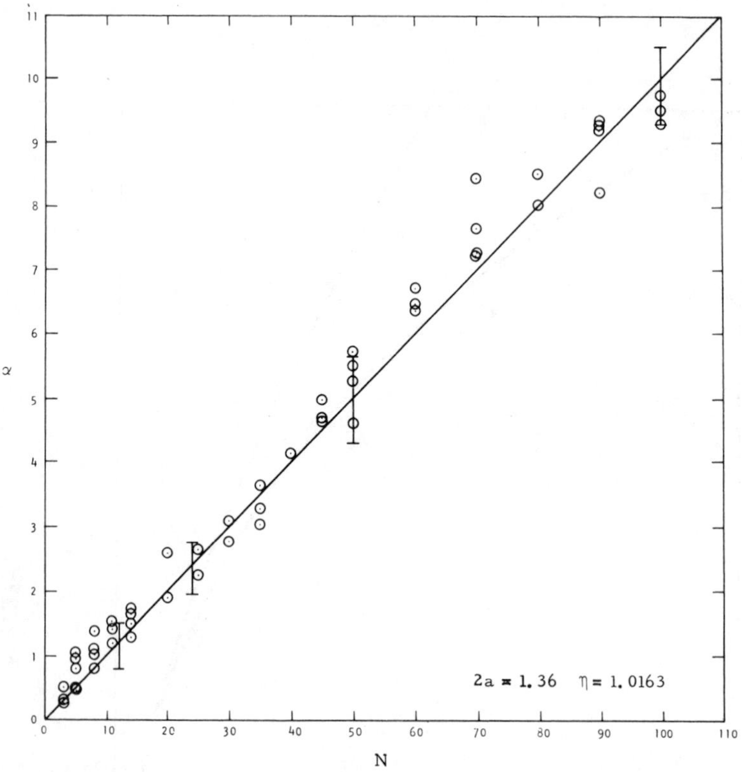

Fig. 24a

Fig. 24 Data for α (deg), β, S^2, versus N: The solid lines are theory for 2a = 1.36", η = 1.0163, λ = 0.205", V/d = 366 in.^{2}, and Z = 21.7". The dashed line for S^2 is fitted for $N \leq 60$; discrepancies may arise from clumping.

the solid circles are $e^{-2\beta} + \langle I^2 \rangle$ with β as in Fig. 24 and $\langle I^2 \rangle$ as in Fig. 27. Corresponding points of the two sets for the average total intensity generally differ by less than one percent; we record both as a check. Figure 29 gives the maximum correlation $\mu_{\wedge} = 2S^2/\langle I^2 \rangle$ with S^2 as in Fig. 24

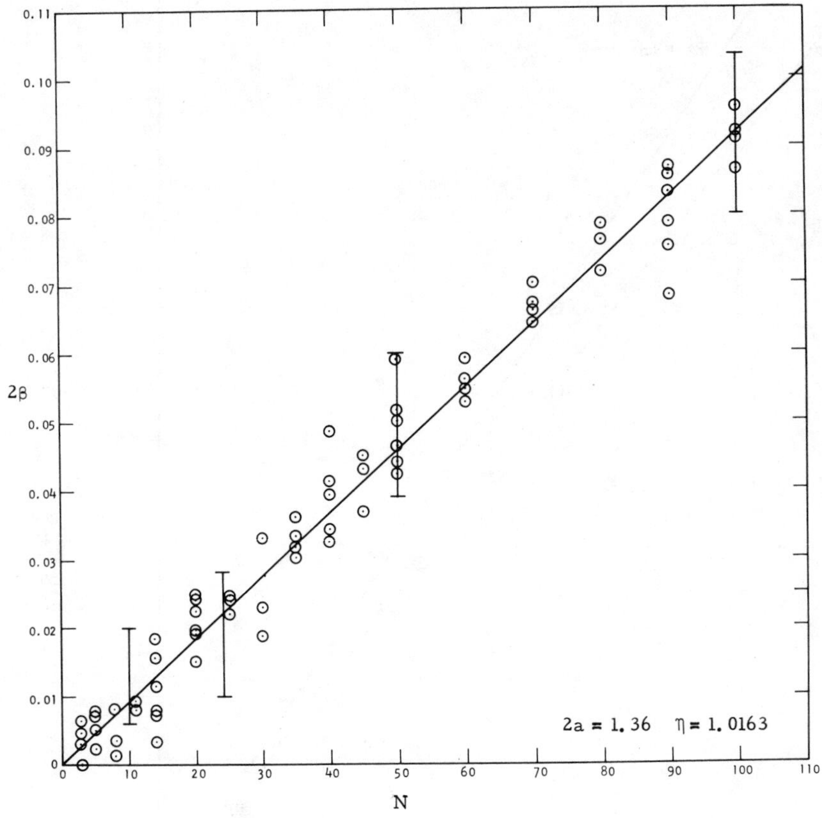

Fig. 24b

and $<I^2>$ as in Fig. 27; theory line based on

$$\mu_{\wedge} = \frac{\pi |f(0)|^2}{kZ \int_{\gamma} |f(\theta)|^2 d\Omega} \tag{161}$$

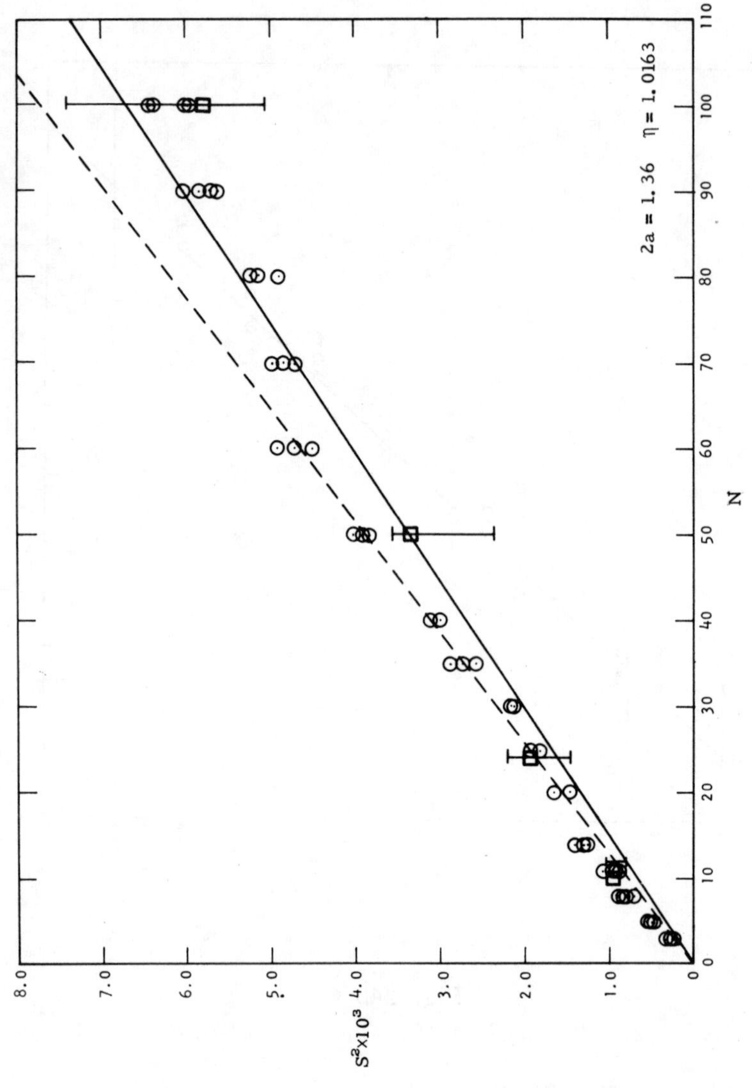

$S^2 \times 10^3$
N
2a = 1.36
η = 1.0163
0
1.0
2.0
3.0
4.0
5.0
6.0
7.0
8.0
10
20
30
40
50
60
70
80
90
100
110

Fig. 24c

is for parameters of Figs. 24 and 27. Fig. 30 shows

$$g(\gamma) = \frac{\langle I^2 \rangle}{1 - C^2} = \frac{\int_\gamma |f(\theta)|^2 d\Omega}{\int_\pi |f(\theta)|^2 d\Omega} \tag{162}$$

obtained from data of Figs. 24 and 27. The solid line corresponds to $\gamma = 5.72°$ as in Figs. 27 and 28; the fitted dashed line compared with Fig. 21 gives $\gamma = 5.92°$. Discrepancies may arise from clumping [20, 4].

IV. 2 Oscillating Curves for the Moments

Having determined the fundamental parameters of the scattering problem in Sec. IV. 1, we could apply them directly to the explicit approximations (118), (120), and (135) to construct the corresponding oscillating theoretical curves of the various moments versus the reference angle ν; we knew Z, we now know a, η, V/d for each set of N spheres, and we have an overall approximation for γ. We did this initially to compare with the data of Figs. 12, 13, 18, 19, and 20 using the parameters given in the figures and the overall average value $\gamma = 5.72°$, and found adequate accord for the amplitudes of the oscillating data and some discrepancies for the phases. To emphasize the periodicities, we shifted the theoretical curves along ν (slight variations of theoretical values of the theoretical phases q) and shifted the height of the base line in $\langle x_\nu^2 \rangle$ and $\langle x_\nu^4 \rangle$ (slight variations of Q_{20} and Q_{40} corresponding to different values of γ than the average 5.72°). Thus most of the curves versus ν are partly fitted. We delineate the discrepancies in the following.

The solid curves for $\langle X_\nu \rangle$ and $\langle Y_\nu \rangle$ of Fig. 12 are the unshifted theoretical curves for the stated parameters. The solid curves of $\langle x_\nu y_\nu \rangle$ of Fig. 13 have the theoretical amplitudes for the stated parameters, but have been shifted somewhat to the left (the N = 50 curve 4.7° and the N = 100 curve by 6.3°), so that the computed values of $s = q_{22}/2 = \Phi + 45° = \arc f + \alpha + 45°$ are correspondingly less than the fitted values obtain by the shifting. The amplitudes $Q_{22} = S^2$ of the solid curves for $\langle x_\nu^2 \rangle$ of Fig. 13 are the theoretical values; the curves have been shifted to the left by the same amounts as for $\langle x_\nu y_\nu \rangle$. The base line Q_{20} for N = 50 is the theoretical value based on the

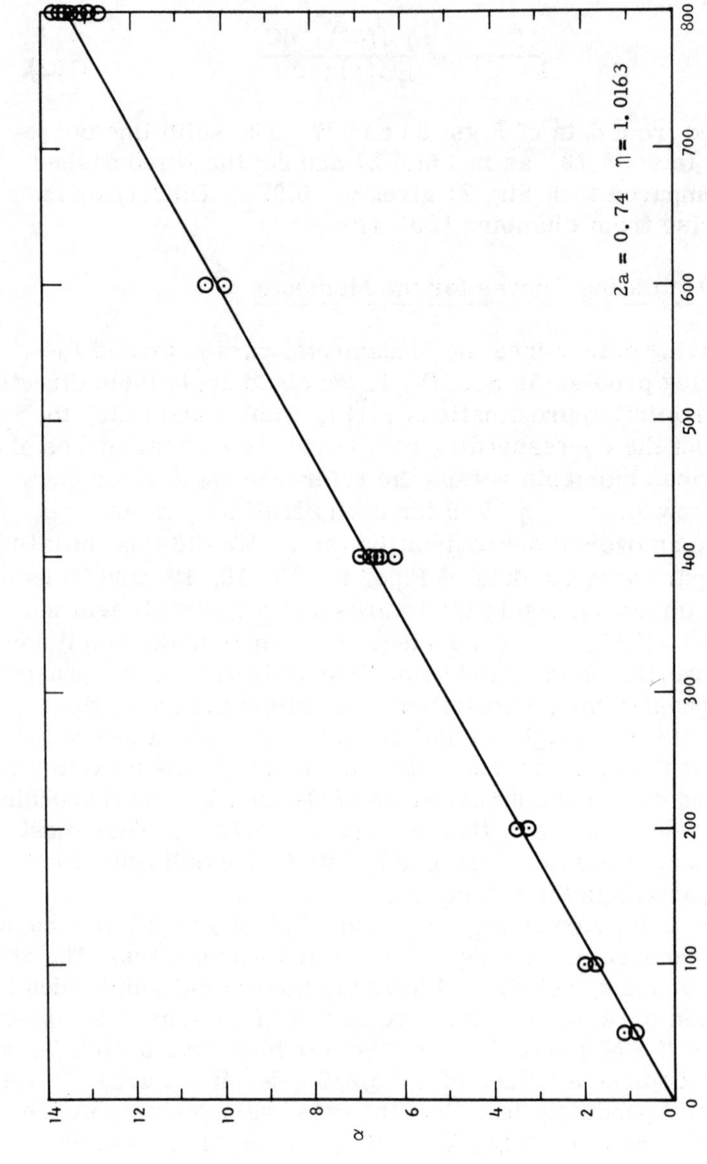

Fig. 25a

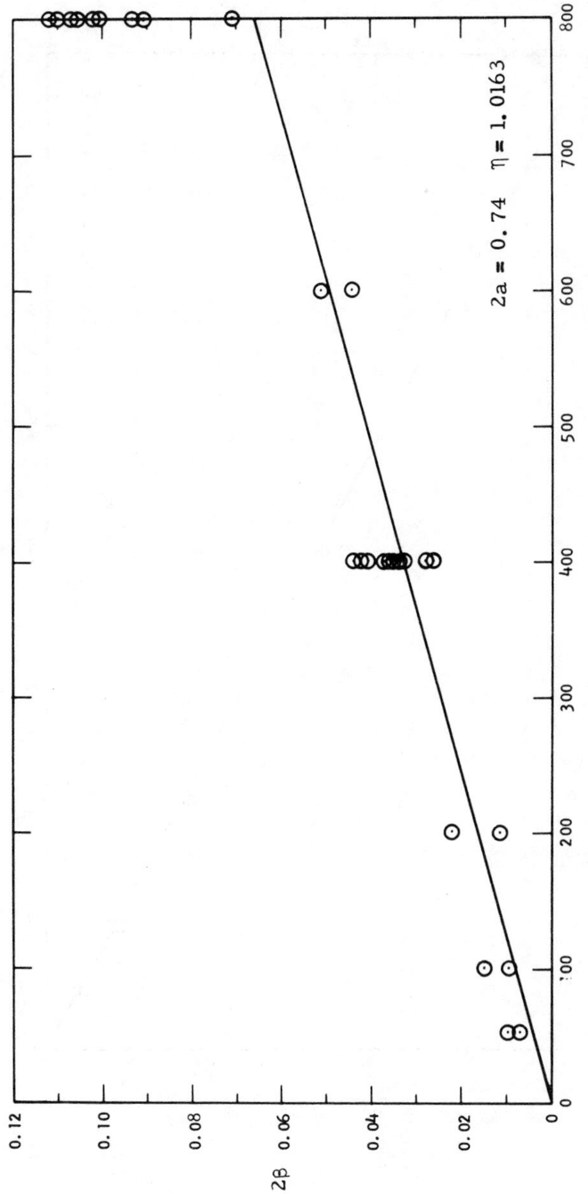

Fig. 25b

Fig. 25. Data for α (deg), β, ζ^2, versus N: The solid lines are theory for 2a = 0.74", η = 1.0163.

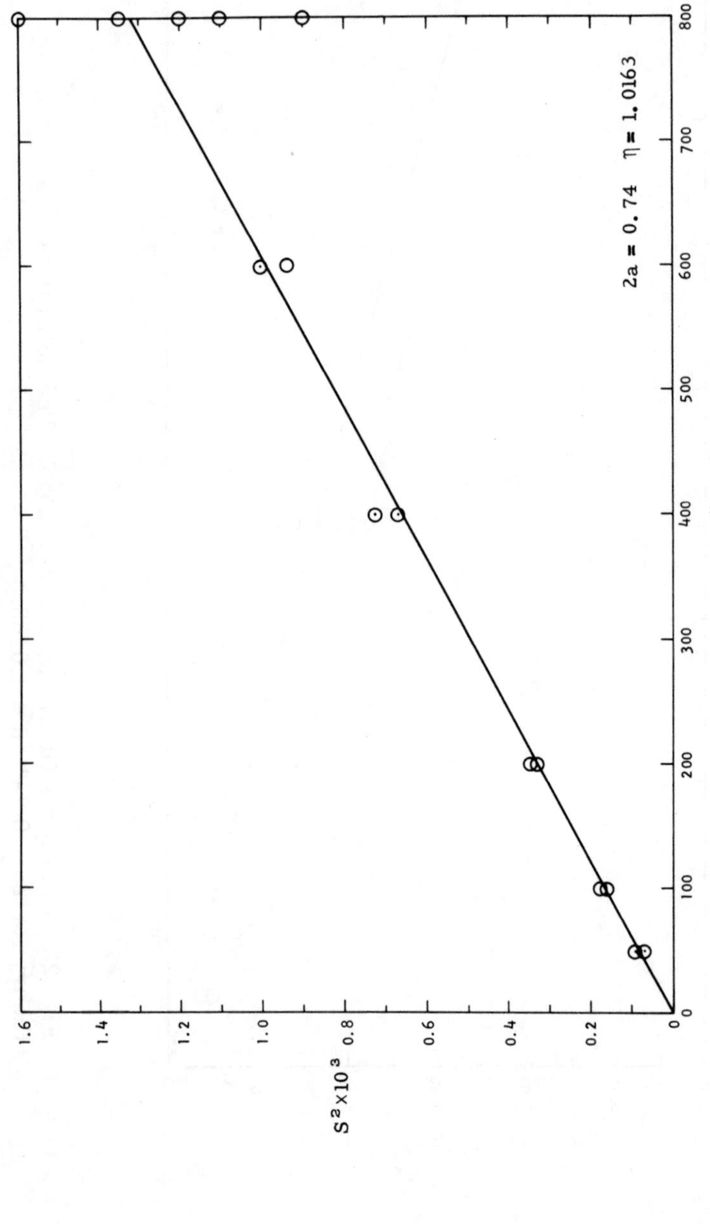
2a = 0.74 η = 1.0163
N
S²×10³
0
100
200
300
400
500
600
700
800
0.2
0.4
0.6
0.8
1.0
1.2
1.4
1.6

Fig. 25c

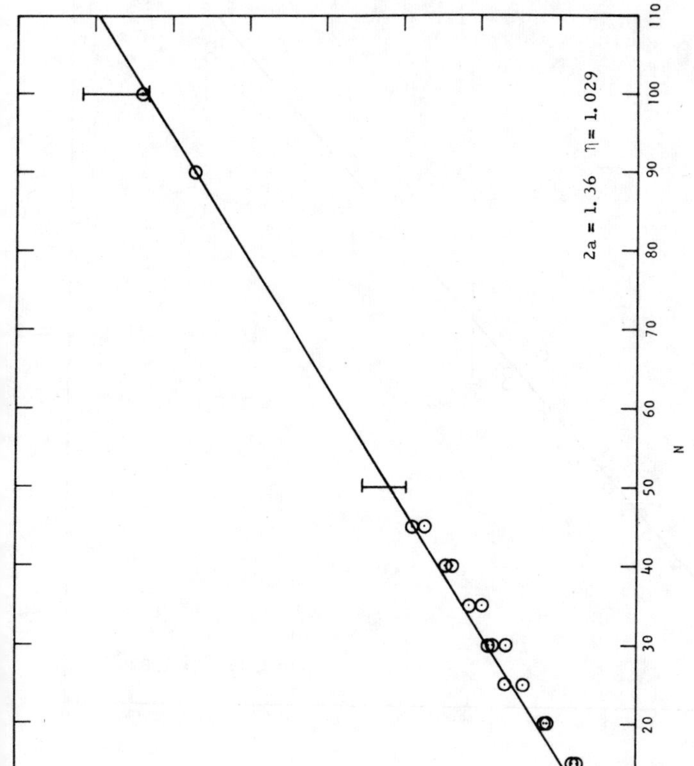

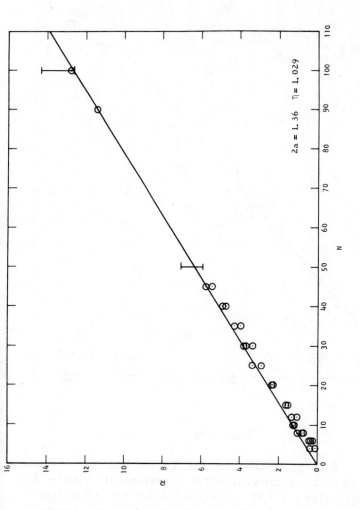

Fig. 26a

Fig. 26. Data for α (deg), β, S^2, versus N: The solid lines are theory for 2a = 1.36", η = 1.029.

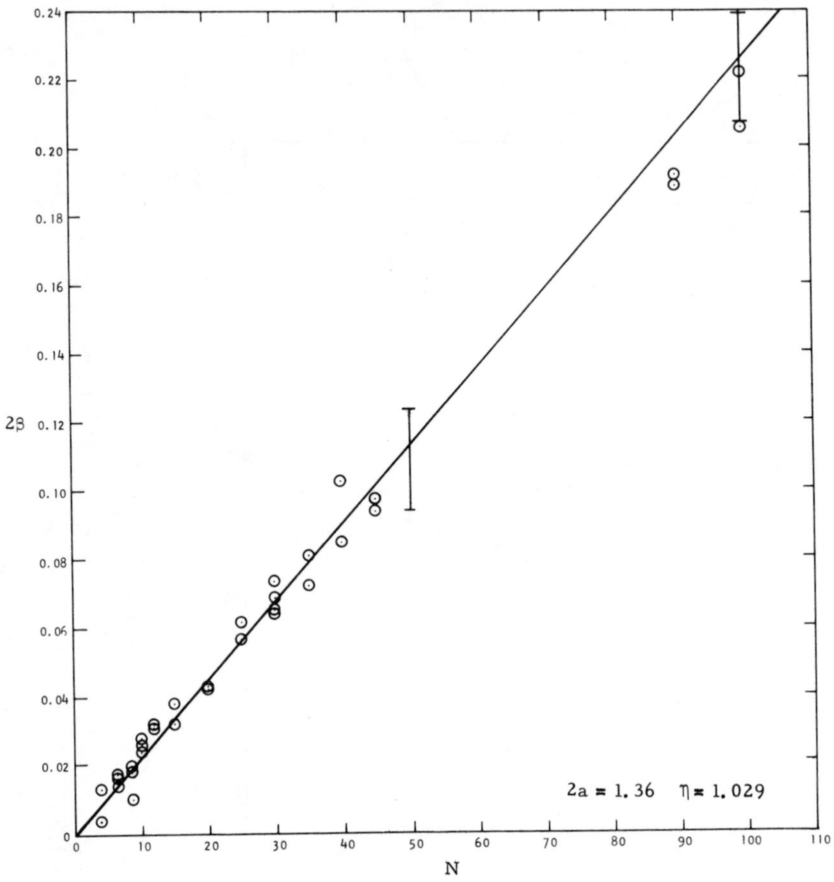

Fig. 26b

average $\gamma = 5.72°$; the base line for N = 100 has been lowered by 2.54% to obtain somewhat better agreement than gotten for the average value $\gamma = 5.72°$; for N = 100 the fitted baseline corresponds to $\gamma = 5.9°$. The amplitudes of the solid curves for $\langle x^3_\nu \rangle$ of Fig. 18 are the theoretical values based on (119) and (120) for the stated parameters. The curves have been shifted to the right (about 10° for N = 50, and about 5° for N = 100), the computed values are correspondingly

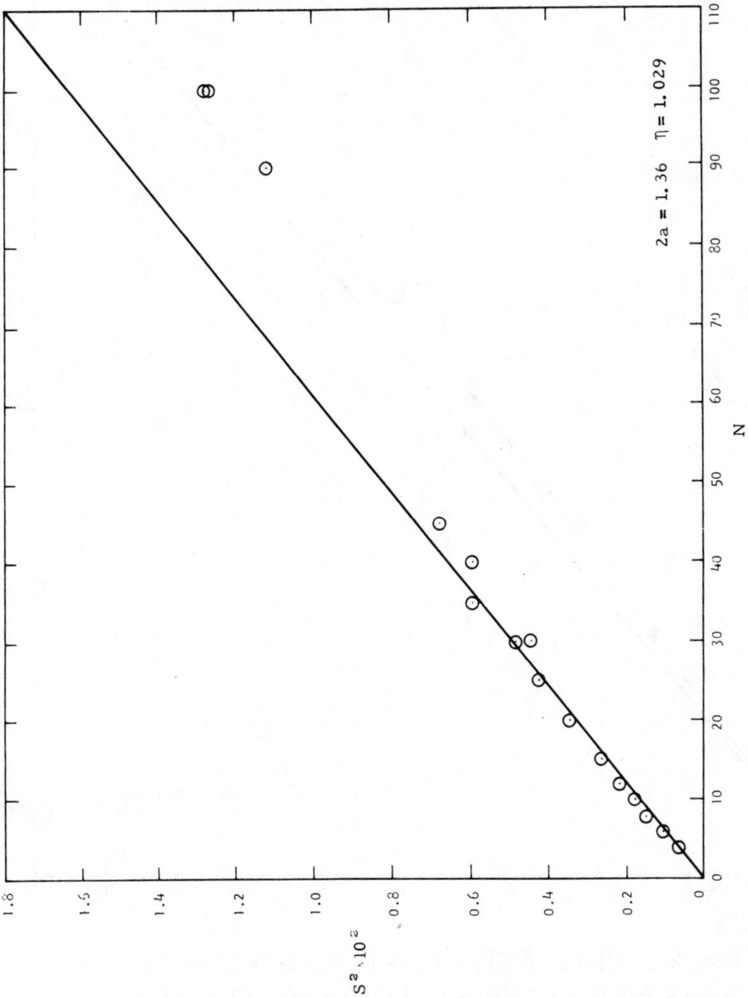
2a = 1.36 η = 1.029
N
0 10 20 30 40 50 60 70 80 90 100 110
0 0.2 0.4 0.6 0.8 1.0 1.2 1.4 1.6 1.8

Fig. 26c

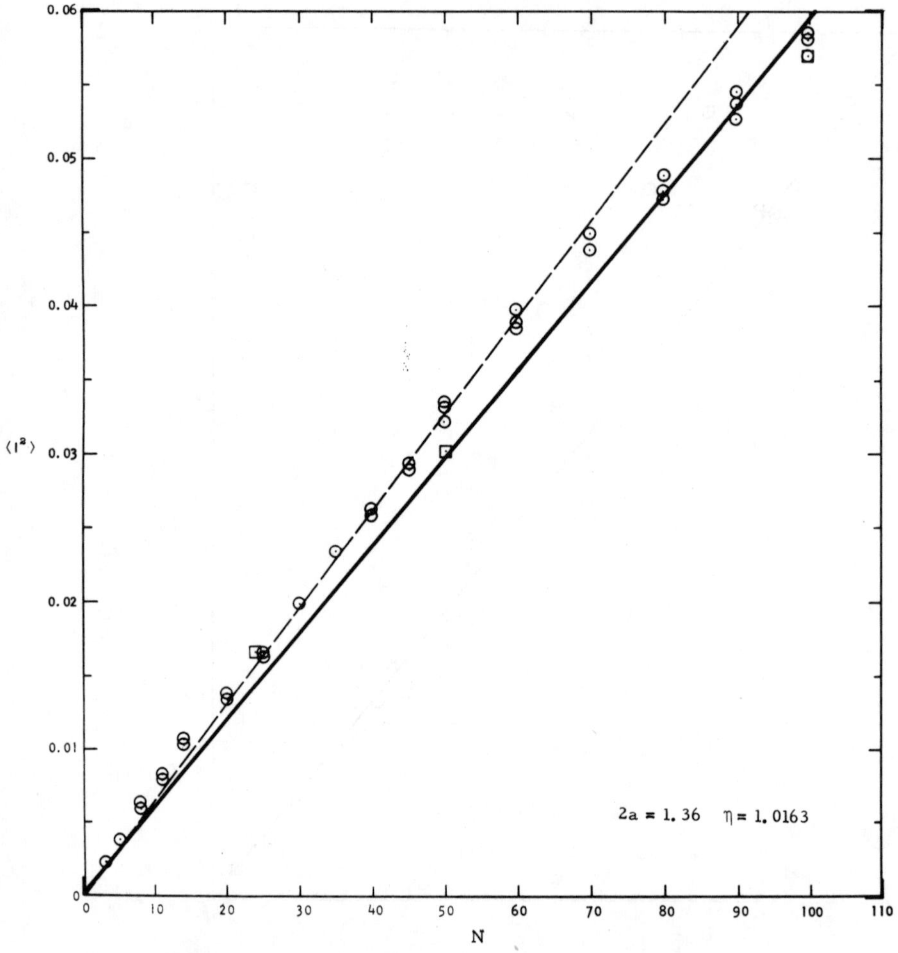

Fig. 27. Plots of $\langle I^2 \rangle$ versus N. Solid line is theory for parameters of Fig. 24 and horn angle $\gamma = 5.72°$. The dashed line is fitted for $N \leq 60$; discrepancies may arise from clumping.

higher than the fitted values of Φ obtained by the shift. Similarly for $\langle x_\nu^4 \rangle$ of Fig. 19 the amplitudes of the oscillating terms of (132) are the theoretical values for the stated parameters. The fitted base lines are lower than the theoretical values Q_{40} of (135) based on the average value $\gamma = 5.72°$ (used to compute Q^1_{40} by means of Fig. 22 and Q_{20} by means of Fig. 21); for N = 50 the fitted line is about 8% lower, and for N = 100, it is about 3% lower. The curves have been shifted to the left by about 8°, so that the computed values of Φ are correspondingly lower. From the shifted base-lines we obtain horn-angle factors γ for the integral in $Q^1_{40}(\gamma)$ that are about half the values obtained from $Q_{20}(\gamma)$; however, in view of the simplified forms of the integrals, it would be surprising if the accord were better. Thus the base-line fits determine essentially the appropriate γ's, and these should be the same for a given order of the moments. For the $\langle x_\nu^2 y_\nu^2 \rangle$ curves of Fig. 20 we used the same theoretical values and the same shifts as for $\langle x_\nu^4 \rangle$ of Fig. 19.

The discrepancies may be due to a neglected 'absorption coefficient' arising from fine-scale scattering (essentially dipole scattering) by the cellular styrofoam material. Such scattering effects would divert a small part of the incident energy omnidirectionally and could be accounted for by introducing ξ as in (106) into our computations; the effects on the amplitudes would be negligible, but the effects on the phases of the higher moments might account for the several degrees difference between measurements and computations based on uniform homogeneous spheres. In all cases the data records have been divided by the corresponding power of D, e.g., the $\langle x^4 \rangle$ data is normalized by D^4; thus a one-percent change in D shows up as a four-percent change in $\langle x^4 \rangle$, and this is a factor that limits the accuracy of the magnitudes of the higher moments.

Similar results for the smaller set of spheres with the same index as the above, and for the denser set of spheres with the same diameters as the above are given in Ref. 12.

ACKNOWLEDGEMENTS

The writer is very pleased to acknowledge the help he has received from his associates. The recent innovations in the millimeter wave facility described in Sec. II were made by T. H. Kays with

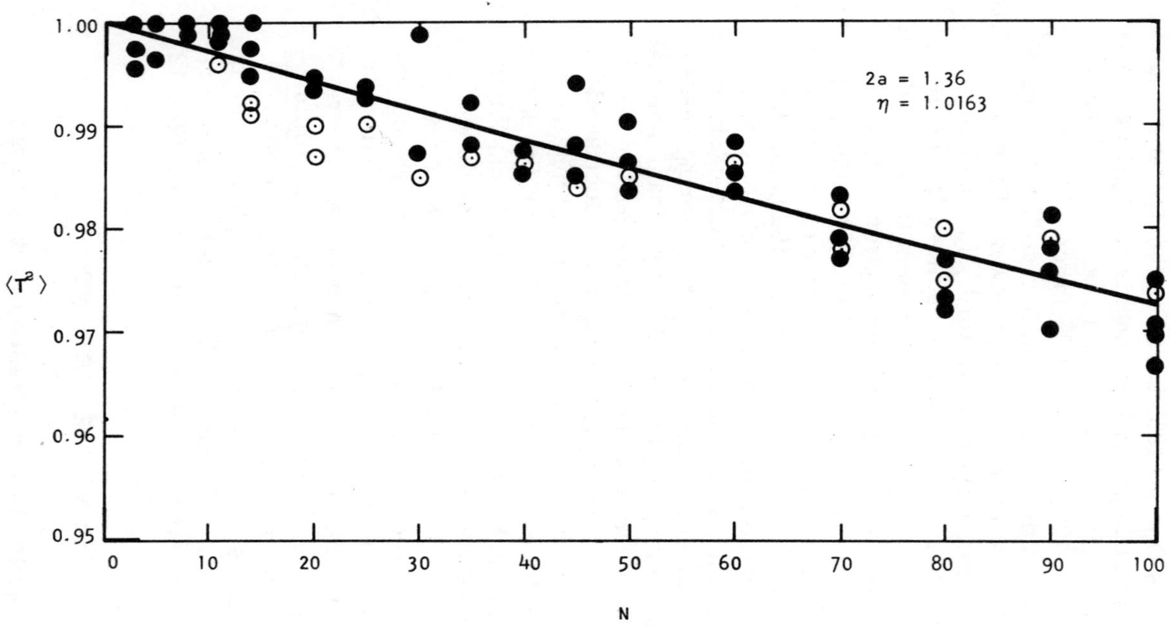

Fig. 28. Data for $\langle T^2 \rangle$ and theory for $C^2 + \langle I^2 \rangle$ based on parameters of Figs. 24 and 27. The empty circles are averages of T^2 with T obtained from the direct channel of Fig. 6; the solid circles are data for $e^{-2\beta} + \langle I^2 \rangle$ with 2β of Fig. 24 and $\langle I^2 \rangle$ of (27).

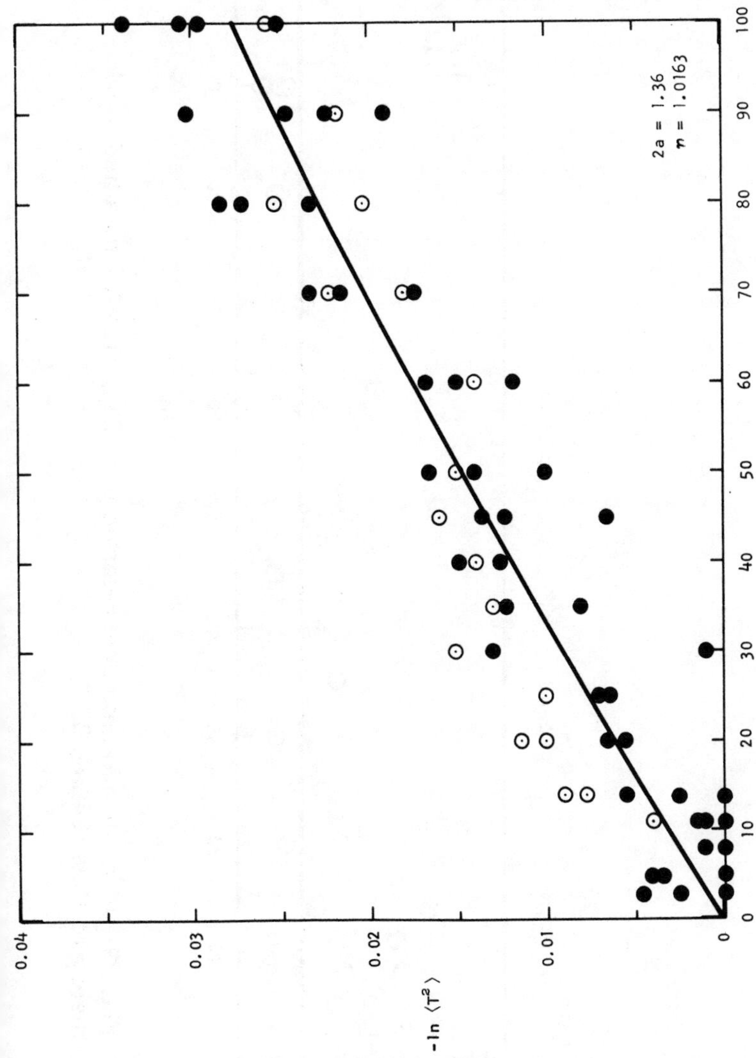
2a = 1.36
η = 1.0163
N
0
10
20
30
40
50
60
70
80
90
100
-ln ⟨T²⟩
0
0.01
0.02
0.03
0.04

Fig. 28b.

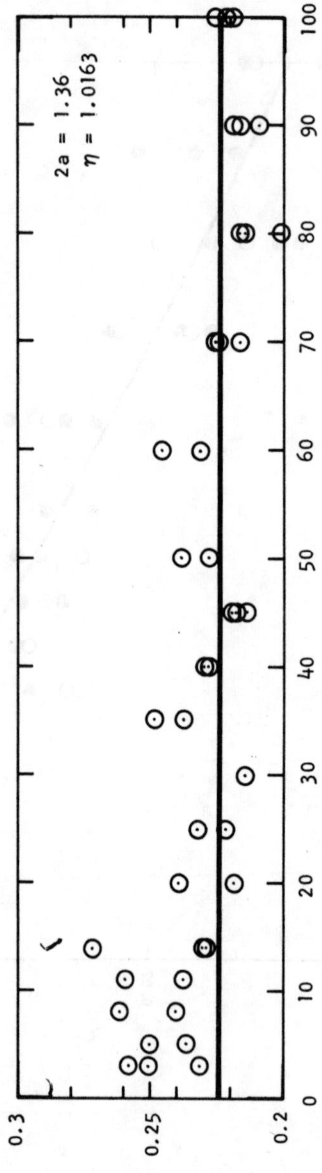

Fig. 29. Plots of maximum correlation $\mu_{\wedge} = 2S^2/\langle I^2 \rangle$ for data and theory of Figs. 24 and 27.

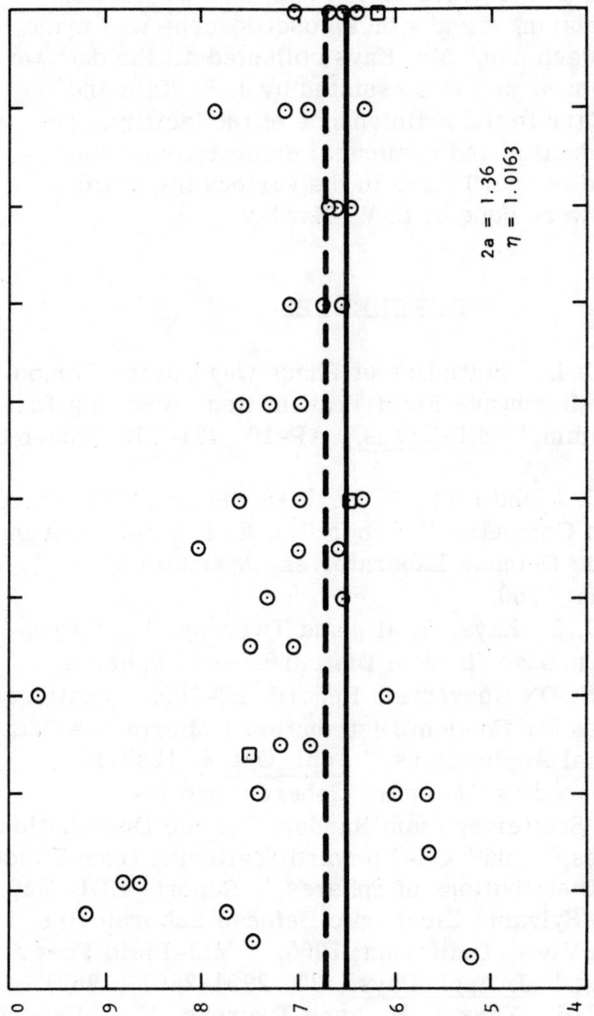

Fig. 30. Plot of $g(\gamma) = \langle I^2 \rangle/(1 - C^2)$ with data as in Figs. 24 and 27; solid line is theory for $\gamma = 5.72°$ and fitted dashed line corresponds to $\gamma = 5.92°$.

the aid of J. L. Kulp, and much of the original facility was developed by C. I. Beard who was a member of the group until 1962. The suggestion for displaying x and y on an oscilloscope was made by N. Blachman. Mr. Kays collected all the data we have shown, and was assisted by J. L. Kulp and J. M. Carr in the maintenance of the facility. The data reduction and numerical computations summarized in Sec. IV and in the various theoretical curves were done by S. W. Hawley.

REFERENCES

(1) Beard, C. I., "Statistics of Phase Quadrature Components of Microwave Field Transmitted Through a Random Medium," IRE Trans., **AP-10**, 721-731 (November, 1962).

(2) Beard, C. I. and Kulp, J. L., "An Electronic Standard Deviation Computer," Report No. EDL-M282, Sylvania Electronic Defense Laboratories, Mountain View, California; 1960.

(3) Beard, C. I., Kays, T. H., and Twersky, V., "Propagation Through Random Distributions of Spheres," 1958 WESCON Convention Record, 87-100. "Scattered Intensities for Random Distributions; Microwave Data and Optical Applications," Appl. Opt. **4**, 1299-1315 (1965); based on "Forward Coherent and Incoherent Scattering from Random Volume Distributions of Spheres," and "Off-Forward Scattering from Random Volume Distributions of Spheres," Reports EDL-E46 and E47, Sylvania Electronic Defense Laboratories, Mountain View, California; 1960. "Mid-Field Forward Scattering," J. Appl. Phys., **37**, 2851-2867 (1962).

(4) Beard, C. I., Kays T. H., and Twersky, V., "Experiment and Theory for Scattering by Random Distributions of Spheres versus Fractional Volume," Report No. EDL-E74, Sylvania Electronic Defense Laboratories, Mountain View, California; 1963. To appear in IEEE Trans **AP 15** (Jan. 1967).

(5) Beckmann, P., "The Probability Distribution of the Vector Series of n Unit Vectors with Arbitrary Phase

Distribution," Czechoslovak Academy of Sciences, Institute of Radio Engineers and Electronics, Prague, Report No. Z-29, 1958.

(6) Bremmer, H., "Propagation of Electromagnetic Waves," in Handbuch der Physik, Springer, Berlin, Germany, **16**, 432-639 (1958); see particularly 587-601.

(7) Foldy, L. L., "The Multiple Scattering of Waves," Phys. Rev. (2), **67** 107-119 (1945).

(8) Fox, A. G., "An Adjustable Waveguide Phase Changer," Proc. IRE, **35**, 1489-1498 (1947).

(9) Goldstein, H., in Kerr, D. E., Propagation of Short Radio Waves, MIT Radiation Laboratory Series, **13**, McGraw-Hill Book Co., New York, N. Y., 553-561 (1951).

(10) Hawley, S. W., Kays, T. H., and Twersky, V., "Fundamental Scattering Parameters Obtained from Low-N Data," Report No. EDL-M808, Sylvania Electronic Defense Laboratories, Mountain View, California; 1965.

(11) James, R. W., "The Optical Principles of the Diffraction of X-Rays" (G. Bell and Sons, Ltd., London, 1954), p. 474ff.

(12) Kays, T. H., and Twersky, V., "Theory and Experiment for Higher Moments of Fields Scattered by Random Distributions," Report No. EDL-M809, Sylvania Electronic Defense Laboratories, Mountain View, California; 1965.

(13) Lawson, J. L., and Uhlenbeck, G. E., Threshold Signals, MIT Radiation Laboratory Series, **24**, McGraw-Hill Book Co., New York, N. Y., Ch. 6 (1950).

(14) Lax, M., "Multiple Scattering of Waves," Rev. Mod. Phys., **23**, 287-310, (1951); "The Effective Field in Dense Systems," Phys. Rev. (2), **88**, 621-629 (1952).

(15) Rice, S. O., "The Mathematical Analysis of Noise," B.S.T.J., **23**, 282, (1944) and **24**, 46 (1945). See also Rice, "Statistical Properties of a Sine Wave Plus Random Noise," Bell Sys. Tech. J., **10**, 109-157, (January, 1948); "Distribution of the Duration of Fades in Radio Transmission," Bell Sys. Tech. J., **37**, 581-635 (May, 1958).

(16) Ring, D. H., "Millimeter Wave Research," Report No. 24261-15, Ch. 2, Bell Telephone Labs., N.Y., 1955.

(17) Saxon, D. D., "Lectures on the Scattering of Light," Scientific Report No. 9, University of California, Los Angles, Department of Meteorology (1955).

(18) Twersky, V., "On Scattering of Waves by Random Distributions. I. Free-Space Scatterer Formalism," J. Math. Phys. **3**, 700-715; (1962); "II. Two-Space Scatterer Formalism," J. Math. Phys., **3**, 724-734 (1962).

(19) Twersky, V., "Signals, Scatterers, and Statistics," IEEE Trans., **AP-11**, 668-690 (1963).

(20) Twersky, V., "Multiple Scattering of Waves in Dense Distributions of Large Tenuous Scatterers," Electromagnetic Scattering, edited by M. Kerker, 523-546, Pergamon Press, New York (1963).

(21) Twersky, V., "On Propagation in Random Media of Discrete Scatterers," Proc. Amer. Math. Soc. Symposium on Stochastic Processes in Mathematical Physics and Engineering, **16**, 84-166 (McGraw-Hill 1964).

(22) Twersky, "Multiple Scattering by Arbitrary Configurations in Three Dimensions," J. Math. Phys., **3**, 83-91 (1962); "Multiple Scattering of Electromagnetic Waves by Arbitrary Configurations," Report No. EDL-L30, Sylvania Electronic Defense Laboratories, Mountain View, California; 1965.

(23) van de Hulst, H. C., Light Scattering by Small Particles (John Wiley and Sons, Inc., New York, 1957) pp. 174 ff.

(24) Wheelon, A. D., "Radio Wave Scattering by Tropospheric Irregularities," J. Res. NBS, **63D**, 205-233 (1959).

(25) Yaw, D. F., "A K-Band Superheterodyne System Using a Rotating Phase Shifter," Report No. 444-19, Antenna Lab., Ohio State University Research Facilities, Columbus, Ohio. 1955.

DISCUSSION FOLLOWING PAPER BY V. TWERSKY

W. Egan: How did you obtain the polarization and phase in your analysis?

V. Twersky: In our microwave scattering range, we work with an incident **E** field perpendicular to the plane of the track (the floor is the **H** plane of the transmitter's rectangular horn), and we measure the polarization of the scattered field by rotating the rectangular receiving horn around its axis. However, the present scatterers are so very large compared to wavelength and their index of refraction is so close to unity, that we detect no cross polarization, i.e., the scattered fields have the same polarization as the incident. We picked such "easy scatterers" deliberately because we wanted to concentrate on the statistical aspects of the problem. For such scatterers most of the energy is scattered right around the forward direction (i.e., for ka = 20, more than 90 percent of the total scattering cross section is concentrated within a ten degree cone around the forward direction), so that we are not troubled by reflection into the transmitter horn, etc., and the entire analysis is relatively simple.

We obtain the phase of the instantaneous field because we measure the component (X) in phase with the direct signal in the absence of scatterers, as well as the component (Y) in phase quadrature with the direct field, i.e., the required instantaneous phase is arctan (Y/X). For the present statistical studies, we determine the time averages $<Y>$ and $<X>$ electronically and from these we obtain the coherent phase arctan ($<Y>/<X>$).

Multiple Scattering in Homogeneous Plane-Parallel Atmospheres*

T. W. Mullikin
Division of Mathematical Sciences, Purdue University,
Lafayette, Indiana

ABSTRACT

Steady state multiple scattering problems for homogeneous plane-parallel atmospheres have been extensively studied by means of the principles of invariance of Ambartsumian and Chandrasekhar. These nonlinear integral equations have been used for computing intensities of radiation on the faces of the atmosphere. Using linear integral equation theory, we show how to compute the source function interior to an atmosphere with optical depth entering the computation only parametrically. Intensities, throughout the atmosphere, are expressed by nonlinear combinations of the computed source function, giving, on the faces, the familiar scattering and transmission functions. By a reduction due to Sekera, this analysis is applied to Rayleigh polarization scattering.

*The research reported in this paper was sponsored in part by the United States Air Force under Project RAND - Contract No. 65-362.

I. INTRODUCTION

We consider that part of the theory of radiative transfer which is concerned with a plane-parallel atmosphere which scatters and absorbs radiation but does not re-emit absorbed radiation. We consider the multiple scattering problem in the steady state for monochromatic radiation. At least three stages are evident in the development of the mathematical theory of this subject.

The first stage deals with the formulation and study of linear equations [21, 22, 13, 9]. The equations are linear integrodifferential equations of Boltzmann type and linear integral equations of Fredholm type. The theory of the existence and uniqueness of solutions to these mathematical equations is thoroughly discussed in the book of Hopf [9].

The second stage deals with nonlinear integral and integrodifferential equations introduced by Ambartsumian [1] and extensively developed by him, by Chandrasekhar [6] and by Sobolev [25]. This work can be viewed as an attempt to translate existence and uniqueness results into feasible computational formulations. The derivations of these equations is often heuristic; use being made of certain principles of invariance.

The third stage is one in which a rigorous study is made of the connection between the linear and the nonlinear formulations. There is, for example, the work of Sobolev [25], Kourganoff [10] and Busbridge [2]. The Laplace transform provides the means for passing from linear to nonlinear equations. That this should be so is clear from the Wiener-Hopf method for solving the Milne problem for the semi-infinite atmosphere [5, 9].

In this third stage comes existence theorems [2] for the solutions to the nonlinear X and Y equations of Chandrasekhar. The uniqueness questions for these equations were not completely answered until recent years [14]. We show [14] that in most cases these equations are not a complete set which determine the desired functions, but that certain equations must be added, which had been overlooked in the heuristic derivations of the nonlinear equations. In the special case of conservative scattering, Chandrasekhar had recognized nonuniqueness of solutions [6, Chap. 8], but even in this case he only partially determined the multiplicity of solutions [17].

The purpose of the present paper is to report on the results obtained from a fruitful combination of the linear and nonlinear theories. This combination of the two methods gives a way of reducing the complexity of numerical computations for homogeneous atmospheres. Even for Rayleigh polarization scattering, we have a relatively simple computational procedure for computing Stokes parameters at any position within a finite or semi-finite atmosphere. These solutions are exact for any atmospheric thickness and yield asymptotic formulae for thick atmospheres.

This introduction should be read only as a brief outline of one aspect of the theory of radiative transfer and neutron transport. There is a vast amount of literature devoted to these subjects for which a partial bibliography is given in [20].

II. ISOTROPIC SCATTERING

We first illustrate various methods for the simple case of isotropic scattering in a finite homogeneous atmosphere. This will also serve as a vehicle for reporting on the stage of development of the program of study outlined in our presentation [16] at the first ICES at Potsdam, New York in 1962. We use isotropic scattering solely for simplicity of formulas, since everything we say has been extended to anisotropic scattering and to Rayleigh polarization scattering.

We begin with the steady state transfer equation in slab geometry

$$\mu \frac{\partial I}{\partial x}(x, \mu, \nu) + I(x, \mu, \nu) = J(x, \nu) \qquad (2.1)$$

for $-1 \leq \mu \leq 1$ and $0 \leq x \leq \tau$, where x measures optical depth in the atmosphere of thickness τ and μ is the cosine of an angle made with the x-axis. This is an equation for the intensity of diffuse radiation due to a steady flux of incident radiation on the face, $x = 0$, of the atmosphere from a direction ν. The boundary conditions are

$$I(0, \mu, \nu) = I(\tau, -\mu, \nu) = 0 \tag{2.2}$$

for $0 \leq \mu \leq 1$. The source function J is given by the sum of the reduced incident radiation field and of radiation scattered from other directions

$$J(x, \nu) = \frac{\omega}{2} \int_{-1}^{1} I(x, s, \nu)\, ds + \exp(-x/\nu) \tag{2.3}$$

The constant ω for radiation transfer satisfies $0 \leq \omega \leq 1$, and is the albedo of single scattering.

Now the function $I(x, \mu, \nu)$ is given in terms of the function J by integrating the ordinary differential equations (2.1) with boundary conditions (2.2) to obtain

$$I(x, \mu, \nu) = \frac{1}{\mu} \int_0^x J(y, \nu) \exp[(y - x)/\mu]dy, \tag{2.4}$$

$$I(x, -\mu, \nu) = \frac{1}{\mu} \int_x^\tau J(y, \nu) \exp[(x - y)/\mu]dy,$$

$$\text{for } 0 \leq \mu \leq 1.$$

Then from Eq. (2.3) we see that the function J satisfies the familiar integral equation [9]

$$J(x, \nu) = \exp(-x/\nu) + \Lambda(J)(x, \nu) \tag{2.5}$$

where

$$\Lambda(J)(x, \nu) \equiv \frac{\omega}{2} \int_0^1 \int_0^\tau \exp[-|x-y|/\mu]\, J(y, \nu)\, dy \frac{d\mu}{\mu}. \tag{2.6}$$

The equation for J has a unique bounded solution for $0 \leq \omega \leq 1$ and $0 \leq \tau \leq \infty$ [9]. This solution can be computed by iteration so that

$$J_{n+1} = \exp(-x/\nu) + \Lambda(J_n) \tag{2.7}$$

determines a sequence of functions which converges to the solution of equation (2.5). As a numerical procedure this gives $J(x, \mu)$ for each μ for a set of values x_i of x, $0 \leq x \leq \tau$ chosen in the numerical work. This method is not practical for ω near 1 and τ large. The rate of convergence is determined by the largest eigenvalue λ of the integral operator Λ. This is estimated very accurately by the following upper bound [15].

$$\lambda \leq \omega\left[1 - \cos^2 a + \tau/2\left(\ln \frac{\pi}{2a} + \int_{2a}^{\pi} \frac{\cos t}{t}\, dt\right)\right],$$

$$2a \tan a = \tau. \qquad (0 \leq 2a \leq \pi).$$

It should also be noted that a change of the parameter ν requires a complete new computation of the function J. It is desirable for some applications to have a computational procedure for computing $J(x, \nu)$ in which the variable x can be treated as a parameter. We shall give one such later.

Now for special values of x, namely $x = 0$ and $x = \tau$, there are the nonlinear equation of Ambartsumian and Chandrasekhar [1, 6]. We define scattering and transmission functions by

$$S(\mu, \nu) \equiv \mu I(0, -\mu, \nu),$$

$$T(\mu, \nu) \equiv \mu I(\tau, \mu, \nu), \quad (0 \leq \mu \leq 1). \tag{2.8}$$

Then it is easily shown [2, 6] that S and T are given by

$$S(\mu, \nu) = \frac{\mu\nu}{\mu + \nu}\left[X(\mu)\, X(\nu) - Y(\mu)\, Y(\nu)\right], \tag{2.9}$$

$$T(\mu, \nu) = \frac{\mu}{\mu - \nu}\left[Y(\mu)\, X(\nu) - X(\mu)\, Y(\nu)\right],$$

where X and Y are given in terms of the function J by [2]

$$X(\mu) \equiv J(0, \mu), \tag{2.10}$$

$$Y(\mu) \equiv J(\tau, \mu).$$

The functions X and Y, so defined, also can be shown to satisfy the following nonlinear integral equations [1, 2, 6]

$$X(\mu) = 1 + \frac{\mu\omega}{2} \int_0^1 \frac{X(\mu)X(\nu) - Y(\mu)\, Y(\nu)}{\mu + \nu}\, d\nu,$$

$$Y(\mu) = \exp(-\tau/\mu) + \frac{\mu\omega}{2} \int_0^1 \frac{Y(\mu)\, X(\nu) - X(\mu)\, Y(\nu)}{\mu - \nu}\, d\nu \tag{2.11}$$

These equations have been extensively used for computation by iteration [7, 29]. The above representation of the functions S and T is, of course, very desirable since it effectively separates the variables μ and ν.

We have shown [14] that the equations (2.11) never have a unique solution for isotropic scattering. For the special case $\omega = 1$, this is shown by Chandrasekhar [6, Chap. 8]. We give in [14] necessary and sufficient conditions on the characteristic function ψ for general X and Y equations to have a unique solution. Additional constraints must be added in case of nonuniqueness [16, 17]. For isotropic scattering these constraints are for $\omega < 1$, given by

$$2/\omega = \int_0^1 \frac{X(\nu)\, d\nu}{1 \pm k\nu} + \exp(\pm k\tau) \int_0^1 \frac{Y(\nu)\, d\nu}{1 \mp k\nu} \tag{2.12}$$

for k the root of the equation

$$2k = \omega \ln \frac{1 + k}{1 - k} \qquad (0 \leq k \leq 1).$$

For $\omega = 1$ they are given by

$$1 = \frac{1}{2} \int_0^1 [X(\nu) + Y(\nu)]\, d\nu, \tag{2.13}$$

$$\tau \int_0^1 Y(\nu)\, d\nu = \int_0^1 [X(\nu) - Y(\nu)]\, \nu\, d\nu. \tag{2.13}$$

These constraints serve to determine arbitrary constants in the representation [17] of all solutions to the equations (2.11).

We have also treated the general scalar transfer equations for anisotropic scattering in three papers [11, 18, 19]. We have shown that Chandrasekhar's ψ_l and ϕ_l equations often have a multiplicity of solutions [19]. Correct constraints have been given in cases of nonuniqueness. In addition, we have derived singular linear integral equations for anisotropic scattering analogous to those given in following sections III and IV for isotropic scattering [18, See also 1 and 25].

III. X AND Y FUNCTIONS

We outlined in our 1962 ICES paper an alternative procedure to both of the above computational methods. The theoretical work has been completed [17] and an operational computer program now exists at the RAND Corporation, Santa Monica, California for computing X and Y functions for any characteristic function and any optical thickness. This work is summarized in a paper [4] in the Astrophysical Journal Supplement Series, which also contains tables of X and Y functions for the case of isotropic scattering.

Our method extends some work of Sobolev [24, 25] and Busbridge [3] in the application of singular integral equation theory to the following equations [2]

$$\lambda(\mu)\, X(\mu) = 1 - \frac{\mu\omega}{2} \int_0^1 \frac{X(\nu)}{\mu - \nu}\, d\nu - \frac{\mu\omega}{2} \exp(-\tau/\mu) \int_0^1 \frac{Y(\nu)}{\mu + \nu}\, d\nu$$

$$\lambda(\mu)\, Y(\mu) = \exp(-\tau/\mu)\left[1 - \frac{\mu\omega}{2} \int_0^1 \frac{X(\nu)}{\mu + \nu}\, d\nu\right] - \frac{\mu\omega}{2} \int_0^1 \frac{Y(\nu)}{\mu - \nu}\, d\nu \tag{3.1}$$

The function λ is given by

$$\lambda(\mu) = 1 - \omega\mu^2 \int_0^1 \frac{d\nu}{\mu^2 - \nu^2} . \tag{3.2}$$

All singular integrals are computed as Cauchy principal values. These equations can be obtained from the nonlinear X and Y equations [2] or, in more general form, from the integral Eq. (2.5). We will return to this in the next section and show the connection with the Wiener-Hopf method for solving semi-infinite problems.

We simply give the final form of the solution to the Eq. (3.1) and constraints (2.12). We first take the case $\tau = \infty$ where $Y \equiv 0$ and X is customarily denoted by H. We have

$$H(\mu) = \frac{1+\mu}{1+k\mu} \exp\left[\mu \int_0^1 \frac{\theta(t)}{t(t+\mu)} dt\right] \tag{3.3}$$

where the function θ is given by

$$\theta(\mu) = \frac{1}{\pi} \tan^{-1}\left[\frac{\pi\mu}{2 + \mu\omega \ln \frac{1-\mu}{1+\mu}}\right] \quad (0 \leq \theta \leq 1).$$

The constant k satisfies the familiar equation [5]

$$2k = \omega \ln \frac{1+k}{1-k} \qquad (0 \leq k \leq 1), \tag{3.4}$$

and its values are given in Table 1 [See also [5]].

This representation of the H function is obviously equivalent to the solution obtained from Eq. (2.5) by Wiener-Hopf method of Fourier transforms [2, 5, 9, 25]. The advantage of this form of the solution over that given by Sobolev [25], say, is that our representation, obtained

Table 1

ω	k	-B	C exp $(k\tau)$
.3	.997414	76.6795	.528923
.4	.985624	19.6089	.537221
.5	.957504	8.51623	.539418
.6	.907332	4.63077	.532150
.7	.828635	2.76239	.511143
.8	.710412	1.65677	.468454
.9	.525430	.877357	.382675
.95	.379485	.528204	.299425
.99	.172511	.197025	.153812
1.00	.000000		

from such a representation by analytic continuation methods, does not contain any Cauchy principle value integrals; all integrals are simple quadratures. This makes computation extremely simple.

This method of solution gives results for finite τ as corrections to the solution for $\tau = \infty$. We have the result [4, 17]

$$X(\mu) = H(\mu)\left[1 + f(\mu) + \frac{k^2\mu(f(\mu) - f(1/k))}{\sqrt{1-\omega}\,N(1/k)(1 - k\mu)} + \frac{\mu\omega}{2}\int_0^1 \frac{f(t) - f(\mu)}{H(t)\Delta(t)(t-\mu)}\,dt\right] \tag{3.5}$$

and a similar expression for $Y(\mu)$ containing a function $g(\mu)$ in place of $f(\mu)$. The functions f and g satisfy certain integral equations. We do not give the details here but refer to our papers [4, 17].

One can ask whether the mathematical gymnastics required to go from the integral Eq. (2.5) or Eqs. (2.11) to another set of equations for the functions f and g is worth the effort. For three reasons this seems worthwhile. Most important is the fact that the integral equations for f and g can be solved by iteration with rapid convergence, since the convergence is geometric with ratio less than $\exp(-\tau)$

[17]. The kernel function is a positive continuous function, which is nice as compared with the kernel of the operator in equation (2.5), which has a logarithmic singularity along the diagonal. Finally, the above computation is for a range of values of μ with x as a parameter; the reverse of the situation in equation (2.5).

The rapid convergence of the equations for the functions f and g also provides a means for obtaining very good asymptotic formulae [4] for X and Y functions for large values of τ. For conservative scattering ($\omega = 1$) we get

$$X(\mu) = H(\mu)\left[1 - \frac{\mu}{\tau + A}\right] + 0(\tau e^{-\tau}) \qquad (3.6)$$

$$Y(\mu) = \frac{\mu H(\mu)}{\tau + A} + 0(\tau e^{-\tau}),$$

where

$$A = 2\left(1 - \int_0^1 \theta(t)\, dt\right) \qquad (3.7)$$

$$= 1.42089$$

Sobolev [26, 27] has obtained similar results as well as van de Hulst [30]. At $\tau = 3.5$ and $\mu = 1$ error terms in the above are 0.002 and 0.012 respectively. In [4] we give a more accurate, but more complicated asymptotic form, in which errors are less than 10^{-6} for $\tau = 3.5$.

For nonconservative scattering the results are more complicated since they change in character from $1/\tau$ to $\exp(-k\tau)$. The simplest such estimates are

$$X(\mu) = H(\mu) + \frac{2k\mu C[k^2\mu(1-\omega)^{-1/2}\exp(-\tau/\mu) - C(1+k\mu)H(\mu)]}{[B^2 - C^2][1 - (k\mu)^2]}$$

$$Y(\mu) = \frac{C}{B}[X(\mu) - H(\mu)]$$

$$+ \frac{k\mu[k(1-\omega)^{-1/2}\exp(-\tau/\mu) - 2CH(\mu)]}{B(1 - k\mu)} \qquad (3.8)$$

where

$$B = - \frac{k}{1 - k} \exp \left[k \int_0^1 \frac{\theta(t)}{1 - kt} dt \right]$$

$$C = \frac{k}{1 + k} \exp \left[-k\tau - k \int_0^1 \frac{\theta(t)}{1 + kt} dt \right] \qquad (3.9)$$

Values of B and C $\exp(k\tau)$ are given in Table 1. Less complete results are given by Sobolev [28] which are poor when k is near 1.

More accurate asymptotic formulas are given in [4] where we have computed, for isotropic scattering, exact X and Y values for τ ranging from 0 to the value at which differences from the asymptotic formulas is less than 10^{-6}.

IV. INTERIOR COMPUTATIONS

All of the results about singular integral equations for X and Y functions can be obtained in an easier and more direct manner from the Eq. (2.5). At the same time this can be generalized to give computations interior to the atmosphere.

We take Eq. (2.5) and apply the integral operator Λ to both sides. When $\Lambda(\exp(-x/\mu)$ is computed, we obtain an integral equation for the function $\Lambda(J)$ whose solution can be expressed in terms of integrals on the function J. We simply give the result and refer to our papers for details [20]. When $\Lambda(J)$, so expressed, is combined with equation (2.5), we see that the unique solution J to the Eq. (2.5) also satisfies the equation

$$\lambda(\mu)\, J(x, \mu) = \exp(-x/\mu) - \frac{\mu\omega}{2} \int_0^1 \frac{J(x, t)}{\mu - t} dt$$

$$- \frac{\mu\,\omega}{2} \exp(-\tau/\mu) \int_0^1 \frac{J(\tau - x, t)}{\mu + t} dt, \qquad (4.1)$$

and a similar one with x replaced by τ - x.

Since the function J is analytic in the complex variable μ for $|\mu| > 0$ [2], we obtain in addition to the above equations the two constraints, for $\omega < 1$,

$$\exp(\pm kx) = \frac{\omega}{2}\int_0^1 \frac{J(x,t)}{1 \pm kt}dt + \frac{\omega}{2}\exp(\pm k\tau)\int_0^1 \frac{J(\tau - x, t)}{1 \mp kt} \tag{4.2}$$

For $\omega = 1$ there are constraints analogous to (2.13).

The study of this system of singular integral equations differs from that for the X and Y equations only in the fact that x is now a free parameter rather than being fixed at x = 0 and x = τ. The X and Y equations (3.1) are the special case of the above equation for x = 0 and x = τ.

Any computer program for X and Y function can be trivially modified to compute $J(x, \mu)$ and $J(\tau - x, \mu)$ for any x, $0 \leq x \leq \tau$ and any μ, $|\mu| > 0$. We obtain results similar to those for X and Y functions: for $\omega < 1$

$$J(x, \mu) = H(\mu)\Big[F(x, \mu) + \frac{k^2\mu}{\sqrt{1-\omega}\,B}\;\frac{F(x,\mu) - F(x, 1/k)}{1 - k\mu} \tag{4.3}$$

$$+ \frac{\mu\omega}{2}\int_0^1 \frac{F(x,t) - F(x,\mu)}{H(t)\,\Delta(t)\,(t-\mu)}\,dt\Big].$$

The function F is determined [4] from rapidly convergent iteration of a linear Fredholm equation which differs from that for the function f of last section by containing the terms $\exp(-x/\mu)$ in place of 1 and $\exp(-(\tau - x)/\mu)$ in place of $\exp(-\tau/\mu)$.

With this reduction of the computation of the J function, it is possible to give a representation of the Green's functions for homogeneous plane-parallel and spherical atmospheres [12, 27, 28]. For simplicity we give only the result for $\omega < 1$. For the plane parallel atmosphere

$$R(x, y) = \frac{k\omega(1-k^2)\exp[-k|x-y|]}{\omega - 1 + k^2} + \frac{1}{2}\,\frac{\exp[-|x-y|/t]}{\Delta(t)}\,\frac{dt}{t}$$

$$- R_0(x, y) - R_0(\tau - x, \tau - y),$$

where

$$R_o(x, y) = \frac{1}{2}\int_0^1 J(x,t)\left[\frac{k(1-k^2)}{\omega - 1 + k^2} \quad \frac{\exp(-ky)}{1+kt} + \frac{1}{2}\int_0^1 \frac{\exp(-y/s)}{\Delta(s)(s+t)}\,ds\right] dt,$$

and

$$\Delta(s) = \left[1 - \frac{\omega s}{2}\ \ln\frac{1+s}{1-s}\right]^2 + \left[\frac{\pi\,\omega s}{2}\right]^2.$$

For the sphere of radius $\tau/2$ we have, for $0 \le x,\ y \le \tau/2$, the Green's function for the sphere expressed in terms of that for the slab by

$$R_s(x, y) = \frac{y}{x}\left[R(x + \tau/2,\ y + \tau/2) - R(x + \tau/2,\ \tau/2 - y)\right]$$

As an application, we find that the flux due to a point source of unit strength at the origin of a sphere of radius $\tau/2$ for $\omega = 1$, say, is given by

$$\rho(x) = \frac{1}{2\pi x}\left\{\frac{3}{4} + \frac{1}{2}\int_0^1 \frac{\exp(-x/t)}{\Delta(t)}\frac{dt}{t^2} + \frac{1}{2}\int_0^1 \left[J(x+\tau/2,\ t) - J(\tau/2 - x,\ t)\right] \left[\frac{3}{4} + \frac{1}{2}\int_0^1 \frac{\exp(-\tau/2s)}{\Delta(s)\ (s+t)}\ \frac{ds}{s}\right] dt\right\}.$$

We can also directly use the results for the source

function J for the purpose of computing intensities $I(x, \mu, \nu)$ interior to the atmosphere. The main point to be observed in the discussion below is the fact that in the final result the variable x enters solely as a parameter. Thus, computations of interior intensities can be done utilizing the dependence of functions on variations of angular variables rather than on variations of the position variable. This is in the spirit of the principles of invariance [1, 6]. However, we do not simply state these principles, which are in themselves expressed as integral equations, but we give results which are in effect the solutions of these integral equations.

A formal statement of the result is this. The intensities are given for $0 \leq \mu \leq 1$ by

$$\mu I(x, \mu, \nu) = U[J(\tau - x)](\mu)\, T(\mu, \nu) - \frac{\mu\nu}{\mu - \nu}[J(x, \nu) - J(x, \mu)\{[1 - U(X)(\mu)]X(\nu) + U(Y)(\mu)\, Y(\nu)\}]$$

and (4.4)

$$\mu I(x, -\mu, \nu) = U[J(x)](\mu)\, S(\mu, \nu) + \frac{\mu\nu}{\mu+\nu}[J(x, \nu) - J(\tau - x, \mu)\{U(Y)(\mu)X(\nu) + [1 - U(X)(\mu)]\, Y(\nu)\}.] ,$$

where we have introduced the notation, for brevity,

$$U(J(x)(\mu) \equiv \frac{\mu\omega}{2}\int_0^1 \frac{J(x, t)}{\mu + t}\, dt.$$

$$V(J(x)(\mu) \equiv \frac{\mu\omega}{2}\int_0^1 \frac{J(x, t)}{\mu - t}\, dt. \tag{4.5}$$

A proof of this is based on a use of the following well-known result [2, p. 91]

$$\frac{\partial J}{\partial x}(x, \nu) + \frac{1}{\nu} J(x, \nu) = X(\nu) \frac{\omega}{2} \int_0^1 J(x, t) \frac{dt}{t}$$

$$- Y(\nu) \frac{\omega}{2} \int_0^1 J(\tau - x, t) \frac{dt}{t} . \tag{4.6}$$

We change x to y, multiply by exp $[-(\tau - x - y)/\mu]$ and integrate on y over $0 \leq y \leq \tau - x$ to obtain

$$J(\tau - x, \nu) - X(\nu) \exp[-(\tau - x)/\mu] + \frac{\mu - \nu}{\mu\nu} \mu I(\tau - x, \mu, \nu) =$$

$$B(x, \mu) X(\nu) - A(x, \mu) Y(\nu) \tag{4.7}$$

The functions A and B are defined by

$$A(x, \mu) = \frac{\omega}{2} \int_0^1 \mu I(x, -\mu, t) \frac{dt}{t} ,$$

$$B(x, \mu) = \frac{\omega}{2} \int_0^1 \mu I(\tau - x, \mu, t) \frac{dt}{t} . \tag{4.8}$$

If we change x to y in Eq. (4.6) multiply by $\exp[-(y-x)/\mu]$ and integrate on y over $x \leq y \leq \tau$ we find

$$Y(\nu) \exp[-(\tau - x)/\mu] - J(x, \nu) + \frac{\mu + \nu}{\mu\nu} \mu I(x, -\mu, \nu) =$$

$$A(x, \mu) X(\nu) - B(x, \mu) Y(\nu). \tag{4.9}$$

We have simultaneous equations for A and B which we proceed to solve. The functions $I(x, \pm\mu, \nu)$ are defined for complex values of μ by (2.4).

We now fix the variables x and μ. For the moment we assume that μ is outside the interval $[-1, 1]$. We multiply Eq. (4.9) by $(\mu\omega)/[2(\mu + \nu)]$ and equation (4.7) by

$(\mu\omega)/[2(\mu-\nu)]$, change ν to t and integrate on t over $0 \leq t \leq 1$. We obtain successively the equations

$$A[1 - U(X)] + BU(Y) = U(J(x)) - U(Y) \exp[-(\tau - x)/\mu]$$

$$A\, V(Y) + B\,[1 - V(X)] = V(X) \exp[-(\tau - x)/\mu] - V(J(\tau - x))$$

This system of linear algebraic equations for A and B has a determinant which satisfies the known identity [2]

$$\lambda \equiv [1 - U(X)]\,[1 - V(X)] - U(Y)\, V(Y)$$

We omit the details of the calculation, but making use of this identity, of Eqs. (3.1) and Eqs. (4.1), written for x and τ - x, we obtain the solution for A and B in the form obviously valid for any value of μ outside the interval [-1, 0]

$$A = U(J(x))X - J(\tau - x)\; U(Y)$$

$$B = U(J(x))\,Y + J(\tau - x)\;[1-U(X)] - \exp[-(\tau - x)/\mu].$$

When these expressions are substituted into Eqs. (4.7) and (4.9) we obtain Eqs. (4.4).

V. RAYLEIGH POLARIZATION SCATTERING

The mathematical model for polarization scattering introduced by Chandrasekhar [6] is a vector integro-differential equation for the four Stokes parameters. The basic ideas presented in previous sections for isotropic scalar transfer equations carry over to this problem [31]. The primary difficulty is in the profusion of details rather than in any requirement of new ideas.

The difficult part of the analysis of the transfer equation for Stokes parameters is in dealing with the azimuth independent terms. We discuss this briefly. By making use of a matrix factorization first observed by Sekera [23], we can reduce the problem for the azimuth independent terms to a study of the matrix equation for a 2 x 2 source matrix $\mathbf{J}$

$$\mathbf{J} = \mathbf{I} \exp(-x/\nu) + \Lambda(\mathbf{J}) \quad , \tag{5.1}$$

where $\mathbf{I}$ is the 2 x 2 identity matrix and the operator Λ is defined by

$$\Lambda(\mathbf{J})\ (x) = \int_0^1 \psi(\mu) \int_0^\tau \mathbf{J}(y) \exp[-|x-y|/\mu]\, dy \frac{d\mu}{\mu} \tag{5.2}$$

The matrix ψ is given by

$$\psi(\mu) = \frac{3}{8} \begin{pmatrix} 1+\mu^4 & 2\mu^2(1-\mu^2) \\ \mu^2(1-\mu^2) & 2(1-\mu^2)^2 \end{pmatrix} \tag{5.3}$$

This is the analogue of equation (2.5).

One can show that this matrix equation can be solved by iteration. This computational procedure has been used for this equation recently [8]. It becomes difficult for large values of τ. In analogy with Eq. (4.1) we can also show that

$$\mathbf{J}(x, \mu)\ \lambda(\mu) = \mathbf{I} \exp(-x/\mu) - \mu \int_0^1 \frac{\mathbf{J}(x, t)\, \psi(t)}{\mu - t}\, dt$$

$$- \mu \exp(-\tau/\mu) \int_0^1 \frac{\mathbf{J}(\tau - x, t)\, \psi(t)}{\mu + t}\, dt, \tag{5.3}$$

with

$$\lambda(\mu) = \mathbf{I} - 2\mu^2 \int_0^1 \frac{\psi(t)\, dt}{\mu^2 - t^2} \ . \tag{5.4}$$

We obtain constraints

$$\begin{pmatrix}2\\1\end{pmatrix} = \frac{3}{4}\int_0^1 [\mathbf{J}(x, t) + \mathbf{J}(\tau - x, t)]\begin{pmatrix}1 + t^2\\ 1 - t^2\end{pmatrix} dt, \tag{5.5}$$

$$\left(\frac{\tau}{2} - x\right)\begin{pmatrix}2\\1\end{pmatrix} = \frac{3}{4}\int_0^1 (t + \tau/2)\,[\mathbf{J}(x, t) - \mathbf{J}(\tau - x, t)]\begin{pmatrix}1 + t^2\\ 1 - t^2\end{pmatrix} dt.$$

The solution to equations for Rayleigh polarization scattering can be expressed in terms of solutions to scalar equations.

$$\lambda^i(\mu) J^{i)}(x, \mu) = \exp(-x/\mu) - \mu\int_0^1 \frac{J^i(x, t)\psi^i(t)\,dt}{\mu - t}$$

$$- \mu\exp(-\tau/\mu)\int_0^1 \frac{J^i(\tau - x, t)\,\psi^i(t)\,dt}{\mu + t}$$

$i = 1, 2, 3, 4, 5,$ where

$$\psi^1 = \frac{3}{8}(1 - \mu^2)(1 + 2\mu^2) \qquad \psi^4 = \frac{3}{8}(1 - \mu^2)$$

$$\psi^2 = \frac{3}{16}(1 + \mu^2)^2 \qquad \psi^5 = \frac{3}{4}(1 - \mu^2) \tag{5.7}$$

$$\psi^3 = \frac{3}{4}\mu^2$$

The computation of solutions to the scalar equations follows the method outlined for isotropic scattering. Except for the characteristic function $\psi^{(4)}$ (ψ_r in Chandrasekhar's notation [6]), additional constraints have to be added to the above equations, namely for $i = 1, 2, 3$

$$\exp(\pm k_i x) = \int_0^1 \frac{J^i(x, t)\,\psi^i(t)\,dt}{1 \pm k_i t}$$

$$+ \exp \pm k_i \tau)\int_0^1 \frac{J^i(\tau - x, t)}{1 \mp k_i t}\,dt$$

where

$$1 = 2 \int_0^1 \frac{\psi^{(i)}(t)\, dt}{1 - (k_i\ t)^2}$$

For the special value x = 0, these constraints were omitted by Chandrasekhar [6, Chap. 10] in his reduction of Rayleigh polarization scattering and transmission matrices to X and Y functions. They are required for the nonlinear X and Y equations also to specify the uniquely desired solution.

For the special case of characteristic function $\psi^{(5)}$ (ψ_l in Chandrasekhar's notation) we express solutions in terms of functions which are analytic in μ for $|\mu| > 0$. These solutions are obtained by adding the constraints

$$1 = \int_0^1 [J_o^{(5)}(x, \mu) + J_o^{(5)}(\tau - x, \mu)]\, \psi^{(5)}(\mu)\, d\mu$$

$$\tau/2 - x = \int_0^1 (\tau/2 + \mu)\, [J_o^{(5)}(x, \mu) - J_o^{(5)}(\tau - x, \mu]\, \psi^{(5)}(\mu)\, d\mu.$$

The general solution then to Eq. (5.6) for i = 5 is

$$J^{(5)}(x, \mu) = J_o^{(5)}(x, \mu) + a(x)\mu\, [X^{(5)}(\mu) + Y^{(5)}(\mu)]$$

$$+ b(x)\mu\, [\gamma(X^5(\mu) - Y^{(5)}(\mu)) + \mu(X^{(5)}(\mu) + Y^{(5)}(\mu))]$$

where γ is a ratio of certain moments of the $X^{(5)}$ and $Y^{(5)}$ functions [17]. The arbitrary functions a(x) and b(x) are eventually evaluated by means of the constraints (5.5).

In the special case of x = 0, Chandrasekhar [6, Chap. 8] selects standard solutions to the X and Y equations for i = 5 by adding the constraints

$$1 = \int_0^1 \psi^{(5)}(\mu)\, [X^*(\mu) \pm Y^*(\mu)]\, d\mu$$

His standard solutions X* and Y* are related to our $X^{(5)}$

and $Y^{(5)}$ functions by

$$X^*(\mu) = X^{(5)}\mu + \frac{\mu}{2\gamma}[X^{(5)}(\mu) + Y^{(5)}(\mu)]$$

$$Y^*(\mu) = Y^{(5)}(\mu) - \frac{\mu}{2\gamma}[X^{(5)}(\mu) + Y^{(5)}(\mu)].$$

The entire computation of source matrices is reduced then to the computing of solutions to scalar equations and to the computation of various moments of these solutions. In all of these computations the optical depth can be considered as a mere parameter.

To obtain Stokes parameters interior to an atmosphere we need the analogue of Eq. (4.4). Since we are dealing with matrices, the derivation of this result is a little more subtle than that given for scalar equations. We have obtained results which we give here for the azimuth independent terms only. Expressions for Stokes parameters interior to an atmosphere follow from formulas which are obtained from Eqs. (4.4), if the scalar functions there are replaced by 2 x 2 matrices with the order of matrix products correctly indicated in Eq. (4.4). The operators U and V of (4.5) are replaced by matrix integral operators with the matrix ψ of Eq. (5.3) replacing the constant $\omega/2$ but written to the right of the matrix $\mathbf{J}$. The scalar functions X and Y are replaced by matrices defined by

$$\mathbf{X}(\mu) \equiv \mathbf{J}(0, \mu),$$

$$\mathbf{Y}(\mu) \equiv \mathbf{J}(\tau, \mu).$$

The scalar functions S and T are replaced by matrices

$$\mathbf{S}(\mu, \nu) = \frac{\mu\nu}{\mu+\nu}\Pi[\mathbf{X}^t(\mu)\Pi^{-1}\mathbf{X}(\nu) - \mathbf{Y}^t(\mu)\Pi^{-1}\mathbf{Y}(\nu)]$$

$$\mathbf{T}(\mu, \nu) = \frac{\mu\nu}{\mu-\nu}\Pi[\mathbf{Y}^t(\mu)\Pi^{-1}\mathbf{X}(\nu) - \mathbf{X}^t(\mu)\Pi^{-1}\mathbf{Y}(\nu)],$$

where

$$\Pi = \begin{pmatrix} 2 & 0 \\ 0 & 1 \end{pmatrix} ,$$

and the superscript "t" denotes matrix transposition. For the special values of x, x = 0 and x = τ, our representation for Stokes parameters interior to an atmosphere can be shown to reduce to that given by Chandrasekhar [6, Chap. 10] for scattering and transmission matrices.

Thus the Stokes' parameters for Rayleigh polarization can be computed for any position within an atmosphere by simple extension of the existing computer program for scalar equations. This is similar in spirit to Chandrasekhar's reduction for scattering and transmission matrices, but by the use of linear equations for the source matrices we have been able to do interior computations as easily as those on the bounding faces. With the recent results of Sekera [24] concerning the matrix factorizations of general phase matrices, the same procedure can be applied to other types of polarization scattering, not just the Rayleigh. As is well-known, however, the number of scalar equations and the complexity of algebraic manipulations increase rapidly as the number of terms in the expansion of the phase matrix increases.

REFERENCES

(1) Ambartsumian, V. A., Theoretical Astrophysics, Pergamon Press, London, 1958 (Gosudarstv. Izdat. Tehn.-Teor. Lit., Moscow, 1952.)

(2) Busbridge, I. W., The Mathematics of Radiative Transfer, Cambridge Tracts, No. **50** (1960).

(3) ______, Astrophys. J., **122**, 327-348 (1955).

(4) Carlstedt, J. L., Mullikin, T. W., Chandrasekhar's X- and Y-Functions, Astrophys. J. Suppl., XII, No. **113**, 449 - 585 (1966).

(5) Case, K. M., DeHoffman, F. Placzek, G., Introduction to the Theory of Neutron Diffusion, Vol. I, U. S. Government Printing Office (1953).

(6) Chandrasekhar, S., Radiative Transfer, Dover, New York, 1960 (Oxford University Press, 1950).
(7) Chandrasekhar, S., Elbert, D., Astrophys. J., **115**, 244-278 (1952).
(8) Dave, J. V., Journal of Atmospheric Sciences (to appear).
(9) Hopf, E., Mathematical Problems of Radiative Equilibrium, Cambridge Tracts, No. **31** (1934).
(10) Kourganoff, V., Basic Methods in Transfer Problems, Oxford, 1952.
(11) Leonard, A., Mullikin, T. W., J. Math. Phys. **5**, 399-411 (1964).
(12) ______, Proc, Nat. Acad. Sci. USA, **52**, 683-688 (1964).
(13) Milne, E. A., Monthly Notices Royal Astron. Soc., **81**, 361 (1921).
(14) Mullikin, T. W., Astrophys. J., **136**, 627-635 (1962).
(15) ______, J. of Math. Anal. and Appl., **5**, 184-199 (1962).
(16) ______, "Uniqueness Problems in the Mathematics of of Multiple Scattering," Proceedings of Interdisciplinary Conference on Electromagnetic Scattering, Pergamon Press, 1963.
(17) ______, Trans. Amer. Math. Soc., **113**, 316-332 (1964).
(18) ______, Astrophys. J., **139**, 379-396 (1964).
(19) ______, Astrophys. J., **139**, 1267-1289 (1964).
(20) ______, "Non linear Integral Equations of Radiative Transfer," Nonlinear Integral Equations, University of Wisconsin Press, 1964.
(21) Schuster, A., Astrophys. J., **21**, 1 (1905).
(22) Schwarzschild, K., Gottinger Nachr. **41** (1906).
(23) Sekera, Z., Radiative Transfer in a Planetary Atmosphere with Imperfect Scattering, The RAND Corporation, R-413-PR (1963).
(24) ______, "Reduction of Equations of Radiative Transfer in a Planetary Plane-parallel Atmosphere," The RAND Corp., RM-4951-PR and RM-5056-PR (1966).
(25) Sobolev, V. V., A Treatise on Radiative Transfer, Van Nostrand, Princeton, 1963 (Moscow, 1956).

(26) ______, Astron. Zh. **34**, 336-348 (1957).
(27) ______, Dokl. Akad. Nauk SSSR, **11**, 39-50 (1958).
(28) ______, Dokl. Akad. Nauk SSSR, **155**, 316-320 (1964).
(29) Sobouti, Y., Astrophys. J. Suppl. 7, **72**, 411 (1963).
(30) van de Hulst, H. C., Icarus, **3**, 336-341 (1964).
(31) Mullikin, T. N., Astrophys. J., 145, 886-931 (1966).

DISCUSSION FOLLOWING PAPER BY T. W. MULLIKIN

W. M. Irvine: For large (and fixed) τ is it possible to obtain simple expressions for the quantities of interest as a function of ω (perhaps in the limit of $(1 - \omega) \ll 1$) ?

T. Mullikin: The given asymptotic formulas are relatively simple expressions. They contain, however, various transcendental functions of ω which do not seem to have good approximations which can be simply expressed as functions of ω, e.g. the function θ.

J. B. Keller: Your asymptotic expansion for large τ is not uniform at $\omega = 1$. You should be able to find an expansion near $\omega = 1$ which is uniform.

T. Mullikin: This should be possible, but I have not done it. The data on values of τ at which the asymptotic formulas are accurate to 10^{-6} (presented in the talk, but deleted from the text) are taken from numerical computations using more accurate, but more complicated, asymptotic formulas. The formulas given may be uniform, but I have not checked this.

Exact Analytical Solution and Numerical Treatment of Transport Problems in the Case of an Arbitrary Anisotropic Scattering Law

F. R. Vanmassenhove
and
C. C. Grosjean
Computing Laboratory, University of Ghent,
Ghent, Belgium

ABSTRACT

The rigorous mathematical expression for the steady-state density of particles emitted by an isotropic point source and undergoing multiple scattering in an infinitely extended homogeneous medium is re-examined in full detail in the case of a general anisotropic single scattering law with rotational symmetry around the direction of incidence. The phase function is represented by an arbitrarily large sum of Legendre polynomials. It is shown how the particle density first described by a Fourier integral can be transformed by suitable integration in the complex plane into a sum of elementary functions representing the asymptotic density and various possible transient contributions to the density, and an integral representing the transient part of shortest range.

The integrand of the latter part can be enormously simplified on account of a remarkable proof. As a by-product of this proof, it becomes clear that the various determinantal functions and equations entering the practical calculation of the particle density can all be reduced to a small set of basic functions which can be rigorously generated by means of very simple recurrence formulas. As a consequence, even on a medium-size electronic computer, it becomes possible to treat multiple scattering problems in which the single scattering law involves several tens of Legendre polynomials in its expansion. This limit can be pushed to a much higher number if a large-size computer is available. A few typical examples are discussed to some extent and illustrated by means of graphical representations. The paper ends with the consideration of the exact particle density around a plane source of uniform strength in an infinitely extended homogeneous medium. In this problem, the same simplifications as in the point source case can still be carried out. The most relevant formulas are derived and briefly discussed.

I. INTRODUCTION

It is a well-known fact that Legendre polynomials and spherical harmonics are endowed with a multitude of properties which make them particularly suitable for the rigorous probabilistic treatment of three-dimensional multiple scattering problems. Indeed, in the idealized situations of certain standard transport problems, these functions have made it possible to obtain exact integral representations of the particle density and current throughout space, in the case of a completely arbitrary single scattering law with rotational symmetry around the direction of incidence. (See, e.g., Grosjean, 3). However, because of the appearance of heavy mathematical expressions such as, for example, high order determinants whose elements are themselves complicated functions of the integration variable, it looks at first sight that, in actual density and current computations, one can only make use of such general solutions in cases where the single scattering law can be represented by a sum of very few Legendre polynomials. For this reason, it has often been said that a multiple scattering formalism based on a spherical harmonics expansion of the phase function is of purely theoretical rather than practical interest. Well, contrary to this opinion, we shall show in the present article that, after a few remarkable mathematical transformations of the results to which it gives rise, such a formalism can ultimately lead to simple iterative calculating schemes permitting the practical solution of transport problems in which the representation of the scattering law requires a large number of Legendre polynomials. The standard problems which we have selected for this purpose, consist in calculating the steady-state scalar particle density around an isotropic point source and an isotropic plane source of uniform strength situated in an infinitely extended homogeneous medium.* The applicability of our final results will be illustrated by means of a few typical examples in which the particle density will be plotted as a function of distance in the case of various single scattering laws of a certain type with gradually increasing anisotropy. Phase functions corresponding to pronounced forward as well as backward anisotropic scattering will be considered and in the cases which come closest to purely forward or purely backward scattering, no less than 44 Legendre polynomials (i.e., from P_0 to P_{43}) are needed in

---

* The reason that we limit ourselves to studying only the scalar density in the present paper is simply limitation of space. As will be shown in a more extensive publication, the particle current and, if necessary, other contributions of higher order to the angular density can be subjected to transformations which are entirely similar to those which we shall apply to the scalar density.

the expansion of the scattering law in order to represent it with sufficient accuracy. The limitation to a maximum of 44 Legendre polynomials in our examples of practical application stems from the fact that, at the moment of the calculations, we had only a computer of intermediate size at our disposition, namely, an IBM 1620 data processing system with standard core memory of 20,000 decimal positions. With a large and high-speed computer at hand, our new algorithms would permit the satisfactory treatment of problems in which the accurate description of the phase function requires several hundreds of Legendre polynomials.

II. EXACT STEADY-STATE PARTICLE DENSITY AROUND AN ISOTROPIC POINT SOURCE IN AN INFINITELY EXTENDED HOMOGENEOUS MEDIUM IN THE CASE OF AN ARBITRARY, AZIMUTH-INDEPENDENT ANISOTROPIC SCATTERING LAW (One-velocity Theory)

Let S_0 be the total strength of an isotropic point source of particles undergoing multiple scattering in a uniform infinite medium. Due to the spherical symmetry of the problem, the particle distribution will solely depend upon the distance coordinate r measured from the source as fixed origin. By v, we symbolize the velocity of the particles which we assume to remain unaltered by the scattering collisions. Further, let ω represent the average number of secondaries emitted after a collision. As the scattering medium is infinitely extended, a finite steady-state particle density distribution will establish itself around the point source only in all nonmultiplicative cases. Therefore, in what follows, we shall assume

$$0 \leqslant \omega \leqslant 1.$$

By λ, we characterize the total mean free path of the particles so that

$$\exp\left(-\frac{l}{\lambda}\right)\frac{dl}{\lambda} \qquad (l \geqslant 0) \qquad (1)$$

describes the elementary probability distribution of the true path lengths l. As for the single scattering law, it is usually denoted by

$$f(\boldsymbol{\Omega}' \rightarrow \boldsymbol{\Omega})d\Omega \qquad (2)$$

representing the elementary probability that a secondary will be moving within the elementary solid angle $d\Omega$ around $\boldsymbol{\Omega}$ after a collision of a primary travelling in the direction $\boldsymbol{\Omega}'$. As we assume that the scattering possesses axial symmetry around the direction of incidence, the probability density in (2) depends only upon the angle of scattering given by

$$\gamma = \arccos(\boldsymbol{\Omega}' \cdot \boldsymbol{\Omega})$$

and its spherical harmonics expansion involves solely Legendre polynomials. Calling N the degree of the highest order Legendre polynomial in this expansion, we have:

$$f(\boldsymbol{\Omega}' \rightarrow \boldsymbol{\Omega})d\Omega = \left[1 + \sum_{n=1}^{N} A_n P_n(\cos\gamma)\right]\frac{d\Omega}{4\pi} \qquad (3)$$

$$(A_N \neq 0)$$

where

$$A_n = (2n+1)\langle P_n(\cos\gamma)\rangle_{av.}$$

$$= (2n+1)\iint f(\boldsymbol{\Omega}' \rightarrow \boldsymbol{\Omega}) P_n(\cos \boldsymbol{\Omega}' \cdot \boldsymbol{\Omega})d\Omega. \qquad (4)$$

That the isotropic contribution to $f(\boldsymbol{\Omega}' \rightarrow \boldsymbol{\Omega})$ is always described by 1 between the square brackets follows from the normalization condition of the elementary probability (2):

$$\iint f(\Omega' \to \Omega)\,d\Omega = 1.$$

As for N, it can theoretically be infinite, but in practical calculations, it will generally be given a finite positive integer value taken sufficiently large to ensure an accurate or even the exact description of the anisotropic single scattering event. In the case of isotropic scattering, evidently $N=0$ corresponding to the disappearance of the sum in (3).

The rigorous probabilistic treatment of the multiple scattering problem under study, as it was described in detail by Grosjean in his 1951 monograph (see also: Grosjean, 4) and briefly recalled in a later publication (Grosjean, 5), leads to the following expression for the scalar particle density:

$$\rho(r) = \frac{S_0\, e^{-\frac{r}{\lambda}}}{4\pi v r^2} + \frac{S_0\,\omega}{2\pi^2 \lambda v r}\int_0^\infty u\,\frac{G_N(\omega,u)}{\Delta_N(\omega,u)}\,\sin\frac{r}{\lambda}u\,du \qquad (5)$$

where $\Delta_N(\omega,u)$ and $G_N(\omega,u)$ are shorthand notations for the following determinantal functions:

$$\Delta_N(\omega,u) = \begin{vmatrix} 1-\omega F_{00}(u) & -\omega A_1 F_{01}(u) & \dots & -\omega A_N F_{0N}(u) \\ -\omega F_{10}(u) & 1-\omega A_1 F_{11}(u) & \dots & -\omega A_N F_{1N}(u) \\ \vdots & \vdots & \ddots & \vdots \\ -\omega F_{N0}(u) & -\omega A_1 F_{N1}(u) & \dots & 1-\omega A_N F_{NN}(u) \end{vmatrix} \qquad (6)$$

$$G_N(\omega,u) = \begin{vmatrix} F_{00}^2(u) & -A_1 F_{01}(u) & \dots & -A_N F_{0N}(u) \\ [1+\omega F_{00}(u)]F_{10}(u) & 1-\omega A_1 F_{11}(u) & \dots & -\omega A_N F_{1N}(u) \\ \vdots & \vdots & \ddots & \vdots \\ [1+\omega F_{00}(u)]F_{N0}(u) & -\omega A_1 F_{N1}(u) & \dots & 1-\omega A_N F_{NN}(u) \end{vmatrix} \qquad (7)$$

The F-functions are defined by

$$F_{km}(u) = \int_0^\infty e^{-z}\left[i^m P_m\left(\frac{d}{iudz}\right) j_k(uz)\right] dz$$
$$= \frac{i^{m-k}}{2}\int_{-1}^{1} \frac{P_k(\mu)P_m(\mu)}{1-iu\mu}\, d\mu \tag{8}$$

in which

$$j_k(x) = \left(\frac{\pi}{2x}\right)^{\frac{1}{2}} J_{k+\frac{1}{2}}(x)$$

and $i^m P_m(d/iudz)$ is a real differential operator acting on $j_k(uz)$. They can be calculated explicitly in terms of the Legendre functions of the second kind, but their expressions become lengthy and complicated as k and m increase. Hence, for large N, Δ_N and G_N are indeed extremely voluminous mathematical objects and our main task consists in bringing them in a more tractable form.

In (5), the "direct beam" and the "multiple scattering" contributions to $\rho(r)$ are clearly separated so that

$$\rho(r) = \rho_d(r) + \rho_s(r). \tag{9}$$

In the extreme case of pure absorption ($\omega = 0$), multiple scattering does not take place and $\rho(r)$ simply reduces to $\rho_d(r)$. Hence, from here on, we may without limitation consider $0 < \omega \leqslant 1$. To start the simplification of (5), it is particularly convenient to represent $\rho_d(r)$ formally as a Fourier integral and to add it to $\rho_s(r)$. This transformation gives rise to a new integral form of $\rho(r)$ which is oscillatory divergent from the strict mathematical point of view so that it represents $\rho(r)$ only in the sense of Cesàro summability. This oscillatory divergence is entirely similar to that occurring in the isotropic case (Case *et al*, 1, p. 71 and p. 169) and is completely unimportant. There comes:

$$\rho(r) = \frac{S_0}{2\pi^2 \lambda v r}\int_0^\infty u\,\frac{g_N(\omega,u)}{\Delta_N(\omega,u)}\,\sin\frac{r}{\lambda}u\, du \tag{10}$$

where

$$g_N(\omega,u) = F_{00}(u)\Delta_N(\omega,u) + \omega G_N(\omega,u)$$

$$= \begin{vmatrix} F_{00}(u) & -\omega A_1 F_{01}(u) & \dots & -\omega A_N F_{0N}(u) \\ F_{10}(u) & 1-\omega A_1 F_{11}(u) & \dots & -\omega A_N F_{1N}(u) \\ \vdots & \vdots & \ddots & \vdots \\ F_{N0}(u) & -\omega A_1 F_{N1}(u) & \dots & 1-\omega A_N F_{NN}(u) \end{vmatrix} . \quad (11)$$

Studying the F-functions in detail by means of the last integral representation in (8), one discovers that they are endowed with interesting properties among which there are recurrence relations showing a marked similarity to those satisfied by the Legendre polynomials. For instance, one finds :

$$\left.\begin{aligned} & F_{km}(0) = \frac{\delta_{km}}{2k+1}, \quad F_{mk}(u) = (-1)^{k-m} F_{km}(u) = F_{km}(-u) \\ & F_{km}(u) = \frac{2m-1}{mu} F_{k,m-1}(u) + \frac{m-1}{m} F_{k,m-2}(u) - \frac{\delta_{k,m-1}}{mu} \\ & F_{km}(u) = -\frac{2k-1}{ku} F_{k-1,m}(u) + \frac{k-1}{k} F_{k-2,m}(u) + \frac{\delta_{k-1,m}}{ku} \\ & F_{k0}(u) = \frac{1}{\mathrm{i}^{k+1} u} Q_k\left(\frac{1}{\mathrm{i}u}\right), \quad F_{0m}(u) = \frac{1}{\mathrm{i}^{m-1} u} Q_m\left(\frac{\mathrm{i}}{u}\right) \end{aligned}\right\} (12)$$

in which δ_{km} is the usual Kronecker symbol and Q_k represents Legendre's function of the second kind and order k. Making use of one of these equalities each time after a clever combination of three consecutive rows in the determinants (6) and (11), proceeding from the bottom to the top row, and carrying out a few other operations, we have succeeded in proving that $\Delta_N(\omega,u)$ and $g_N(\omega,u)$ can be rewritten in the following form :

$$\Delta_N(\omega,u) =$$

$$\begin{vmatrix} 1+\frac{\omega}{iu}Q_0\left(\frac{i}{u}\right) & \frac{\omega A_1}{(iu)^2}Q_1\left(\frac{i}{u}\right) & \frac{\omega A_2}{(iu)^3}Q_2\left(\frac{i}{u}\right) & \frac{\omega A_3}{(iu)^4}Q_3\left(\frac{i}{u}\right) & \cdots & \frac{\omega A_N}{(iu)^{N+1}}Q_N\left(\frac{i}{u}\right) \\ 1-\omega & 1 & 0 & 0 & \cdots & 0 \\ -\frac{1}{2}u^2 & \frac{1}{2}(3-\omega A_1) & 1 & 0 & \cdots & 0 \\ 0 & -\frac{2}{3}u^2 & \frac{1}{3}(5-\omega A_2) & 1 & \cdots & 0 \\ \vdots & \vdots & \vdots & \vdots & \ddots & \vdots \\ 0 & 0 & 0 & 0 & \cdots & 1 \end{vmatrix} \tag{13}$$

and

$$g_N(\omega,u) =$$

$$\begin{vmatrix} -\frac{1}{iu}Q_0\left(\frac{i}{u}\right) & \frac{\omega A_1}{(iu)^2}Q_1\left(\frac{i}{u}\right) & \frac{\omega A_2}{(iu)^3}Q_2\left(\frac{i}{u}\right) & \frac{\omega A_3}{(iu)^4}Q_3\left(\frac{i}{u}\right) & \cdots & \frac{\omega A_N}{(iu)^{N+1}}Q_N\left(\frac{i}{u}\right) \\ 1 & 1 & 0 & 0 & \cdots & 0 \\ 0 & \frac{1}{2}(3-\omega A_1) & 1 & 0 & \cdots & 0 \\ 0 & -\frac{2}{3}u^2 & \frac{1}{3}(5-\omega A_2) & 1 & \cdots & 0 \\ \vdots & \vdots & \vdots & \vdots & \ddots & \vdots \\ 0 & 0 & 0 & 0 & \cdots & 1 \end{vmatrix}. \tag{14}$$

Compared to (6) and (11), these new determinantal expressions imply a tremendous simplification in the representation of the functions Δ_N and g_N. The method by which we have accomplished this simplification is described in full detail in a previous paper (Grosjean, 5, pp. 32-36).

III. TRANSFORMATION OF THE FOURIER INTEGRAL REPRESENTATION OF THE SCALAR DENSITY BY CONTOUR INTEGRATION IN THE COMPLEX PLANE

Precisely as in the case of isotropic scattering (Cfr. : Case *et al*, 1, pp. 167-170), it is advisable to carry out a further transformation of $\rho(r)$ by means of an appropriate contour integration in the complex u-plane. The main reason is that, due to the oscillatory nature of the sine function which entails a great deal of mutual cancellations, a Fourier integral is not very suitable for accurate numerical calculations.

From (13) and (14), it easily follows that Δ_N and g_N are even functions of u so that

$$u\frac{g_N(\omega,u)}{\Delta_N(\omega,u)} \tag{15}$$

is an odd function of the same variable. Replacing $\sin(ru/\lambda)$ by its exponential form, this permits us to rewrite (10) as a complex Fourier integral:

$$\rho(r) = \frac{S_0}{4\pi^2 i\lambda v r}\int_{-\infty}^{+\infty} u_1\frac{g_N(\omega,u_1)}{\Delta_N(\omega,u_1)}\exp(i\frac{r}{\lambda}u_1)du_1 \tag{16}$$

where the variable of integration u_1 will now be regarded as the real part of the complex variable

$$u = u_1 + iu_2 .$$

The purpose of the contour integration in the u-plane is to carry the integration along the real u_1-axis over into an integration along the imaginary u_2-axis permitting us to find the various exponential-type contributions to $\rho(r)$. In this context, it is essential to study the general behavior of (15) in the complex u-plane.

From (6) and (11), it is clear that $\Delta_N(\omega,u)$ and $g_N(\omega,u)$ are both expressible as algebraic sums of products of a finite number of F-functions. As all these functions can be developed in Maclaurin series, this is also the case for Δ_N and g_N. Further, considering that

$$\frac{1}{i^{k+1}u} Q_k\left(\frac{i}{u}\right) = -\frac{1}{i^k}\left[P_k\left(\frac{i}{u}\right)\frac{\operatorname{arctg} u}{u} - \frac{i}{u} W_{k-1}\left(\frac{i}{u}\right)\right]$$
$$(k = 0, 1, 2, \ldots)$$

where W_{k-1} represents a polynomial of degree $(k-1)$ (with $W_{-1} \equiv 0$), one deduces from (13) and (14) that (15) is of the form

$$u \frac{f_1'\left(\frac{1}{u^2}\right)\frac{\operatorname{arctg} u}{u} + f_2'\left(\frac{1}{u^2}\right)}{f_1\left(\frac{1}{u^2}\right)\frac{\operatorname{arctg} u}{u} + f_2\left(\frac{1}{u^2}\right)}$$

where f_1, f_2, f_1' and f_2' are four polynomials in $1/u^2$. Thus, the behavior of (15) is largely dictated by that of the arctangent function: the ratio has branch points at $u = \pm i$ and it is single-valued in the u-plane cut by branch cuts from $+i$ to $+i\infty$ and from $-i$ to $-i\infty$ along the u_2-axis. In addition to this, the integrand in (16) is an analytic function throughout the complex plane except in all points of the branch cuts and at its poles which appear to arise from the zeros of $\Delta_N(\omega, u)$. On physical grounds as well as on account of further mathematical considerations, we can state that, for $0 < \omega < 1$, all the roots of $\Delta_N(\omega, u) = 0$ are single and situated in the interval $(-i, +i)$ (endpoints included) on the imaginary u_2-axis. As $\Delta_N(\omega, u)$ is even with respect to u, these roots come in conjugate pairs (see also: Davison, 2, p. 242). For any physically acceptable single scattering law of the type (3) (by this, we mean that the A_n-coefficients are such that the probability density $f(\Omega' \to \Omega)$ to which they correspond is non-negative for all possible scattering angles $(0 \leqslant \gamma \leqslant \pi)$), we know that if we let ω vary from 0 toward 1, there is always a pair of conjugate imaginary zeros of $\Delta_N(\omega, u)$ which arise at $-i$ and $+i$, respectively, and move toward each other. At $\omega = 1$, they join at the origin $u = 0$. In an earlier paper (Grosjean, 5), we have rigorously proved, for $0 < \omega < 1$, that in the case of a physically acceptable scattering law of the type (3) with $N = 1$ or $N = 2$, this pair of zeros is the only one that can exist. In contrast, as soon as N is larger than 2, additional pairs of conjugate imaginary roots may appear at the ends of the cuts and move toward one another, but without reaching $u = 0$ as ω increases and eventually attains $\omega = 1$. Anyway, let us in what follows consider the ω-values which satisfy

$$0 < \omega < 1$$

and let us represent whatever pairs of roots the equation

$$\Delta_N(\omega, u) = 0$$

possesses, by

$$\pm i\kappa_0,\ \pm i\kappa_1,\ \ldots,\ \pm i\kappa_p \qquad (p = 0,\ 1,\ 2,\ \ldots)$$

with

$$0 < \kappa_0 < \kappa_1 < \ldots < \kappa_p \leqslant 1. \tag{17}$$

In conclusion, we may state that as long as $0 < \omega < 1$, the behavior of the integrand in (16) over the entire complex plane is the same as in the case of isotropic scattering except that, from $N = 3$ on, the integrand may possess more than one pair of poles in $(-i, +i)$ on the u_2-axis. Hence, for any physically acceptable anisotropic single scattering law, the contour integration may be carried out along the

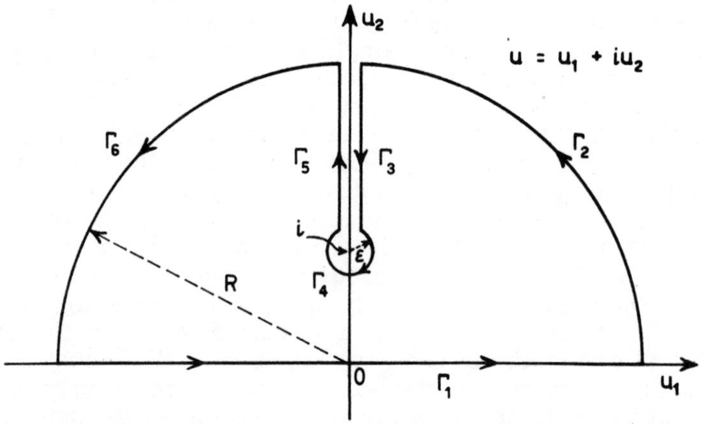

Fig. 1 Contour of integration in the complex u-plane needed in the transformation of the integral in (16).

same path as in the case of isotropic scattering, namely that depicted on Fig. 1, and the theory of residues enables us to write in a straightforward manner:

$$\oint u \frac{g_N(\omega,u)}{\Delta_N(\omega,u)} \exp\left(i\frac{r}{\lambda}u\right)du$$

$$= 2\pi i \sum_{m=0}^{p} \lim_{u\to i\kappa_m} \frac{(u-i\kappa_m)u g_N(\omega,u)}{\Delta_N(\omega,u)} \exp\left(i\frac{r}{\lambda}u\right)$$

$$= \pi i \sum_{m=0}^{p} C_m(\omega) \exp\left(-\kappa_m\frac{r}{\lambda}\right) \; * \tag{18}$$

where

$$C_m(\omega) = -\frac{g_N(\omega, i\kappa_m)}{\left(\dfrac{\partial \Delta_N(\omega, i\kappa)}{\partial(\kappa^2)}\right)_{\kappa=\kappa_m}}\,. \tag{19}$$

Now, again as in the isotropic scattering case, one succeeds in proving that the integrations along the parts Γ_2, Γ_4 and Γ_6 do not contribute effectively to the contour integration in the limit of infinite R and vanishing ε. Therefore, we deduce from (18):

$$\left(\int_{\Gamma_1} + \int_{\Gamma_3} + \int_{\Gamma_5}\right) u \frac{g_N(\omega,u)}{\Delta_N(\omega,u)} \exp\left(i\frac{r}{\lambda}u\right)du$$

$$= \pi i \sum_{m=0}^{p} C_m(\omega) \exp\left(-\kappa_m\frac{r}{\lambda}\right)$$

in which the first integral becomes identical to the one in (16) in the limit $R = +\infty$. Hence:

* In this equation, the upper limit of the summation index m may always be taken equal to p because for such ω-values for which $\kappa_p = 1$, the corresponding coefficient $C_p(\omega)$ appears to vanish anyway.

$$\rho(r) = \frac{S_0}{4\pi\lambda v r}\sum_{m=0}^{p} C_m(\omega)\exp(-\kappa_m \frac{r}{\lambda})$$

$$+\frac{S_0}{4\pi^2 i\lambda v r}\int_1^{\infty} s\left[\frac{g_N(\omega,-0+is)}{\Delta_N(\omega,-0+is)}-\frac{g_N(\omega,+0+is)}{\Delta_N(\omega,+0+is)}\right]\exp(-\frac{r}{\lambda}s)ds \tag{20}$$

in which $(+0+is)$ and $(-0+is)$ $(s \geqslant 1)$ symbolize respectively all points on Γ_3 and on Γ_5 as one lets these straight lines converge towards the u_2-axis and coincide with it in the limit. Thus, the contour integration transforms the Fourier integral representation (10) of $\rho(r)$ into a sum of one or more contributions of the so-called "asymptotic density" type and a transient contribution still in integral form which we shall call $\rho_{tr}(r)$. The next section is devoted to a detailed study of the latter part.

For the sake of completeness, let us point out that, again as for isotropic scattering (Cfr.: Case *et al,* 1, p. 171), the case of $\omega = 1$ can be obtained from the preceding theory most simply by passing to the limit $\omega \to 1$. Form. (20) remains perfectly valid, but as κ_0 and $C_0(\omega)$ become resp. equal to 0 and $3 - A_1$ in the limit $\omega = 1$, the first term in the sum on the right hand side of (20) which is actually the asymptotic density, reduces to

$$\frac{(3 - A_1) S_0}{4\pi\lambda v}\frac{1}{r}.$$

IV. FURTHER SIMPLICATION OF THE TRANSIENT CONTRIBUTION $\rho_{tr}(r)$ AND DEFINITIVE FORM OF THE TOTAL DENSITY $\rho(r)$

In this section, we shall prove that the integrand in the transient contribution $\rho_{tr}(r)$ on the right hand side of (20) can be tremendously simplified. Let us first concentrate on the various determinantal functions appearing between the square brackets. Making use of a well-known property of the Legendre functions of the second kind in the complex domain, we can write for $s > 1$:

$$Q_k\left(\frac{i}{\mp 0 + is}\right) = \frac{1}{2}\left[\ln\frac{s+1}{s-1} \pm i\pi\right] P_k\left(\frac{1}{s}\right) - W_{k-1}\left(\frac{1}{s}\right)$$
$$(k = 0,\ 1,\ 2, \ldots).$$

Substituting this in the elements of the first row of the determinants $\Delta_N(\omega, \mp 0 + is)$ deduced from (13) permits us to express them in terms of two new determinantal functions:

$$\Delta_N(\omega, \mp 0 + is) = -\frac{\omega}{2s}\left[\ln\frac{s+1}{s-1} \pm i\pi\right]\Psi_N(\omega, s) + \Phi_N(\omega, s) \tag{21}$$

where

$$\Psi_N(\omega, s) = \begin{vmatrix} 1 & -\frac{A_1}{s}P_1\left(\frac{1}{s}\right) & \frac{A_2}{s^2}P_2\left(\frac{1}{s}\right) & -\frac{A_3}{s^3}P_3\left(\frac{1}{s}\right) & \cdots & (-1)^N\frac{A_N}{s^N}P_N\left(\frac{1}{s}\right) \\ 1-\omega & 1 & 0 & 0 & \cdots\cdots & 0 \\ \frac{s^2}{2} & \frac{1}{2}(3-\omega A_1) & 1 & 0 & \cdots\cdots & 0 \\ 0 & \frac{2}{3}s^2 & \frac{1}{3}(5-\omega A_2) & 1 & \cdots\cdots & 0 \\ \vdots & \vdots & \vdots & \vdots & \ddots & \vdots \\ 0 & 0 & 0 & 0 & \cdots\cdots & 1 \end{vmatrix} \tag{22}$$

and

$$\Phi_N(\omega, s) = \begin{vmatrix} 1 & -\frac{\omega A_1}{s^2}W_0\left(\frac{1}{s}\right) & \frac{\omega A_2}{s^3}W_1\left(\frac{1}{s}\right) & -\frac{\omega A_3}{s^4}W_2\left(\frac{1}{s}\right) & \cdots & (-1)^N\frac{\omega A_N}{s^{N+1}}W_{N-1}\left(\frac{1}{s}\right) \\ 1-\omega & 1 & 0 & 0 & \cdots\cdots & 0 \\ \frac{s^2}{2} & \frac{1}{2}(3-\omega A_1) & 1 & 0 & \cdots\cdots & 0 \\ 0 & \frac{2}{3}s^2 & \frac{1}{3}(5-\omega A_2) & 1 & \cdots\cdots & 0 \\ \vdots & \vdots & \vdots & \vdots & \ddots & \vdots \\ 0 & 0 & 0 & 0 & \cdots\cdots & 1 \end{vmatrix} \tag{23}$$

Expanding these determinants in terms of the elements of the first column, we obtain:

$$\Psi_N(\omega, s) = 1 + \frac{1-\omega}{s}\Psi_N^{(1)}(\omega, s) - \frac{s}{2}\Psi_N^{(2)}(\omega, s) \quad (24)$$

$$\Phi_N(\omega, s) = 1 + \frac{\omega(1-\omega)}{s^2}\Phi_N^{(1)}(\omega, s) - \frac{\omega}{2}\Phi_N^{(2)}(\omega, s) \quad (25)$$

in which

$$\Psi_N^{(1)}(\omega, s) = \begin{vmatrix} A_1 P_1\left(\frac{1}{s}\right) & -\frac{A_2}{s}P_2\left(\frac{1}{s}\right) & \frac{A_3}{s^2}P_3\left(\frac{1}{s}\right) & \cdots & (-1)^{N-1}\frac{A_N}{s^{N-1}}P_N\left(\frac{1}{s}\right) \\ \frac{1}{2}(3-\omega A_1) & 1 & 0 & \cdots\cdots & 0 \\ \frac{2}{3}s^2 & \frac{1}{3}(5-\omega A_2) & 1 & \cdots\cdots & 0 \\ \vdots & \vdots & \vdots & \ddots & \vdots \\ 0 & 0 & 0 & \cdots\cdots & 1 \end{vmatrix} \quad (26),$$

$$\Psi_N^{(2)}(\omega, s) = \begin{vmatrix} \frac{A_2}{s}P_2\left(\frac{1}{s}\right) & -\frac{A_3}{s^2}P_3\left(\frac{1}{s}\right) & \frac{A_4}{s^3}P_4\left(\frac{1}{s}\right) & \cdots & (-1)^{N}\frac{A_N}{s^{N-1}}P_N\left(\frac{1}{s}\right) \\ \frac{1}{3}(5-\omega A_2) & 1 & 0 & \cdots\cdots & 0 \\ \frac{3}{4}s^2 & \frac{1}{4}(7-\omega A_3) & 1 & \cdots\cdots & 0 \\ \vdots & \vdots & \vdots & \ddots & \vdots \\ 0 & 0 & 0 & \cdots\cdots & 1 \end{vmatrix} \quad (27),$$

$$\Phi_N^{(1)}(\omega, s) =$$

$$\begin{vmatrix} A_1 W_0\left(\frac{1}{s}\right) & -\frac{A_2}{s} W_1\left(\frac{1}{s}\right) & \frac{A_3}{s^2} W_2\left(\frac{1}{s}\right) & \cdots & (-1)^{N-1}\frac{A_N}{s^{N-1}} W_{N-1}\left(\frac{1}{s}\right) \\ \frac{1}{2}(3-\omega A_1) & 1 & 0 & \cdots & 0 \\ \frac{2}{3}s^2 & \frac{1}{3}(5-\omega A_2) & 1 & \cdots & 0 \\ \vdots & \vdots & \vdots & \ddots & \vdots \\ 0 & 0 & 0 & \cdots & 1 \end{vmatrix} \quad (28),$$

and

$$\Phi_N^{(2)}(\omega, s) =$$

$$\begin{vmatrix} \frac{A_2}{s} W_1\left(\frac{1}{s}\right) & -\frac{A_3}{s^2} W_2\left(\frac{1}{s}\right) & \frac{A_4}{s^3} W_3\left(\frac{1}{s}\right) & \cdots & (-1)^{N}\frac{A_N}{s^{N-1}} W_{N-1}\left(\frac{1}{s}\right) \\ \frac{1}{3}(5-\omega A_2) & 1 & 0 & \cdots & 0 \\ \frac{3}{4}s^2 & \frac{1}{4}(7-\omega A_3) & 1 & \cdots & 0 \\ \vdots & \vdots & \vdots & \ddots & \vdots \\ 0 & 0 & 0 & \cdots & 1 \end{vmatrix} \quad (29).$$

The determinantal functions $g_N(\omega, \mp 0 + is)$ can also be expressed in terms of the preceding determinants. In an entirely similar manner, we find on the basis of (14):

$$g_N(\omega, \mp 0 + is) = \frac{1}{2s}\left[\ln\frac{s+1}{s-1} \pm i\pi\right]\left[1 - \frac{\omega}{s}\Psi_N^{(1)}(\omega, s)\right] + \frac{\omega}{s^2}\Phi_N^{(1)}(\omega, s). \quad (30)$$

With the aid of (21), (24), (25) and (30), it is now possible to calculate the integrand in $\rho_{tr}(r)$ explicitly. After a few intermediate steps, there comes:

$$\rho_{tr}(r) = \frac{S_0}{4\pi\lambda v r}\int_1^\infty \frac{\mathcal{T}_N(\omega,s)}{\mathcal{N}_N(\omega,s)}\exp(-\frac{r}{\lambda}s)ds \tag{31}$$

with

$$\mathcal{T}_N(\omega,s) = 1 - \frac{\omega}{s}\Psi_N^{(1)}(\omega,s) + \frac{\omega}{s^2}\Phi_N^{(1)}(\omega,s) - \frac{\omega}{2}\Phi_N^{(2)}(\omega,s) + \frac{\omega^2}{2s}\left[\Psi_N^{(1)}(\omega,s)\Phi_N^{(2)}(\omega,s) - \Psi_N^{(2)}(\omega,s)\Phi_N^{(1)}(\omega,s)\right] \tag{32}$$

and

$$\mathcal{N}_N(\omega,s) = \left\{\Phi_N(\omega,s) - \frac{\omega}{2s}\Psi_N(\omega,s)\ln\frac{s+1}{s-1}\right\}^2 + \left\{\frac{\pi\omega}{2s}\Psi_N(\omega,s)\right\}^2. \tag{33}$$

We shall now prove that, for any N, the following truly remarkable equality holds :

$$\boxed{\mathcal{T}_N(\omega,s) \equiv 1} \tag{34}$$

For $N = 0$ (the isotropic case), this property is well-known (Cfr. : Case *et al*, 1, p. 170). For $N = 1$ and $N = 2$, it can quite easily be verified in a direct manner. This permits us to proceed by the method of complete induction for $N = 3, 4, \ldots$. Thus, from the assumption

$$\mathcal{T}_{N-1}(\omega,s) = 1, \tag{35}$$

we shall deduce that necessarily

$$\mathcal{T}_N(\omega,s) = 1. \tag{36}$$

We start by expanding $\Psi_N^{(1)}$, $\Psi_N^{(2)}$, $\Phi_N^{(1)}$ and $\Phi_N^{(2)}$ with respect to their last column. This leads to:

$$\begin{aligned}
\Psi_N^{(1)}(\omega,s) &= \Psi_{N-1}^{(1)}(\omega,s) + \frac{A_N}{s^{N-1}}P_N\left(\frac{1}{s}\right)\varepsilon_{N-1}^{(1)}\\
\Psi_N^{(2)}(\omega,s) &= \Psi_{N-1}^{(2)}(\omega,s) + \frac{A_N}{s^{N-1}}P_N\left(\frac{1}{s}\right)\varepsilon_{N-1}^{(2)}\\
\Phi_N^{(1)}(\omega,s) &= \Phi_{N-1}^{(1)}(\omega,s) + \frac{A_N}{s^{N-1}}W_{N-1}\left(\frac{1}{s}\right)\varepsilon_{N-1}^{(1)}\\
\Phi_N^{(2)}(\omega,s) &= \Phi_{N-1}^{(2)}(\omega,s) + \frac{A_N}{s^{N-1}}W_{N-1}\left(\frac{1}{s}\right)\varepsilon_{N-1}^{(2)}
\end{aligned} \tag{37}$$

where

$$\mathcal{E}_{N-1}^{(1)} = \begin{vmatrix} \frac{1}{2}(3-\omega A_1) & 1 & 0 & \cdots\cdots & 0 \\ \frac{2}{3}s^2 & \frac{1}{3}(5-\omega A_2) & 1 & \cdots\cdots & 0 \\ 0 & \frac{3}{4}s^2 & \frac{1}{4}(7-\omega A_3) & \cdots\cdots & 0 \\ \vdots & \vdots & \vdots & \ddots & \vdots \\ 0 & 0 & 0 \cdots & \frac{1}{N}(2N-1-\omega A_{N-1}) \end{vmatrix} \tag{38}$$

and $\mathcal{E}_{N-1}^{(2)}$ is defined as the determinant resulting from $\mathcal{E}_{N-1}^{(1)}$ by the omission of the first row and the first column. As we shall need them further on, let us also introduce the determinants $\mathcal{E}_{N-1}^{(3)}, \mathcal{E}_{N-1}^{(4)}, \ldots, \mathcal{E}_{N-1}^{(N-1)}$ resulting each time from the preceding one by simply omitting the first row and the first column. Expanding $\mathcal{E}_{N-1}^{(k)}$ in terms of the elements of the first column, one easily shows that these $\mathcal{E}$-determinants are related by way of the following recurrence formula :

$$\mathcal{E}_{N-1}^{(k)} = \frac{1}{k+1}(2k+1-\omega A_k)\,\mathcal{E}_{N-1}^{(k+1)} - \frac{k+1}{k+2}s^2\mathcal{E}_{N-1}^{(k+2)} \tag{39}$$

applicable for $k = 1, 2, \ldots, N-3$, and also for $k = N-2$ and $N-1$ if we define

$$\mathcal{E}_{N-1}^{(N)} = 1, \qquad \mathcal{E}_{N-1}^{(N+1)} = 0$$

solely for the sake of convenience. Introducing (37) in (32) and taking (35) into account, $\mathcal{T}_N(\omega, s)$ becomes

$$\mathcal{T}_N(\omega, s) = 1 + \frac{\omega A_N}{s^{N-1}}\left\{\frac{\mathcal{E}_{N-1}^{(1)}}{s^2}W_{N-1}\left(\frac{1}{s}\right) - \frac{\mathcal{E}_{N-1}^{(1)}}{s}P_N\left(\frac{1}{s}\right) - \frac{\mathcal{E}_{N-1}^{(2)}}{2}W_{N-1}\left(\frac{1}{s}\right)\right.$$

$$\left. + \frac{\omega}{2s}\left(\mathcal{E}_{N-1}^{(1)}\delta_{N-1}^{(2)} - \mathcal{E}_{N-1}^{(2)}\delta_{N-1}^{(1)}\right)\right\} \tag{40}$$

in which $\delta_{N-1}^{(1)}$ and $\delta_{N-1}^{(2)}$ are again two determinantal functions defined by

$$\delta_{N-1}^{(1)} = P_N\left(\frac{1}{s}\right)\Phi_{N-1}^{(1)}(\omega, s) - W_{N-1}\left(\frac{1}{s}\right)\Psi_{N-1}^{(1)}(\omega, s)$$

or

$$\delta_{N-1}^{(1)} = \begin{vmatrix} A_1 R_1\left(\frac{1}{s}\right) & -\frac{A_2}{s} R_2\left(\frac{1}{s}\right) & \frac{A_3}{s^2} R_3\left(\frac{1}{s}\right) & \cdots & (-1)^{N-2} \frac{A_{N-1}}{s^{N-2}} R_{N-1}\left(\frac{1}{s}\right) \\ \frac{1}{2}(3-\omega A_1) & 1 & 0 & \cdots\cdots & 0 \\ \frac{2}{3}s^2 & \frac{1}{3}(5-\omega A_2) & 1 & \cdots\cdots & 0 \\ \vdots & \vdots & \vdots & \ddots & \vdots \\ 0 & 0 & 0 & \cdots\cdots & 1 \end{vmatrix} \tag{41}$$

with

$$R_k\left(\frac{1}{s}\right) \equiv P_N\left(\frac{1}{s}\right) W_{k-1}\left(\frac{1}{s}\right) - W_{N-1}\left(\frac{1}{s}\right) P_k\left(\frac{1}{s}\right) \tag{42}$$

and $\delta_{N-1}^{(2)}$ is the cofactor of the element of the second row and the first column in $\delta_{N-1}^{(1)}$. In the same way as for the ε-determinants, let us also introduce the determinantal functions

$$\delta_{N-1}^{(3)}, \ \delta_{N-1}^{(4)}, \ \ldots, \ \delta_{N-1}^{(N-1)}, \ \delta_{N-1}^{(N)}, \ \delta_{N-1}^{(N+1)}$$

where

$$\delta_{N-1}^{(N)} = \delta_{N-1}^{(N+1)} = 0$$

and every other $\delta_{N-1}^{(k)}$ being the cofactor of the element of the second row and the first column in $\delta_{N-1}^{(k-1)}$. They satisfy the following recurrence relation:

$$\delta_{N-1}^{(k)} = \frac{A_k}{s^{k-1}} R_k\left(\frac{1}{s}\right) + \frac{1}{k+1}(2k+1-\omega A_k)\,\delta_{N-1}^{(k+1)} - \frac{k+1}{k+2} s^2 \delta_{N-1}^{(k+2)}$$

$$(k = 1,\ 2,\ \ldots\ldots,\ N-1). \tag{43}$$

Now, returning to (40), it is clear that our statement (36) is proven as soon as we have shown that

$$\frac{\varepsilon_{N-1}^{(1)}}{s} R_1\left(\frac{1}{s}\right) + \frac{\varepsilon_{N-1}^{(2)}}{2} W_{N-1}\left(\frac{1}{s}\right) - \frac{\omega}{2s}\left(\varepsilon_{N-1}^{(1)} \delta_{N-1}^{(2)} - \varepsilon_{N-1}^{(2)} \delta_{N-1}^{(1)}\right) \equiv 0. \tag{44}$$

This can be accomplished by examining, in succession, the dependence of the left hand side on $A_1, A_2, \ldots, A_{N-1}$. It will turn out that this expression does not depend on the A-coefficients and, at the same time, we shall find that its value is exactly zero. Applying the recurrence formulas (39) and (43) for $k = 1$ in order to eliminate $\varepsilon_{N-1}^{(1)}$ and $\delta_{N-1}^{(1)}$ in terms of other quantities, the left hand side in (44) goes over into

$$\frac{3\,\varepsilon_{N-1}^{(2)}}{2s^2}\left[\frac{3}{2s}R_1\left(\frac{1}{s}\right)+\frac{1}{2}W_{N-1}\left(\frac{1}{s}\right)\right]-\frac{\varepsilon_{N-1}^{(3)}}{s}R_1\left(\frac{1}{s}\right)$$
$$-\frac{\omega}{2s}\left(\varepsilon_{N-1}^{(2)}\delta_{N-1}^{(3)}-\varepsilon_{N-1}^{(3)}\delta_{N-1}^{(2)}\right)$$

after complete cancellation of the A_1-dependent terms and multiplication by $3/2s^2$. But,

$$\frac{3}{2s}R_1\left(\frac{1}{s}\right)+\frac{1}{2}W_{N-1}\left(\frac{1}{s}\right)=\frac{3}{2s}P_N\left(\frac{1}{s}\right)+\left(\frac{1}{2}-\frac{3}{2s^2}\right)W_{N-1}\left(\frac{1}{s}\right)$$
$$=P_N\left(\frac{1}{s}\right)W_1\left(\frac{1}{s}\right)-W_{N-1}\left(\frac{1}{s}\right)P_2\left(\frac{1}{s}\right)=R_2\left(\frac{1}{s}\right)$$

and therefore, the proof of the identity (44) is reduced to that of the new identity

$$\frac{3\,\varepsilon_{N-1}^{(2)}}{2s^2}R_2\left(\frac{1}{s}\right)-\frac{\varepsilon_{N-1}^{(3)}}{s}R_1\left(\frac{1}{s}\right)-\frac{\omega}{2s}\left(\varepsilon_{N-1}^{(2)}\delta_{N-1}^{(3)}-\varepsilon_{N-1}^{(3)}\delta_{N-1}^{(2)}\right)\equiv 0. \quad (45)$$

Continuing in the same manner, namely, applying the recurrence relations (39) and (43) for $k = 2$ and replacing $\varepsilon_{N-1}^{(2)}$ and $\delta_{N-1}^{(2)}$ by the resulting expressions, the above left hand side is transformed into:

$$\frac{4\,\varepsilon_{N-1}^{(3)}}{3s^3}\left[\frac{5}{2s}R_2\left(\frac{1}{s}\right)-R_1\left(\frac{1}{s}\right)\right]-\frac{3\,\varepsilon_{N-1}^{(4)}}{2s^2}R_2\left(\frac{1}{s}\right)$$
$$-\frac{\omega}{2s}\left(\varepsilon_{N-1}^{(3)}\delta_{N-1}^{(4)}-\varepsilon_{N-1}^{(4)}\delta_{N-1}^{(3)}\right) \quad (46)$$

again after total cancellation of the A_2-dependent terms and multiplication by $4/3s^2$. In order to work out the difference between the square brackets, we make use of the recurrence relation between the R-functions. From the well-known recurrence formulas relating three consecutive Legendre polynomials and three consecutive Legendre functions of the second kind, we deduce:

$$(k+2)W_{k+1}\left(\frac{1}{s}\right) = \frac{2k+3}{s} W_k\left(\frac{1}{s}\right) - (k+1)W_{k-1}\left(\frac{1}{s}\right)$$

and

$$(k+2)P_{k+2}\left(\frac{1}{s}\right) = \frac{2k+3}{s} P_{k+1}\left(\frac{1}{s}\right) - (k+1)P_k\left(\frac{1}{s}\right).$$

Multiplying these equalities on both sides by $P_N(1/s)$ and $W_{N-1}(1/s)$ resp., and subtracting them, we obtain, recalling the definition (42):

$$(k+2)R_{k+2}\left(\frac{1}{s}\right) = \frac{2k+3}{s} R_{k+1}\left(\frac{1}{s}\right) - (k+1)R_k\left(\frac{1}{s}\right)$$

$$(k = 0,\ 1,\ \ldots). \quad (47)$$

Applying this formula for $k = 1$ in (46), we can conclude that the proof of (45) comes down to showing that

$$\frac{4\,\varepsilon_{N-1}^{(3)}}{2s^3} R_3\left(\frac{1}{s}\right) - \frac{3\,\varepsilon_{N-1}^{(4)}}{2s^2} R_2\left(\frac{1}{s}\right) - \frac{\omega}{2s}\left(\varepsilon_{N-1}^{(3)}\delta_{N-1}^{(4)} - \varepsilon_{N-1}^{(4)}\delta_{N-1}^{(3)}\right) \equiv 0. \quad (48)$$

Comparing the left hand sides in (44), (45) and(48) with one another, we see that they are of the same type, with the indices gradually increasing. It is therefore logical that, proceeding along the same lines, the transformation method outlined above will generate a sequence of similar left hand sides whose identity to zero will each time follow from the vanishing of the next expression. After $(k-1)$ transformations, the general form of the identity to be shown is:

$$\frac{(k+1)\,\varepsilon_{N-1}^{(k)}}{2s^k} R_k\left(\frac{1}{s}\right) - \frac{k\,\varepsilon_{N-1}^{(k+1)}}{2s^{k-1}} R_{k-1}\left(\frac{1}{s}\right) - \frac{\omega}{2s}\left(\varepsilon_{N-1}^{(k)}\delta_{N-1}^{(k+1)} - \varepsilon_{N-1}^{(k+1)}\delta_{N-1}^{(k)}\right) \equiv 0. \quad (49)$$

When k reaches the value $N-1$, the identity to be proven (which is still fully equivalent to showing (36)) becomes

$$\frac{N\,\varepsilon_{N-1}^{(N-1)}}{2s^{N-1}} R_{N-1}\left(\frac{1}{s}\right) - \frac{N-1}{2s^{N-2}} R_{N-2}\left(\frac{1}{s}\right) + \frac{\omega}{2s}\delta_{N-1}^{(N-1)} \equiv 0 \quad (50)$$

since $\varepsilon_{N-1}^{(N)} = 1$, $\delta_{N-1}^{(N)} = 0$. Now, considering that

$$\varepsilon_{N-1}^{(N-1)} = \frac{1}{N}(2N - 1 - \omega A_{N-1}), \; \delta_{N-1}^{(N-1)} = \frac{A_{N-1}}{s^{N-2}} R_{N-1}\left(\frac{1}{s}\right),$$

the left hand side in (50) can be rewritten as

$$\frac{2N-1}{2s^{N-1}} R_{N-1}\left(\frac{1}{s}\right) - \frac{N-1}{2s^{N-2}} R_{N-2}\left(\frac{1}{s}\right)$$

or

$$\frac{N}{2s^{N-2}} R_N\left(\frac{1}{s}\right)$$

on account of (47). That this expression really vanishes identically follows directly from (42) as

$$R_N\left(\frac{1}{s}\right) = P_N\left(\frac{1}{s}\right) W_{N-1}\left(\frac{1}{s}\right) - W_{N-1}\left(\frac{1}{s}\right) P_N\left(\frac{1}{s}\right) \equiv 0 .$$

This completes our proof of (34) and in conclusion, the scalar particle density given by (20) finally reduces to

$$\boxed{\rho(r) = \frac{S_0}{4\pi\lambda v r} \sum_{m=0}^{p} C_m(\omega) \exp\left(-\kappa_m \frac{r}{\lambda}\right) + \frac{S_0}{4\pi\lambda v r} \int_1^{\infty} \frac{\exp(-rs/\lambda)}{\mathcal{N}_N(\omega, s)} \, ds} \tag{51}$$

in which $\mathcal{N}_N(\omega, s)$ is given by (33). In the case of $\omega = 0$, we have:

$$p = 0, \qquad \kappa_0 = 1, \qquad C_0(0) = 0 \quad \text{and} \quad \mathcal{N}_N(0, s) = 1$$

so that $\rho(r)$ reduces to the direct beam contribution $\rho_d(r)$. For $0 < \omega \leqslant 1$, we know that $0 \leqslant \kappa_0 < 1$ and that κ_0 always represents the smallest among the possible κ-values if $p > 0$ (see (17)). Thus, the exponential function

$$\exp\left(-\kappa_0 \frac{r}{\lambda}\right)$$

dies out more slowly with increasing r than any other exponential term that may appear in the sum or any infinitesimal contribution to the integral in (51). Hence, the part of $\rho(r)$ containing κ_0 can be called the asymptotic density, i.e.:

$$\rho_{as}(r) = \frac{S_0}{4\pi\lambda v r} C_0(\omega)\exp(-\kappa_0 \frac{r}{\lambda}) . \qquad (52)$$

The remaining parts in (51) are of shorter range and, therefore, of transient behavior. They can logically be put together to form the so-called non-asymptotic density:

$$\rho_{nas}(r) = \frac{S_0}{4\pi\lambda v r}\left[\sum_{m=1}^{p} C_m(\omega)\exp(-\kappa_m \frac{r}{\lambda}) + \int_1^{\infty} \frac{\exp(-rs/\lambda)}{\mathcal{N}_N^2(\omega, s)} ds\right] . \qquad (53)$$

Clearly, the numerical evaluation of $\rho_{as}(r)$, $\rho_{nas}(r)$ and $\rho(r)$ on the basis of the above formulas comes down to:

1) the tabulation of $1/\mathcal{N}_N^2(\omega, s)$ as a function of s from 1 up to a sufficiently high value so that from there on the integrand in $\rho_{tr}(r)$ becomes negligibly small on account of the exponential function $\exp(-rs/\lambda)$;
2) the determination of the κ-roots of $\Delta_N(\omega, i\kappa) = 0$;
3) the calculation of the corresponding coefficients $C_m(\omega)$.

In the next section, we shall discuss these questions more in detail.

V. NUMERICAL ASPECTS OF THE PRACTICAL CALCULATION OF $\rho(r)$

The principal merit of the proof which we have given in Sect. IV lies not so much in the important simplification which the result (34) brings about in the rigorous expression of $\rho(r)$, but rather in the fact that it gives rise to a set of very useful recurrence formulas which make it possible, for the first time, to treat multiple scattering problems involving complicated, highly anisotropic phase functions. These recurrence relations lead to practical calculating schemes which are particularly suitable for machine computation.

(a) Practical Calculating Scheme for the Transient Part $\rho_{tr}(r)$

Since the integral appearing in $\rho_{tr}(r)$ cannot be worked out explicitly in closed form, it must necessarily be evaluated numerically. Whatever the method adopted, one must always be in a position to calculate the integrand in any point of the integration interval. In the present case, this amounts to the calculation of $\mathcal{N}_N(\omega, s)$ as a function of s. This can be carried out by means of (33) in which $\Psi_N(\omega, s)$ and $\Phi_N(\omega, s)$ are the determinantal functions given by (22) and (23), respectively. In this form, these functions would generally lead to voluminous computations. Fortunately, their evaluation can be enormously simplified using the following formulas. Expanding the determinant in (22) in terms of the elements of the last column, we find:

$$\Psi_N(\omega, s) = \Psi_{N-1}(\omega, s) + \frac{A_N}{s^N} P_N\left(\frac{1}{s}\right) \varphi_N(\omega, s)$$

and repeating the same operation for $\Psi_{N-1}, \Psi_{N-2}, \ldots$, there comes:

$$\Psi_N(\omega, s) = 1 + \sum_{n=1}^{N} \frac{A_n}{s^n} P_n\left(\frac{1}{s}\right) \varphi_n(\omega, s) \tag{54}$$

with

$$\varphi_n(\omega, s) = \begin{vmatrix} 1-\omega & 1 & 0 & \cdots & 0 \\ \frac{1}{2}s^2 & \frac{1}{2}(3-\omega A_1) & 1 & \cdots & 0 \\ 0 & \frac{2}{3}s^2 & \frac{1}{3}(5-\omega A_2) & \cdots & 0 \\ \vdots & \vdots & \vdots & \ddots & \vdots \\ 0 & 0 & 0 & \cdots & \frac{1}{n}(2n-1-\omega A_{n-1}) \end{vmatrix} \tag{55}$$

In the same manner, we deduce from (23):

$$\Phi_N(\omega, s) = 1 + \frac{\omega}{s} \sum_{n=1}^{N} \frac{A_n}{s^n} W_{n-1}\left(\frac{1}{s}\right) \varphi_n(\omega, s). \tag{56}$$

The φ-functions themselves can be calculated by means of the simple recurrence relation

$$\varphi_n(\omega, s) = \frac{1}{n}(2n-1-\omega A_{n-1})\varphi_{n-1}(\omega, s) - \frac{n-1}{n} s^2 \varphi_{n-2}(\omega, s)$$

$$(n = 2, 3, \ldots) \tag{57}$$

starting from

$$\varphi_0(\omega, s) = 1, \qquad \varphi_1(\omega, s) = 1 - \omega.$$

Thus, generating the consecutive $P_n(1/s)$- and $W_{n-1}(1/s)$-functions by means of their well-known recurrence formulas and $\varphi_n(\omega, s)$ by means of (57), task which is particularly suited for automatic computation, we are in the possibility to attain Ψ_N and Φ_N, and through them, the function $\mathcal{N}_N(\omega, s)$. Due to its iterative character and striking simplicity, this calculating scheme requires very little storage space in the memory units of an electronic computer and the calculation proceeds very rapidly.

Let us also note that from (33), (54), (56) and (57), one can deduce that $1/\mathcal{N}_N(\omega, s)$ is zero at $s = 1$ and approaches unity, its asymptotic value, as $s \to +\infty$ like in the isotropic case. In further analogy with this case, $\rho_{tr}(r)$ stays real as one lets ω exceed 1. It can therefore be tabulated for $\omega > 1$ in view of future work on multiplicative multiple scattering in finite media.

(b) Practical Calculating Scheme for the Evaluation of the Zeros of $\Delta_N(\omega, i\kappa)$

The κ-values appearing in the exponential terms of (51) are the roots of the determinantal equation:

$$\Delta_N(\omega, i\kappa) = 0. \, ^* \tag{58}$$

We recall that, for $0 < \omega \leqslant 1$, all the κ's are real and belonging to the interval (0, 1), with the smallest one becoming zero for $\omega = 1$. Written explicitly, (58) becomes:

* In this paragraph, we shall always talk about the κ-roots, in plural, for the sake of generality, although we have previously indicated that in various cases, Eq. (58) has only one non-negative root.

$$\begin{vmatrix} 1-\frac{\omega}{\kappa}Q_0(\frac{1}{\kappa}) & \frac{\omega A_1}{\kappa^2}Q_1(\frac{1}{\kappa}) & -\frac{\omega A_2}{\kappa^3}Q_2(\frac{1}{\kappa}) & \ldots & (-1)^{N+1}\frac{\omega A_N}{\kappa^{N+1}}Q_N(\frac{1}{\kappa}) \\ 1-\omega & 1 & 0 & \ldots\ldots & 0 \\ \frac{1}{2}\kappa^2 & \frac{1}{2}(3-\omega A_1) & 1 & \ldots\ldots & 0 \\ \vdots & \vdots & \vdots & \ddots & \vdots \\ 0 & 0 & 0 & \ldots\ldots & 1 \end{vmatrix} = 0. \quad (59)$$

Using the same expansion procedure as in the case of Ψ_N and Φ_N, this determinantal equation can be reduced to

$$1-\frac{\omega}{\kappa}Q_0(\frac{1}{\kappa})-\omega\sum_{n=1}^{N}\frac{A_n}{\kappa^{n+1}}Q_n(\frac{1}{\kappa})\,\varphi_n(\omega,\kappa) = 0 \quad (60)$$

with the same φ-functions as in (54) and (56). Thus, using an appropriate recurrence procedure for the accurate calculation of the Q-functions and generating the φ-functions by means of (57), one can easily tabulate the value of the left hand side in (60) as a function of κ in (0, 1). This makes it possible to localize the κ-roots and to obtain accurate approximations for them by means of the false position method (regula falsi) or any other convenient iterative process currently used for the solution of transcendental equations.

There exists another form of (58) which is more of theoretical interest, but nevertheless fully worth to mention. Expressing the Legendre functions by means of the formula

$$Q_k(\frac{1}{\kappa}) = \frac{1}{2}P_k(\frac{1}{\kappa})\ln\frac{1+\kappa}{1-\kappa} - W_{k-1}(\frac{1}{\kappa}) \quad (k = 0, 1, \ldots)$$

in (59) and comparing the resulting determinant to (22) and (23), we conclude that (58) goes over into:

$$\Phi_N(\omega,\kappa) - \omega\frac{\operatorname{argth}\kappa}{\kappa}\Psi_N(\omega,\kappa) = 0 \quad (61)$$

which generalizes the known equation appearing in the theory of multiple isotropic scattering, i.e.:

$$1-\omega\frac{\operatorname{argth}\kappa}{\kappa} = 0.$$

On the basis of (61), we have been able to establish various properties of the κ-roots, but because of limitation of space, it is not possible to describe them in full detail in this paper. They will be included in a future extensive account of our work on multiple anisotropic scattering. We shall limit ourselves here to two examples.

Equation (61) enables us to find the ω-values at which a given multiple scattering problem possesses at least one κ-root equal to 1. The functions $\Phi_N(\omega,\kappa)$ and $\Psi_N(\omega,\kappa)$ are simply polynomials in $1/\kappa^2$, ω and the A-coefficients. Putting $\kappa = 1$ in (61), it follows that Φ_N and Ψ_N are finite for any ω, but argthκ becomes infinite. Hence, the left hand side of (61) cannot vanish unless

$$\omega \Psi_N(\omega, 1) = 0. \tag{62}$$

This equality is satisfied for $\omega = 0$ at which the first and only κ-value, namely κ_0, appears at 1, and for

$$\Psi_N(\omega, 1) = 1 + \sum_{n=1}^{N} A_n \varphi_n(\omega, 1) = 0 \tag{63}$$

according to (54). This is an algebraic equation in ω. Its roots which can always be determined either analytically or numerically can *a priori* be real or complex, but physically only those roots which are real and non-negative are of interest. As for the maximum number of these ω-roots, we deduce from (22) that $\Psi_N(\omega, 1)$ is a polynomial in ω of a degree equal to the number of non-zero A-coefficients in the expansion (3) of the phase function. Indeed, the explicit calculation of the determinant representing $\Psi_N(\omega, 1)$ leads to a sum of the form:

$$\frac{A_N(1-\omega)}{N!} \prod_{n=1}^{N-1} (2n+1-\omega A_n) + \text{(terms of the same or an inferior degree in } \omega).$$

Thus, for a given single scattering law, the total number of ω-values at which a κ-root may become equal to 1 is at most equal to the number of Legendre polynomials (including P_0) which appear *effectively* in its expansion. In fact, studying the determinants representing Ψ_N and Φ_N more closely, we establish that exactly the same conclusion about the maximum number of ω-values satisfying Eq. (61) can be drawn for *any* physically acceptable κ. The reason simply is that Φ_N and $\omega\Psi_N$ are both polynomials in ω of a degree equal to the total number of Legendre polynomials appearing effectively in (3).

Studying the variation of the κ's as functions of ω, one finds that in general every κ-value has the tendency to decrease toward zero as ω increases. It is therefore also interesting to find out at what ω-values one finds a κ-root equal to zero. Taking into account the results

$$\lim_{\kappa \to 0} \frac{Q_n(1/\kappa)}{\kappa^{n+1}} = \frac{2^n (n!)^2}{(2n+1)!} \qquad (n = 0, 1, \ldots)$$

and

$$\varphi_n(\omega, 0) = \frac{1}{n!} \prod_{k=0}^{n-1} (2k + 1 - \omega A_k)$$

$$(A_0 \equiv 1; n = 1, 2, \ldots),$$

Eq. (60) becomes for $\kappa = 0$:

$$1 - \omega - \omega \sum_{n=1}^{N} \frac{2^n n! A_n}{(2n+1)!} \prod_{k=0}^{n-1} (2k + 1 - \omega A_k) = 0.$$

After suitable rearrangement, this leads to

$$\Delta_N(\omega, 0) = \prod_{n=0}^{N} \left(1 - \frac{\omega A_n}{(2n+1)}\right) = 0. \qquad (64)$$

This result also follows directly from putting $u = 0$ in (6) which reduces $\Delta_N(\omega, 0)$ to a purely diagonal determinant since

$$F_{km}(0) = \frac{\delta_{km}}{2k+1} \qquad \text{(see: (12))}.$$

Eq. (64) is satisfied for $\omega = 1$ as well as for those values

$$\omega = \frac{2n+1}{A_n} \qquad (1 \leqslant n \leqslant N) \qquad (65)$$

which are finite, hence for those n's for which $A_n \neq 0$. However, to be acceptable, an ω-value must be non-negative. Therefore, it is clear that the total number of significant

ω-values at which a κ-root becomes zero, is at most equal to the number of Legendre polynomials (including P_0) appearing with a positive coefficient in the expansion (3) of the phase function.*

Finally, we note that, on account of (4):

$$-(2n+1) \leqslant A_n \leqslant (2n+1) \quad (n = 1, 2, \ldots),$$

but it can be shown that, for any physically acceptable single scattering law, the right hand equality is never satisfied except in the extreme cases of purely forward scattering, purely backward scattering or any mixture of the two. Indeed,

$$A_n = 2n+1 \qquad (n = 1, 2, \ldots) \quad (66)$$

means that necessarily

$$< P_n(\cos\gamma)>_{\text{av.}} = 1. \quad (67)$$

Now, for any odd positive n, we have:

$$P_n(\cos 0) = 1 \quad \text{and} \quad P_n(\cos\gamma) < 1 \quad \text{for} \quad 0 < \gamma \leqslant \pi.$$

Thus, averaging $P_n(\cos\gamma)$ over a normalized phase function which is non-negative for all scattering angles can only lead to (67) if

$$f(\Omega' \to \Omega) \begin{cases} > 0 & \text{for} \quad \gamma = 0 \\ = 0 & \text{for} \quad 0 < \gamma \leqslant \pi, \end{cases}$$

that is, in the case of purely forward scattering described by

$$f(\Omega' \to \Omega)\,\mathrm{d}\Omega = \frac{1}{2\pi}\delta(1 - \cos\gamma)\,\mathrm{d}\Omega \quad **$$
$$= \left[1 + 3P_1(\cos\gamma) + 5P_2(\cos\gamma) + \ldots\right]\frac{\mathrm{d}\Omega}{4\pi}.$$

---

* We use the term "at most" because it is not excluded that certain positive ω-values among those given by (65) are equal to one another.

** Here, the point of discontinuity of the Dirac δ-function should be treated as if it were an internal point of the closed γ-interval $(0,\pi)$.

At the same time, we note that as soon as (66) is satisfied for one odd n-value, it holds for all $n = 1, 2, \ldots$. Similarly, for any even positive n, we can write:

$$P_n(\cos 0) = P_n(\cos\pi) = 1 \quad\text{and}\quad P_n(\cos\gamma) < 1 \quad \text{for } 0 < \gamma < \pi,$$

and hence, (67) can only be satisfied for a non-negative, normalized phase function in which solely the scattering angles $\gamma = 0$ and $\gamma = \pi$ have a probability to occur, i.e.:

$$f(\Omega' \to \Omega)\,d\Omega = \frac{1}{2\pi}\left[a\,\delta(1 - \cos\gamma) + (1-a)\,\delta(1 + \cos\gamma)\right] d\Omega^{*}$$

$$= \left[1 + 3(2a - 1)\,P_1(\cos\gamma) + 5\,P_2(\cos\gamma) + \ldots\right]\frac{d\Omega}{4\pi} \qquad (0 \leqslant a \leqslant 1).$$

If (66) is satisfied for one even positive n, it evidently holds for all even n. Consequently, for any physically acceptable single scattering law other than those just considered, all the finite positive ω-values included in (65) are larger than 1 showing that as long as $0 < \omega < 1$, no κ-root can be equal to zero. As ω reaches 1, only the smallest κ, namely κ_0, becomes equal to zero, confirming an earlier statement.

(c) Practical Calculating Scheme for the Coefficients $C_m(\omega)$

Recalling (19), the coefficient $C_m(\omega)$ associated with κ_m is given by

$$C_m(\omega) = -\frac{g_N(\omega, i\kappa_m)}{\left(\dfrac{\partial\Delta_N(\omega, i\kappa)}{\partial(\kappa^2)}\right)_{\kappa=\kappa_m}} \qquad (m = 0, 1, \ldots, p). \quad (68)$$

From (14), we easily deduce:

$$g_N(\omega, i\kappa_m) = \frac{\operatorname{argth}\kappa_m}{\kappa_m}\left[1 - \frac{\omega}{\kappa_m}\Psi_N^{(1)}(\omega, \kappa_m)\right] + \frac{\omega}{\kappa_m^2}\Phi_N^{(1)}(\omega, \kappa_m).$$

* In this right hand side, the points of discontinuity of the various Dirac δ-functions should be treated as if they were internal points of the closed γ-interval $(0,\pi)$.

But, considering that κ_m is a root of Eq. (58), we have:

$$\frac{\operatorname{argth}\kappa_m}{\kappa_m} = \frac{\Phi_N(\omega,\kappa_m)}{\omega\Psi(\omega,\kappa_m)} \qquad \text{(see: (61))}$$

and using the formulas (24) and (25), we obtain :

$$g_N(\omega, i\kappa_m) = \frac{\mathcal{C}_N(\omega,\kappa_m)}{\omega\Psi_N(\omega,\kappa_m)}.$$

Again because of (34), this result can be simplified to

$$g_N(\omega, i\kappa_m) = \frac{1}{\omega\Psi_N(\omega,\kappa_m)}. \tag{69}$$

Next, we have to transform the denominator in (68) into an expression suitable for practical computation. Considering that $\Delta_N(\omega, i\kappa)$ is given by the left hand side in (60), we get:

$$-\frac{\partial\Delta_N(\omega, i\kappa)}{\partial(\kappa^2)} = \omega\frac{d}{d(\kappa^2)}\left(\frac{Q_0(1/\kappa)}{\kappa}\right)$$

$$+\omega\sum_{n=1}^{N}A_n\varphi_n(\omega,\kappa)\frac{d}{d(\kappa^2)}\left(\frac{Q_n(1/\kappa)}{\kappa^{n+1}}\right)$$

$$+\omega\sum_{n=1}^{N}A_n\frac{Q_n(1/\kappa)}{\kappa^{n+1}}\frac{\partial\varphi_n(\omega,\kappa)}{\partial(\kappa^2)} \tag{70}$$

in which the φ-functions still satisfy the recurrence relation (57). From this formula, we easily deduce a similar recurrence formula for the derivatives of the φ-functions:

$$\frac{\partial\varphi_n(\omega,\kappa)}{\partial(\kappa^2)} = \frac{1}{n}(2n-1-\omega A_{n-1})\frac{\partial\varphi_{n-1}(\omega,\kappa)}{\partial(\kappa^2)}$$

$$-\frac{n-1}{n}\kappa^2\frac{\partial\varphi_{n-2}(\omega,\kappa)}{\partial(\kappa^2)} - \frac{n-1}{n}\varphi_{n-2}(\omega,\kappa)$$

$$(n \geqslant 2) \quad (71)$$

where

$$\frac{\partial\varphi_0(\omega,\kappa)}{\partial(\kappa^2)} = \frac{\partial\varphi_1(\omega,\kappa)}{\partial(\kappa^2)} = 0.$$

As for the remaining derivatives involving the Q-functions, they can be expressed in terms of these functions themselves using some of their well-known recurrence relations. We can write:

$$\frac{d}{d(\kappa^2)}\left(\frac{Q_n(1/\kappa)}{\kappa^{n+1}}\right) = \frac{n+1}{2(1-\kappa^2)}\left[\frac{Q_n(1/\kappa)}{\kappa^{n+1}} - \frac{Q_{n+1}(1/\kappa)}{\kappa^{n+2}}\right] \qquad (n \geqslant 0) \qquad (72)$$

and

$$\frac{d}{d(\kappa^2)}\left(\frac{Q_n(1/\kappa)}{\kappa^{n+1}}\right) = \frac{1}{2\kappa^2(1-\kappa^2)}\left\{n\left[\frac{Q_{n-1}(1/\kappa)}{\kappa^n} - (2-\kappa^2)\frac{Q_n(1/\kappa)}{\kappa^{n+1}}\right] - (1-\kappa^2)\frac{Q_n(1/\kappa)}{\kappa^{n+1}}\right\} \quad (n \geqslant 1). \; (73)$$

Applying (72) for $n = 0$ and (73) for $n = 1, 2, \ldots, N$ in (70), replacing κ by the root κ_m and taking into account that (60) holds for a κ-root, we obtain:

$$-\left(\frac{\partial \Delta_N(\omega, i\kappa)}{\partial(\kappa^2)}\right)_{\kappa=\kappa_m} = \frac{1}{2\kappa_m^2(1-\kappa_m^2)}\left\{\kappa_m^2 - 1 + \omega + \omega\sum_{n=1}^{N} nA_n \varphi_n(\omega,\kappa_m)\left[\frac{Q_{n-1}(1/\kappa_m)}{\kappa_m^n} - (2-\kappa_m^2)\frac{Q_n(1/\kappa_m)}{\kappa_m^{n+1}}\right] + 2\omega\kappa_m^2(1-\kappa_m^2)\sum_{n=1}^{N} A_n \frac{Q_n(1/\kappa_m)}{\kappa_m^{n+1}}\left(\frac{\partial\varphi_n(\omega,\kappa)}{\partial(\kappa^2)}\right)_{\kappa=\kappa_m}\right\}.$$

In this way, we are led to the final result:

$$C_m(\omega) = \frac{2\kappa_m^2(1-\kappa_m^2)}{\omega \mathcal{M}_m} \qquad (74)$$

with

$$\mathcal{M}_m = \Psi_N(\omega,\kappa_m)\left\{\kappa_m^2 - 1 + \omega + \omega\sum_{n=1}^{N} nA_n\varphi_n(\omega,\kappa_m)\left[\frac{Q_{n-1}(1/\kappa_m)}{\kappa_m^n} - (2-\kappa_m^2)\frac{Q_n(1/\kappa_m)}{\kappa_m^{n+1}}\right] + 2\omega\kappa_m^2(1-\kappa_m^2)\sum_{n=1}^{N} A_n\frac{Q_n(1/\kappa_m)}{\kappa_m^{n+1}}\left(\frac{\partial\varphi_n(\omega,\kappa)}{\partial(\kappa^2)}\right)_{\kappa=\kappa_m}\right\} \qquad (74')$$

result which generalizes the well-known formula of multiple isotropic scattering theory:

$$C_0(\omega) = \frac{2\kappa_0^2(1-\kappa_0^2)}{\omega(\kappa_0^2 - 1 + \omega)} .$$

Generating in succession the values of the various Q-functions, φ-functions and the derivatives of the latter with respect to κ^2 in the point κ_m, one deduces $\mathcal{M}_m$ from (74') and $C_m(\omega)$ from (74).

In analogy with the case of the equation $\Delta_N(\omega, i\kappa) = 0$, there also exists another expression for the coefficients $C_m(\omega)$ which is again more of theoretical interest but worthwhile to mention. We deduce it as follows. Considering that the left hand sides in (58) and (61) are equal, we find by differentiation:

$$\frac{\partial \Delta_N(\omega, i\kappa)}{\partial \kappa} = \frac{\partial \Phi_N(\omega,\kappa)}{\partial \kappa} - \omega \frac{\operatorname{argth}\kappa}{\kappa} \frac{\partial \Psi_N(\omega,\kappa)}{\partial \kappa} - \frac{\omega}{\kappa}\Psi_N(\omega,\kappa)\left[\frac{1}{1-\kappa^2} - \frac{\operatorname{argth}\kappa}{\kappa}\right]$$

Putting $\kappa = \kappa_m$ and taking into account that κ_m is a root of Eq. (61), we get

$$\left(\frac{\partial \Delta_N(\omega, i\kappa)}{\partial(\kappa^2)}\right)_{\kappa=\kappa_m} = \frac{1}{2\kappa_m}\left\{\left(\frac{\partial \Phi_N(\omega,\kappa)}{\partial\kappa}\right)_{\kappa=\kappa_m} - \frac{\Phi_N(\omega,\kappa_m)}{\Psi_N(\omega,\kappa_m)}\left(\frac{\partial \Psi_N(\omega,\kappa)}{\partial\kappa}\right)_{\kappa=\kappa_m} + \frac{1}{\kappa_m}\Psi_N(\omega,\kappa_m)\left(\frac{\Phi_N(\omega,\kappa_m)}{\Psi_N(\omega,\kappa_m)} - \frac{\omega}{1-\kappa_m^2}\right)\right\} .$$

Finally, when we introduce this into (68) taking also (69) into account, we obtain:

$$C_m(\omega) = \frac{2\kappa_m^2(1-\kappa_m^2)}{\omega\,\mathcal{M}_m} \tag{75}$$

where

$$\mathcal{M}_m = \left[(\kappa_m^2 - 1)\Phi_N(\omega, \kappa_m) + \omega\Psi_N(\omega,\kappa_m)\right]\Psi_N(\omega,\kappa_m) + \kappa_m(1-\kappa_m^2)\left[\Phi_N(\omega,\kappa_m)\left(\frac{\partial \Psi_N(\omega,\kappa)}{\partial \kappa}\right)_{\kappa=\kappa_m} - \Psi_N(\omega,\kappa_m)\left(\frac{\partial \Phi_N(\omega,\kappa)}{\partial \kappa}\right)_{\kappa=\kappa_m}\right]. \qquad (75')$$

We terminate by drawing the attention upon the fact that the various formulas in this section are valid and applicable for N as large as one wishes. In practice, however, generating the required functions by means of recurrence relations, one must ascertain that the chosen formulas are the appropriate ones capable of yielding the functions with sufficient accuracy. We shall discuss this technical question in full detail in a future publication.

VI. EXAMPLES OF PRACTICAL APPLICATION

To show the applicability of the preceding formalism, we have tabulated the particle density $\rho(r)$ as a function of r for two typical ω-values, namely $\omega = 0.3$ and $\omega = 0.9$, in the case of a number of single scattering laws obtained by putting different g-values in the normalized probability distribution:

$$f(\boldsymbol{\Omega}'\to\boldsymbol{\Omega})d\Omega = \frac{1-g^2}{(1-2g\cos\gamma + g^2)^{3/2}}\frac{d\Omega}{4\pi} \quad (-1 \leqslant g \leqslant +1) \qquad (76)$$

This scattering law which has also been considered by H.C. van de Hulst presents the advantage that, when one lets g vary from 0 to 1, it gradually changes from isotropic scattering over more and more pronounced anisotropic to purely forward scattering. Similarly, as g varies from 0 to -1, it corresponds to backward scattering situations with increasingly stronger anisotropy up to purely backward scattering. In our calculations, we have chosen $g = \pm 0.1$, ± 0.3, ± 0.5 and ± 0.7 and compared the obtained results to those corresponding to the case of $g = 0$ (deduced from multiple isotropic scattering theory) and the cases of $g = +1$ and $g = -1$. Table 1 provides an idea of the degree of anisotropy contained in (76) for the considered g-values.

TABLE 1

Comparison Between the Values of $(1-g^2)/(1-2g\cos\gamma+g^2)^{3/2}$ in the Forward and Backward Directions

g	$\gamma = 0$	$\gamma = \pi$
-1	0	$+\infty$
-0.7	0.1038	18.89
-0.5	0.2222	6
-0.3	0.4142	2.653
-0.1	0.7438	1.358
0	1	1
0.1	1.358	0.7438
0.3	2.653	0.4142
0.5	6	0.2222
0.7	18.89	0.1038
1	$+\infty$	0

The above scattering law can easily be expanded in a rigorous infinite series of Legendre polynomials:

$$f(\boldsymbol{\Omega}'\to\boldsymbol{\Omega})\,d\Omega = \left[\sum_{n=0}^{\infty}(2n+1)g^n P_n(\cos\gamma)\right]\frac{d\Omega}{4\pi} \qquad (77)$$

so that

$$A_n = (2n+1)g^n.$$

For every considered g-value, we have truncated this expansion in such a manner that $f(\boldsymbol{\Omega}'\to\boldsymbol{\Omega})$ is approximated by the resulting finite sum of Legendre polynomials to an accuracy better than 0.5×10^{-4} for all $0 \leqslant \gamma \leqslant \pi$. In the present case, it is particularly easy to find an upper limit to the error resulting from the truncation. Indeed we have:

$$\left|4\pi f(\boldsymbol{\Omega}'\to\boldsymbol{\Omega}) - \sum_{n=0}^{N}(2n+1)\,g^n P_n(\cos\gamma)\right| \leqslant \sum_{n=N+1}^{\infty}(2n+1)\left|g^n P_n(\cos\gamma)\right|$$

$$\leqslant \sum_{n=N+1}^{\infty} (2n+1)|g|^n = \frac{|g|^{N+1}}{1-|g|}\left\{2N+3+\frac{2|g|}{1-|g|}\right\}.$$

Table 2 lists the number of Legendre polynomials needed for this purpose.

TABLE 2

g	number of Legendre polynomials (including P_0)
± 0.1	6
± 0.3	12
± 0.5	21
± 0.7	44

As we mentioned in the introduction, the calculations have been carried out on an IBM 1620 with standard core memory of 20,000 decimal positions. It is only this fact that has prevented us from including still higher positive and negative values of g requiring much larger numbers of Legendre polynomials in our study. The κ-values have been determined by successive approximation on the basis of the formulas of Sect. V(b). After that, the corresponding $C(\omega)$'s have been obtained using the results in Sect. V(c). As for the transient part $\rho_{tr}(r)$, the infinite upper limit of the integral appearing in it has been replaced by 360 and the interval $1 \leqslant s \leqslant 360$ has been split in a number of properly chosen smaller intervals each themselves subdivided in 8 equal intervals on which the Newton-Cotes numerical integration formula was applied. To know the accuracy of the final results, the numerical integration was every time repeated with the groups of 8 equal intervals replaced by groups of 16 equal intervals of half length and the overlapping digits in corresponding results were regarded as meaningful. With the adopted subdivision, the overlap was generally of four to six significant digits.

Figures 2 and 3 depict some of the obtained curves. Since $\rho(r)$ always behaves approximately as $S_0/4\pi v r^2$ in the vicinity of $r = 0$, it is particularly convenient to plot the dimensionless quantity

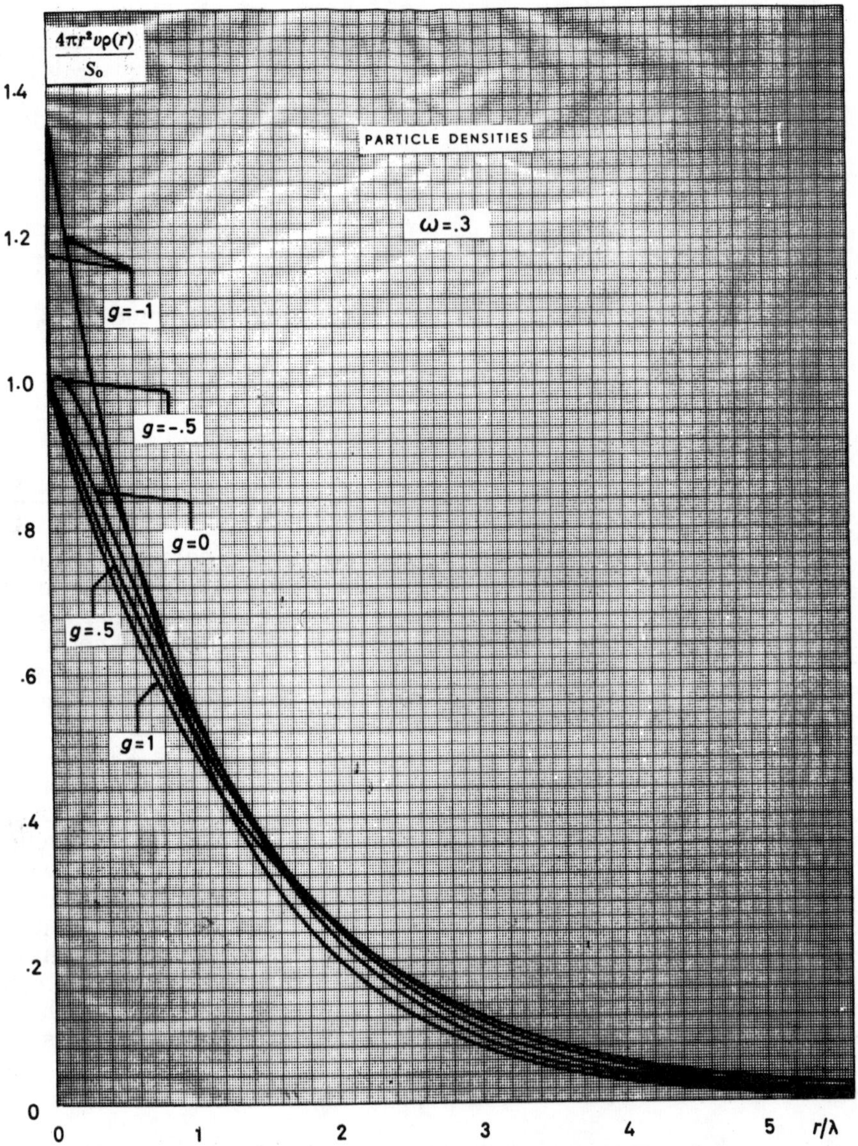

Fig. 2 Graphical representation of $4\pi r^2 v\rho(r)/S_0$ as a function of r/λ for $g = 0, \pm 0.5$ and ± 1 in the case of $\omega = 0.3$.

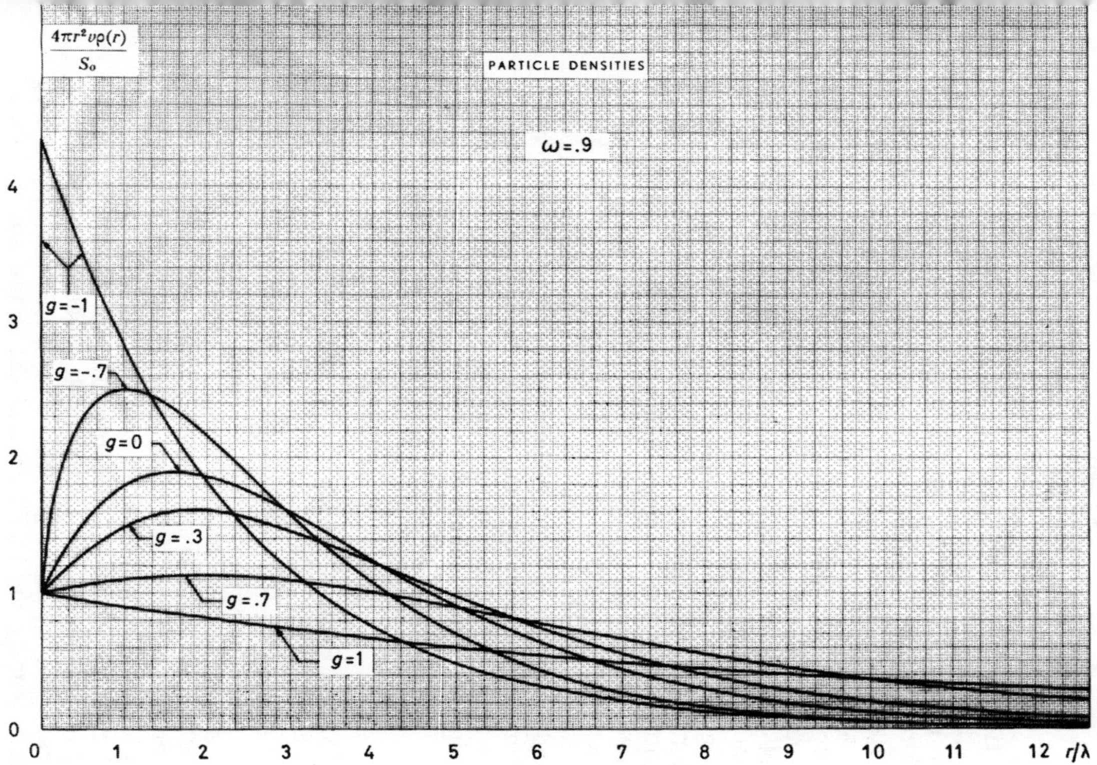

Fig. 3 Graphical representation of $4\pi r^2 v\rho(r)/S_0$ as a function of r/λ for $g = 0,\ 0.3,\ \pm 0.7$ and ± 1 in the case of $\omega = 0.9$.

$$\frac{4\pi r^2 v \rho(r)}{S_0}$$

as a function of the dimensionless distance r/λ instead of $\rho(r)$ itself. In the case of $\omega = 0.3$ (Fig. 2) which corresponds to reasonably strong absorption, the obtained curves stay so close to one another that it was preferable, for the sake of clarity, to plot them only for $g = 0$ and $g = \pm 0.5$, together with the curves for the extreme cases $g = \pm 1$. The latter were obtained, not on the basis of the present theory, but by the use of formulas resulting from a direct treatment of purely forward and purely backward multiple scattering (Grosjean, 5, Appendix II). In the case of $\omega = 0.9$ (Fig. 3), where the scattering largely dominates the absorption, the situation is different. Here, the obtained distributions differ more drastically from one another and without overloading the diagram, it was possible to plot the curves for $g = 0$, $g = 0.3$, $g = \pm 0.7$ and $g = \pm 1$. As one lets g vary from -1 over 0 to $+1$, one can nicely follow and interpret the gradual changes of shape of the lines from the sharp-peaked curve corresponding to purely backward multiple scattering to the smooth exponentially decreasing curve for purely forward multiple scattering.

VII. EXACT PARTICLE DENSITY AROUND A PLANE SOURCE OF UNIFORM STRENGTH IN AN INFINITELY EXTENDED HOMOGENEOUS MEDIUM

The case of the isotropic plane source can be treated independently on the basis of an entirely similar theory as the one which we outlined in the preceding sections. The beautiful results which we obtained for the isotropic point source can, however, be transferred directly to the plane source case by means of the well-known trick of considering the scalar density produced around the plane source as a linear superposition of densities created by an infinity of uniformly distributed point sources. This leads to the well-known relations:

$$\rho_{pl}(z) = 2\pi \int_{|z|}^{\infty} \rho_{pt}(r) r \, dr \quad \text{and} \quad \rho_{pt}(r) = -\frac{1}{2\pi r}\left(\frac{d\rho_{pl}(z)}{dz}\right)_{z=r} \tag{78}$$

where z is the cartesian coordinate measured on an axis perpendicular to the source plane. The independent treatment leads to the convergent integral representation:

$$\rho_{pl}(z) = \frac{S_0}{\pi v}\int_0^{\infty} \frac{g_N(\omega,u)}{\Delta_N(\omega,u)} \cos\frac{z}{\lambda}u\,du$$

$$= \frac{S_0}{2\pi v}\int_{-\infty}^{\infty} \frac{g_N(\omega,u)}{\Delta_N(\omega,u)} \exp(i\frac{z}{\lambda}u)du \qquad (-\infty < z < +\infty)$$

where Δ_N and g_N have the same meaning as in the point source case. By means of the same contour integration or by means of (51) applied in (78), one establishes that the practical form of $\rho_{pl}(z)$ is:

$$\rho_{pl}(z) = \frac{S_0}{2v}\left\{\sum_{m=0}^{p}\frac{C_m(\omega)}{\kappa_m}\exp(-\kappa_m\frac{|z|}{\lambda}) + \int_1^{\infty}\frac{\exp(-|z|s/\lambda)}{s\mathcal{N}_N^2(\omega,s)}ds\right\} \tag{79}$$

where $1/\mathcal{N}_N^2(\omega,s)$, the κ_m's and the $C_m(\omega)$-coefficients are again evaluated as in Sect. V. Hence, as could be expected, no new difficulties arise.

We are convinced that it must also be feasible to develop similar formalisms for the cases of an anisotropic point source and a uniform anisotropic plane source in an infinite homogeneous medium. This would then open up the possibility of extending our calculating techniques to certain standard problems involving a finite medium. In practice, the number of Legendre polynomials permitted in the expansion of the phase function would again be limited only by the particular characteristics (size and speed) of the computing facilities at one's disposition.

REFERENCES

(1) Case, K.M., de Hoffmann, F. and Placzek, G., *Introduction to the Theory of Neutron Diffusion* — I. Los Alamos Scientific Laboratory, Los Alamos, N.M. (1953).

(2) Davison, B., *Neutron Transport Theory*. - Clarendon Press, Oxford (1957).

(3) Grosjean, C. C., "The exact mathematical Theory of Multiple Scattering of Particles in an infinite Medium," *Verhand. Kon. Vl. Ac. Wet. België*, XIII, No. 36, (1951)
(4) Grosjean, C. C., *Physica,* XIX, 29 (1953).
(5) Grosjean, C. C., "A new approximate one-velocity Theory for treating both isotropic and anisotropic multiple scattering Problems. Part I : Infinite homogeneous scattering Media, " *Verhand. Kon. Vl. Ac. Wet. België,* XXV, No. 70 (1963).

DISCUSSION FOLLOWING PAPER BY F. VANMASSENHOVE AND C. C. GROSJEAN

J. B. Keller : Did you evaluate the integral in calculating $\rho(r)$?
F. Vanmassenhove : Of course, since $\rho(r)$ represents the *total* particle density. We have calculated the integral by means of an appropriate process of numerical integration.
J.B. Keller : Is that included in the plots ?
F. Vanmassenhove : Yes, certainly, the graphs really represent the total density.
Z. Sekera : Could you define more clearly what is the proper meaning of particle density ?
F. Vanmassenhove : In the presence of radiating sources, a certain distribution of particles (or photons) undergoing multiple scattering will establish itself throughout space at any considered time instant. By particle density at a given point in space, I mean as usually, the number of particles (or photons) present in a unit volume around the considered point, whatever their direction of motion. It results from the so-called angular density by integrating the latter over all directions of motion of the traveling particles.

Scattering and Absorption of Light in Turbid Media

J. K. Beasley, J. T. Atkins,

and

F. W. Billmeyer, Jr.*
Plastics Department
E. I. du Pont de Nemours & Co., Inc.
Wilmington, Delaware

ABSTRACT

Although the optics of turbid media have been widely studied, there has appeared no satisfactory theory of the transmittance and reflectance properties of such materials as opal glass or translucent plastics. This paper describes new equations relating these properties to fundamental optical constants of turbid materials. The equations allow for change in refractive index at the sample boundaries and for any combination of collimated and diffuse illuminations. The ratio of forward to backward scattering in an elementary volume and the ratio of path lengths for collimated and diffuse fluxes appear as adjustable parameters. Pre-

*Present address: Department of Chemistry, Rensselaer Polytechnic Institute, Troy, N. Y.

liminary tests of the new equations with translucent plastic samples show them to be markedly superior to previous theories for predicting the optical properties of turbid media.

INTRODUCTION

Although the optics of turbid media have been widely studied, no satisfactory theory has found practical use for relating the transmittance and reflectance of such translucent materials as opal glass and pigmented plastics to more fundamental optical parameters. The shortcomings of existing theories result primarily from the adoption of overly simplified models, necessary for mathematical tractability but failing to describe adequately the particular system under investigation. For example, the widely used Kubelka-Munk analysis (23) makes the assumptions of diffuse illumination and diffuse viewing of the sample, with no optical discontinuity at the sample-air interface. In the three decades since the original Kubelka-Munk paper, no instrument manufacturer has commercialized an instrument embodying the conditions of the first assumption. The second assumption corresponds to conditions obtained in some systems, such as colored papers for which the model was developed and to which the analysis has been successfully applied in the past. However, numerous other applications have been made with varying degrees of success to materials such as plastics and oil-base paint films for which the assumption is decidely not valid.

Mathematical descriptions of the optics of turbid media, which is a particular case of the phenomenon of radiative transfer, may be divided into two categories: extremely general and broad treatments, often by astrophysicists, which lead in most cases to systems of integro-differential equations which cannot be solved analytically; and restricted special cases which may not describe the physical situation precisely, but do so adequately with respect to observable phenomena, and are mathematically tractable.

The work described in this paper was undertaken in 1957

with the objective of developing a theory which is a significantly better approximation than previously available to the actual phenomena of light scattering and absorption in turbid media, yet retains mathematical simplicity commensurate with the capacity of small or medium size digital computers.

After the oral presentation of this paper (30 June, 1965) our attention was called (37) to the papers (36) of H. G. Völz, who derived, apparently quite independently, essentially the same equations presented here, with differences in notation explained later. Völz did not, however, present any experimental data. Although an experimental test of the theory is not a major purpose of this paper, but will be the subject of a later presentation, a few preliminary experimental results have been included at this time.

HISTORICAL REVIEW

The more inclusive treatment of radiative transfer is summarized in the works of Chandrasekhar (7), Kourganoff (21), and Sobolev (33), to which the reader is referred. In this review, attention is focused on the more simplified methods of which the present work is an outgrowth.

A comprehensive and detailed review of the simplified treatments has not been published, although Judd (18) and Duntley (10) have each published short reviews. The following is not intended to be exhaustive, but merely to trace broadly the introduction and development of new concepts into the theory. A number of papers which merely restate the approach in other terms, or which utilize it in the solution of problems, are not mentioned. Judd (18) lists a number of such papers which discuss applications.

The earliest work related to (although not specifically concerned with) turbid media appears to be a paper by Stokes (34) in 1862. He was interested in evaluating the reflectance of a pile of glass plates each of which may or may not exhibit absorption. In essence, he computed the reflectance and transmittance of such pile of identical plates by taking the reflectance and transmittance values for a single plate and summing the infinite series obtained when the inter-reflections between all of the plates were included.

The first major contribution appears to be by the astronomer Schuster (30) in 1905 who sought to explain generally the escape of light from the self-luminous, foggy atmosphere of a star and more particularly, why some stars showed bright line spectra while others showed dark line spectra. In his paper, he proposed the concept of two diffuse light fluxes moving in opposite directions, with each contributing backscattered light to the other. Since the scattering particles were of molecular dimensions, he assumed that the scattered light was divided equally between the forward and backward directions. All light energy was considered to be emitted by the gas molecules within the atmosphere and none was incident upon the atmosphere from without.

In 1927, Silberstein (31) published a modified treatment which introduced the concept of a collimated flux within the medium which was the result of a collimated beam incident upon the front surface. He also removed the restriction that the scattered light was divided equally in two directions and permitted the beam to be divided into any arbitrary fractions. However, he assumed that the scattering coefficient was the same for both the collimated and diffuse beams and that there was no optical interface at the surface of the medium.

In 1931, Ryde (27, 28) extended Silberstein's work by developing the concept that the scattering coefficient of the diffuse beam should be different from the scattering coefficient of the collimated beam. He attempted to determine the scattering coefficient from the Rayleigh-Gans (35) single particle scattering theory. He also applied correction factors to account for the effect of the optical discontinuity at the medium-air interface.

Also in 1931, Kubelka and Munk (23) published what is probably the most widely known and used treatment of the subject. They reverted back to the two flux assumption, and in essence, their work is very similar to Schuster's with the omission of the emission terms. The Kubelka-Munk analysis has found wide-spread practical application, particularly since Kubelka (22) published sequels giving new analytical solutions to the differential equations, thus permitting easier numerical computation. The assumptions made in setting up the differential equations were somewhat restrictive, however, and for many systems of interest, the Kubelka-Munk treatment is not applicable. In particular, this treatment assumes that the light is completely diffuse, both internally and externally. It is also assumed that there is no optical discontinuity at the medium-air interface. Only backward scattering is considered.

The popularity of this treatment over that of Schuster is apparently due to the fact that the integrated solutions of the Kubelka-Munk equations were in terms of quantities familiar to the paper industry, where the technique was first applied, while Schuster's were in unfamiliar terms.

In 1942, Saunderson (29) made a new attempt to account for the effect of the optical discontinuity at the boundary of the medium. He limited his treatment to the case of an opaque medium and computed a correction term to be applied to the integrated equations of Kubelka and Munk, rather than applying a new set of boundary conditions.

Also in 1942, Duntley (10) published a short review of the previous work and a major extension to the treatment. He combined the three flux treatment of Silberstein with the collimated and diffuse scattering coefficient treatment of Ryde, and included the effect of optical interfaces and the fact that the absorption coefficient is different in collimated and diffuse light, to develop a theory involving eight parameters: two absorption coefficients, four scattering coefficients and two surface reflection coefficients. The experimental measurements which he reported were made under conditions where the reflection coefficients were zero. This was done deliberately in an effort to reduce the number of experimental measurements which had to be made and to simplify the numerical calculations. In the single example quoted, he predicted the reflectance and transmittance of a sample two units thick using data taken from samples one and three units thick. The agreement of the predicted values with the experimental values was significantly better for the six-constant theory than for the two-constant treatment.

The next theoretical advance was by Hulburt (15) in 1943 who published a mathematical paper dealing with the conditions involved in the illumination of the earth's atmosphere by the sun and with the subsequent illumination in the sea. The only new feature of Hulburt's treatment was permitting the collimated beam to enter at an angle other than normal.

Richmond (26) in 1963 solved the original Kubelka-Munk differential equations for the case where there is an optical discontinuity at the boundaries, rather than applying a correction factor after the fact as Saunderson had done.

All of the treatments discussed so far have neglected the effect of the angular distribution of light scattering, other than the division of the light beam into two (not necessarily equal) streams moving in opposite directions. Giovanelli (12) in 1955, considering only the case of opaque samples, attempted to introduce the effect of the angular distribution of scattered light. He assumed an arbitrary distribution function and set up the appropriate differential equations. Because of mathematical complexity he was forced to use approximation methods in obtaining solutions to the equations. In 1962 Blevin and Brown (5), co-workers of Giovanelli, attempted to demonstrate experimentally the validity of Giovanelli's results. They concluded that present experimental techniques were not sufficiently precise to distinguish between the Kubelka-Munk and the Giovanelli treatments. However, from the description of their experiments, it is expected that deviations from the Kubelka-Munk equations would be small. Like Giovanelli, they considered only opaque, semi-infinite samples.

Diffuse light which is internally incident upon a boundary is partially reflected. The coefficient of reflection for internally incident diffuse light, r_i, is not subject to direct experimental measurement. Rather, it is derived from transmittance and reflectance data. Various workers have obtained values of about 0.4 for r_i for opal glass (28), paint (19), and polystyrene (29). Judd (17) has calculated the theoretical value of this coefficient for perfectly diffuse light for a wide range of refractive index, n. He found that r_i = 0.60 for n = 1.50. The lower values in the literature were variously attributed to imperfect diffusion, surface roughness and refraction effects at the surface. Giovanelli (13), using perfectly diffuse light, showed that a rough surface did not result in a low value of the coefficient. In fact, the observed value was slightly higher than that for an optical surface whose observed value agreed with the theoretical one. Kottler (20), working with opal glass, presented evidence to support his postulate that the low values were the result of incompletely diffuse light. He attributed an apparent variation of the coefficient with sample thickness to a breakdown of the Schuster equations.

In 1962, Butler (6) considered the effect of the increased path length encountered by diffuse light in a scattering medium and used this effect to intensify the absorption spectra of natural products in which he was interested. He concluded that the path length was easily increased by a factor of 20, possibly as much as 100, over the path length for a collimated beam by the addition of a scattering substance to the solution under test. Prior to this time, it apparently had been tacitly assumed that the maximum average path length for completely diffuse light in a scattering matrix was twice that for collimated light, the factor gradually dropping to one as the radiation proceeded through the material. The factor of 2 is exact for completely diffuse light in an absorbing but non-scattering medium (22, 15).

Other workers, in particular Channon (8), Gurevic (14), Smith (32), Neugebauer (24), and Amy (1) have derived two-constant theories which are similar to if not identical to or which are special cases of those discussed above. Ingle (16) has shown that the work by Smith, Amy, and Stokes (34) are merely special cases of the Kubelka-Munk (23) analysis. Kubelka (22) has shown that the work by Gurevic is also a special case of the Kubelka-Munk analysis.

THEORY

Features and Restrictive Assumptions

The theory developed in this paper is the first, to our knowledge, to incorporate simultaneously all of the following features, most of them used in one or more previous treatments:

1. Incident radiation can be any combination of diffuse and normally-incident collimated radiations from either or both sides of the sample.
2. The ratio of forward to backward scattering is treated as an adjustable parameter.
3. The ratio of the path lengths of diffuse and collimated beams is an adjustable parameter.
4. Provision is made for a change in refractive index at the sample boundaries.
5. If the sample is illuminated from only one side, then the other side may have a partially-reflecting boundary, either in optical contact or not in optical contact with the sample.

In common with those of earlier workers, the theory is is subject to several restrictions and assumptions:

1. All energy is generated external to the medium in question.
2. Polarization effects are neglected.
3. The infinite sheet approximation is adopted.
4. The medium is assumed isotropic.
5. Illumination is considered to be monochromatic.
6. Scattering particles are assumed to be sufficiently far apart that they scatter independently. Consequently, the total scattering coefficient is directly proportional to the number of scattering particles in the medium.

The Model

Consider a sheet of turbid material infinite in lateral extent but of finite thickness, d (Fig. 1). The sheet is illuminated on the front face by a beam of collimated light,

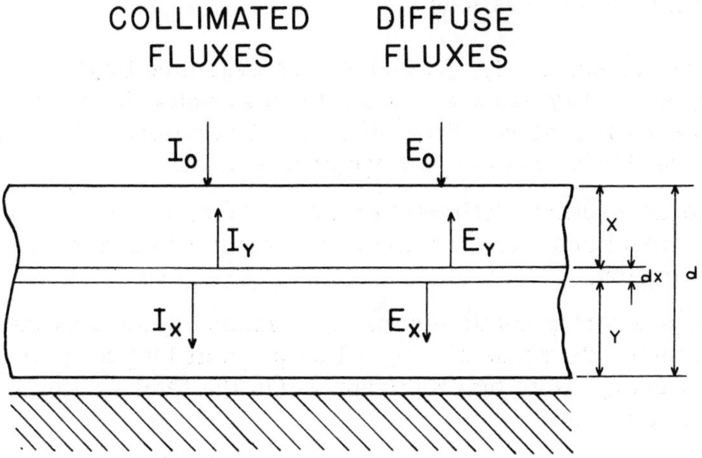

Fig. 1. Model for derivation of turbid medium equations.

normally incident, of intensity I_0, and a beam of completely diffuse light of intensity E_0. Internally, it is assumed that the light is resolved into four fluxes: a collimated beam I_x, and a diffuse beam E_x, propagating in the direction of the incident light, and a collimated beam I_y, and a diffuse beam E_y, moving in the opposite direction.

With the additional condition that there is a refractive index change at the front and back surfaces, and hence need to consider the appropriate reflection coefficients; and normalizing I_0 and E_0 so that $I_0 + E_0 = 1$, the reflectance and transmittance of the sheet can be written

$$R = I_0 r_0 + E_0 r_e + I_y (1-r_0) + E_y (1-r_i)$$

where I_y and E_y are evaluated at the front surface, and

$$T = I_x (1-r_0) + E_x (1-r_i)$$

where I_x and E_x are evaluated at the rear surface. The constants r_0, r_e and r_i are, respectively, the reflection coefficients for collimated light, diffuse light externally incident, and diffuse light internally incident on the specimen boundary.

The Differential Equations

The fluxes, I_x, I_y, E_x and E_y are evaluated by establishing an energy balance across the differential layer, dx, and integrating the resulting differential equations. Several additional terms must be defined at this point:

k The absorption coefficient of the medium, defined as the fractional decrease of a light flux per unit length due to absorption.

S The scattering coefficient of the medium, defined as the fractional decrease of a light flux per unit length due to scattering. Note that this represents the total scattering from the beam.

α The ratio of the average path length of the diffuse beam in the medium to the path length of the collimated beam. The assumption is made that the value of α is constant throughout the medium.

β The fraction of the scattered light that is scattered in the forward direction, i. e., the direction in which the beam is propagating. The fraction of backward scattering is therefore $(1-\beta)$.

Within an elemental layer of thickness dx, the changes in intensity with distance for the collimated fluxes I_x and I_y are:

$$\frac{dI_x}{dx} = -(k + S)\, I_x \tag{1}$$

$$\frac{dI_y}{dy} = -\frac{dI_y}{dx} = -(k + S)\, I_y \tag{2}$$

The diffuse flux, E_x, undergoes several changes in intensity:

A. an increase in flux, due to light scattered into the diffuse beam from I_x, equal to $(\beta S I_x)$, and from I_y, equal to $(1 - \beta)\, S I_y$

B. A decrease in flux equal to $(\alpha k E_x)$, due to light absorbed from E_x

C. A decrease in flux equal to (αSE_x), due to light scattered from E_x

D. an increase in flux equal to $(\alpha\beta SE_x)$, due to light scattered from E_x in the x direction

E. an increase in flux, due to light scattered from E_y in the x direction, equal to $\alpha(1-\beta)\, SE_y$

Combining these terms gives:

$$\frac{dE_x}{dx} = \beta SI_x + (1-\beta)SI_y + \alpha\beta SE_x + \alpha(1-\beta)SE_y - \alpha(k+S)E_x \qquad (3)$$

Similar considerations for E_y lead to a similar expression:

$$\frac{dE_y}{dy} = -\frac{dE_y}{dx} = (1-\beta)SI_x + \beta SI_y + \alpha(1-\beta)SE_x + \alpha\beta SE_y - \alpha(k+S)E_y \qquad (4)$$

By means of differentiation and algebraic manipulation, it is possible to obtain an equation from (3) and (4) which does not contain either E_y or its derivatives. This equation is:

$$-\frac{d^2E_x}{dx^2} + A_2E_x = A_3A_x\exp[-(k+S)x] + A_4A_y\exp[(k+S)x] \qquad (5)$$

where

$$A_2 = \alpha^2k(k+2S(1-\beta)) \qquad (6)$$

$$A_3 = S(\beta(k+S) + \alpha\beta k + \alpha(1-\beta)S) \qquad (7)$$

$$A_4 = S(1-\beta)(\alpha-1)(k+S) \qquad (8)$$

An equation containing only E_y and its derivatives is obtained in a similar manner

$$-\frac{d^2E_y}{dx^2} + A_2E_y = A_4A_x\exp[-(k+S)x] + A_3A_y\exp[(k+S)x] \qquad (9)$$

Solutions to the Equations

Equations (1) and (2) for the collimated fluxes have the general solutions:

$$I_x = A_x \exp[-(k+S)x] \text{ and} \tag{1A}$$

$$I_y = A_y \exp[(k+S)x] \tag{2A}$$

where A_x and A_y are constants of integration determined by the boundary conditions, considered later.

Equations (5) and (9) for the diffuse fluxes are linear differential equations with constant coefficients to which the method of undetermined coefficients may be applied. Thus the general plus the particular solutions are

$$E_x = C_1 \exp[\sqrt{A_2}\, x] + C_2 \exp[-\sqrt{A_2}\, x] + M_x \exp[(k+S)x] + N_x \exp[-(k+S)x] \tag{5A}$$

and

$$E_y = C_3 \exp[\sqrt{A_2}\, x] + C_4 \exp[-\sqrt{A_2}\, x] + M_y \exp[(k+S)x] + N_y \exp[-(k+S)x] \tag{9A}$$

where M_x, N_x, M_y and N_y are the undetermined coefficients, and C_1, C_2, C_3 and C_4 are constants of integration. Since the original differential equations are first order but were differentiated in the process of obtaining a solution, only two of the constants are truly independent, the other two being functions of the first two.

The undetermined coefficients, M_x, N_x, M_y and N_y are found to be

$$M_x = \frac{A_4 A_y}{A_2 - (k+S)^2} \tag{10}$$

$$N_x = \frac{A_3 A_x}{A_2 - (k+S)^2} \tag{11}$$

$$M_y = \frac{A_3 A_y}{A_2 - (k+S)^2} \tag{12}$$

$$N_y = \frac{A_4 A_x}{A_2 - (k+S)^2} \tag{13}$$

The functional relationship between C_1, C_2, C_3 and C_4 is

$$C_3 = \frac{(A_5 + \sqrt{A_2})}{(\quad A_6 \quad)} C_1 \tag{14}$$

$$C_4 = \frac{(A_5 - \sqrt{A_2})}{(A_6)} C_2 \tag{15}$$

$$A_5 = \alpha (k + S - \beta S) \tag{16}$$

$$A_6 = \alpha (1 - \beta) S \tag{17}$$

The Boundary Conditions

The above equations are general, and may be applied to a wide variety of experimental conditions. In this work, the particular conditions chosen are:

A. There is an optical discontinuity, i.e., a change in refractive index, at each surface of the medium. As a result, the following reflection coefficients exist at the surfaces:

r_0 reflection coefficient for the collimated beam at the air-medium interface.

r_i reflection coefficient for the diffuse beam incident upon the air-medium interface from the medium (the internal diffuse reflection coefficient).

r_e reflection coefficient for the diffuse beam incident upon the air-medium interface from air (the external diffuse reflection coefficient).

B. The medium is illuminated by a collimated, normally-incident flux of intensity I_0, and a diffuse flux of intensity E_0. The fluxes are incident from the x-direction.

C. There is a backing material, not in optical contact with the medium, which has a diffuse reflection coefficient r_b.

For the collimated beam, where Eqs. (1A) and (2A) apply, the boundary conditions are:
at x = 0,

$$I_x = I_0 (1 - r_0) + I_y r_0 \tag{18}$$

and at x = d,

$$I_y = I_x r_0 \tag{19}$$

For the diffuse beam, where Eqs. (5A) and (9A) apply, the boundary conditions are:
at x = 0,

$$E_x = E_0\ (1 - r_e) + E_y\, r_i \tag{20}$$

and at x = d,

$$E_y = E_x r_i + ((E_x\ (1 - r_i) + I_x\ (1 - r_0))\, r_b\ (1 - r_e))$$
$$(1 + r_b r_e + r_b^2\ r_e^2 + r_b^3\ r_e^3\ \ldots) \tag{21}$$

simplifying:

$$E_y = E_x r_i + \frac{(E_x\ (1 - r_i) + I_x\ (1 - r_0\ ))\ r_b\ (1 - r_e)}{1 - r_b\, r_e} \tag{21A}$$

Let

$$A_7 = r_i + \frac{(1 - r_i)\ r_b\ (1 - r_e)}{1 - r_b\ r_e} \tag{22}$$

$$A_8 = \frac{(1 - r_0)\ r_b\ (1 - r_e)}{1 - r_b\ r_e} \tag{23}$$

then, at x = d

$$E_y = A_7\, E_x + A_8\, I_x \tag{21B}$$

<u>Evaluation of Constants of Integration</u>

Substituting Eqs. (1A) and (2A) into the boundary conditions and solving simultaneously for A_x and A_y gives:

$$A_x = \frac{I_0\ (1 - r_0\ )}{1 - r_0^2\ \exp[-2(k + S)\, d]} \tag{24}$$

$$A_y = \frac{I_0(1 - r_0)\ r_0 \exp[-2(k + S)\, d]}{1 - r_0^2\ \exp[-2(k + S)\, d]} \tag{25}$$

Substituting Eqs. (5A) and (9A) into the boundary conditions and solving for C_1 and C_2 gives

$$C_1 = \frac{A_{11}\ A_{12}\ - A_9\ A_{14}}{A_{13}\ A_{11}\ - A_{10}\ A_{14}} \tag{26}$$

$$C_2 = \frac{A_9\ - A_{10}\ \ C_1}{A_{11}} \tag{27}$$

where

$$A_9 = E_0 (1 - r_e) + r_i (M_y + N_y) - (M_x + N_x) \quad (28)$$

$$A_{10} = 1 - \frac{(A_5 + \sqrt{A_2})}{(A_6)} r_i \quad (29)$$

$$A_{11} = 1 - \frac{(A_5 - \sqrt{A_2})}{(A_6)} r_i \quad (30)$$

$$\begin{aligned} A_{12} = {} & A_7 (M_x \exp[(k + S) d] + N_x \exp[-(k + S) d]) \\ & - M_y \exp[(k + S) d] - N_y \exp[-(k + S) d] \\ & + A_8 A_x \exp[-(k + S) d] \end{aligned} \quad (31)$$

$$A_{13} = \left(\frac{A_5 + \sqrt{A_2}}{A_6} - A_7 \right) \exp[\sqrt{A_2}\, d] \quad (32)$$

$$A_{14} = \left(\frac{A_5 - \sqrt{A_2}}{A_6} - A_7 \right) \exp[-\sqrt{A_2}\, d] \quad (33)$$

Comparison with Notation of Völz (36)

Brockes (37) has pointed out the following correspondences between our notation and that of Völz, who independently derived equations similar to Eqs. (5) and (9):

Quantity	Symbol: This Work	Symbol: Völz
Forward scattering, parallel flux	βS	S_1
Backward scattering, parallel flux	$(1 - \beta) S$	S_2
Forward scattering, diffuse flux	$\alpha \beta S$	0
Backward scattering, diffuse flux	$\alpha (1 - \beta) S$	s
Absorption, parallel flux	k	K
Absorption, diffuse flux	αk	k

The major point of difference, other than notation, is that Völz neglects forward diffuse scattering as indistinguishable from the forward diffuse flux, whereas it is included in our treatment. The solutions derived by Völz are expressed in terms of hyperbolic functions, rather than the exponentials we use. This, again, is merely a matter of notation.

COMPARISON WITH EXPERIMENT

The equations derived above were tested by comparing observed and computed values of the spectral transmittance and reflectance of plastic samples containing a mixture of a dye ($S = 0$) and a white pigment ($k = 0$). Full details of the tests and results will be given elsewhere (2). The samples were prepared by mixing known amounts of a dye, C. I. Disperse Red 9, C. I. 60505, and a pigment, rutile TiO_2, in an acrylic resin, using standard plastics industry techniques. Measurements were made with a General Electric Recording Spectrophotometer (11, 25) equipped with a digital readout unit (9) similar in function to that described by Billmeyer (4). For the purposes of this investigation, transmittance and reflectance were measured at 500 nm, corrected for zero-and 100%-line errors and expressed in percent with the perfect diffuser at 100.0. The measurement conditions correspond to collimated incident radiation and diffuse viewing. The specular reflected component was, of course, included.

The results of only one of many tests are described here. It involved a least squares analysis of spectral transmittance and spectral reflectance (with a black background of reflectance substantially zero, not in optical contact with the specimen) data at 500 nm for 23 specimens. Numerical values were fitted to the parameters k, S, α, β, and r_i, with the following results:

$$k = 70,600 \text{ cm}^{-1}$$
$$S = 49,700 \text{ cm}^{-1}$$
$$\alpha = 2.40$$
$$\beta = 0.90$$
$$r_i = 0.46$$

The results of this test are given in Table 1. The standard error of estimate for reflectance and transmittance was 1.9. When α and r_i were allowed to vary with k and S in an arbitrary but defined way, the standard error of estimate was reduced slightly to 1.6.

The values of k and S obtained in this test are approximately equal to those obtained in independent experiments

TABLE 1

Predicted Transmittance and Reflectance, Theory of This Work

Sample	Predicted Transmittance	Transmittance Difference, Predicted Minus Observed	Predicted Reflectance	Reflectance Difference, Predicted Minus Observed
16702	43.87	2.00	44.13	-0.48
16703	39.28	2.13	39.46	-0.25
16704	30.55	3.74	32.80	-0.37
16705	21.09	0.61	24.48	-0.40
16706	10.43	-0.60	16.62	-0.51
16707	3.11	-1.30	11.01	0.20
16802	64.64	2.07	26.26	1.91
16803	61.37	2.62	22.98	2.19
16804	52.56	0.75	18.76	2.25
16805	41.28	-0.16	13.33	1.31
16806	28.71	-2.57	8.69	0.33
16807	15.82	-2.48	6.02	0.01
17402	71.38	-0.34	10.68	3.10
17403	64.41	-0.06	13.87	3.94
17404	53.52	-1.10	18.73	4.19
17405	41.50	0.96	25.07	2.13
17406	31.17	0.39	32.78	1.24
17407	19.65	1.04	42.62	0.64
17502	46.20	-1.88	6.18	0.76
17503	39.28	-3.06	7.07	0.83
17504	28.71	-3.17	8.69	0.71
17505	18.51	-2.51	11.69	0.64
17506	9.74	-1.72	16.59	0.32

using samples containing only dye (yielding $k = 72,800$ cm^{-1}) or only white pigment (yielding $S = 57,500$ cm^{-1}). The differences are attributed (2, 3) to experimental errors involving loss of light through the sides of the samples, which were approximately 1 mm thick. The observed value of β, ~ 0.9, is qualitatively consistent with the values of β, 0.9 - 0.98, predicted by Rayleigh-Gans single particle scattering theory for 0.2 - 0.3 μ particles.

TABLE 2

Predicted Transmittance and Reflectance, Modified Theory of Kubelka-Munk

Sample	Predicted Transmittance	Transmittance Difference, Predicted Minus Observed	Predicted Reflectance	Reflectance Difference, Predicted Minus Observed
16702	45.88	4.01	45.82	1.20
16703	42.45	5.30	42.35	2.63
16704	34.89	8.08	37.46	4.28
16705	25.89	5.41	30.09	5.20
16706	14.06	3.02	22.02	4.88
16707	4.57	0.15	15.11	4.30
16802	69.43	6.86	23.33	-1.01
16803	65.86	7.11	21.12	0.33
16804	56.31	4.50	18.73	2.22
16805	42.73	1.28	14.81	2.79
16806	26.42	-4.86	10.63	2.27
16807	10.90	-7.40	7.54	1.53
17402	68.01	-3.71	9.84	2.26
17403	64.37	-0.10	13.02	3.09
17404	57.19	2.56	18.56	4.02
17405	46.98	6.44	26.92	3.98
17406	35.53	4.75	37.31	5.77
17407	22.73	4.12	48.87	6.89
17502	33.47	-14.61	6.24	0.82
17503	31.12	-11.22	7.83	1.59
17504	26.42	-5.46	10.63	2.65
17505	20.92	-0.10	15.27	4.22
17506	13.26	1.79	22.02	5.75

For comparison, the same set of data was fitted to the equations with α fixed at 1.00, β at 0.50, and r_i at 0.40. This case was selected as representative of the best treatment which would have been available from previous theories. It differs from the Kubelka-Munk treatment primarily in the inclusion of corrections for change in refractive index at the sample boundaries. The results of this test are given in Table 2; the standard error of estimate was 5.1, nearly three times as great as with the new theory. The absorption coefficient (k = 127, 500 cm^{-1}) and the scattering coefficient (S = 21.600 cm^{-1}) are significantly different from the values determined in separate experiments.

REFERENCES

(1) Amy. L., Rev. Opt., 16, 81 (1937).
(2) Atkins, J. T., Ph.D. Dissertation, University of Delaware, June 1965; Dissertation Abstr. XX, XXXX (1966).
(3) Atkins, J. T. and Billmeyer, F. W., J. Opt. Soc. Am., 54, 1407 (FD 14) (1960).
(4) Billmeyer, F. W., J. Opt. Soc. Am., 50, 137 (1960).
(5) Blevin, W. R. and Brown, W. J., J. Opt. Soc. Am., 52, 1250 (1962).
(6) Butler, Warren L., J. Opt. Soc. Am., **52**, 292 (1962).
(7) Chandrasekhar, S., Radiative Transfer, Dover, New York, 1960.
(8) Channon, H. J., Renwick, F. F., and Storr, B. V., Proc. Roy. Soc. (London), **A94**, 222 (1918).
(9) Davidson and Hemmendinger, Easton, Pennsylvania.
(10) Duntley, S. Q., J. Opt. Soc. Am., **32**, 61 (1942).
(11) General Electric Company, Schenectady, New York.
(12) Giovanelli, R. G., Optica Acta, **2**, 153 (1955).
(13) Giovanelli, R. G., Optica Acta, **3**, 127 (1956).
(14) Gurevic, M., Physik. Z., **31**, 753 (1930).
(15) Hulburt, E. O., J. Opt. Soc. Am. **33**, 42 (1943) errata, ibid., 33, 505 (1943).
(16) Ingle, George W., Am Soc. Testing Mater., Bull., **1942**, 32 (May, 1942).
(17) Judd, D. B., J. Research NBS., **29**, 329 (1942).
(18) Judd, Deane B., and Wyszecki, Gunter, Color in Business, Science, and Industry, Second Edition, Wiley, New York, 1963, pp. 387-405.

(19) Kawahata, H., Science of Light (Tokyo), 10, 127 (1961).
(20) Kottler, F., J. Opt. Soc. Am., 50, 483 (1960).
(21) Kourganoff, V., Basic Methods in Transfer Problems, Dover, New York, 1963.
(22) Kubleka, P., J. Opt. Soc. Am., 38, 448 (1948); errata, ibid., 38, 1067 (1948); ibid., 44, 330 (1954).
(23) Kubleka, P., and Munk, F., Z. Tech. Physik, 12, 593 (1931).
(24) Neugebauer, H. E. I., Z. Tech. Physik, 18, 137 (1937).
(25) Pritchard, B. S., and Holmwood, W. A., J. Opt. Soc. Am., 45, 690 (1955).
(26) Richmond, J. C., J. Res. Natl. Bur. Std., 67C, 217 (1963).
(27) Ryde, J. W., Proc. Roy. Soc. (London), A131, 451 (1931).
(28) Ryde, J. W., and Cooper, B. S., Proc. Roy. Soc. (London), A131, 464 (1931).
(29) Saunderson, J. L., J. Opt. Soc. Am., 32, 727 (1942).
(30) Schuster, A., Astrophys. J., 21, 1 (1905).
(31) Silberstein, L., Phil. Mag., 4, 1291 (1927).
(32) Smith, F. A., Paper Trade J., 100, 37 (1935).
(33) Sobolev, V. V., A Treatise on Radiative Transfer, translated by Gaposchkin, S. I., Van Nostrand, Princeton, 1963.
(34) Stokes, G. G., Proc. Roy. Soc. (London), 11, 545 (1860-1862).
(35) Van de Hulst, Light Scattering by Small Particles, Wiley, New York, 1957. Chapter 7.
(36) Völz, H. G., Proceedings, VI Congress F.A.T.I.P.E.C., 1962, pp. 98-103; Proceedings, VII Congress F.A.T.I.P.E.C., 1964, pp. 194-201.
(37) We are indebted to Dr. A. Brockes, Farbenfabriken Bayer AG, for calling our attention to the Völz papers.

DISCUSSION FOLLOWING PAPER BY J. K. BEASLEY, J. T. ATKINS and F. W. BILLMEYER

R. Munis: How does your treatment differ from that of Ryde and Cooper?

J. Atkins: We have a backward collimated beam since our incident collimated beam goes almost unattenuated to the back surface where it is specularly reflected. This was not in the Ryde and Cooper treatment. They have also separate sets of absorption and scattering coefficients for the collimated and diffuse beams where we have only one set since these are a function of the particle and not the type of illumination.

P. Latimer: Do you assume that your path lengths are independent of absorption? If multiple scattering occurs the effective path length will be a function of absorption.

J. Atkins: We use a fixed path length but multiply it by an empirical factor "α" which effectively accounts for this absorption dependence.

Multiple Scattering in Plane-Parallel Layers*

H. C. van de Hulst
Sterrewacht, Leiden, Netherlands

ABSTRACT

A program on multiple scattering calculations is presented, in which the derivation of formulae and the interpretation of numerical results are based on physical rather than mathematical definitions. The fundamental concepts are reflection and transmission function and point-direction gain. Computation methods for plane-parallel homogeneous layers with anisotropic scattering are briefly outlined. The illustrations refer to isotropic scattering. They give the distribution of incident energy over reflection, absorption and transmission and the extension of the H-function to virtual angles.

I. GENERAL PHILOSOPHY

The problem discussed in this paper is: multiple scattering in a homogeneous plane-parallel layer, single scattering in each volume element being characterized by a

---

*Invited paper; not presented at Conference.

pattern $\Phi(\alpha)$ and albedo a. The quantities to be determined are functions of combinations of the following variables

a = albedo for single scattering, $0 \leq a \leq 1$ (sometimes > 1)
b = total optical depth, $0 < b \leq \infty$
g = asymmetry parameter for single scattering, $-1 \leq g \leq 1$
τ = optical depth inside layer, $0 \leq \tau \leq b$
μ_0 = cosine of angle of incidence, $0 \leq \mu_0 \leq 1$ (sometimes > 1)
μ = cosine of angle of emergence, $0 \leq \mu \leq 1$ (sometimes > 1)

When reviewing this problem some years ago (7), we concluded that, although the solutions of most problems in this class were well-known for isotropic scattering and known in principle for anisotropic scattering, few numerical results were readily available. We then embarked on a program aimed at:

(a) producing numerical data in a convenient format;
(b) presenting the theory in a physically clear manner.

Since then the work has branched out in different directions but the general philosophy has remained:

- to prepare tables and graphs of quantities which have a physical meaning that can be directly understood.
- to use exclusively methods which can give unlimited accuracy, depending only on the fineness of integration chosen.
- to emphasize physical meaning from the start and to derive the basic formulae from physical definitions rather than from the equation of transfer. In this context, a physical definition of a quantity is the description of a physical measurement in a fictitious experiment that would yield the value of the said quantity.
- to emphasize the reciprocity principle and to employ it for frequent checks on formulae and numbers.
- to go all the way in the range of variables, i.e., to include the limits for $b = \infty$, for $\mu = 0$, etc., wherever appropriate, even if they necessitate special programming.
- to test the influence of anisotropy by a continuous set of phase functions, the Henyey-Greenstein functions, in which g is the only parameter. The program is suitable for arbitrary phase functions.

The results so far obtained along these lines are encouraging. The general impression is that the advantages gained by this more physical approach are marginal for the "classical" problem of homogeneous atmospheres with isotropic scattering, but that they make the step towards more complicated problems of anisotropic scattering, inhomogeneous layers, etc., a great deal easier.

This paper presents a few results obtained in this program. The majority of results is being worked up into a monograph.

II. FUNCTIONS COMPUTED

The functions computed are first of all the reflection and transmission functions:

$$R\,(a,\ b,\ g,\ \mu_0,\ \mu) \text{ and } T\,(a,\ b,\ g,\ \mu_0,\ \mu).$$

These are symmetric in μ_0 and μ; the transmission can be separated into a singular (direct) and non-singular (diffuse) part. We compute these values for the values μ_0 or μ = 0, 0.1, 0.3, 0.5, 0.7, 0.9, 1. In addition, moments and bi-moments are given by integrating over μ_0 or μ, or both, with two different weighting functions expressed by the operators:

U { physical meaning at incidence: radiation from Lambert surface
physical meaning at emergence: flux integral

N { physical meaning at incidence: radiation from thin layer of isotropic sources
physical meaning at emergence: average intensity or radiation density

Quantities referred to in the literature by a variety of names, like "albedo of the layer", "reflection coefficient", etc., are expressible in these moments or bi-moments.

Many functions which have τ as an independent variable can be reduced to a basic quantity, the <u>point-direction gain</u> (5, 6)

$$G\,(a,\ b,\ g,\ \mu,\ \tau).$$

The general gain concept (inspired by a similar concept employed in antenna theory) defines the gain between points P and Q in, near, or away from an arbitrary cloud of scattering particles as

$$\text{gain} = \frac{\text{radiation density created at P by isotropic source in Q}}{\text{outcome of same experiment in absence of the cloud}}$$

By the reciprocity principle, the gain from P to Q equals the gain from Q to P.

This general gain definition is here applied to one point inside the layer at optical depth τ and a second point far away outside the layer in a direction characterized by the direction cosine μ. We may again define moments of G by integrating over μ. Special applications to homogeneous layers with isotropic scattering (g = 0) have been in the literature for some time and are now linked together in one systematic concept. The functions which can thus be expressed are, with the omission of trivial factors:

- source function at depth τ created by radiation incident from direction μ_0.
- escape probability into direction μ of radiation emitted by an isotropic point source at depth τ_0.
- X-function = gain for $\tau = 0$.
- Y-functions = gain for $\tau = b$.
- H-functions = X-function for $b = \infty$

III. METHODS USED

A variety of methods were reviewed and tried in sample problems. However, the majority of the computations were performed by three methods:

(a) For $b \leq 2$ the direct method, or method of successive scattering was used. This consists of summing the terms due to n^{th} order scattering in an infinite series, which is the NEUMANN solution of the equation of transfer. Eigenvalues $\eta_n(b, g)$, n = 1, 2, characterizing the convergence have been tabulated.

(b) For $b \geq 1$ the doubling method was used. This method, first derived in 1962, gives an infinite series representing the results of diffuse reflection back and forth between equally thick layers. The convergence is fast and to reach 4-figure accuracy in a doubling sequence from $b = \frac{1}{2}$ to $b = 32$ is no problem. Again, eigenvalues $\alpha_n(a, b, g)$, $n = 1, 2$, have been tabulated.

(c) For $b \geq 8$ we usually are well within the thick-layer theory, which enables an accurate transition to $b = \infty$ to be made. In the conservative case ($a = 1$, arbitrary g) this takes the simple form that the reflection function for $b = \infty$ is found by adding the reflection and transmission functions for any large b (2, 6). In the non-conservative case the same is true if the transmission function for finite b is weighed down by a certain factor, which follows from the asymptotic theory, before being added to the reflecting function for finite b (Sobolev, 1964 for $g = 0$; similar results hold for anisotropic scattering).

All solutions have the form of series of definite integrals so that no questions of uniqueness arise. The programming was in the able hands of Dr. K. Grossman working with the I.B.M. 7094 at the N.A.S.A. Institute for Space Studies at New York. Usually τ-integration was performed with 51 to 201 points and μ-integration with a 7 pt. or 11 pt. Gauss or Radau formula. The accuracy is 4 to 5 figures.

The methods (a) to (c) circumvent the use of expansion into Legendre functions, or of a characteristic function, or of a characteristic matrix. It is not certain that this is always an advantage. Our work on anisotropic scattering has not progressed far enough to judge this point. It is quite possible that, in dealing with more complicated scattering diagrams or diagrams involving polarization, it will be profitable to switch in some stage to such a separation method, e.g., in one of the advanced forms discussed at this Symposium by Sekera and by Grosjean.

It was also noted that a computing program written for unpolarized scattering, as in (a) and (b), may be used directly for scattering with arbitrary polarization. It is only

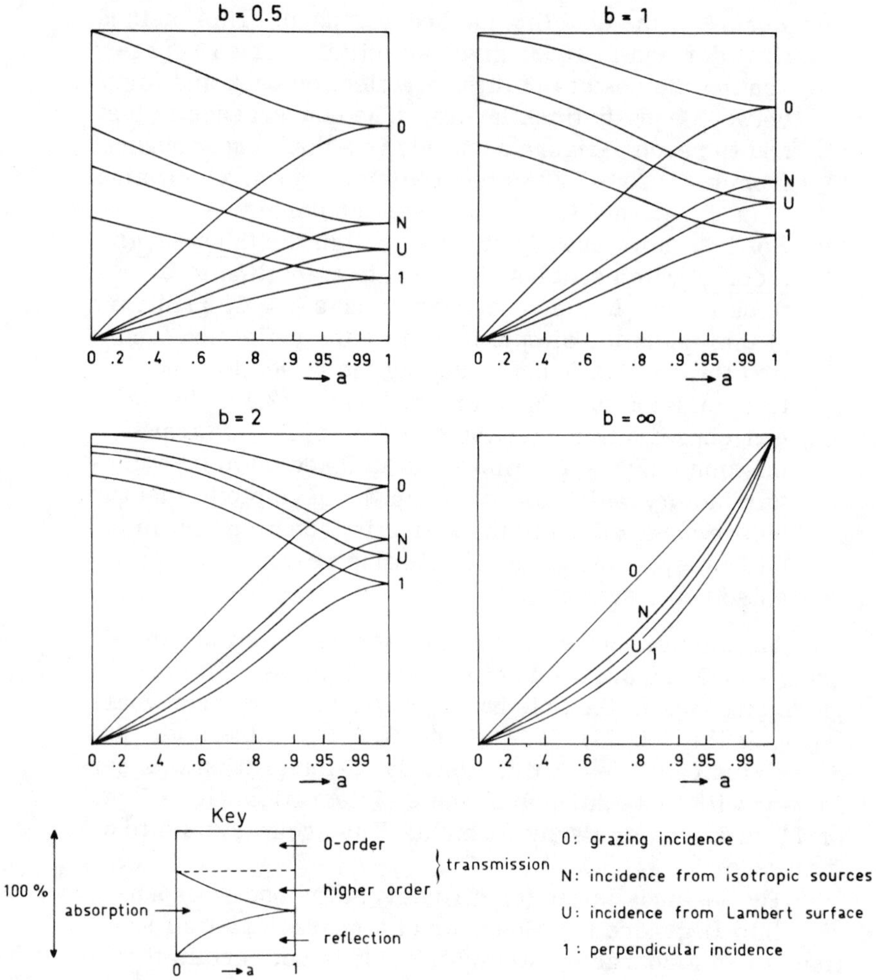

Figure 1

necessary to extend the angular domain of θ over $4 \times 90°$ and to specify the phase matrix in more detail.

IV. SOME RESULTS

The energy incident upon a layer (say from above) is

conserved. It must end up in three parts, together 100 per cent, namely

energy reflected (emerging from top)
energy absorbed (not emerging)
energy transmitted (emerging from bottom).

These fractions are functions of a, b, g, μ_0. Figure 1 shows these fractions for isotropic scattering (g = 0), for four values of the optical thickness b. The abscissa is $(1 - a)^{1/2}$ in a linear scale. Besides values for two discrete angles of incidence we have plotted the corresponding fractions for the two forms of distributed incidence, U and N, defined above. The order is always 0, N, U, 1. Absorption vanishes for a = 1; transmission vanishes for b = ∞. The plotted functions can be expressed in terms of the X- and Y-functions and their moments α_n and β_n as follows:

	lower curve, r	upper curve, 1 - t
0	$1/2\, a\, \alpha_0$	$1 - 1/2\, a\, \beta_0$
N	$\alpha_0 - 1$	$1 - \beta_0$
U	$1 - 2\alpha_1 + a(\alpha_0\alpha_1 - \beta_0\beta_1)$	$1 - 2\beta_1 + a(\alpha_0\beta_1 - \beta_0\alpha_1)$
1	$1 - (1 - 1/2a\alpha_0)\, X(a, 1)$	$1 - 1/2a\beta_0\, X(a, 1)$
	$- 1/2a\beta_0 Y(a, 1)$	$- (1 - 1/2a\alpha_0)\, Y(a, 1)$

As a further illustration, Fig. 2 shows the bi-moment of the reflection function URU, again for g = 0, over the range of combinations (a, b) for which it remains finite. This quantity is physically defined as the fraction of the energy reflected, if the incidence is distributed with constant brightness (Lambert's law). The abscissa is a linear scale of $(b + 1)^{-1}$. The plot is limited by a curve showing at what thickness b, a layer with a certain value $a > 1$ (i.e., with energy generation instead of absorption losses), becomes critical.

A graph like this is insufficient to read accurate values. We have found that, if accurate values are sought, it is invariably possible to use along with available numerical data the asymptotic formulae for large thickness (6). This permits us to transform a precarious extrapolation into a secure interpolation.

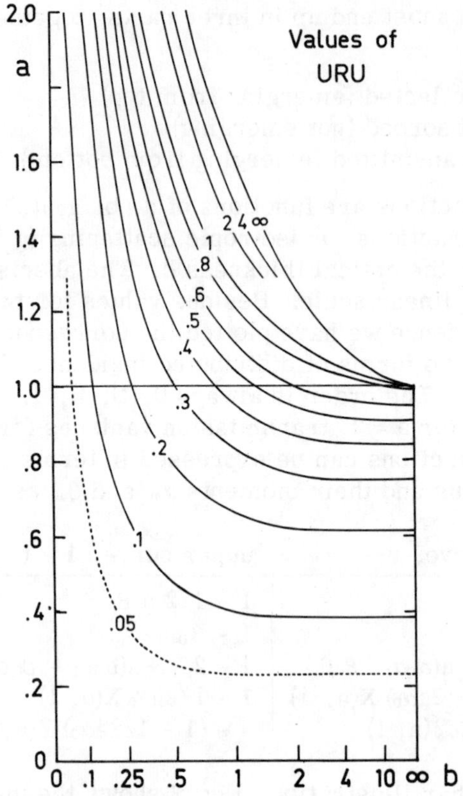

Figure 2

An illustration which has no such direct physical meaning is shown in Fig. 3. The meaning of the familiar H-functions in the interval $0 \leq \mu \leq 1$ has been stated above: point-direction gain for a point outside a semi-infinite layer. The figure shows a smooth extension of this function into the interval $1 < \mu < \infty$ and beyond that in $-\infty < \mu < -p^{-1}$. Here $p = p(a)$ is the characteristic coefficient which occurs in the statement, that the intensity of radiation diffusing by multiple scattering through an unbounded non-conservative medium decreases as $e^{-p(a)z}$, where z is measured in units of optical depth. The graph shows the following remarkable points, which we shall not here explain in detail:

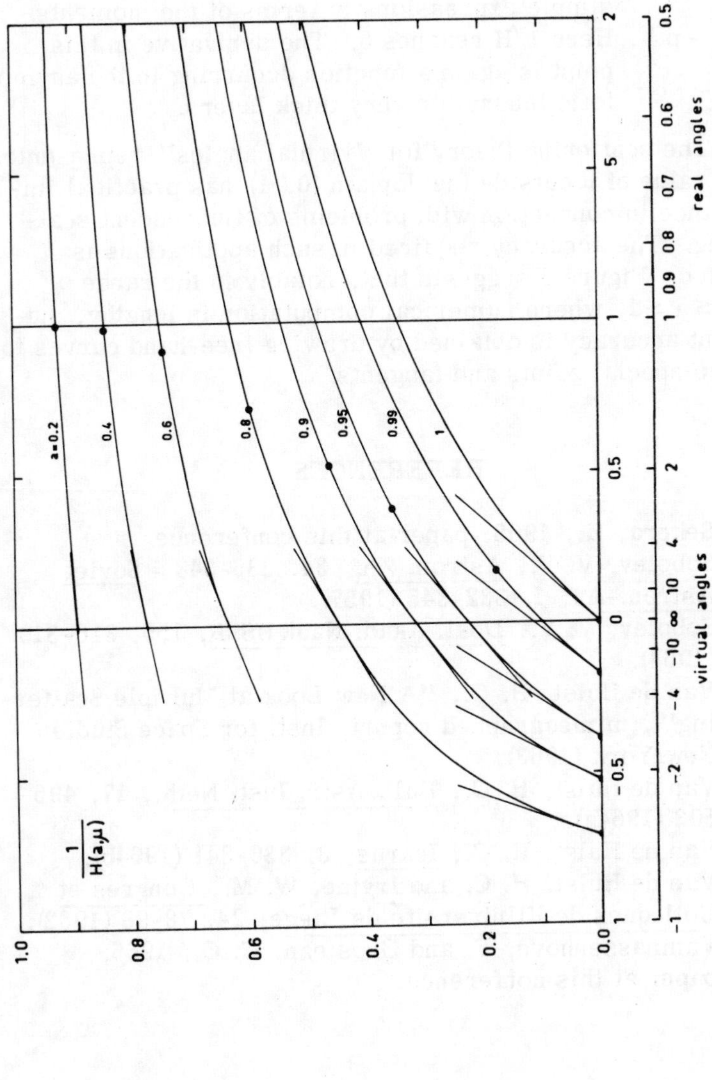
1/H(a,μ)
1.0
0.8
0.6
0.4
0.2
0.0
a=0.2
0.4
0.6
0.8
0.9
0.95
0.99
1
1 −0.5 0 0.5 1 1/μ
−1 −2 −4 −10 ∞ 10 4 2 5 2 μ
1 0.9 0.8 0.7 0.6 0.5
virtual angles
real angles

Figure 3

$\mu < 1$	Point-direction gain for oblique directions,
$\mu = 1$	Point-direction gain for perpendicular direction,
$\mu = p^{-1}$	The value reached here occurs as a coefficient in the asymptotic theory for very thick layers.
$\mu = \infty$	Value and derivative at this point follow from simple expressions in terms of the moments.
$\mu = -p^{-1}$	Here 1/H reaches 0. The derivative in this point is again a function occurring in the asymptotic theory for very thick layers.

The scattering theory for "virtual angles" represented by a value of μ outside the domain (0, 1) has practical importance in connection with problems of fluorescent scattering. The accuracy required in such applications is limited. Figure 3 suggests that, notably in the range $0.9 \leq a \leq 1$, where numerical computation is lengthy, sufficient accuracy is obtained by drawing free-hand curves to fit the special points and tangents.

REFERENCES

(1) Sekera, Z., 1965, paper at this conference.

(2) Sobolev, V. V., Astron. Zh., **34**, 336-348 = Soviet Astron.-AJ, 1, 332-345 (1957).

(3) Sobolev, V. V., Dokl. Akad. Nauk USSR, **155**, 316-319 (1964).

(4) Van de Hulst, H. C., "A New Look at Multiple Scattering", mimeographed report, Inst. for Space Studies, New York (1963).

(5) Van de Hulst, H. C., Bull. Astr. Inst. Neth., **17**, 495-503 (1964a).

(6) Van de Hulst, H. C., Icarus, **3**, 336-341 (1964b).

(7) Van de Hulst, H. C. and Irvine, W. M., Congrès et Colloques de l'Université de Liège, 24, 78-98 (1962).

(8) Vanmassenhove, F. and Grosjean, C. C., 1965, paper at this conference.

SESSION IV:
RELATED NON-ELECTROMAGNETIC SCATTERING

Nuclear Scattering and the Optical Model of the Nucleus*

David S. Saxon
University of California
Los Angeles, California

INTRODUCTION

The study of the scattering of nuclear particles is the primary source of information about the detailed nature of nuclear interactions. Although the details of the forces are, in fact, still not very precisely known, despite an enormous and continuing effort extending over many years, at least their qualitative features have been determined by now with some certainty. It turns out that nuclear forces are just about as complicated as it is possible for them to be; they are very strong and of very short range, they are spin-dependent, they are not central and they are not monatonic. This means that, unlike electromagnetic theory, physically interesting but mathematically elementary problems simply do not exist in the nuclear domain. Nevertheless, there is a broad class of nuclear scattering problems where in spirit, at least, the methods are those of electromagnetic theory. There are problems in which an incident nucleon (neutron or proton) is elastically scattered from a complex nucleus. This complicated process can be analysed

* Supported in part by a grant from the United States National Science Foundation.

with remarkable success by treating the nucleus as if it were an optical medium characterized by appropriate constitutive parameters. This so-called optical model of the nucleus will be our principal topic of discussion. We shall first describe the model and its parametrization. We shall then discuss the properties of the optical model Schroedinger's equation and the nature of its solution. We next provide a formal basis for the optical model and discuss the non-local nature of the nuclear medium. We conclude with a brief reference to the interesting subject of inelastic scattering. Throughout we shall repeatedly emphasize both the similarities and differences between nuclear and electromagnetic scattering.

II. PHENOMENOLOGICAL DESCRIPTION OF THE NUCLEAR OPTICAL MODEL

We consider the following kind of process. An incident particle a is incident with energy E upon a target nucleus A in its ground state. As a result of the collision a particle (or set of particles) b is emitted and the residual nucleus A^1 is formed. In the process the total energy of the system, its linear momentum and its angular momentum must all be conserved. When the emitted particle is the same as the incident particle and the target nucleus is left in its ground state, the process is that of elastic scattering. If the target is left in an excited state, the scattering is called inelastic. If the emitted particle differs from the incident particle, or if more than one particle is emitted, the process is called a nuclear reaction.

The earliest theory of nuclear scattering and reactions was dominated by the compound nucleus model suggested by Niels Bohr in 1936. According to that model the process proceeds in two well-defined and quite separate stages. In the first the incoming particle strikes the nucleus, is completely absorbed by it and, because of the enormous strength of nuclear forces, quickly shares its energy with all of the particles in the target. This amalgamated homogenized excited system is called the compound nucleus. Eventually some or all of the excitation energy of the system becomes concentrated by chance in such a way that a particle (or a series of particles) can be emitted. This evaporation like decay of the compound system is the second stage of the process.

Note that in this model the nucleus is taken to be a completely black object in so far as the incident particles are concerned. There are thus two distinct contributions to elastic scattering. One involves an intermediate stage in the process and it is called compound elastic scattering. The other is associated with the shadow necessarily cast by the opaque nucleus and is called shape elastic scattering.

The compound nucleus model satisfactorily accounts for at least some of the main features of nuclear scattering and reactions. Most particularly, the extremely sharp resonances which are observed in processes at low energies can be understood only in terms of the formation of the long-lived compound nucleus. However, the successes of the nuclear shell model and the increasing weight of experimental evidence on the detailed properties of elastic scattering gradually led to a moderation of the extreme black and white world of the compound nuclear model. Specifically, it was realized that there was no compelling reason to assume that the nucleus is completely opaque, that all incident particles are completely absorbed. Instead the nucleus is treated as a relatively transparent but partly absorbing medium, in short, rather like a lossy dielectric. The absorption accounts for the removal of incident particles through compound nucleus formation or other reaction processes. Note that the compound nucleus is by no means eliminated by the optical model, although the probability of its formation is somewhat decreased.

It must be mentioned that the nuclear optical model emphasizes only elastic scattering and indeed only that part which used to be called shape elastic scattering. All else is counted as absorption. The optical model also accounts for the total absorption cross-section of the nucleus, but it cannot account for the subsequent fate of the absorbed particles since that fate depends on the actual microscopic structure of the nucleus. This is in complete analogy to the macroscopic description of the interaction of electromagnetic waves with the complex system of charged particles which makes up a material medium. The electromagnetic constitutive parameters permit a description of scattering and of total absorption but certainly furnish no information on the ultimate fate of the absorbed radiation.

We have seen that in a general way the phenomenological description of material media in optical terms is rather similar in the nuclear and electromagnetic cases. The mathematical details are somewhat different, however, as we now show.

Consider first the scattering of electromagnetic waves of frequency ω by an inhomogeneous isotropic dielectric medium (for simplicity we take the medium to have the magnetic properties of the vacuum). It is recalled that the wave equation for the electric field vector in such a medium can be expressed in the form

$$\nabla^2 E - \nabla(\nabla \cdot E) + k^2 \epsilon (r) E = 0 \qquad (1)$$

where the Laplacian is understood to act only on the rectangular components of E, where $\epsilon(r)$ is the dielectric constant of the medium relative to that of the vacuum, and where k is the free space wave number. Note that E is not divergenceless but rather that

$$\nabla \cdot (\epsilon E) = 0 \qquad (2)$$

As a consequence we can write

$$\nabla \cdot E = -\nabla \cdot (\epsilon - 1) E$$

and hence Eq. (1) can be re-expressed in the dyadic form

$$(\nabla^2 + k^2) E = -(k^2 \mathfrak{F} + \nabla\nabla) \cdot (\epsilon - 1) E \qquad (3)$$

where $\mathfrak{F}$ is the unit dyad. Written in this way, the right hand side, proportional to the deviation of $\epsilon(r)$ from unity, can be regarded as the source of the scattered field. The $\nabla\nabla$ term is particularly interesting since it couples the field components together and hence is responsible for many of the major complications in the analysis of electromagnetic scattering by an inhomogeneous medium. Suppose for the moment that this term were absent. If this were so, we see at once that no matter the nature of the inhomogeneity (so long as the medium is isotropic) the problem would reduce to three identical scalar problems in the three uncoupled rectangular components of E. Otherwise stated, the induced polarization of the medium would be exactly proportional to that of the incident field and all polarization effects in the scattered field would be trivial and uninteresting. Note, however, that the scattered field so obtained would not be transverse! In a sense, then, the $\nabla\nabla$ term appears in the equation to maintain the transversality of the scattered field. Indeed, by rewriting Eq. (3) in the form of an integral equation and examining its asymptotic form, it is easy to show that the $\nabla\nabla$ term precisely cancels the longitudinal component of the scattered field generated by the first term on the right of Eq. (3). Physically, the secondary waves generated in an inhomogeneous medium combine with the incident wave to produce a continuous bending of the rays, this bending is accompanied by polarization changes as required by the transversality requirement, the induced polarization is correspondingly altered from that of the incident wave and this in turn alters the secondary waves generated in the medium. The wave equation is a complicated prescription for constructing a self-consistant solution to the problem.

Next consider nuclear scattering. Here the governing equation is Schroedinger's equation. The optical model version of that equation, describing the interaction of an incident nucleon with a complex nucleus, can be expressed in the form

$$(\nabla^2 + k^2)\,\psi = \frac{2m}{\hbar^2}\,[V_{opt}\,(r) + z\,e\,\phi(r)]\,\psi \qquad (4)$$

where $k^2 = (2mE)/\hbar^2$, with E the energy of the system in the center of mass system of coordinates and m the reduced mass, $V_{opt}\,(r)$ is the optical model potential, ze is the electrostatic potential generated by the electrical charge distribution in the target nucleus. This last is quite well known from the study of electron scattering by nuclei and its effects are well understood. However, the long range of the electrostatic interaction introduces significant complications into the analysis and solution of Schroedinger's equation; for simplicity, therefore, we shall restrict our attention primarily to the case of neutron scattering ($z=0$), when this term is absent. Temporarily neglecting the effects of spin and of polarization, the state function is described by a scalar field ψ. Ignoring polarization effects in the electromagnetic case as well, we then obtain upon comparison of Eq. (3) and Eq. (4) a simple (but not entirely precise) correspondence between the dielectric constant and the optical potential,

$$\epsilon(n) - 1 \longleftrightarrow -\frac{2mV_{opt}}{\hbar^2 k^2} = -\frac{V_{opt}}{E} \qquad (5)$$

This relationship is the main link between the two classes of phenomena and it at once provides a basis for relating the principal qualitative features of electromagnetic and nuclear scattering. These features, which are rather insensitive to polarization, include the structure of the main diffraction peak, the regularities of the pronounced maxima and minima in the differential cross-section as a function of angle, the dependence of this structure on wavelength and on the size of the scattering object, the effect of absorption in damping that structure, and the generally smooth dependence of the total cross-section on wavelength and size.

The parametric description of the optical potential, which turns out to be rather complicated, has gradually evolved along the following lines. Because it has not yet been possible to construct this potential from first principles with any quantitative reliability, its properties have instead been largely phenomenologically determined by the slow process of choosing families of potentials, computing cross-sections and comparing with experiment. The first attempts, the simplest possible, used a central square well potential

$$\begin{aligned} -V_{opt} &= V_0 + iW \quad , \quad r < R \\ &= 0 \qquad\qquad , \quad r > R \end{aligned} \qquad (6)$$

where the nuclear radius R for a nucleus of mass number A is taken to have the form

$$R = r_0 A^{1/3} \tag{7}$$

In a sense, in the square well model, each nucleus is regarded as an appropriate sized sphere of uniform nuclear matter. This simple three parameter model proved inadequate in two respects. It predicted too much backward scattering and it did not account for the fact that the particles scattered out of an unpolarized incident beam are observed to be partially polarized. It was quickly realized that the backward angle difficulty was generated by the abrupt change in optical properties of the square well model and that a smooth transition from the interior of the nucleus to the exterior is required. The polarization effects can only be accounted for by introducing a spin-dependent term into the optical potential. Unlike the electromagnetic case, the mere presence of an inhomogeneous medium does not produce polarization and so the interaction itself must be intrinsically anisotropic. Since polarization effects are experimentally observed even for spherically symmetrical, spinless nuclei, this anisotropy cannot reside in the properties of the nuclear medium alone. Instead it is a mutual property of the incoming particle and the medium and its directional properties must be expressible in terms of the spin orientation of the incident particle relative to its direction of motion, more precisely to its orbital angular momentum vector. Specifically, the spin-dependent interaction is of the spin-orbit type, that is, proportional to $\sigma \cdot L$, where σ is the Pauli spin operator,

$$\sigma = e_x \sigma_x + e_y \sigma_y + e_z \sigma_z \tag{8}$$

$$\sigma_x = \begin{pmatrix} 0 & 1 \\ 1 & 0 \end{pmatrix} \qquad \sigma_y = \begin{pmatrix} 0 & -i \\ i & 0 \end{pmatrix} \qquad \sigma_z = \begin{pmatrix} 1 & 0 \\ 0 & -1 \end{pmatrix}$$

and where L is the orbital angular momentum operator in units of $\hbar$,

$$L = \frac{1}{i} \; (r \times \nabla) \tag{9}$$

The state function is now a two component object, with one component corresponding to spin up along a given axis, the other to spin down.

The optical potential can now be written in its full glory and in its most general form as

$$-V_{opt} = V f_c (r) + iWf_I (r) + V_s f_s(r)\sigma \cdot L \qquad (10)$$

Here, V and W are the strengths of the real and imaginary parts of the central part of the potential and V that of the spin-orbit term. The f's describe the radial dependence of each of these terms. Each f must contain at least two parameters, a radius and a fall-off distance. If all parameters are treated independently, there are thus at least nine parameters in the model, three dynamical and six geometrical. It turns out that the dynamical parameters all depend on energy (frequency) and the medium is thus highly dispersive, to add to the complications. In practice, however, the geometrical parameters are not taken to be independent. In the simplest version f_c and f_I are taken to be the same and, almost always, of the reasonable form

$$f_I = f_c = (1 + \exp\frac{r-R}{a})^{-1} \qquad (11)$$

For $a \ll R$, as is the case in practice, note that f is practically unity over the central region of the nucleus and that it begins to fall off smoothly when r becomes comparable with R. The parameter R is thus a measure of the nuclear radius and it is assumed to vary with mass number according to Eq. (7). The parameter a characterizes the thickness of the surface region, that is, the distance over which the potential decreases significantly from its value at the center of the nucleus. The spin-orbit term is generally taken to be of the so-called Thomas form, that is proportional to $r^{-1} df_c/dr$. In this version, called the volume absorption model, there are thus five parameters.

The volume absorption model accounts remarkably well for the differential cross-section and polarization data but not so well for the absorption cross-section, at least at energies below 40 Mev or so. On theoretical grounds, it is expected that in this energy region, absorption should be inhibited in the nuclear interior because of the effects of the Pauli exlusion principle. Hence a somewhat more complicated version has been introduced in which the absorption is concentrated to some degree in the nuclear surface. This surface absorption model, involving a total of six or seven parameters depending on circumstances, indeed gives an improved account of the moderate energy data, and particularly of the absorption cross-section data. Presumably there is a gradual transition between surface absorption at moderate energies and volume absorption at high energies, but this has not yet been traced through in any detail.

For orientation, the significant parameter values, expressed in optical terms, for a medium sized nucleus such as copper are the following: As the energy increases from 10 Mev to 100 Mev (the most extensively studied energy domain) kR increases from about 3 to about 10, the attenuation length decreases from about one nuclear radius to a few percent of the nuclear radius, ka increases from about 0.3 to about 1.0 and the effective dielectric constant decreases from about 6 to about 1.2. The last two quantities are approximately the same for all nuclei, since the surface thickness and the strength of the optical model interactions turn out to be more or less independent of nuclear species, while the former two vary linearly with nuclear radius.

III. SCATTERING CROSS-SECTIONS AND POLARIZATION FOR SPHERICAL NUCLEI

The particular solution of the optical model Schroedinger's equation appropriate to the scattering of a beam of particles incident from infinity along the direction n_0 is characterized by the requirement that the asymptotic field have the form

$$\psi = \exp(ikn_0 \cdot r)\, \chi_{inc} + F(n_0, n)\, \frac{e^{ikr}}{r}\, \chi_{inc} \qquad (12)$$

where the first term gives the incident field, the second the purely outgoing scattered field. The quantity χ_{inc} is the two component spin function of the incident wave, while $F(n_0, n)$ is the amplitude for scattering in the direction n.

The amplitude F is an operator in the spin space of the scattered particle. Its general structure is easily determined for spherically symmetric nuclei from the requirement that it be invariant under combined rotations in ordinary and spin space. This requirement follows from the fact that V_{opt} exhibits the same invariance. Regarded as a function of the Pauli operator σ, F can always be expressed as a superposition of a term independent of σ, which we call $f(n_0, n)$, and a term linear in σ. This follows because the three components of σ and the identity operator form a complete set of two by two matrices and thus of operators in spin space. Now σ, being an angular momentum, is an axial vector and to generate an invariant we must construct a second axial vector from the other vectors which define the scattering. These are only the polar vectors n_0 and n, which can be combined to yield the axial unit vector

$$n_\rho = \frac{n x n_0}{| n x n_0 |} = \frac{n x n_0}{\sin\theta} \qquad (13)$$

where θ is the angle of scattering. The vector n_ρ is, of course, perpendicular to the plane of the scattering. The quantity $\sigma \cdot n_\rho$ is properly invariant and it is the only such invariant which can be constructed. Hence F must be expressible in the form

$$F(n_0, n) = f(n_0, n) + \sigma \cdot n_p \, g(n_0, n) \qquad (14)$$

where f and g are scalar functions of the scattering angles. The first term involves no change in the spin state of the incident particle, the second can involve such a change and it is therefore frequently called the spin-flip part of the scattering amplitude.

For an unpolarized incident beam it can be shown that the differential cross-section and polarization are expressed in terms of f and g as follows:

$$\begin{aligned} \sigma(n_0, n) &= |f|^2 + |g|^2 \\ P(n_0, n) &= n_p \frac{f^*g + fg^*}{|f|^2 + |g|^2} \end{aligned} \qquad (15)$$

To understand physically the fact that scattering produces polarization in an originally unpolarized beam, let us examine the classical trajectories in a given scattering plane. Let us choose the axis of spin quantization to be perpendicular to that plane. Consider first a beam completely polarized upward say. The angular momentum vector of a particle incident along a trajectory to the right of the scattering center has its angular momentum component oppositely oriented to that of a particle incident along a trajectory to the left. Hence the spin-orbit contribution to the potential has opposite sign in the two cases and the number of particles scattered through a given angle to the right and to the left will be different. The polarization still remains up, of course. Suppose, for example, that more particles are scattered to the right than to the left. Then, conversely, for a beam polarized with spin down, more particles will be scattered to the left than to the right and the polarization of these will be down. An unpolarized beam can be regarded as a superposition of a spin-up and a spin-down beam of equal intensities and hence, for this example, the particles scattered to the right will have net upward polarization, those scattered to the left will have net downward polarization. Of course the total number of particles scattered to right and left are the same; the differential cross-action is a function only of scattering angle for an unpolarized beam in agreement with the first of Eq. (15).

If the incident beam is polarized, then the scattering cross-section becomes asymmetric as the above argument shows. It turns out that, if P_1 is the magnitude of the polarization of the incident beam, then

$$P = \frac{1}{P_1} \frac{\sigma_{\text{right}} - \sigma_{\text{left}}}{\sigma_{\text{right}} + \sigma_{\text{left}}} \tag{16}$$

where P is the magnitude of the polarization which would be produced by the single scattering of an unpolarized beam. In the past the experimental determination of polarization involved a difficult double scattering experiment, the first scattering serving as polarizer, the second as analyser, upon measurement of the asymmetry in the scattering. Recently, however, polarized sources have become available and these have considerably simplified the experimental problem.

The discussion above on the mechanism causing polarization can easily be translated into optical language. The differing forces on particles depending on their spin orientation means a differing index of refraction. Thus the velocity of propagation of a ray depends on its spin and this birefringence is quite peculiar, compared to that in an optical medium, since its magnitude is proportional to the angular momentum that is to the impact parameter of a ray. There is no birefringence at all for a ray passing through the center of the nuclear sphere, the birefringence is a maximum for rays which graze the nuclear surface. As we said in a somewhat different way earlier, nuclear birefringence is not an intrinsic and constant property of the nuclear medium as in optical birefringence, but rather a mutual property of the medium and the incident particle, and it is tied to their relative state of motion.

IV. PARTIAL WAVE ANALYSIS FOR NEUTRAL PARTICLES

The solution of the partial differential optical model Schroedinger's equation can be reduced to the solution of a set of ordinary differential equations by introducing an appropriate partial wave decomposition. This decomposition is slightly more complicated than usual because of the spin-orbit term in the potential. In particular, there are two radial wave functions for each spherical harmonic of order l, (except l = 0), corresponding to the two orientations of the spin relative to the orbital angular momentum. These radial functions, which we call U_l^+ and U_l^- satisfy the ordinary differential equations

$$\frac{d^2 U_l^{\pm}}{dr^2} + \left[k^2 - \frac{l(l+1)}{r^2} - \frac{2m}{\hbar^2} V_{opt}^{\pm}\right] U_l^{\pm} = 0 \qquad (17)$$

where

$$\begin{aligned} V_{opt}^{+} &= - Vf_c - iWf - V_s f_s l \\ V_{opt}^{-} &= - Vf_c - iWf_I + V_s f_s (l+1) \end{aligned} \qquad (18)$$

which clearly exhibits the terms responsible for birefringence as essentially proportional to l and of the expected sign.

With the boundary condition that $U_l^\pm$ be regular at the origin, Eq. (17) determines the radial functions up to a normalization constant. This normalization is fixed by the requirement that, for $r \to \infty$,

$$\frac{U_l^\pm(r)}{kr} \simeq h_l^{(2)}(kr) + \eta_l^\pm h_l^{(1)}(kr) \tag{19}$$

Of course, we have

$$|\eta_l^\pm| \leq 1$$

since there can only be absorption of particles.

The quantities f and g which appear in the scattering amplitude, Eq. (14), can be expressed in terms of the $\eta_l^\pm$ as

$$\begin{aligned} f(n_0, n) &= \frac{1}{2ik} \sum_l [(l+1)(\eta_l^+ - 1) + l(\eta_l^- - 1)] P_l(n_0 \cdot n) \\ g(n_0, n) &= -\frac{I}{2k} \sum_l (\eta_l^+ - \eta_l^-) P_l^1(n_0 \cdot n) \end{aligned} \tag{20}$$

The absorption cross-section σ_r can also be expressed in terms of these quantities and one finds,

$$\sigma_r = \frac{\pi}{k^2} \sum [(2l+1) - (l+1)|\eta_l^+|^2 - l|\eta_l^-|^2] \tag{21}$$

The analysis of charged particle scattering is similar but more complicated. The asymptotic condition involves the confluent hypergeometric Coulomb functions rather than the spherical Bessel functions of Eq. (19). Equation (21) is unaltered in form but Eq. (20) is modified in two ways. The Coulomb scattering amplitude must be added to the expression for f and each term in the summations for f and g is multiplied by $e^{2i\sigma_l}$, where σ_l is the Coulomb phase shift.

The actual solution of the radial equations, the calculation of differential cross-sections, polarizations and absorption cross-sections, and a χ^2 comparison with the experiment can all be routinely carried out in a few seconds on digital computors such as the IBM 7094. The search for an optimum least-squares fit to the data is a major problem because of the multidimensional nature of the optical model parameter space and because often more than one set of parameters give equivalent fits to the data. It is not yet known whether such ambiguities are a consequence of incompleteness and uncertainty in experimental results or if their occurance implies an inadequate parametization of the model. In either case, the existence of ambiguities is a very unpleasant feature of the optical model at present, although it in no way detracts from the astonishing success of the model in correlating an enormous amount of data and in correctly predicting the results of scattering measurements.

V. BASIC THEORY, NON-LOCAL EFFECTS AND INELASTIC SCATTERING

We now provide a brief description of the theory of the optical model. We emphasize that our treatment will be formal; we ignore all questions of convergence, existence and the like. For simplicity, we also ignore the exclusion principle and center of mass effects, although both can be taken into account.

Nuclear scattering is a many body problem described by the Schroedinger equation

$$[-\frac{\hbar^2}{2m}\nabla^2 + V(r, r_A) + H_A]\,\Psi(r, r_A) = E\,\Psi \qquad (22)$$

Here r_A denotes the set of coordinates of the A particles in the target, $V(r, r_A)$ is the sum of two body interactions between the incoming particle and the target nucleons and H_A is the Hamiltonian operator of the target nucleons. Introduce now the complete orthonormal set of target nuclear states $\phi_n(r_A)$ defined by

$$H_A\,\phi_n(r_A) = \epsilon_n\,\phi_n(r_A) \qquad (23)$$

and express ψ as a superposition of these states,

$$\Psi(r, r_A) = \sum_n \psi_n(r)\,\phi_n(r_A) \qquad (24)$$

The coefficients $\psi_n(r)$ are the state functions of the incident particle when the target is in its nth state. In particular $\psi_0(r)$ is the state function for elastic scattering, and it is this function we are especially interested in.

Next, substitute Eq. (24) into Eq. (22), multiply by ϕ_m^* and integrate over the set of coordinates r_A. Using Eq. (23), we then obtain the infinite set of coupled differential equations,

$$m = 0: \quad -\frac{\hbar^2}{2m}\nabla^2\psi_0 + V_{00}\psi_0 + \sum_{n\neq 0} V_{0n}\psi_n = E\psi_0 \tag{25}$$

$$m \neq 0: \quad -\frac{\hbar^2}{2m}\nabla^2\psi_m + \sum_{n\neq 0} V_{mn}\psi_n + V_{no}\psi_0 = (E-\epsilon_m)\psi_m \tag{26}$$

where the $V_{mn}(r)$ are the matrix elements of $V(r, r_A)$ connecting ϕ_m and ϕ_n and where we have chosen the zero of energy in such a way that $\epsilon_0 = 0$. The boundary condition on this set of equations is that only ψ_0 contains an incoming part at infinity. All of the other ψ_n contain only outgoing parts, corresponding to inelastic scattering, or else vanish at infinity if inelastic scattering to the state in question is energetically impossible. From this point of view, ψ_0, through its incoming part, is the source of the entire field.

We cannot actually solve Eq. (25) and (26), of course, but we formally do so by inverting (26) and expressing ψ_m in terms of ψ_0. In other words, we write

$$\psi_m = G_m V_{mo}\psi_0$$

where G is a complicated linear integral operator (since we have inverted a set of differential equations), that is to say an outgoing Green's function for the mth state. In any case, substitution into Eq. (25) then yields

$$\left(-\frac{h^2}{2m}\nabla^2 + \tilde{V}_{opt}\right)\psi_0 = E\psi_0 \tag{27}$$

where

$$\tilde{V}_{opt} = V_{00} + \sum_{n\neq 0} V_{0m} G_m V_{m0} \tag{28}$$

and this is the true optical model interaction*.

Although we cannot evaluate Eq. (28) in any real sense, the fact that it is a linear integral operator means that it is expressible in the form

$$\widetilde{V}_{opt}\ \psi_0 = \int K(r, r')\,\psi_0(r')\,d^3 r' \qquad (29)$$

and it is this non-local operator which is phenomenologically represented by the local potential of Eq. (10). It thus appears rather surprising that the phenomenological model works at all and very surprising that it works so well. This can be understood however, in the following way. Consider the behavior of $K(r, r')$. It certainly must fall rapidly to zero whenever r or r' lies outside of the nuclear domain. The overall spatial dependence of K is thus fixed by the nuclear dimensions. Additionally however, we expect K to vanish rapidly when r and r' differ appreciably. The distance over which K diminishes appreciably as a function of $(r-r')$ we call the range β of the non-locality. It then turns out that if β is small enough it is possible to define a local potential which is equivalent to the non-local one in the sense that it gives rise to the same asymptotic field and hence to the same scattering.

To make this more explicit, we rewrite K without loss of generality in the form

$$K(r, r') = U(r, r')\,H(|r-r'|) \qquad (30)$$

The non-locality factor H can be regarded as a smeared out δ-function of range β. Our fundamental assumption is that $U(r, r')$ varies slowly over a distance β in either of its variables. Introducing a new variable s by writing $r'=r+s$, Eq. (29) can now be written in the form

$$\widetilde{V}_{opt}\ \psi_0 = \int U(r, r+s)\ H(s)\ \psi_0(r+s)\,d^3 s \qquad (31)$$

* Strictly speaking this is not so at sufficiently low energies that resonances are important. The resonant part of the scattering, which involves compound nuclear formation, is contained in $\widetilde{V}_{opt}$ as defined in Eq. (28). This must be removed by averaging over resonances before the true optical model interaction is actually obtained.

For definiteness, we take H to be so normalized that

$$\int H(s)\, d^3 s = 1 \qquad (32)$$

Now the main contribution to the integral in Eq. (31) comes from a small volume of radius β about r. Over this volume, U changes little and ψ oscillates with its local wave number, say κ, to be defined in a moment. It is then easy to see that to first approximation

$$\widetilde{V}_0 \quad \psi_0 \sim U(r, r)\, H(\kappa^2)\, \psi_0(r) \qquad (33)$$

where $H(\kappa^2)$ is the Fourier transform of H(s). To this approximation, $U(r, r)\, H(\kappa^2)$ is the local potential equivalent to $\widetilde{V}$. Since κ^2 is the local wave number, it is determined implicitly by the relation

$$\kappa^2 = k^2 - \frac{2m}{h^2}\, U(r, r)\, H(\kappa^2) \qquad (34)$$

A more complete and careful analysis along these lines yields surface term corrections to Eq. (33) and also leads to a difference between the true wave function and the local equivalent wave function in the nuclear interior. Specifically

$$\psi_{\text{non-local}} \sim \sqrt{H(\kappa^2)/H(k^2)}\; \psi_{\text{local}} \qquad (35)$$

Note that for large r, κ^2 approaches k^2 and the two functions are thus the same asymptotically. In the nuclear interior, however, the true wave function is reduced by as much as ten or twenty percent for numbers which are relevant. This has consequences for processes which depend on the wave function in the interior, such as inelastic scattering.

Although our discussion has been completely heuristic, there is some evidence that it bears some relation to reality. For one thing, the phenomonological energy dependence of the local optical model potential is resonably well accounted for by the prescription of Eq. (33). For another, the analysis of inelastic scattering indicates that the true wave function in the nuclear interior should indeed be reduced by ten or twenty percent.

We conclude with the briefest of remarks on inelastic

scattering. This is not a common topic in electromagnetic scattering but it is highly interesting, none the less. The most frequently used and simplest method for analysing inelastic scattering is a phenomenological generalization of the optical model in which the incoming and outgoing particles each move in the optical potential appropriate to the initial and final states of the system and in which the interaction producing the transition is treated only in first order perturbation theory. This method is usually called the distorted wave Born approximation. It works quite well, particularly in giving the angular distribution of the outgoing particles. More recently a much more complicated and complete treatment has been developed in which the inelastic states of interest and the elastic state are all treated on an equal footing in Eq. (25) and Eq. (26). Only the unwanted states are eliminated in favor of an optical model type of potential, and the remaining coupled equations are solved without further approximation. This coupled channel method, as it is called, has been very successful but it is unfortunately a difficult and time consuming approach. Its usefulness is likely to be limited therefore to cases in which one or more particular states are so strongly coupled to the ground state that no other method is adequate.

REFERENCES

A useful and general discussion of the optical model, of the history of its development and of its application to a wide variety of problems is given in P. E. Hodgson, The Optical Model of Elastic Scattering, Oxford, Clarendon Press (1964). Inelastic scattering is discussed in W. Tobocman, Theory of Direct Nuclear Reactions, London, Oxford University Press (1961). For a discussion of more recent developments see Calculation of Inelastic Scattering in terms of Elastic Scattering, N. Austern and J. S. Blair (to be published). The equivalence between local and nonlocal potentials is discussed by Perey and Saxon, Phys. Lett. 10, 107 (1964). The most sophisticated and powerful computer programs for elastic and inelastic scattering are those written at Oak Ridge National Laboratory by R. Satchelor and collaborators. For a complete and detailed description of an earlier and very influential program see Melkanoff, Nodvik, Saxon and Cantor, "A FORTRAN Program for Elastic Scattering Analyses with the Nuclear Optical Model," University of California Press Publications in Automatic Computing No. 1 (1961).

DISCUSSION FOLLOWING PAPER BY D. SAXON

V. Twersky: For the low energy case, in connection with the kind of inverse skin-effect that was mentioned, can you bring the energy into the description of it? Do you have to introduce more parameters?

D. Saxon: Well, there really have been two kinds of extreme cases that have been studied: volume absorption and surface absorption. In these treatments we have additional parameters and if we want to bridge the gap between the two we must take linear combinations. But with these simple models we can correlate a vast amount of data.

S. Borowitz: How many data points are correlated by the 5 parameters?

D. Saxon: For a given nucleus at a given energy, fifty to one-hundred; however, since the optical model parameters are about the same for all but the lightest nucleii, one set of optical-model parameters can satisfactorily account for an enormous amount of data.

Atomic Scattering

Sidney Borowitz
Physics Department, New York University,
New York, N.Y.

ABSTRACT

The basic problem of describing theoretically the low energy scattering of electrons or positrons by atoms is to find an effective one body potential which is simple enough to be used in the Schrödinger Equation and accurate enough to describe the physical situation. The indications are that the principal physical effect that must be included is the distortion of the atomic charge distribution by the incoming particle. Attempting to do this by considering only the potential of the induced dipole is too crude, although this can be used as the basis of an adiabatic approximation. A more general approach is to expand the wave function of the distorted atom in terms of atomic wave functions. Some guide as to how many terms of the expansion are necessary can be had by noting that in the case of hydrogen 66 percent of the polarizability of the atom is accounted for by the excitation to the first excited state. For heavier atoms such as sodium over 90 percent of the polarizability can be accounted for in this way. In the former case addition of terms from the continuum makes a significant difference in the calculation of the cross section. Continuum states can be included by supplementing the expansion in terms of the bound state of the incoming particle with the proton in the case of electron-hydrogen scattering and in terms of bound states of the positron in the case of position-hydrogen scattering. An evaluation of the correct approaches has been made possible by the calculation of bounds for scattering lengths and of phase shifts in electron and positron scattering by hydrogen. Calculation of the scattering cross section electrons and positrons by atoms more complicated than hydrogen is in quite a primitive state. Other interesting atomic scattering problems exist–among them are high energy scattering, charge exchange processes and rearrangement collisions in general. These however have not been discussed.

REFERENCES

(1) Bates, D. R. (Editor), Atomic and Molecular Processes, Academic Press, (1962).

(2) Burke, P. G. and Schey, H., Phys. Rev., 126, 147 (1962).

(3) Burke, P. G. and Smith, K., Rev. Mod. Phys., 34, 458 (1962).

(4) Castillejo, L., Percival, I. C. and Seaton, M. J., Proc. Roy. Soc. (London) A254, 259 (1960).

(5) Chen A., Tani, S. and Borowitz, S., Phys. Rev., 137, 2B, 236 (1965).

(6) Clanot, W. R. and Mann, A., Phys. Rev., 130, 658 (1963).

(7) Crown, J. C. and Russek, A., Phys. Rev., 138, 3A, 669 (1965).

(8) Gerjuoy, E., Ann. Phys., 5, 1, 58 (1958).
(9) Hahn, Y., O'Malley, T. F. and Spruch, L., Phys. Rev., 134, 2, 397 (1964). Phys. Rev., 134, 4, 911 (1964).
(10) Massey, H. S. W., Handbuch der Physik, Vol. **36**, Theory of Atomic Collisons Excitation and Ionization of Atoms by Electron Impact (Springer Verlag) 1956.
(11) Morse, P. M. and Allis, W. P., Phys. Rev., **44**, 269 (1933).
(12) Mott, N. F. and Massey, H. S. W., Theory of Atomic Collisions, Clarendon Press, Oxford, England (1949).
(13) Omidvar, K., Research Report No. CX-37 (1959), Division of Electromagnetic Research, New York University (Unpublished).
(14) Robinson, L. B., Phys. Rev., 127, 2076 (1961).
(15) Rosenberg, L. and Spruch, L., Phys. Rev., 120, 2, 472 (1960).
(16) Rosenberg, L., Spruch, L. and O'Malley, T. F., Phys. Rev. 119, 1, 1964 (1960). Phys. Rev., 117, 1, 143 (1960).
(17) Ruffine, R. and Borowitz, S., 2nd International Conference on the Physics of Electronic and Atomic Collisions, W. A. Benjamin Inc., New York, (1961), p. 144.
(18) Seaton, M. J., Proc. Roy. Soc., (London) A241, 522 (1957).
(19) Seaton, M. J. and Salmona, A., Proc. Phys. Soc., (London) 77, 617 (1961).
(20) Spruch, L. and Rosenberg. L., J. Appl. Phys., 31, 2, 2104 (1960).
(21) Temkin, A., Phys. Rev., 116, 2, 358 (1959).
(22) Temkin, A., Phys. Rev., 126, 1, 130 (1962).

DISCUSSION FOLLOWING PAPER BY S. BOROWITZ

V. Twersky: Could these variational methods be applied to the electromagnetic analog of a wave incident on a sphere with a radially varying index of refraction?

S. Borowitz: Yes, as a matter of fact I think Spruch himself has worked out some electromagnetic problems. The method will certainly work in problems involving dielectrics.

The Velocity and Attenuation of Waves in a Random Medium*

Joseph B. Keller
Courant Institute of Mathematical Sciences
New York University, New York, N. Y.

ABSTRACT

A general method is presented for the determination of the average solution of a linear equation with random coefficients. It is used to derive the dispersion equation relating the frequency and propagation constant of a coherent wave in a random medium. This equation contains as special cases various equations which have been derived before for electromagnetic, acoustic and elastic waves. In addition it applies to many other types of waves.

I. INTRODUCTION

A common occurrence in the propagation of waves of all kinds is propagation through a medium which is very complex. By this we mean a medium with properties which vary in a complicated way in space and time. In such

*This research was supported by the Air Force Cambridge Research Laboratories, Office of Aerospace Research, under Contract No. AF 19(628)3868. Reproduction in whole or in part is permitted for any purpose of the U. S. Government.

cases it is impractical to determine the actual variation of the properties but it may be more convenient to determine their statistics. Correspondingly only statistical properties of the wave can be determined. In the theoretical analysis of wave propagation in such media it is appropriate to consider the medium to be random. Then the propagating wave must also be treated as random.

It is our objective to analyze wave propagation in a random medium from a general point of view applicable to all kinds of waves governed by linear equations. Our analysis is based upon a method which we have introduced previously (3, 4) but the present treatment is self-contained, more general and includes some novel features. We shall utilize it to derive an equation for the average or mean wave, which is often called the coherent wave, in a random medium. From this equation we shall deduce the exact dispersion equation relating the angular frequency and propagation vector of a coherent time harmonic plane wave in a statistically steady, statistically homogeneous medium. Then we shall simplify this equation by supposing that the random inhomogeneities are of small magnitude compared with the corresponding non-random quantities. In this way we obtain a dispersion equation involving only the mean values and the two point two time cörrelation functions of the random inhomogeneities. From the dispersion equation the propagation velocity and attenuation coefficient of the wave can be obtained. The same method can be used to obtain an equation for the two point two time correlation function of the field, which describes the incoherent wave, and for other moments of the field.

The final dispersion equation is a generalization of equations we have derived before in special cases. The first of these was for the reduced wave equation (4), which applies to scalar waves in a time dependent medium, such as sound waves in a fluid in slow turbulent motion. Together with F. C. Karal Jr. (2, 5) we investigated elastic and electromagnetic waves in time independent random media. The results of this analysis should apply to seismic waves in the earth and to radio waves in the atmosphere. In it we also determined the effective dielectric constant, magnetic permeability and conductivity of the medium in the electromagnetic case. We have also applied the present method to waves in a medium of discrete scatterers (4) such as the molecules of a gas or liquid. Then together with D. J. Vezzetti (6) we used a slight variant of the present method to treat electromagnetic wave propagation in a medium of polarizable point dipoles. In this case we also deduced the dielectric constant and magnetic permeability of the medium. This generalized J. Yvon's method and results, which concern static fields. (See W.F. Brown (1).) In view of the fact that all these applications of the method have been published, we have not included any applications here.

Needless to say, the present method has much in common with other methods of treating waves in random media. References to such methods and results, and comparisons of them with the present ones, are given in the articles cited above. Additional references are given in the articles by V. Twersky and some others in this volume.

Let us conclude by emphasizing that the similarity of the phenomena occurring in different fields of wave propagation makes it possible to transfer to each field the methods of analysis developed in others. With this view in mind it is desirable to isolate the general features of such methods and to formulate them in such a way that they can be applied to any field. It is the object of this article to illustrate this possibility for one type of process--coherent wave propagation in a random medium.

II. DERIVATION OF THE EXACT DISPERSION EQUATION

Let us consider a linear equation of the form

$$Lu = g \tag{1}$$

Here L is a linear operator, $\mathbf{u}$ is an unknown vector in the space on which L acts and $\mathbf{g}$ is a given vector. If L is invertible, the solution of (1) is

$$u = L^{-1} g \tag{2}$$

From (2) we see that if L is a random operator and g is a non-random vector, then u is a random vector. The mean or expectation value of u, denoted by $\langle u \rangle$, is

$$\langle u \rangle = \langle L^{-1} \rangle g \tag{3}$$

Here $\langle L^{-1} \rangle$ is the expectation of L^{-1}.

For many purposes the expression (3) for $\langle u \rangle$ is very useful, but for other purposes it is conveneient to multiply (3) by $\langle L^{-1} \rangle^{-1}$ to obtain

$$\langle L^{-1} \rangle^{-1} \langle u \rangle = g \tag{4}$$

This may be thought of as an equation to be solved for $\langle u \rangle$ or as an expression for g in terms of $\langle u \rangle$. An important special case of (4) is the homogeneous one $g = 0$, when (4) becomes

$$\langle L^{-1} \rangle^{-1} \langle u \rangle = 0 \tag{5}$$

Our first application of (5) is to the determination of the propagation velocity and attenuation coefficient of a wave in a random medium. To this end we assume that the wave is represented by a vector function u(x, t) of position **x** and time t. We also assume that the medium is statistically homogeneous in space and time. Then $\langle L^{-1} \rangle$ is translationally invariant in **x** and t. In fact this could be taken as the meaning of statistical homogeneity of the medium. Translational invariance of an operator implies that its eigendifferentials (i.e. "eigenfunctions" corresponding to its continuous spectrum) are exponential functions. Therefore we seek solutions of (5) in which the mean wave $\langle u \rangle$, which is also called the coherent wave, is a time harmonic plane wave of the form

$$\langle u(\mathbf{x}, t) \rangle = \mathbf{A} \exp[i(\mathbf{k} \cdot \mathbf{x} - \omega t)] \tag{6}$$

Here **A**, **k** and ω are constants called the amplitude vector, the propagation vector and the angular frequency respectively.

Upon inserting (6) into (5) and multiplying on the left by $\exp[-i(\mathbf{k} \cdot \mathbf{x} - \omega t)]$ we obtain

$$\exp[-i(\mathbf{k}\cdot\mathbf{x}-\omega t)]<L^{-1}>^{-1}\exp[i(\mathbf{k}\cdot\mathbf{x}-\omega t)]\,\mathbf{A}=0 \tag{7}$$

This may be thought of as a system of linear algebraic equations for the vector **A**. The coefficient of **A** is a matrix which is independent of **x** and t due to the translational invariance of $<L^{-1}>^{-1}$. The condition that (7) have a non-trivial solution is that the determinant of this matrix vanish

$$\det[\exp[-i(\mathbf{k}\cdot\mathbf{x}-\omega t)]<L^{-1}>^{-1}\exp[i(\mathbf{k}\cdot\mathbf{x}-\omega t)]]=0 \tag{8}$$

The relation (8) is the exact dispersion equation for the coherent wave $<u>$. It relates the propagation vector k and the angular frequency ω. Once (8) is satisfied, **A** can be found from (7).

Further applications of (5) are possible when the medium is statistically homogeneous with respect to some but not all of the components of **x** and t. In this case we seek a solution u(x, t) which is an exponential function of these variables multiplied by an undetermined function ψ of the remaining variables. Then (5) simplifies to a similar equation for ψ which we shall not write out.

III. SIMPLIFICATION OF THE DISPERSION EQUATION

In order to solve the dispersion equation (2.8) we must be able to evaluate the operator $<L^{-1}>^{-1}$. To do this we shall suppose that L is the sum of a non-random operator M and a random part V,

$$L = M + V \tag{1}$$

Then we have, if M is invertible,

$$L^{-1} = [M(1+M^{-1}V)]^{-1} = (1+M^{-1}V)^{-1}M^{-1} \tag{2}$$

Now we suppose that the operator norm of $M^{-1}V$ is less than one so that we can use the binomial theorem in (2) to obtain

$$L^{-1} = \sum_{n=0}^{\infty} (-M^{-1}V)^n M^{-1} \tag{3}$$

Then we take the expectation of each side of (3) and separate out the term with n = 0 which yields

$$<L^{-1}> = \left[1 + \sum_{n=1}^{\infty} <(-M^{-1}V)^n> \right. M^{-1} \tag{4}$$

Finally we invert each side of (4) and assume that the binomial theorem is again valid. Thus we obtain

$$<L^{-1}>^{-1} = M \sum_{q=0}^{\infty} \left(- \sum_{n=1}^{\infty} <(-M^{-1}V)^n> \right)^q \tag{5}$$

When V is small compared to M (in the sense of operator norms), it suffices to retain only the first few terms in (5). To second order in $M^{-1}V$, (5) becomes

$$\begin{aligned} <L^{-1}>^{-1} = M + <V> + <V> M^{-1} <V> - <VM^{-1}V> \\ + 0[(M^{-1}V)^3] \end{aligned} \tag{6}$$

To apply (5) or (6) we must know M^{-1}. When M applies to vector functions of x and t, its inverse M^{-1} can be expressed as an integral operator in the form

$$M^{-1}u(x, t) = \int G(x, x', t, t')\, u(x', t')\, dx'dt' \tag{7}$$

The integral in (7) extends over the domain of definition of the function u. The kernel G is a matrix called the Green's function (or matrix) of the operator M. It is a solution of the equation

$$M\, G(x, x', t, t') = I\, \delta(x-x')\, \delta(t-t') \tag{8}$$

Here I is the unit matrix, $\delta(x-x')$ is the three dimensional delta function and $\delta(t-t')$ is the one dimensional delta function. When M is translationally invariant in t, G is of the form

$$G = G(x, x', t-t') \tag{9}$$

If M is translationally invariant in both x and t, G has the form

$$G = G(x - x', t-t') \tag{10}$$

We shall now write out the dispersion equation (2.8) in

more explicit form by using (6), (7) and (10) in it. We obtain upon omitting terms of order $(M^{-1}V)^3$,

$$\det\Big[\exp[-i(k\cdot x-\omega t)]\,\{M\exp[i(k\cdot x-\omega t)]+\langle V\rangle\exp[i(k\cdot x-\omega t)]$$

$$+\langle V\rangle\int G(x-x',t-t')\langle V'\rangle\exp[i(k\cdot x'-\omega t')]\,dx'\,dt'$$

$$-\int\langle VG(x-x',t-t')\,V'\rangle\exp[i(k\cdot x'-\omega t')]\,dx'dt'\}\Big]=0 \qquad (11)$$

$V' = V' = V(x',t')$. When $\langle V\rangle = 0$, (11) becomes

$$\det\Big[\exp[-i(k\cdot x-\omega t)]\,\{M\exp[i(k\cdot x-\omega t)]$$

$$-\int\langle VG(x-x',t-t')\,V'\rangle\exp[i(k\cdot x'-\omega t')]\,dx'dt'\}\Big]=0 \qquad (12)$$

Either (11) or (12) is the dispersion equation relating the angular frequency ω and propagation vector k of a time harmonic plane wave.

IV. WAVES GOVERNED BY DIFFERENTIAL EQUATIONS

The results (3.11)-(3.12) of the previous section can be made still more explicit by specializing them to waves governed by linear ordinary or partial differential equations. Then both M and V are matrices whose elements are differential operators. These operators are polynomials in the gradient operator ∇ and the time derivative operator ∂_t.

The coefficients of these polynomials are functions of x and t. Therefore we may write $M = M(x, t, \nabla, \partial_t)$ and $V = V(x, t, \nabla, \partial_t)$. However if M is translationally invariant in t, the coefficients in M are independent of t so we have $M = M(x, \nabla, \partial_t)$. If M is also translationally invariant in x then $M = M(\nabla, \partial_t)$. When $\langle V\rangle$ is translationally invariant in t its coefficients are also independent of t and we shall denote it by $\langle V(x, \nabla, \partial_t)\rangle$. If $\langle V\rangle$ is also invariant in x we shall write $\langle V(\nabla, \partial_t)\rangle$.

Let us now specialize the dispersion equation (3.11) to waves governed by differential equations translationally invariant in x and t. Using the above notation we can write (3.11) as

$$\det \Big[M(ik, -i\omega) + \langle V(ik, -i\omega) \rangle$$

$$+ \exp[-i(k\cdot x-\omega t)] \langle V(\nabla, \partial_t) \rangle$$

$$\int G(x-x', t-t') \exp[i(k\cdot x'-\omega t')]\, dx'dt' \langle V(ik, -i\omega) \rangle$$

$$- \exp[-i(k\cdot x-\omega t)]$$

$$\int \langle V(x, t, \nabla, \partial_t)\, G(x-x', t-t')\, V(x', t', ik, -i\omega) \rangle$$

$$\exp[i(k\cdot x'-\omega t')]\, dx'dt' \Big] = 0 \tag{1}$$

By introducing t'' = t-t' and **x**'' = **x**-**x**' into the integrals, we can simplify (1) to

$$\det \Big[M(ik, -i\omega) + \langle V(ik, -i\omega) \rangle + \langle V(ik, -i\omega) \rangle$$

$$\int G(x'', t'') \exp[-i(k\cdot x''-i\omega t'')]\, dx''dt'' \langle V(ik, -i\omega) \rangle$$

$$- \exp[-i(k\cdot x-\omega t)]$$

$$\int \langle V(x, t, \nabla, \partial_t)\, G(x'', t'')\, V(x-x'', t-t'', ik, -i\omega) \rangle$$

$$\exp[i(k\cdot x-\omega t)]\, \exp[-i(k\cdot x''-\omega t']dx''\, dt'' \Big] = 0 \tag{2}$$

The first integral in (2) is just the space time Fourier transform of G, which we shall denote by $\hat{\hat{G}}(k, \omega)$. It is defined by

$$\hat{\hat{G}}(k, \omega) = \int G(x'', t'') \exp[-i(k\cdot x''-\omega t'')]\, dx''\, dt'' \tag{3}$$

From (3) and (3.8) it follows that $\hat{\hat{G}}$ is given by

$$\hat{\hat{G}}(k, \omega) = M^{-1}(ik, -i\omega) \tag{4}$$

Thus $\hat{\hat{G}}$ is given explicitly as the inverse of the matrix M(ik, -iω).

The second integral in (2) can be simplified by using the shift formulas

$$\exp[i\omega t]\ \partial_t\ \exp[-i\omega t] = \partial_t - i\omega \qquad (5)$$

$$\exp[ik\cdot x]\ \nabla\ \exp[-ik\cdot x] = \nabla - ik \qquad (6)$$

By doing this and using (4) we can write the dispersion equation (2) as

$$\det\Big[M(ik, -i\omega) + \langle V(ik, -i\omega)\rangle + \langle V(ik, -i\omega)\rangle M^{-1}(ik. -i\omega)\ \langle V(ik, -i\omega)\rangle - \int \langle V(x, t, \nabla + ik, \partial_t - i\omega)\ G(x'', t'')\ V(x-x'', t-t'', ik, -i\omega)\rangle \exp[-i(k\cdot x'' - \omega t)]\ dx''\, dt''\Big] = 0 \qquad (7)$$

To simplify the result (7) further, we must introduce the elements of the matrices G and V, which we shall denote by $G_{\alpha\beta}$ and $V_{\alpha\beta}$. We shall also use the summation convention to express sums. Then the $\alpha\delta$ component of the expectation value in the integral in (7) can be written as

$$(\langle VGV\rangle)_{\alpha\delta} =$$

$$= \langle V_{\alpha\beta}(x, t, \nabla + ik, \partial_t - i\omega)\ G_{\beta\gamma}(x'', t'')\ V_{\gamma\delta}(x-x'', t-t'', ik, -i\omega)\rangle$$

$$= \langle V_{\alpha\beta}(x, t, \nabla + ik, \partial_t - i\omega)\ V_{\gamma\delta}(x-x'', t-t'', ik, -i\omega)\rangle\ G_{\beta\gamma}(x'', t'') \qquad (8)$$

The last equality holds because $G_{\beta\gamma}(x'', t'')$ is a non-random scalar independent of x and t. We can rewrite (8) in terms of the two point two time correlation function $R_{\alpha\beta\gamma\delta}(x'', t'', k, \omega)$ defined by

$$R_{\alpha\beta\gamma\delta}(x'', t'', k, \omega) =$$

$$= \langle V_{\alpha\beta}(x, t, \nabla + ik, \partial_t - i\omega)\ V_{\gamma\delta}(x-x'', t-t'', ik, -i\omega)\rangle \qquad (9)$$

Now (8) becomes

$$(\langle VGV\rangle)_{\alpha\delta} = R_{\alpha\beta\gamma\delta}(x'', t'', k, \omega)\ G_{\beta\gamma}(x'', t'') \qquad (10)$$

By using (10) and omitting the primes we can put the dispersion equation (7) in the simpler form

$$\det \Big[M(ik, -i\omega) + \langle V(ik, -i\omega)\rangle + \langle V(ik, -i\omega)\rangle M^{-1}(ik, -i\omega)\langle V(ik, -i\omega)\rangle - \int R_{\alpha\beta\gamma\delta}(x, t, k, \omega)\, G_{\beta\gamma}(x, t) \exp[-i(k\cdot x-\omega t)]\,dx\,dt \Big] = 0 \tag{11}$$

When $\langle V\rangle = 0$, (11) reduces to

$$\det \Big[M(ik, -i\omega) - \int R_{\alpha\beta\gamma\delta}(x, t, k, \omega)\, G_{\beta\gamma}(x, t) \exp[-i(k\cdot x-\omega t)]\,dx\,dt \Big] = 0 \tag{12}$$

It is to be observed that (11) and (12) involve only the mean value and the two point two time correlation function of the random operator V. Furthermore only the space time Fourier transform of the correlation function multiplied by the Green's function occurs.

If the correlation function is independent of the time difference t, the time integration in (11) and (12) leads to the Fourier time transform G of $\hat{G}$ defined by

$$\hat{G}(x, \omega) = \int G(x, t) \exp[i\omega t]\, dt \tag{13}$$

From (13), (3.8) and (3.10) it follows that $\hat{G}$ satisfies the equation

$$M(\nabla, -i\omega)\, \hat{G}(x, \omega) = I\delta(x) \tag{14}$$

In terms of $\hat{G}$, (11) becomes

$$\det \Big[M(ik, -i\omega) + \langle V(ik, -i\omega)\rangle + \langle V(ik, -i\omega)\rangle M^{-1}(ik, -i\omega)\langle V(ik, -i\omega)\rangle - \int R_{\alpha\beta\gamma\delta}(x, k, \omega)\, \hat{G}_{\beta\gamma}(x, \omega) \exp[-ik\cdot x]\, dx \Big] = 0 \tag{15}$$

When $<V> = 0$ (12) or (15) yields

$$\det \Big[M(ik, -i\omega) - \int R_{\alpha\beta\gamma\delta}(\mathbf{x}, \mathbf{k}, \omega)\, \hat{G}_{\beta\gamma}(\mathbf{x}, \omega) \exp[-i\mathbf{k}\cdot\mathbf{x}]\, d\mathbf{x} \Big] = 0 \tag{16}$$

If the medium is statistically isotropic then M and $<V>$ depend only upon k, the magnitude of **k**, G depends only upon r, the magnitude of **x** and $R_{\alpha\beta\gamma\delta}$ depends only upon r, k and the angle θ between **x** and **k**. Then the dispersion equation (11) and its special cases (12), (15), and (16) involve only k and not the direction of **k**. It follows that the propagation velocity and attenuation of the wave are independent of the direction of **k**. The integrals in all these dispersion equations can also be simplified by introducing polar coordinates (r, θ, φ) to represent **x**, with the polar axis along **k**. Then the φ integration can be performed since the integrands are independent of φ. In this way (11) becomes, in the statistically isotropic case,

$$\det \Big[M(ik, -i\omega) + <V(ik, -i\omega)> + <V(ik, -i\omega)> M^{-1}(ik, -i\omega) <V(ik, -i\omega)> -2\pi \int_{-\infty}^{\infty} \exp[i\omega t] \int_0^{\infty} G_{\beta\nu}(r, t) \int_{-\pi}^{\pi} R_{\alpha\beta\gamma\delta}(r, \theta, t, k, \omega) \exp[-ikr\cos\theta] \sin\theta\, d\theta\, r^2\, dr\, dt \Big] = 0 \tag{17}$$

Similarly (16) becomes for the isotropic time independent medium with $<V> = 0$,

$$\det \Big[M(ik, -i\omega) - 2\pi \int_0^{\infty} \hat{G}_{\beta\gamma}(r, \omega) \int_{-\pi}^{\pi} R_{\alpha\beta\gamma\delta}(r, \theta, k, \omega) \exp[-ikr\cos\Theta] \sin\theta\, d\theta\, r^2\, dr \Big] = 0 \tag{18}$$

If the function $u(\mathbf{x}, t)$ is a scalar, all the subscripts in the preceding formulas, as well as the determinant symbol "det", can be omitted. Thus, for example, (12) becomes

$$M(ik, -i\omega)$$

$$-\int R(x, t, k, \omega)\, G(x, t)\, \exp[-i(k \cdot x - \omega t)]\, dx\, dt = 0 \qquad (19)$$

This is the dispersion equation for a plane time harmonic coherent scalar wave in a statistically stationary, statistically homogeneous medium when $\langle V \rangle = 0$. This result also applies to a component of a vector field provided the original equation (2.1) is written for that component alone, which might be done by eliminating other components from a set of equations.

REFERENCES

(1) Brown, W. F., Handbuch der Physik, 17, Springer-Verlag, Berlin (1956).
(2) Karal, F. C., Jr. and Keller, J. B., J. Math Phys., 5, 537 (1964).
(3) Keller, J. B., Proc. Symp. Appl. Math., 13, 227, Amer. Math. Soc., Providence (1962).
(4) Keller, J. B., Proc. Symp. Appl. Math., 16, 145, Amer. Math. Soc., Providence (1964).
(5) Keller, J. B. and Karal, F. C., Jr., J. Math Phys., 7, 661 (1966).
(6) Vezzetti, D. J. and Keller, J. B., Refractive index, attenuation, dielectric constant and permeability for waves in a polarizable medium. (To be published)

Author Index